Customized Version of

Basic Mathematical Skills with Geometry

Eighth Edition

Stefan Baratto
Clackamas Community College

Barry Bergman
Clackamas Community College

Don Hutchison
Clackamas Community College

El Camino College Compton Center

McGraw Hill Learning Solutions

Boston Burr Ridge, IL Dubuque, IA New York San Francisco St. Louis
Bangkok Bogotá Caracas Lisbon London Madrid
Mexico City Milan New Delhi Seoul Singapore Sydney Taipei Toronto

The McGraw·Hill Companies

Customized Version of
Basic Mathematical Skills with Geometry, Eighth Edition
El Camino College Compton Center

This book is a McGraw-Hill Learning Solutions textbook and contains select material from *Basic Mathematical Skills with Geometry,* Eighth Edition by Stefan Baratto, Barry Bergman and Don Hutchison. Copyright © 2010 by The McGraw-Hill Companies, Inc. Reprinted with permission of the publisher. Many custom published texts are modified versions or adaptations of our best-selling textbooks. Some adaptations are printed in black and white to keep prices at a minimum, while others are in color.

4 5 6 7 8 9 0 DIG DIG 12 11

ISBN-13: 978-0-07-746129-4
ISBN-10: 0-07-746129-0

Learning Solutions Representative: James Doepke
Production Editor: Tina Hermsen
Printer/Binder: Digital Impressions

Geometric Formulas

PLANE GEOMETRY

Rectangle

Area: $A = l \cdot w$
Perimeter: $P = 2 \cdot l + 2 \cdot w$

Square

Area: $A = s^2$
Perimeter: $P = 4 \cdot s$

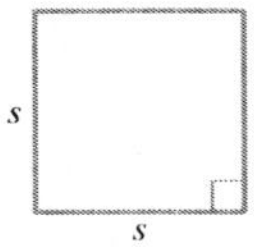

Triangle

Area: $A = \frac{1}{2} \cdot b \cdot h$

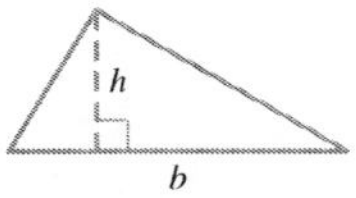

Sum of Angle Measures

$A + B + C = 180°$

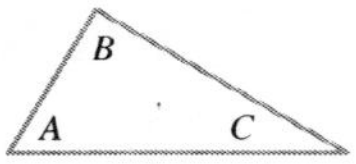

Right Triangle

Pythagorean Theorem:
$a^2 + b^2 = c^2$

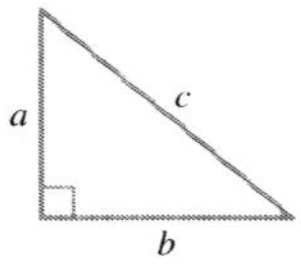

Parallelogram

Area: $A = b \cdot h$

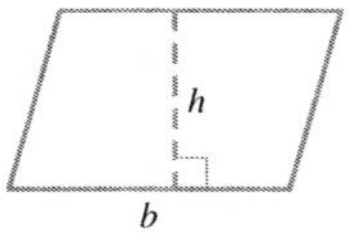

Trapezoid

Area: $A = \frac{1}{2} \cdot h \cdot (a + b)$

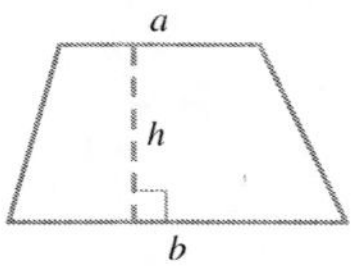

Circle

Area: $A = \pi \cdot r^2$
Circumference:
$C = \pi \cdot d = 2 \cdot \pi \cdot r$
($\frac{22}{7}$ and 3.14 are different approximations for π)

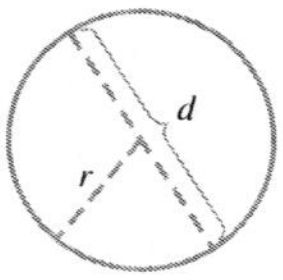

SOLID GEOMETRY

Rectangular Solid

Volume: $V = l \cdot w \cdot h$

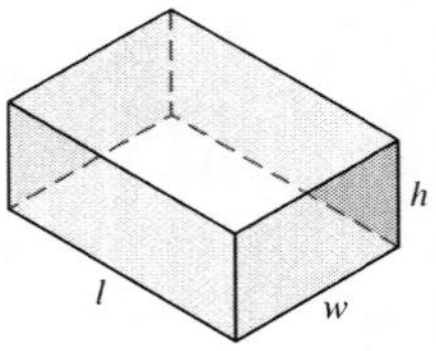

Cube

Volume: $V = s^3$

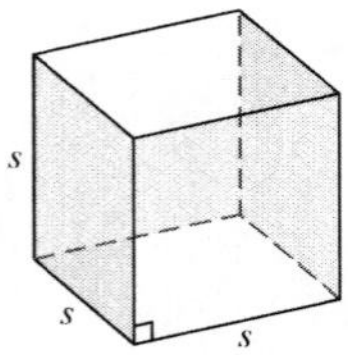

Right Circular Cylinder

Volume: $V = \pi \cdot r^2 \cdot h$
Surface Area:
$S = 2 \cdot \pi \cdot r \cdot h + 2 \cdot \pi \cdot r^2$

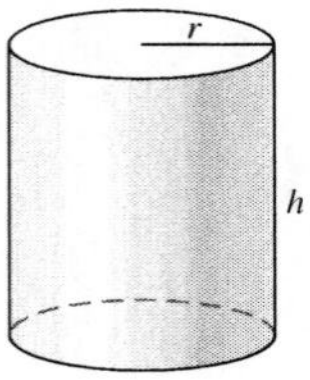

Right Circular Cone

Volume: $V = \frac{1}{3} \cdot \pi \cdot r^2 \cdot h$
Surface Area: $S = \pi \cdot r^2 + \pi \cdot r \cdot s$

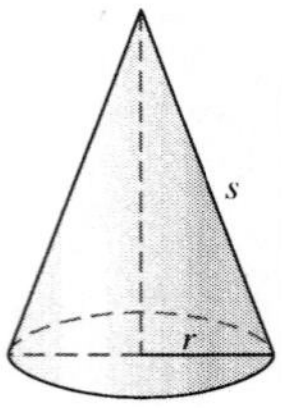

Sphere

Volume: $V = \frac{4}{3} \cdot \pi \cdot r^3$
Surface Area: $S = 4 \cdot \pi \cdot r^2$

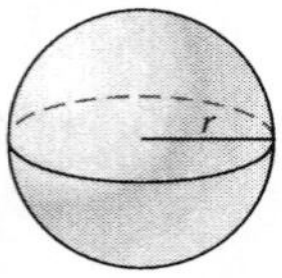

about the authors/dedication

Stefan Baratto

Stefan began teaching math and science in New York City middle schools. He also taught math at the University of Oregon, Southeast Missouri State University, and York County Technical College. Currently, Stefan is a member of the mathematics faculty at Clackamas Community College where he has found a niche, delighting in the CCC faculty, staff, and students. Stefan's own education includes the University of Michigan (BGS, 1988), Brooklyn College (CUNY), and the University of Oregon (MS, 1996).

Stefan is currently serving on the AMATYC Executive Board as the organization's Northwest Vice President. He has also been involved with ORMATYC, NEMATYC, NCTM, and the State of Oregon Math Chairs group, as well as other local organizations. He has applied his knowledge of math to various fields, using statistics, technology, and web design. More personally, Stefan and his wife, Peggy, try to spend time enjoying wonders of Oregon and the Pacific Northwest. Their activities include scuba diving and hiking.

Barry Bergman

Barry has enjoyed teaching mathematics to a wide variety of students over the years. He began in the field of adult basic education and moved into the teaching of high school mathematics in 1977. He taught high school math for 11 years, at which point he served as a K-12 mathematics specialist for his county. This work allowed him the opportunity to help promote the emerging NCTM standards in his region.

In 1990, Barry began the next portion of his career, having been hired to teach at Clackamas Community College. He maintains a strong interest in the appropriate use of technology and visual models in the learning of mathematics.

Throughout the past 32 years, Barry has played an active role in professional organizations. As a member of OCTM, he contributed several articles and activities to the group's journal. He has presented at AMATYC, OCTM, NCTM, ORMATYC, and ICTCM conferences. Barry also served 4 years as an officer of ORMATYC and participated on an AMATYC committee to provide feedback to revisions of NCTM's standards.

Don Hutchison

Don began teaching in a preschool while he was an undergraduate. He subsequently taught children with disabilities, adults with disabilities, high school mathematics, and college mathematics. Although each position offered different challenges, it was always breaking a challenging lesson into teachable components that he most enjoyed.

It was at Clackamas Community College that he found his professional niche. The community college allowed him to focus on teaching within a department that constantly challenged faculty and students to expect more. Under the guidance of Jim Streeter, Don learned to present his approach to teaching in the form of a textbook. Don has also been an active member of many professional organizations. He has been president of ORMATYC, AMATYC committee chair, and ACM curriculum committee member. He has presented at AMATYC, ORMATYC, AACC, MAA, ICTCM, and a variety of other conferences.

Above all, he encourages you to be involved, whether as a teacher or as a learner. Whether discussing curricula at a professional meeting or homework in a cafeteria, it is the process of communicating an idea that helps one to clarify it.

Dedication

We dedicate this text to the thousands of students who have helped us become better teachers, better communicators, better writers, and even better people. We read and respond to every suggestion we get—every one is invaluable. If you have any thoughts or suggestions, please contact us at

Stefan Baratto: sbaratto@clackamas.edu
Barry Bergman: bfbergman@gmail.com
Don Hutchison: donh@collegemathtext.com

Thank you all.

Letter from the Authors

Dear Colleagues,

We believe the key to learning mathematics, at any level, is active participation! We have revised our textbook series to specifically emphasize *GROWING MATH SKILLS* through active learning. Students who are active participants in the learning process have a greater opportunity to construct their own mathematical ideas and make stronger connections to concepts covered in their course. This participation leads to better understanding, retention, success, and confidence.

In order to grow student math skills, we have integrated features throughout our textbook series that reflect our philosophy. Specifically, our *chapter opening vignettes* and an array of section exercises relate to a singular topic or theme to engage students while identifying the relevance of mathematics.

The *Check Yourself* exercises, which include optional calculator references, are designed to keep students actively engaged in the learning process. Our exercise sets include application problems as well as challenging and collaborative writing exercises to give students more opportunity to sharpen their skills.

Originally formatted as a work-text, this textbook allows students to make use of the margins where exercise answer space is available to further facilitate active learning. This makes the textbook more than just a reference. Many of these exercises are designed for insight to generate mathematical thought while reinforcing continual practice and mastery of topics being learned. Our hope is that students who uses our textbook will grow their mathematical skills and become better mathematical thinkers as a result.

As we developed our series, we recognized that the use of technology should not be simply a supplement, but should be an essential element in learning mathematics. We understand that these "millennial students" are learning in different modes than just a few short years ago. Attending course lectures is not the only demand these students face—their daily schedules are pulling them in more directions than ever before. To meet the needs of these students, we have developed videos to better explain key mathematical concepts throughout the textbook. The goal of these videos is to provide students with a better framework—showing them how to solve a specific mathematical topic, regardless of their classroom environment (online or traditional lecture). The videos serve as refreshers or preparatory tools for classroom lecture and are available in several formats, including iPOD/MP3 format, to accommodate the different ways students access information.

Finally, with our series focus on ***growing math skills,*** we strongly believe that ALEKS® software can truly help students to remediate and grow their math skills given its adaptiveness. ALEKS is available to accompany our textbooks to help build proficiency. ALEKS has helped our own students to identify mathematical skills they have mastered and skills where remediation is required.

Thank you for using our textbook! We look forward to learning of your success!

Stefan Baratto
Barry Bergman
Donald Hutchison

Grow Your Mathematical Skills

About the Cover

A flower symbolizes transformation and growth—a change from the ordinary to the spectacular! Similarly, students in an arithmetic/basic math course have the potential to grow their math skills with resources to help them to become stronger math students. Authors Stefan Baratto, Barry Bergman, and Don Hutchison seek to help students to *grow their mathematical skills*—guiding them through the different stages to mathematical success!

Helping students develop study skills is critical for student success. With over 80 years in the classroom, Stefan Baratto, Barry Bergman, and Don Hutchison have helped students sharpen their mathematical skills and learn how to use their mathematical knowledge in everyday life! The Hutchison Series helps ***grow mathematical skills*** to motivate students to learn!

"This is a good book. The best feature, in my opinion is the readability of this text. It teaches through example and has students immediately check their own skills. This breaks up long text into small bits easier for students to digest."

— Robin Anderson, Southwestern Illinois College

Grow Your Mathematical Skills Through Better Conceptual Tools!

Stefan Baratto, Barry Bergman, and Don Hutchison know that students succeed once they have built a strong conceptual understanding of mathematics. ***"Make the Connection"*** chapter-opening vignettes help students to better understand mathematical concepts through everyday examples. Further reinforcing real-world mathematics, each vignette is accompanied by activities and exercises in the chapter to help students focus on the mathematical skills required for mastery.

- ***Make the Connection***
- ***Chapter-Opening Vignettes***
- ***Activities***
- ***Reading Your Text***
- ***Learning Objectives***
- ***Self-Tests***
- ***Cumulative Reviews***
- ***Group Activities***

Grow Your Mathematical Skills Through Better Exercises, Examples, and Applications!

A wealth of exercise sets is available for students at every level to actively involve them through the learning process in an effort to grow mathematical skills, including:

- ***Prerequisite Tests***
- ***Check Yourself Exercises***
- ***Career Application Exercises***
- ***End-of-Section Exercises***
- ***Summary Exercises***

Grow Your Mathematical Study Skills Through Better Active Learning Tools!

In an effort to meet the needs the "millennial student," we have made active-learning tools available to sharpen mathematical skills and build proficiency.

- ***ALEKS***
- ***MathZone***
- ***Conceptual Videos***
- ***Lecture Videos***

"The Baratto/Bergman/Hutchison textbook gives the student a well-rounded foundation into many concepts of algebra, taking the student from prior knowledge, to guided practice, to independent practice, and then to assessment. Each chapter builds upon concepts learned in other chapters. Items such as Check Yourself exercises and Activities at the end of most chapters help the student to be more successful in many of the concepts taught."

– Karen Day, Elizabethtown Technical & Community College

Grow Your Mathematical Skills

"Make the Connection"—***Chapter-Opening Vignettes*** provide interesting, relevant scenarios that will capture students' attention and engage them in the upcoming material. Exercises and *Activities* related to the *Opening Vignette* are available to utilize the theme most effectively for better mathematical comprehension (marked with an icon).

36. ______

37. ______

38. ______

Los Angeles–Long Beach, Calif.	360,300	1,056,600	$181,455,900
New York	282,000	1,077,900	193,572,200
Chicago	260,200	1,108,800	161,200,900
Washington, D.C.	193,600	440,000	56,644,000
Philadelphia	144,600	695,900	90,231,000
Atlanta	138,700	331,800	50,206,800
Houston	136,400	560,100	78,180,300
Dallas	123,900	431,900	63,114,900
Detroit	123,600	371,400	50,060,700
Minneapolis–St. Paul, Minn.	119,600	337,400	51,063,400

(a) How many firms in total are located in Washington, Philadelphia, and New York?

(b) What is the total number of employees in all 10 of the areas listed?

(c) What are the total sales for firms in Houston and Dallas?

(d) How many firms in total are located in Chicago and Detroit?

37. Number Problem The following sequences are called *arithmetic sequences*. Determine the pattern and write the next four numbers in each sequence.

(a) 5, 12, 19, 26, ____, ____, ____, ____

(b) 8, 14, 20, 26, ____, ____, ____, ____

(c) 7, 13, 19, 25, ____, ____, ____, ____

(d) 9, 17, 25, 33, ____, ____, ____, ____

38. Number Problem Fibonacci numbers occur in the sequence

Activities are incorporated to promote *active learning* by requiring students to find, interpret, and manipulate real-world data. The activity seen in the chapter-opening vignette ties the chapter together by way of questions to sharpen student mathematical and conceptual understanding highlighting the cohesiveness of the chapter. Students can complete the activities on their own, but they are best worked on in small groups.

Activity 15 ::
Burning Calories

Many people are interested in losing weight through exercise. An important fact to consider is that a person needs to burn off 3,500 calories more than he or she takes in to lose 1 pound, according to the American Dietetic Association.

The table shows the number of calories burned per hour (cal/h) for a variety of activities, where the figures are based on a 150-pound person.

Activity	Cal/h	Activity	Cal/h
Bicycling 6 mi/h	240	Running 10 mi/h	1,280
Bicycling 12 mi/h	410	Swimming 25 yd/min	275
Cross-country skiing	700	Swimming 50 yd/min	500
Jogging $5\frac{1}{2}$ mi/h	740	Tennis (singles)	400
Jogging 7 mi/h	920	Walking 2 mi/h	240
Jumping rope	750	Walking 3 mi/h	320
Running in place	650	Walking $4\frac{1}{2}$ mi/h	440

NEW! *Reading Your Text* offers a brief set of exercises at the end of each section to assess students' knowledge of key vocabulary terms. These exercises are designed to encourage careful reading for greater conceptual understanding. *Reading Your Text* exercises address vocabulary issues, which students often struggle in learning to understand core mathematical concepts. Answers to these exercises are provided at the end of the book.

Reading Your Text

The following fill-in-the-blank exercises are designed to ensure that you understand some of the key vocabulary used in this section.

SECTION 5.3

(a) A statement that two rates are ____________ is called a proportion.

(b) A letter used to represent an unknown value is called a ____________.

(c) If two fractions form a true ____________, we say that they are proportional.

(d) When writing a proportion for two ____________, corresponding units must be similarly placed.

Self-Tests appear in each chapter to provide students with an opportunity to check their progress and to review important concepts, as well as provide confidence and guidance in preparing for exams. The answers to the *Self-Test* exercises are given at the end of the book. Section references are given with the answers to help the student.

CHAPTER 2

self-test 2

Name ______

Section ______ Date ______

The purpose of this self-test is to help you assess your progress so that you can find concepts that you need to review before the next exam. Allow yourself about an hour to take this test. At the end of that hour, check your answers against those given in the back of this text. If you miss any, go back to the appropriate section to reread the examples until you have mastered that particular concept.

Find the greatest common factor (GCF) for the given numbers.

1. 36 and 84 **2.** 16, 24, and 72

3. Give the mixed number that names the shaded part of the following diagram.

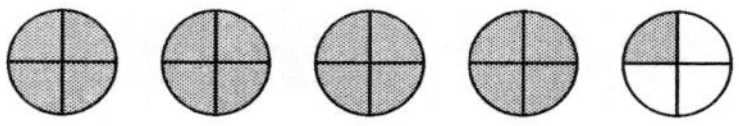

Write the fractions in simplest form.

4. $\frac{21}{27}$ **5.** $\frac{36}{84}$ **6.** $\frac{8}{23}$

Answers

1. ______
2. ______
3. ______
4. ______
5. ______
6. ______
7. ______
8. ______
9. ______

Cumulative Reviews are included starting with Chapter 2, following the *self-tests*. These reviews help students build on previously covered material and give them an opportunity to reinforce the skills necessary in preparing for midterm and final exams. These reviews assist students with the retention of knowledge throughout the course. The answers to these exercises are also given at the end of the book, along with section references.

cumulative review chapters 1–5

Name ______

Section ______ Date ______

The following exercises are presented to help you review concepts from earlier chapters. This is meant as review material and not as a comprehensive exam. The answers are presented in the back of the text. Beside each answer is a section reference for the concept. If you have difficulty with any of these exercises, be certain to at least read through the summary related to that section.

1. Write 45,789 in words.

2. What is the place value of 2 in the number 621,487?

Perform the indicated operations.

3. $2{,}790 + 831 + 22{,}683$ **4.** $84{,}793 - 36{,}987$

5. 76×58 **6.** $72\overline{)5{,}683}$

7. Luis owes $815 on a credit card after a trip. He makes payments of $125, $80, and $90. Interest amounting to $48 is charged. How much does he still owe on the account?

Answers

1. ______
2. ______
3. ______
4. ______
5. ______
6. ______
7. ______

Group Activities offer practical exercises specifically designed to grow student comprehension through group work. Group activities are great for instructors and adjuncts—bringing a more interactive approach to teaching mathematics!

Activity 6 :: Adapting a Recipe

Tom and Susan like eating in ethnic restaurants, so they were thrilled when Marco's Cafe, an Indian restaurant, opened in their neighborhood. The first time they ate there, Susan had a bowl of Mulligatawny soup and she loved it. She decided that it would be a great soup to serve her friends, so she asked Marco for the recipe. Marco said that was no problem. He had already had so many requests for the recipe that he had made up a handout. A copy of it is reproduced here (try it if you are adventurous):

Mulligatawny Soup

This recipe makes 10 gal; recommended serving size is a 12-ounce (12-oz) bowl. Sauté the following in a steam kettle until the onions are translucent:

10 lb	diced onion
10 lb	diced celery
$\frac{1}{2}$ cup	garlic puree
1 cup	madras curry
2 cups	mild curry

Add the following and bring to a boil:

4 cups	white wine

Grow Your Mathematical Skills with Better Worked Examples, Exercises, and Applications!

"Check Yourself" Exercises are a hallmark of the Hutchison series; they are designed to actively involve students in the learning process. Every example is followed by an exercise that encourages students to solve a problem similar to the one just presented and check, through practice, what they have just learned. Answers are provided at the end of the section for immediate feedback.

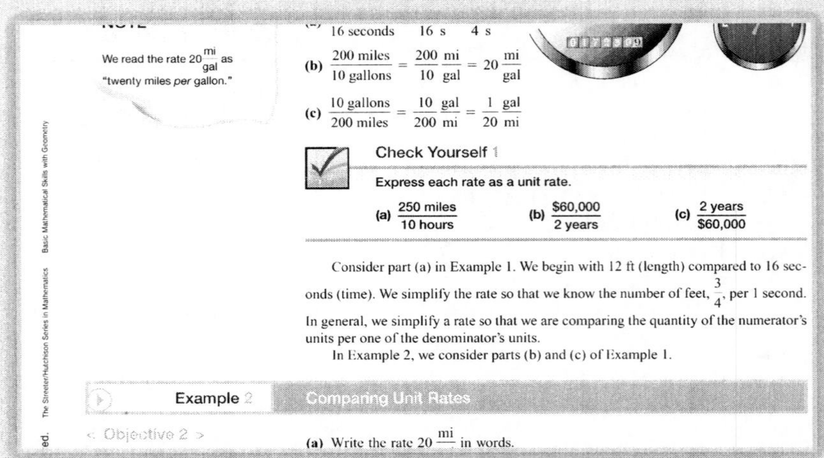
16 seconds 16 s 4 s

We read the rate $20\frac{\text{mi}}{\text{gal}}$ as "twenty miles *per* gallon."

(b) $\frac{200 \text{ miles}}{10 \text{ gallons}} = \frac{200 \text{ mi}}{10 \text{ gal}} = 20 \frac{\text{mi}}{\text{gal}}$

(c) $\frac{10 \text{ gallons}}{200 \text{ miles}} = \frac{10 \text{ gal}}{200 \text{ mi}} = \frac{1 \text{ gal}}{20 \text{ mi}}$

Check Yourself 1

Express each rate as a unit rate.

(a) $\frac{250 \text{ miles}}{10 \text{ hours}}$ (b) $\frac{\$60{,}000}{2 \text{ years}}$ (c) $\frac{2 \text{ years}}{\$60{,}000}$

Consider part (a) in Example 1. We begin with 12 ft (length) compared to 16 seconds (time). We simplify the rate so that we know the number of feet, $\frac{3}{4}$, per 1 second. In general, we simplify a rate so that we are comparing the quantity of the numerator's units per one of the denominator's units.

In Example 2, we consider parts (b) and (c) of Example 1.

Example 2 Comparing Unit Rates

< Objective 2 >

(a) Write the rate $20 \frac{\text{mi}}{\text{gal}}$ in words.

"I like the placement of the 'check yourself's.' Students are confronted with thought provoking questions to answer without mindlessly proceeding through the text."

– Byron D. Hunter, College of Lake County

End-of-Section Exercises enable students to evaluate their conceptual mastery through practice as they conclude each section. These comprehensive exercise sets are structured to highlight the progression in level not only providing clarity for the student, but also making it easier for instructors to determine exercises for assignments. The *application exercises* that are now integrated into every section are a crucial component of this organization.

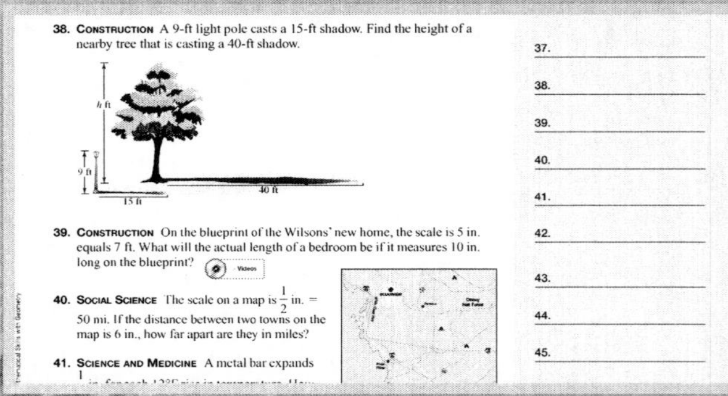
38. CONSTRUCTION A 9-ft light pole casts a 15-ft shadow. Find the height of a nearby tree that is casting a 40-ft shadow.

39. CONSTRUCTION On the blueprint of the Wilsons' new home, the scale is 5 in. equals 7 ft. What will the actual length of a bedroom be if it measures 10 in. long on the blueprint?

40. SOCIAL SCIENCE The scale on a map is $\frac{1}{2}$ in. = 50 mi. If the distance between two towns on the map is 6 in., how far apart are they in miles?

41. SCIENCE AND MEDICINE A metal bar expands

37. 38. 39. 40. 41. 42. 43. 44. 45.

Summary and Summary Exercises at the end of each chapter allow students to review important concepts. The *Summary Exercises* provide an opportunity for the student to practice these important concepts. The answers to odd-numbered exercises are provided in the answers appendix.

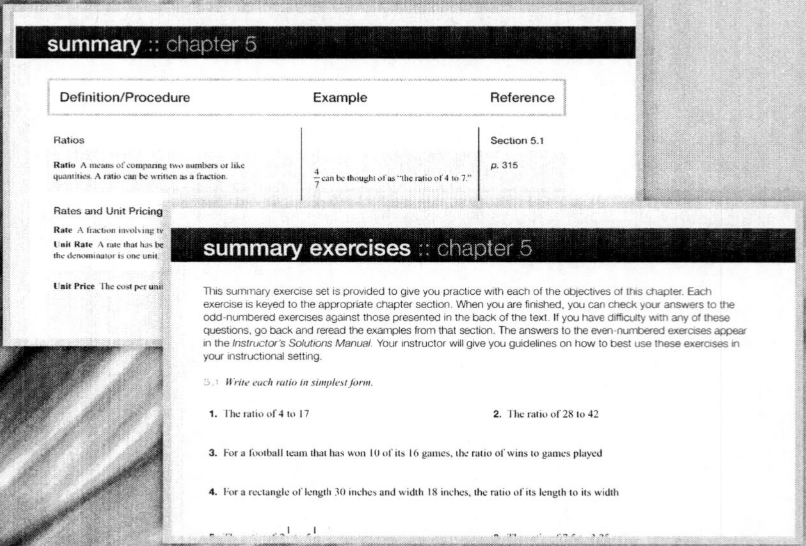
summary :: chapter 5

Definition/Procedure	Example	Reference
Ratios		Section 5.1
Ratio A means of comparing two numbers or like quantities. A ratio can be written as a fraction.	$\frac{4}{7}$ can be thought of as "the ratio of 4 to 7."	p. 315
Rates and Unit Pricing		

summary exercises :: chapter 5

This summary exercise set is provided to give you practice with each of the objectives of this chapter. Each exercise is keyed to the appropriate chapter section. When you are finished, you can check your answers to the odd-numbered exercises against those presented in the back of the text. If you have difficulty with any of these questions, go back and reread the examples from that section. The answers to the even-numbered exercises appear in the *Instructor's Solutions Manual*. Your instructor will give you guidelines on how to best use these exercises in your instructional setting.

5.1 *Write each ratio in simplest form.*

1. The ratio of 4 to 17
2. The ratio of 28 to 42
3. For a football team that has won 10 of its 16 games, the ratio of wins to games played
4. For a rectangle of length 30 inches and width 18 inches, the ratio of its length to its width

Grow Your Mathematical Study Skills [illegible] Better Active Learning Tools!

Tips for Student Success offers a resource to help students learn how to study, which is a problem many new students face, especially when taking their first exam in college mathematics. For this reason, Baratto/Bergman/Hutchison has incorporated *Tips for Student Success* boxes in the beginning of this textbook. The same suggestions made by great teachers in the classroom are now available to students outside of the classroom, offering extra direction to help improve understanding and further insight.

1.1 The Decimal Place-Value System

< 1.1 Objectives >

1 > Write numbers in expanded form
2 > Determine the place value of a digit
3 > Write a number in words
4 > Given its word name, write a number

Tips for Student Success

Throughout this text, we present you with a series of class-tested techniques that are designed to improve your performance in this math class.

Hint #1 Become familiar with your textbook.

Perform each of the following tasks.

1. Use the Table of Contents to find the title of Section 5.1.
2. Use the Index to find the earliest reference to the term *mean*. (By the way, this term has nothing to do with the personality of either your instructor or the textbook authors!)
3. Find the answer to the first Check Yourself exercise in Section 1.1.
4. Find the answers to the odd-numbered exercises in Section 1.1.

Notes and Recalls accompany the step-by-step worked examples helping students **focus on information critical to their success.** ***Recall Notes*** give students a ***just-in-time*** reminder, reinforcing previously learned material through references.

NOTE

In an application involving taxes, the tax paid is always the amount.

RECALL

Multiplying a quantity by 1 does not change the amount it describes.

Cautions are integrated throughout the textbook to alert students to common mistakes and how to avoid them.

> CAUTION

Solving for x does not give us an answer directly. x represents the total volume, which includes both water and serum. We still need to subtract 8.5 from x to get a final answer.

make a $\frac{1}{20}$ dilu

We set up

that should be i

$$\frac{1}{20} = \frac{8.5}{x}$$

$$1 \cdot x = 20 \cdot 8.5$$

$$x = 170$$

Experience Student Success!

ALEKS® ALEKS is a unique online math tool that uses adaptive questioning and artificial intelligence to correctly place, prepare, and remediate students . . . all in one product! Institutional case studies have shown that **ALEKS has improved pass rates by over 20% versus traditional online homework, and by over 30% compared to using a text alone.**

By offering each student an individualized learning path, ALEKS directs students to work on the math topics that they are ready to learn. Also, to help students keep pace in their course, instructors can correlate ALEKS to their textbook or syllabus in seconds.

To learn more about how ALEKS can be used to boost student performance, please visit www.aleks.com/highered/math or contact your McGraw-Hill representative.

ALEKS Pie

Each student is given her or his own individualized learning path.

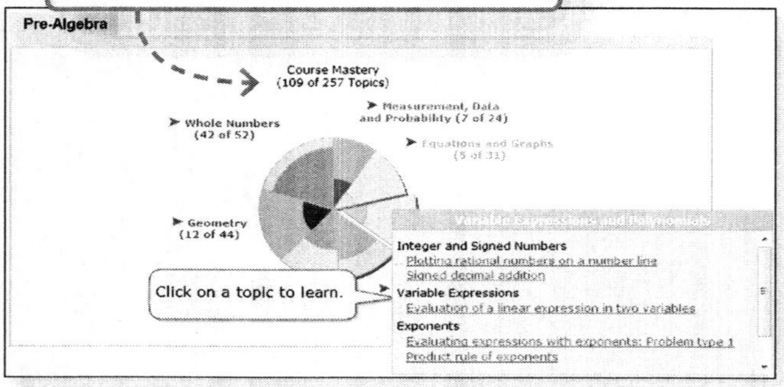

Easy Graphing Utility!

Students can answer graphing problems with ease!

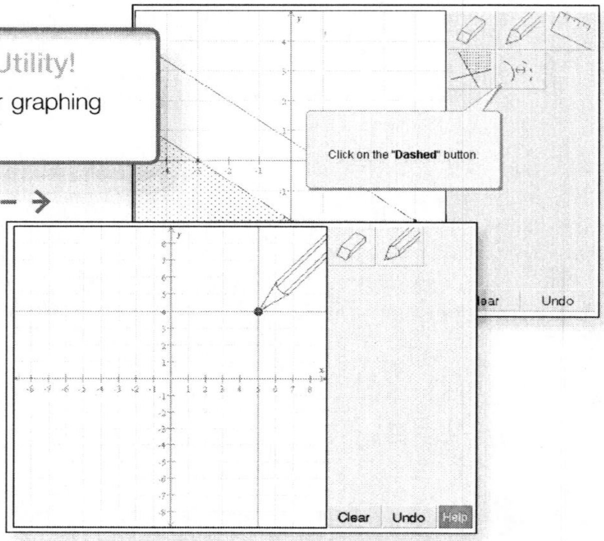

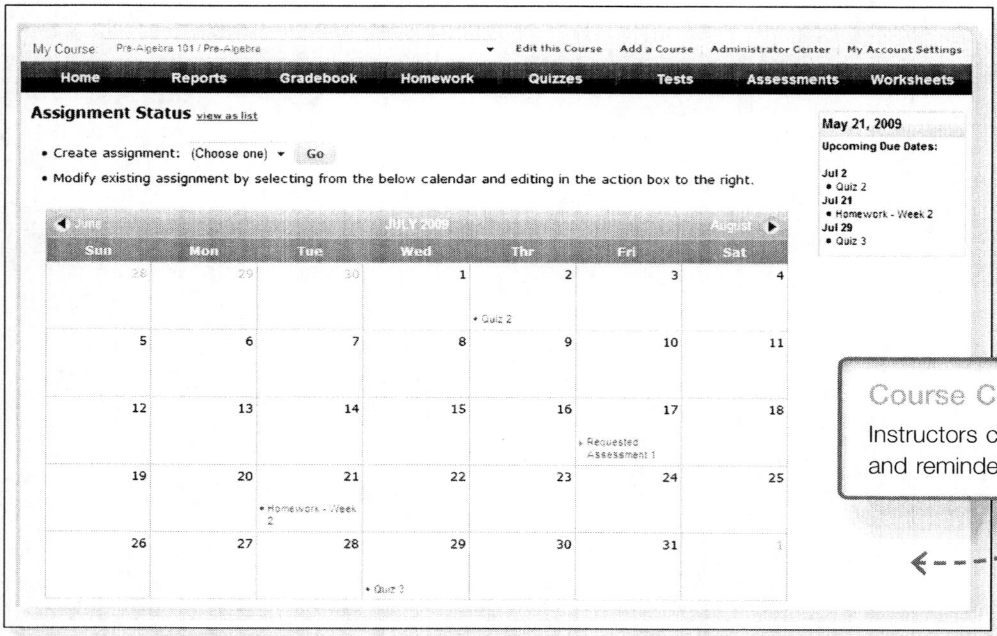

Course Calendar

Instructors can schedule assignments and reminders for students.

New ALEKS Instructor Module

Enhanced Functionality and Streamlined Interface Help to Save Instructor Time

ALEKS® The new ALEKS Instructor Module features enhanced functionality and a streamlined interface based on research with ALEKS instructors and homework management instructors. Paired with powerful assignment-driven features, textbook integration, and extensive content flexibility, the new ALEKS Instructor Module simplifies administrative tasks and makes ALEKS more powerful than ever.

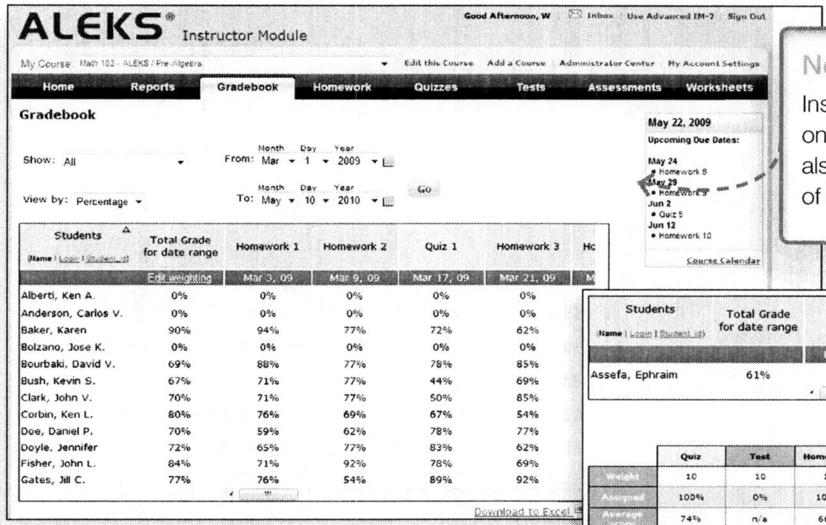

Gradebook view for all students

New Gradebook!

Instructors can seamlessly track student scores on automatically graded assignments. They can also easily adjust the weighting and grading scale of each assignment.

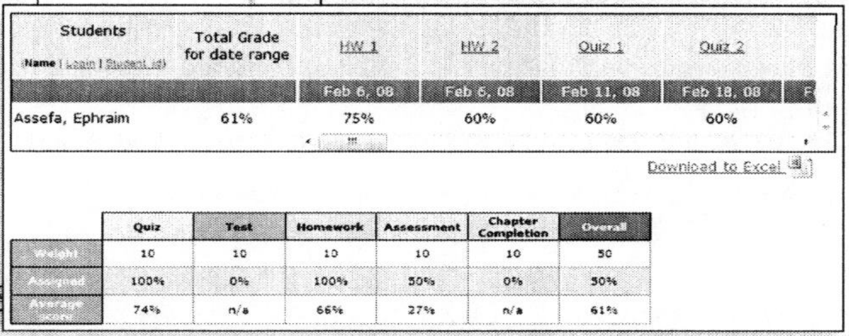

Gradebook view for an individual student

Track Student Progress Through Detailed Reporting

Instructors can track student progress through automated reports and robust reporting features.

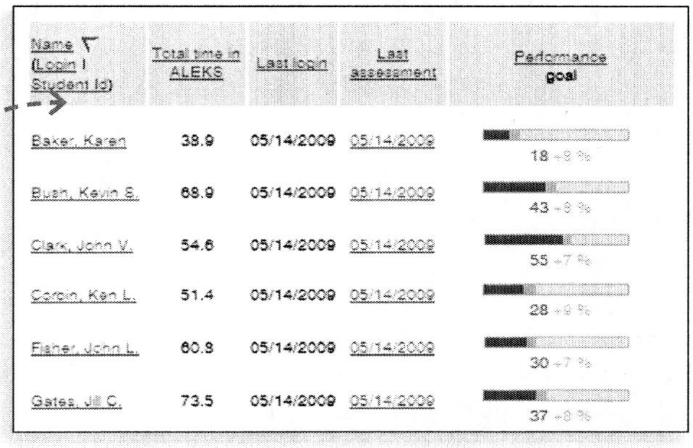

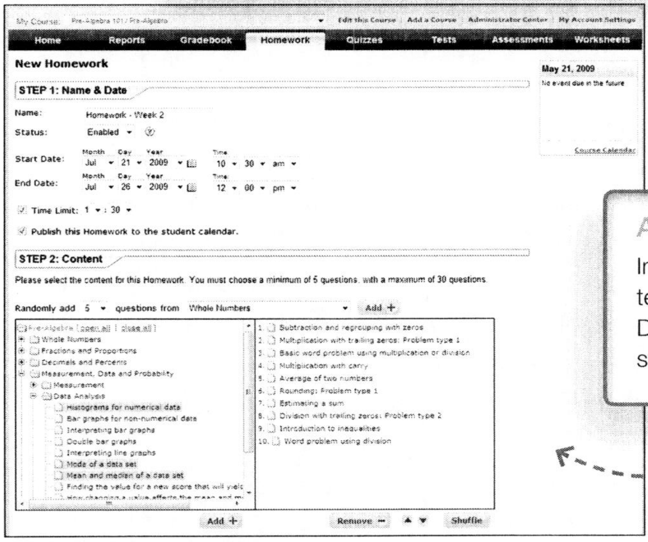

Select topics for each assignment

Automatically Graded Assignments

Instructors can easily assign homework, quizzes, tests, and assessments to all or select students. Deadline extensions can also be created for select students.

Learn more about ALEKS by visiting www.aleks.com/highered/math or contact your McGraw-Hill representative.

360° Development Process

McGraw-Hill's 360° Development Process is an ongoing, never-ending, market-oriented approach to building accurate and innovative print and digital products. It is dedicated to continual large-scale and incremental improvement driven by multiple customer feedback loops and checkpoints. This is initiated during the early planning stages of our new products, and intensifies during the development and production stages, then begins again upon publication, in anticipation of the next edition.

A key principle in the development of any mathematics text is its ability to adapt to teaching specifications in a universal way. The only way to do so is by contacting those universal voices—and learning from their suggestions. We are confident that our book has the most current content the industry has to offer, thus pushing our desire for accuracy to the highest standard possible. In order to accomplish this, we have moved through an arduous road to production. Extensive and open-minded advice is critical in the production of a superior text.

Listening to you...

This textbook has been reviewed by over 300 teachers across the country. Our textbook is a commitment to your students, providing clear explanations, concise writing style, step-by-step learning tools, and the best exercises and applications in developmental mathematics. How do we know? You told us so!

Teachers *just like you* are saying great things about the Baratto/Bergman/Hutchison developmental mathematics series:

"Well written and organized. It tends to get directly into what the students actually are required to do without lengthy preamble. Nice division of exercises into basic/advanced suitable for our students and personal finance exercises they can relate to."

– Jonathan Cornick, Queensborough Community College

"This text is clearly written with developmental students in mind, including numerous examples and exercises to reinforce the concepts presented. The examples are thorough, including step-by-step guidance to students."

– Shelly Hansen, Mesa State College

"A very readable and comprehensive textbook that does a great job of presenting and describing the basic and more advanced concepts. "Practice" and "learning by doing" are themes that penetrate throughout the text, for there is a large volume of (homework) problems from which both teachers and students can choose. Each problem section builds upon the concepts learned previously: a very sound pedagogical approach."

– Bob Rhea, J. Sargeant Reynolds Community College

Acknowledgments and Reviewers

The development of this textbook series would never have been possible without the creative ideas and feedback offered by many reviewers. We are especially thankful to the following instructors for their careful review of the manuscript.

Symposia

Every year McGraw-Hill conducts a general mathematics symposium, which is attended by instructors from across the country. These events are an opportunity for editors from McGraw-Hill to gather information about the needs and challenges of instructors teaching these courses. This information helped to create the book plan for *Basic Mathematical Skills with Geometry*. They also offer a forum for the attendees to exchange ideas and experiences with colleagues they might have not otherwise met.

Napa Valley Symposium

Antonio Alfonso, *Miami Dade College*

Lynn Beckett-Lemus, *El Camino College*

Kristin Chatas, *Washtenaw Community College*

Maria DeLucia, *Middlesex College*

Nancy Forrest, *Grand Rapids Community College*

Michael Gibson, *John Tyler Community College*

Linda Horner, *Columbia State College*

Matthew Hudock, *St. Phillips College*

Judith Langer, *Westchester Community College*

Kathryn Lavelle, *Westchester Community College*

Scott McDaniel, *Middle Tennessee State University*

Adelaida Quesada, *Miami Dade College*

Susan Schulman, *Middlesex College*

Stephen Toner, *Victor Valley College*

Chariklia Vassiliadis, *Middlesex County College*

Melanie Walker, *Bergen Community College*

Myrtle Beach Symposium

Patty Bonesteel, *Wayne State University*

Zhixiong Chen, *New Jersey City University*

Latonya Ellis, *Bishop State Community College*

Bonnie Filer-Tubaugh, *University of Akron*

Catherine Gong, *Citrus College*

Marcia Lambert, *Pitt Community College*

Katrina Nichols, *Delta College*

Karen Stein, *University of Akron*

Walter Wang, *Baruch College*

La Jolla Symposium

Darryl Allen, *Solano Community College*

Yvonne Aucoin, *Tidewater Community College*

Sylvia Carr, *Missouri State University*

Elizabeth Chu, *Suffolk County Community College*

Susanna Crawford, *Solano Community College*

Carolyn Facer, *Fullerton College*

Terran Felter, *Cal State Long Bakersfield*

Elaine Fitt, *Bucks County Community College*

John Jerome, *Suffolk County Community College*

Sandra Jovicic, *Akron University*

Carolyn Robinson, *Mt. San Antonio College*

Carolyn Shand-Hawkins, *Missouri State*

Manuscript Review Panels

Over 150 teachers and academics from across the country reviewed the various drafts of the manuscript to give feedback on content, design, pedagogy, and organization. This feedback was summarized by the book team and used to guide the direction of the text.

Reviewers of the Hutchison/Baratto/Bergman Developmental Mathematics Series

Board of Advisors

Bonnie Filer-Tubaugh, *University of Akron*

Eliane Keane, *Miami Dade College–North*

Jean Olsen, *Pikes Peak Community College*

Sandra Tannen, *Camden County College*

Reviewers

Robin Anderson, *Southwestern Illinois College*

Nieves Angulo, *Hostos Community College*

Arlene Atchison, *South Seattle Community College*

Haimd Attarzadeh, *Kentucky Jefferson Community and Technical College*

Jody Balzer, *Milwaukee Area Technical College*

Rebecca Baranowski, *Estrella Mountain Community College*

Wayne Barber, *Chemeketa Community College*

Bob Barmack, *Baruch College*

Chris Bendixen, *Lake Michigan College*

Karen Blount, *Hood College*

Donna Boccio, *Queensborough Community College*

Steve Boettcher, *Estrella Mountain Community College*

Karen Bond, *Pearl River Community College, Poplarville*

Laurie Braga Jordan, *Loyola University-Chicago*

Kelly Brooks, *Pierce College*

Michael Brozinsky, *Queensborough Community College*

Amy Canavan, *Century Community and Technical College*

Faye Childress, *Central Piedmont Community College*

Kathleen Ciszewski, *University of Akron*

Bill Clarke, *Pikes Peak Community College*

Lois Colpo, *Harrisburg Area Community College*

Christine Copple, *Northwest State Community College*

Jonathan Cornick, *Queensborough Community College*

Julane Crabtree, *Johnson County Community College*

Carol Curtis, *Fresno City College*

Sima Dabir, *Western Iowa Tech Community College*

Reza Dai, *Oakton Community College*

Karen Day, *Elizabethtown Technical and Community College*

Mary Deas, *Johnson County Community College*

Anthony DePass, *St. Petersburg College-Ns*

Shreyas Desai, *Atlanta Metropolitan College*

Robert Diaz, *Fullerton College*

Michaelle Downey, *Ivy Tech Community College*

Ginger Eaves, *Bossier Parish Community College*

Azzam El Shihabi, *Long Beach City College*

Kristy Erickson, *Cecil College*

Steven Fairgrieve, *Allegany College of Maryland*

Jacqui Fields, *Wake Technical Community College*

Rhoderick Fleming, *Wake Tech Community College*

Matt Foss, *North Hennepin Community College*

Catherine Frank, *Polk Community College*
Matt Gardner, *North Hennepin Community College*
Judy Godwin, *Collin County Community College-Plano*
Lori Grady, *University of Wisconsin-Whitewater*
Brad Griffith, *Colby Community College*
Robert Grondahl, *Johnson County Community College*
Shelly Hansen, *Mesa State College*
Kristen Hathcock, *Barton County Community College*
Mary Beth Headlee, *Manatee Community College*
Kristy Hill, *Hinds Community College*
Mark Hills, *Johnson County Community College*
Sherrie Holland, *Piedmont Technical College*
Diane Hollister, *Reading Area Community College*
Denise Hum, *Canada College*
Byron D. Hunter, *College of Lake County*
Nancy Johnson, *Manatee Community College-Bradenton*
Joe Jordan, *John Tyler Community College-Chester*
Sandra Ketcham, *Berkshire Community College*
Lynette King, *Gadsden State Community College*
Jeff Koleno, *Lorain County Community College*
Donna Krichiver, *Johnson County Community College*
Indra B. Kshattry, *Colorado Northwestern Community College*
Patricia Labonne, *Cumberland County College*
Ted Lai, *Hudson County Community College*
Pat Lazzarino, *Northern Virginia Community College*
Richard Leedy, *Polk Community College*
Jeanine Lewis, *Aims Community College-Main Campus*
Michelle Christina Mages, *Johnson County Community College*
Igor Marder, *Antelope Valley College*
Amina Mathias, *Cecil College*
Donna Martin, *Florida Community College-North Campus*
Jean McArthur, *Joliet Junior College*
Carlea (Carol) McAvoy, *South Puget Sound Community College*
Tim McBride, *Spartanburg Community College*
Sonya McQueen, *Hinds Community College*
MariaLuisa Mendez, *Laredo Community College*
Madhu Motha, *Butler County Community College*
Shauna Mullins, *Murray State University*
Julie Muniz, *Southwestern Illinois College*
Kathy Nabours, *Riverside Community College*
Michael Neill, *Carl Sandburg College*
Nicole Newman, *Kalamazoo Valley Community College*
Said Ngobi, *Victor Valley College*
Denise Nunley, *Glendale Community College*
Deanna Oles, *Stark State College of Technology*
Staci Osborn, *Cuyahoga Community College-Eastern Campus*
Linda Padilla, *Joliet Junior College*
Karen D. Pain, *Palm Beach Community College*
George Pate, *Robeson Community College*
Margaret Payerle, *Cleveland State University-Ohio*
Jim Pierce, *Lincoln Land Community College*
Tian Ren, *Queensborough Community College*
Nancy Ressler, *Oakton Community College*
Bob Rhea, *J. Sargeant Reynolds Community College*
Minnie M. Riley, *Hinds Community College*
Melissa Rossi, *Southwestern Illinois College*
Anna Roth, *Gloucester County College*
Alan Saleski, *Loyola University-Chicago*
Lisa Sheppard, *Lorain County Community College*
Mark A. Shore, *Allegany College of Maryland*
Mark Sigfrids, *Kalamazoo Valley Community College*
Amber Smith, *Johnson County Community College*
Leonora Smook, *Suffolk County Community College-Brentwood*
Renee Starr, *Arcadia University*
Jennifer Strehler, *Oakton Community College*
Renee Sundrud, *Harrisburg Area Community College*
Harriet Thompson, *Albany State University*
John Thoo, *Yuba College*
Fred Toxopeus, *Kalamazoo Valley Community College*
Sara Van Asten, *North Hennepin Community College*
Felix Van Leeuwen, *Johnson County Community College*
Josefino Villanueva, *Florida Memorial University*
Howard Wachtel, *Community College of Philadelphia*
Dottie Walton, *Cuyahoga Community College Eastern Campus*
Walter Wang, *Baruch College*
Brock Wenciker, *Johnson County Community College*
Kevin Wheeler, *Three Rivers Community College*
Latrica Williams, *St. Petersburg College*
Paul Wozniak, *El Camino College*
Christopher Yarrish, *Harrisburg Area Community College*
Steve Zuro, *Joliet Junior College*

Finally, we are forever grateful to the many people behind the scenes at McGraw-Hill without whom we would still be on page 1. Most important, we give special thanks to all the students and instructors who will *grow* their *Basic Math Skills!*

Supplements for the Student

MathZone www.mathzone.com

McGraw-Hill's **MathZone** is a powerful Web-based tutorial for homework, quizzing, testing, and multimedia instruction. Also available in CD-ROM format, MathZone offers:

- **Practice exercises** based on the text and generated in an unlimited quantity for as much practice as needed to master any objective
- **Video** clips of classroom instructors showing how to solve exercises from the text, step by step
- **e-Professor** animations that take the student through step-by-step instructions, delivered on-screen and narrated by a teacher on audio, for solving exercises from the textbook; the user controls the pace of the explanations and can review as needed
- **NetTutor,** which offers personalized instruction by live tutors familiar with the textbook's objectives and problem-solving methods

Every assignment, exercise, video lecture, and e-Professor is derived from the textbook.

ALEKS Prep for Developmental Mathematics

ALEKS Prep for Beginning Algebra and Prep for Intermediate Algebra focus on prerequisite and introductory material for Beginning Algebra and Intermediate Algebra. These prep products can be used during the first 3 weeks of a course to prepare students for future success in the course and to increase retention and pass rates. Backed by two decades of National Science Foundation funded research, ALEKS interacts with students much like a human tutor, with the ability to precisely assess a student's preparedness and provide instruction on the topics the student is most likely to learn.

ALEKS Prep Course Products Feature:

- Artificial Intelligence Targets Gaps in Individual Students Knowledge
- Assessment and Learning Directed Toward Individual Students Needs
- Open Response Environment with Realistic Input Tools
- Unlimited Online Access-PC & Mac Compatible

Free trial at www.aleks.com/free_trial/instructor

Student's Solutions Manual

The *Student's Solutions Manual* provides comprehensive, worked-out solutions to the odd-numbered exercises in the Pre-Test, Section Exercises, Summary Exercises, Self-Test and the Cumulative Review. The steps shown in the solutions match the style of solved examples in the textbook.

New connect2Developmental Mathematics video Series!

Available on DVD and the MathZone website, these innovative videos bring essential Developmental Mathematics concepts to life! The videos take the concepts and place them in a real world setting so that students make the connection from what they learn in the classroom to real world experiences outside the classroom. Making use of 3D animations and lectures, Connect2Developmental Mathematics video series answers the age-old questions "Why is this important?" and "When will I ever use it?" The videos cover topics from Arithmetic and Basic Mathematics through the Algebra sequence, mixing student-oriented themes and settings with basic theory.

Video Lectures on Digital Video Disk

The video series is based on exercises from the textbook. Each presenter works through selected problems, following the solution methodology employed in the text. The video series is available on DVD or online as part of MathZone. The DVDs are closed-captioned for the hearing impaired, are subtitled in Spanish, and meet the Americans with Disabilities Act Standards for Accessible Design.

NetTutor

Available through MathZone, NetTutor is a revolutionary system that enables students to interact with a live tutor over the web. NetTutor's Web-based, graphical chat capabilities enable students and tutors to use mathematical notation and even to draw graphs as they work through a problem together. Students can also submit questions and receive answers, browse previously answered questions, and view previous sessions. Tutors are familiar with the textbook's objectives and problemsolving styles.

Supplements for the Instructor

MathZone www.mathzone.com

McGraw-Hill's **MathZone** is a complete online tutorial and course management system for mathematics and statistics, designed for greater ease of use than any other system available. Available with selected McGraw-Hill textbooks, the system enables instructors to **create and share courses and assignments** with colleagues and adjuncts with only a few clicks of the mouse. All assignments, questions, e-Professors, online tutoring, and video lectures are directly tied to **text-specific** materials.

MathZone courses are customized to your textbook, but you can edit questions and algorithms, import your own content, and **create** announcements and due dates for assignments.

MathZone has **automatic grading** and reporting of easy-to-assign, algorithmically generated homework, quizzing, and testing. All student activity within **MathZone** is automatically recorded and available to you through a **fully integrated grade book** that can be downloaded to Excel.

MathZone offers:

- **Practice exercises** based on the textbook and generated in an unlimited number for as much practice as needed to master any topic you study.
- **Videos** of classroom instructors giving lectures and showing you how to solve exercises from the textbook.
- **e-Professors** to take you through animated, step-by-step instructions (delivered via on-screen text and synchronized audio) for solving problems in the book, allowing you to digest each step at your own pace.
- **NetTutor,** which offers live, personalized tutoring via the Internet.

Instructor's Testing and Resource Online

Provides a wealth of resources for the instructor. Among the supplements is a **computerized test bank** utilizing Brownstone Diploma® algorithm-based testing software to create customized exams quickly. This user-friendly program enables instructors to search for questions by topic, format, or difficulty level; to edit existing questions or to add new ones; and to scramble questions and answer keys for multiple versions of a single test. Hundreds of text-specific, open-ended, and multiple-choice questions are included in the question bank. Sample chapter tests are also provided. CD available upon request.

Grow Your Knowledge with MathZone Reporting

MathZone

Visual Reporting

The new dashboard-like reports will provide the progress snapshot instructors are looking for to help them make informed decisions about their students.

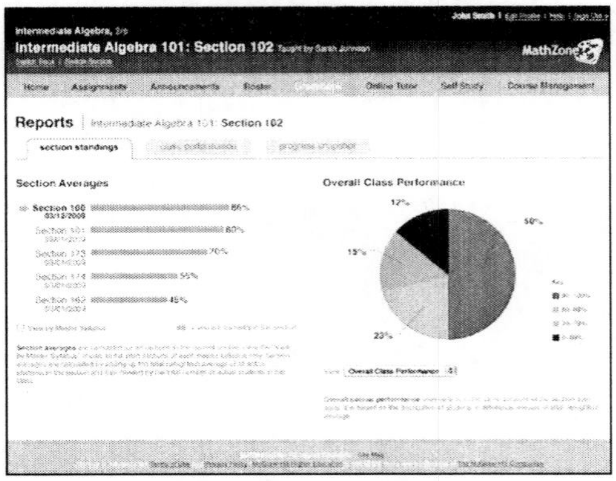

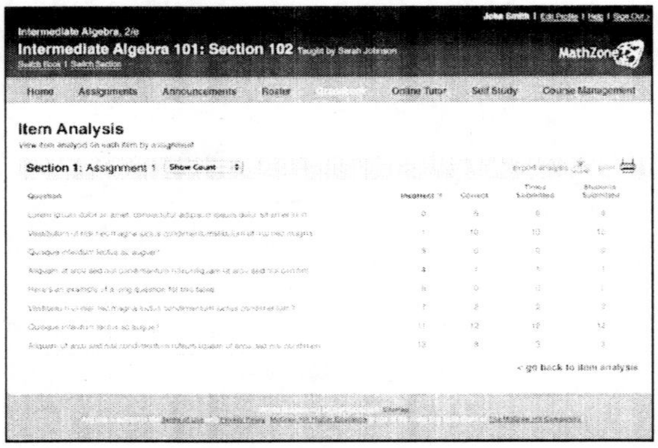

Item Analysis

Instructors can view detailed statistics on student performance at a learning objective level to understand what students have mastered and where they need additional help.

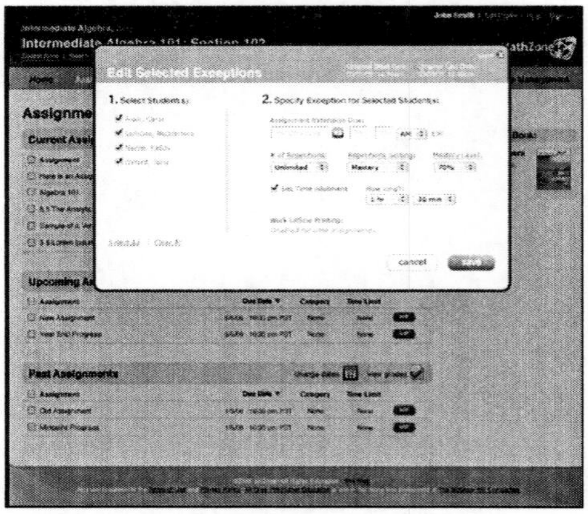

Managing Assignments for Individual Students

Instructors have greater control over creating individualized assignment parameters for individual students, special populations and groups of students, and for managing specific or ad hoc course events.

New User Interface

Designed by You! Instructors and students will experience a modern, more intuitive layout. Items used most commonly are easily accessible through the menu bar such as assignments, visual reports, and course management options.

New ALEKS Instructor Module

The new ALEKS Instructor Module features enhanced functionality and a streamlined interface based on research with ALEKS instructors and homework management instructors. Paired with powerful assignment driven features, textbook integration, and extensive content flexibility, the new ALEKS Instructor Module simplifies administrative tasks and makes ALEKS more powerful than ever. Features include:

Gradebook Instructors can seamlessly track student scores on automatically graded assignments. They can also easily adjust the weighting and grading scale of each assignment.

Course Calendar Instructors can schedule assignments and reminders for students.

Automatically Graded Assignments Instructors can easily assign homework, quizzes, tests, and assessments to all or select students. Deadline extensions can also be created for select students.

Set-Up Wizards Instructors can use wizards to easily set up assignments, course content, textbook integration, etc.

Message Center Instructors can use the redesigned Message Center to send, receive, and archive messages; input tools are available to convey mathematical expressions via email.

Baratto/Bergman/Hutchison Video Lectures on Digital Video Disk (DVD)

In the videos, qualified instructors work through selected problems from the textbook, following the solution methodology employed in the text. The video series is available on DVD or online as an assignable element of MathZone. The DVDs are closed-captioned for the hearing-impaired, are subtitled in Spanish, and meet the Americans with Disabilities Act Standards for Accessible Design. Instructors may use them as resources in a learning center, for online courses, and to provide extra help for students who require extra practice.

Annotated Instructor's Edition

In the *Annotated Instructor's Edition (AIE),* **answers to exercises and tests appear adjacent to each exercise set,** in a color used *only* for annotations. Also found in the *AIE* are icons within the Practice Exercises that serve to guide instructors in their preparation of homework assignments and lessons.

Instructor's Solutions Manual

The *Instructor's Solutions Manual* provides comprehensive, worked-out solutions to all exercises in the Pre-Test, Section Exercises, Summary Exercises, Self-Test, and the Cumulative Review. The methods used to solve the problems in the manual are the same as those used to solve the examples in the textbook.

A commitment to accuracy

You have a right to expect an accurate textbook, and McGraw-Hill invests considerable time and effort to make sure that we deliver one. Listed below are the many steps we take to make sure this happens.

1st Round
Author's Manuscript

↓

✓ Multiple Rounds of Review by College Math Instructors

↓

2nd Round
Typeset Pages

↓

Accuracy Checks by
✓ Authors
✓ Professional Mathematician
✓ 1st Proofreader

↓

3rd Round
Typeset Pages

↓

Accuracy Checks by
✓ Authors
✓ 2nd Proofreader

↓

4th Round
Typeset Pages

↓

Accuracy Checks by
✓ 3rd Proofreader
✓ Test Bank Author
✓ Solutions Manual Author
✓ Consulting Mathematicians for MathZone site
✓ Math Instructors for text's video series

↓

Final Round
Printing

↓

✓ Accuracy Check by
4th Proofreader

Our accuracy verification process

First Round

Step 1: Numerous **college math instructors** review the manuscript and report on any errors that they may find. Then the authors make these corrections in their final manuscript.

Second Round

Step 2: Once the manuscript has been typeset, the **authors** check their manuscript against the first page proofs to ensure that all illustrations, graphs, examples, exercises, solutions, and answers have been correctly laid out on the pages, and that all notation is correctly used.

Step 3: An outside, **professional, mathematician** works through every example and exercise in the page proofs to verify the accuracy of the answers.

Step 4: A **proofreader** adds a triple layer of accuracy assurance in the first pages by hunting for errors, then a second, corrected round of page proofs is produced.

Third Round

Step 5: The **author team** reviews the second round of page proofs for two reasons: (1) to make certain that any previous corrections were properly made, and (2) to look for any errors they might have missed on the first round.

Step 6: A **second proofreader** is added to the project to examine the new round of page proofs to double check the author team's work and to lend a fresh, critical eye to the book before the third round of paging.

Fourth Round

Step 7: A **third proofreader** inspects the third round of page proofs to verify that all previous corrections have been properly made and that there are no new or remaining errors.

Step 8: Meanwhile, in partnership with **independent mathematicians,** the text accuracy is verified from a variety of fresh perspectives:

- The **test bank author** checks for consistency and accuracy as he/she prepares the computerized test item file.
- The **solutions manual author** works every exercise and verifies his/her answers, reporting any errors to the publisher.
- A **consulting group of mathematicians,** who write material for the text's MathZone site, notifies the publisher of any errors they encounter in the page proofs.
- A video production company employing **expert math instructors** for the text's videos will alert the publisher of any errors they might find in the page proofs.

Final Round

Step 9: The **project manager,** who has overseen the book from the beginning, performs a **fourth proofread** of the textbook during the printing process, providing a final accuracy review.

⇒ What results is a mathematics textbook that is as accurate and error-free as is humanly possible. Our authors and publishing staff are confident that our many layers of quality assurance have produced textbooks that are the leaders in the industry for their integrity and correctness.

brief contents

contents

Chapter 5

Ratios and Proportions

Chapter 6

Percents

applications index

CHAPTER

1

Operations on Whole Numbers

INTRODUCTION

To supplement her income while attending college, Nadia answered an ad in a local paper to become a census worker. She got the job at a census bureau in her community. Because she was juggling school, studying, and raising a 4-year-old daughter, she was able to work only part-time. Nadia thought this would be a good way to earn some extra money.

Eventually, Nadia began to realize how important her work was. She spent time studying data pertaining to people and businesses in her county. She saw that by analyzing facts such as age, education, income, and family size, she could formulate certain ideas about her environment. She began working with city planners to help make projections pertaining to population growth. This enabled them to sketch out a blueprint to accommodate new housing, office buildings, roads, and a new school, based on certain predictions. Until this new job, Nadia never realized the impact math has on the lives of ordinary people. She decided to change her major to something that would allow her to continue her work with strategic planning. She also realized that she would need to take more mathematics and statistics classes to continue on this track.

To learn more about the U.S. Census Bureau data, do Activity 1 on page 38.

CHAPTER 1 OUTLINE

1.1 The Decimal Place-Value System

< 1.1 Objectives >

1 > Write numbers in expanded form

2 > Determine the place value of a digit

3 > Write a number in words

4 > Given its word name, write a number

Tips for Student Success

Throughout this text, we present you with a series of class-tested techniques that are designed to improve your performance in this math class.
Hint #1 Become familiar with your textbook.
Perform each of the following tasks.

1. Use the Table of Contents to find the title of Section 5.1.
2. Use the Index to find the earliest reference to the term *mean*. (By the way, this term has nothing to do with the personality of either your instructor or the textbook authors!)
3. Find the answer to the first Check Yourself exercise in Section 1.1.
4. Find the answers to the odd-numbered exercises in Section 1.1.
5. In the margin notes for Section 1.1, find the origin of the term *digit*.

Now you know where some of the most important features of the text are. When you have a moment of confusion, think about using one of these features to help you clear up that confusion. You should also find out whether a solutions manual is available for your text. Many students find these to be helpful.

Number systems have been developed throughout human history. Starting with simple tally systems used to count and keep track of possessions, more and more complex systems were developed. The Egyptians used a set of picturelike symbols called **hieroglyphics** to represent numbers. The Romans and Greeks had their own systems of numeration. We see the Roman system today in the form of Roman numerals. Some examples of these systems are shown in the following table.

Numerals	Egyptian	Greek	Roman
1	I	I	I
10	∩	Δ	X
100	ᑫ	H	C

NOTES

The prefix *deci* means 10. Our word *digit* comes from the Latin word *digitus,* which means finger.

Any number, no matter how large, can be represented using the 10 digits of our system.

Any number system provides a way of naming numbers. The system we use is described as a **decimal place-value system.** This system is based on the number 10 and uses symbols called **digits.** (Other numbers have also been used as bases. The Mayans used 20, and the Babylonians used 60.)

The basic symbols of our system are the digits 0, 1, 2, 3, 4, 5, 6, 7, 8, 9.

These basic symbols, or digits, were first used in India and then adopted by the Arabs. For this reason, our system is called the Hindu-Arabic numeration system.

Numbers may consist of one or more *digits*.

The numbers 3, 45, 567, and 2,359 are examples of the **standard form** for numbers. We say that 45 is a two-digit number, 567 is a three-digit number, and so on.

As we said, our decimal system uses a *place-value* concept based on the number 10. Understanding how this system works will help you see the reasons for the rules and methods of arithmetic that we will be introducing.

Example 1 Writing a Number in Expanded Form

< Objective 1 >

NOTES

Each digit in a number has its own place value.

Here the parentheses are used for emphasis. (4×100) means 4 is multiplied by 100. (3×10) means 3 is multiplied by 10. (8×1) means 8 is multiplied by 1.

Look at the number 438.

We call 8 the *ones digit.* As we move to the left, the digit 3 is the *tens digit.* Again as we move to the left, 4 is the *hundreds digit.*

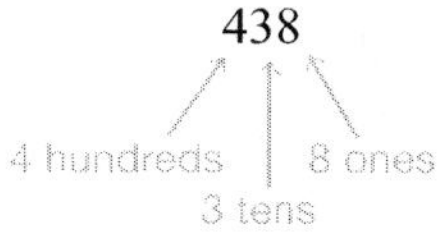

If we rewrite a number such that each digit is written with its units, we have used the **expanded form** for the number.

In expanded form, we write 438 as

$$400 + 30 + 8 \quad \text{or} \quad (4 \times 100) + (3 \times 10) + (8 \times 1)$$

Check Yourself 1

Write 593 in expanded form.

The following place-value diagram shows the place value of digits as we write larger numbers. For the number 3,156,024,798, we have

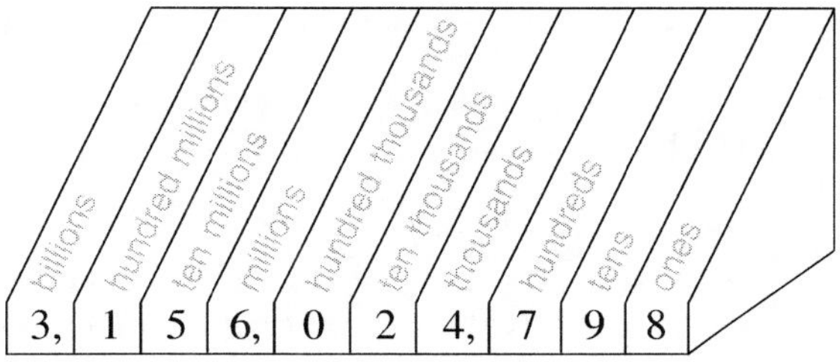

Of course, the naming of place values continues for larger numbers beyond the chart.

For the number 3,156,024,798, the place value of the digit 4 is thousands. As we move to the left, each place value is 10 times the value of the previous place. The place value of 2 is ten thousands, the place value of 0 is hundred thousands, and so on.

Example 2 Identifying Place Value

< Objective 2 >

Identify the place value of each digit in the number 418,295.

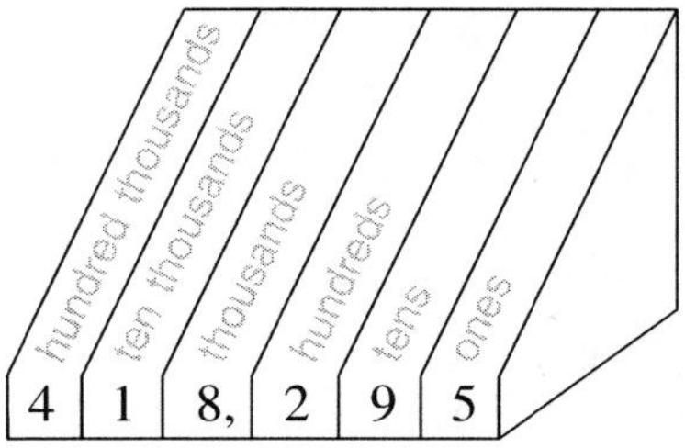

Check Yourself 2

Use a place-value diagram to answer the following questions for the number 6,831,425,097.

(a) What is the place value of 2?
(b) What is the place value of 4?
(c) What is the place value of 3?
(d) What is the place value of 6?

NOTE

A four-digit number, such as 3,456, can be written with or without a comma. We have chosen to write them with a comma in this text.

Understanding place value will help you read or write numbers in word form. Look at the number

7 2,	3 5 8,	6 9 4
Millions	Thousands	Ones

Commas are used to set off groups of three digits in the number. The name of each group—millions, thousands, ones, and so on—is then used as we write the number in words. To write a word name for a number, we work from left to right, writing the numbers in each group, followed by the group name. The following chart summarizes the group names.

Billions Group			Millions Group			Thousands Group			Ones Group		
Hundreds	Tens	Ones	Hundreds	Tens	Ones	Hundreds	Tens	Ones	Hundreds	Tens	Ones

Example 3 Writing Numbers in Words

< Objective 3 >

NOTE

The commas in the word statements are in the same place as the commas in the number.

Write the word name for each of the following.

27,345 is written in words as twenty-seven *thousand,* three hundred forty-five.

2,305,273 is two *million,* three hundred five *thousand,* two hundred seventy-three.

Note: We do *not* write the name of the ones group. Also, the word *and* is not used when a number is written in words. It will have a special meaning later.

Check Yourself 3

Write the word name for each of the following numbers.

(a) **658,942** **(b)** **2,305**

We reverse the process to write the standard form for numbers given in word form. Consider the following.

Example 4 Translating Words into Numbers

< Objective 4 >

Forty-eight thousand, five hundred seventy-nine in standard form is

48,579

Five hundred three thousand, two hundred thirty-eight in standard form is

503,238

Note the use of 0 as a placeholder in writing the number.

Check Yourself 4

Write twenty-three thousand, seven hundred nine in standard form.

Check Yourself ANSWERS

1. $(5 \times 100) + (9 \times 10) + (3 \times 1)$ **2.** **(a)** Ten thousands; **(b)** hundred thousands; **(c)** ten millions; **(d)** billions
3. **(a)** Six hundred fifty-eight thousand, nine hundred forty-two; **(b)** two thousand, three hundred five **4.** 23,709

Reading Your Text

The following fill-in-the-blank exercises are designed to ensure that you understand some of the key vocabulary used in this section.

SECTION 1.1

(a) The system we use for naming numbers is described as a ________ place-value system.

(b) We say the number 567 is a three-____________ number.

(c) A four-digit number can be written with or without a ____________.

(d) In words, the number 2,000,000 is written as two ____________.

1.1 exercises

Basic Skills | Challenge Yourself | Calculator/Computer | Career Applications | Above and Beyond

Boost *your* GRADE at ALEKS.com!

ALEKS®

- Practice Problems
- Self-Tests
- NetTutor
- e-Professors
- Videos

Name ______________

Section ________ Date ________

Answers

1. ______
2. ______
3. ______
4. ______
5. ______
6. ______
7. ______
8. ______
9. ______ 10. ______
11. ______ 12. ______
13. ______
14. ______
15. ______
16. ______
17. ______
18. ______
19. ______
20. ______

< Objective 1 >

Write each number in expanded form.

1. 456

2. 637

3. 5,073 > Videos

4. 20,721

< Objective 2 >

Give the place values for the indicated digits.

5. 4 in the number 416

6. 3 in the number 38,615

7. 6 in the number 56,489

8. 4 in the number 427,083

9. In the number 43,729

(a) what digit tells the number of thousands?

(b) what digit tells the number of tens?

10. In the number 456,719

(a) what digit tells the number of ten thousands?

(b) what digit tells the number of hundreds?

11. In the number 1,403,602

(a) what digit tells the number of hundred thousands?

(b) what digit tells the number of ones? > Videos

12. In the number 324,678,903

(a) what digit tells the number of millions?

(b) what digit tells the number of ten thousands?

< Objective 3 >

Write the word name of each number.

13. 5,618 > Videos

14. 21,812

15. 200,304 > Videos

16. 103,900

< Objective 4 >

Write each number in standard form.

17. Two hundred fifty-three thousand, four hundred eighty-three

18. Three hundred fifty thousand, three hundred fifty-nine

19. Five hundred two million, seventy-eight thousand > Videos

20. Four billion, two hundred thirty million

Write the whole number in each sentence in standard form.

21. **Statistics** The first-place finisher in the 2004 U.S. Open won one million one hundred twenty-five thousand dollars.

22. **Science and Medicine** Scientific speculation is that the universe originated in the explosion of a primordial fireball approximately fourteen billion years ago.

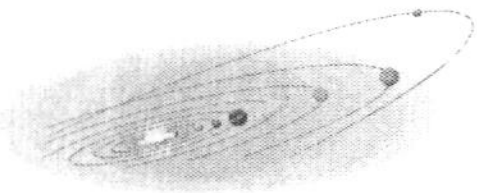

23. **Social Science** The population of Kansas City, Missouri, in 2000 was approximately four hundred forty-one thousand, five hundred.

24. **Social Science** The Nile river in Egypt is about four thousand, one hundred forty-five miles long.

Basic Skills | **Challenge Yourself** | Calculator/Computer | Career Applications | Above and Beyond

Sometimes numbers found in charts and tables are abbreviated. The following table represents the population of the 10 largest cities in the 2000 U.S. census. Note that the numbers represent thousands. Thus, Detroit had a population of 951 thousand or 951,000.

chapter 1 > Make the Connection

Name	Rank	Population (thousands)
New York City, NY	1	8,008
Los Angeles, CA	2	3,695
Chicago, IL	3	2,896
Houston, TX	4	1,954
Philadelphia, PA	5	1,518
Phoenix, AZ	6	1,321
San Diego, CA	7	1,223
Dallas, TX	8	1,189
San Antonio, TX	9	1,145
Detroit, MI	10	951

Source: U.S. Census Bureau

Social Science In exercises 25 to 28, write your answers in standard form, using the preceding table.

25. What was the population of San Diego in 2000?

Answers

21. ____

22. ____

23. ____

24. ____

25. ____

Answers

26. ______

27. ______

28. ______

29. ______

30. ______

31. ______

32. ______

33. ______

34. ______

35. ______

36. ______

26. What was the population of Chicago in 2000?

27. What was the population of Philadelphia in 2000?

28. What was the population of Dallas in 2000?

Determine the number represented by the scrambled place values.

29. 4 thousands
1 tens
3 ten thousands
5 ones
2 hundreds

30. 7 hundreds
4 ten thousands
9 ones
8 tens
6 thousands

Assume that you have alphabetized the word names for every number from one to one thousand.

31. Which number would appear first in the list?

32. Which number would appear last?

33. **Business and Finance** Inci had to write a check for $2,565. There is a space on the check to write out the amount of the check in words. What should she write in this space?

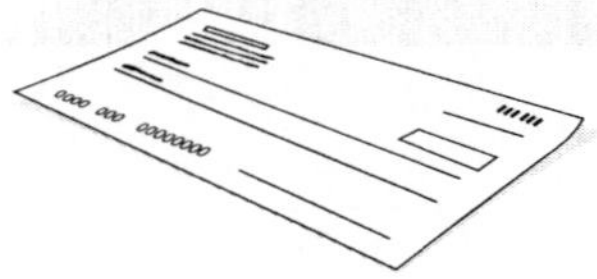

34. **Business and Finance** In a rental agreement, the amount of the initial deposit required is two thousand, five hundred forty-five dollars. Write this amount as a number.

Basic Skills | Challenge Yourself | Calculator/Computer | **Career Applications** | Above and Beyond

35. **Allied Health** Doctor Edwards prescribes four hundred eighty thousand units of penicillin G benzathine to treat a 3-year-old child with a streptococcal infection. Write this amount as a number.

36. **Allied Health** Doctor Hill prescribes one thousand, one hundred eighty-three milligrams (mg) of amifostine to be administered together with an adult patient's chemotherapy to reduce the adverse effects of the treatment. Write this amount as a number.

Use this table to complete exercise 37 on the following page.

Child's Weight (lb)	Dose of Penicillin G Potassium (thousands of units)
30	680
35	795
40	910
45	1,020
50	1,135

37. ALLIED HEALTH Write your answers in standard form using the preceding table.

(a) Carla weighs 35 pounds (lb). What dose of penicillin G potassium should her doctor prescribe?

(b) Nelson weighs 50 lb. What dose of penicillin G potassium should his doctor prescribe?

(c) What dose of penicillin G potassium is required for a child weighing 40 lb?

38. ELECTRONICS Write your answers in standard form using the following table.

Appliance	Estimated Power Consumption [thousands of watts/hour (W/h)]
Drip coffeemaker	301
Electric blanket	120
Laser printer	466
Personal computer	25
Video game system	49

(a) What is the estimated power consumption of a laser printer?

(b) What is the estimated power consumption of a video game system?

(c) What is the estimated power consumption of an electric blanket?

39. NUMBER PROBLEM Write the largest five-digit number that can be made using the digits 6, 3, and 9 if each digit is to be used at least once.

Basic Skills | Challenge Yourself | Calculator/Computer | Career Applications | **Above and Beyond**

40. What are the advantages of a place-value system of numeration?

41. SOCIAL SCIENCE The number 0 was not used initially by the Hindus in our number system (about 250 B.C.E.). Go to your library (or "surf the net"), and determine when a symbol for zero was introduced. What do you think is the importance of the role of 0 in a numeration system?

42. A *googol* is a very large number. Do some research to find out how big it is. Also try to find out where the name of this number comes from.

Answers

We provide the answers for the odd-numbered exercises at the end of each exercise set. The answers for the even-numbered exercises are provided in the instructor's resource manual.

1. $(4 \times 100) + (5 \times 10) + (6 \times 1)$ **3.** $(5 \times 1{,}000) + (7 \times 10) + (3 \times 1)$
5. Hundreds **7.** Thousands **9.** (a) 3; (b) 2 **11.** (a) 4; (b) 2
13. Five thousand, six hundred eighteen
15. Two hundred thousand, three hundred four
17. 253,483 **19.** 502,078,000 **21.** $1,125,000
23. 441,500 **25.** 1,223,000 **27.** 1,518,000 **29.** 34,215
31. Eight **33.** Two thousand, five hundred sixty-five **35.** 480,000
37. (a) 795,000; (b) 1,135,000; (c) 910,000 **39.** 99,963
41. Above and Beyond

Answers

37. ______

38. ______

39. ______

40. ______

41. ______

42. ______

1.2 Addition

< 1.2 Objectives >

1 > Add single-digit numbers
2 > Identify the properties of addition
3 > Add groups of numbers with no carrying
4 > Use the language of addition
5 > Solve simple applications
6 > Add any group of numbers
7 > Find the perimeter of a figure
8 > Solve applications that involve perimeter

Tips for Student Success

Hint #2 Become familiar with your syllabus.
In the first class meeting, your instructor probably handed out a class syllabus. If you haven't done so already, you need to put important information into your calendar and address book.

1. Write all important dates in your calendar. This includes homework due dates, quiz dates, test dates, and the date and time of the final exam. Never allow yourself to be surprised by any deadline!
2. Write your instructor's name, contact number, and office number in your address book. Also include the office hours and e-mail address. Make it a point to see your instructor early in the term. Although this is not the only person who can help clear up your confusion, he or she is the most important person.
3. Make note of other resources that are made available to you. These include CDs, videotapes, Web pages, and tutoring.

Given all these resources, it is important that you never let confusion or frustration mount. If you can't "get it" from the text, try another resource. All the resources are there specifically for you, so take advantage of them!

NOTE

The series of three dots (. . .) is called an **ellipsis;** they mean that the indicated pattern continues.

The *natural* or *counting numbers* are the numbers we use to count objects.

The natural numbers are 1, 2, 3, . . .

When we include the number 0, we have the set of *whole numbers.*

The whole numbers are 0, 1, 2, 3, . . .

Let's look at the operation of *addition* on the whole numbers.

Definition

Addition

Addition is the combining of two or more groups of the same kind of objects.

This concept is extremely important, as we will see in our later work with fractions. We can only combine or add numbers that represent the same kind of objects.

From your first encounter with arithmetic, you were taught to add "3 apples plus 2 apples."

On the other hand, you have probably encountered a phrase such as "that's like combining apples and oranges." That is to say, what do you get when you add 3 apples and 2 oranges?

You could answer "5 fruits," or "5 objects," but you cannot combine the apples and the oranges.

What if you walked 3 miles and then walked 2 more miles? Clearly, you have now walked 3 miles + 2 miles = 5 miles. The addition is possible because the groups are of the same kind.

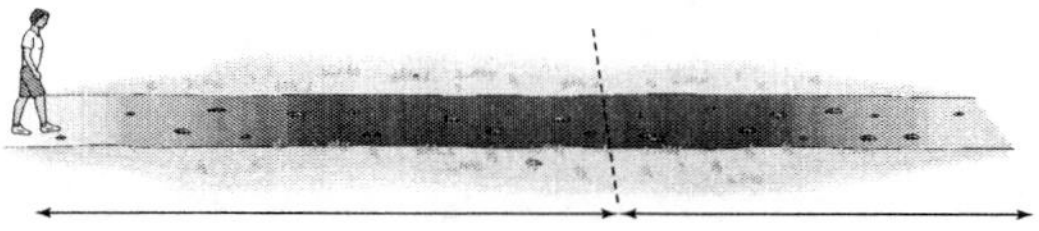

NOTES

The first printed use of the symbol + dates back to 1526 (Smith, *History of Math,* Vol. II.)

The point labeled 0 is called the **origin** of the number line.

Each operation of arithmetic has its own special terms and symbols. The addition symbol + is read **plus.** When we write 3 + 4, 3 and 4 are called the **addends.**

We can use a number line to illustrate the addition process. To construct a number line, we pick a point on the line and label it 0. We then mark off evenly-spaced units to the right, naming each marked point with a successively larger whole number.

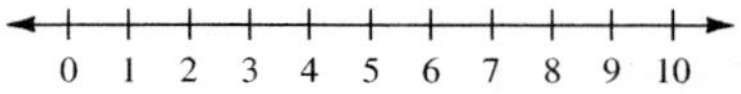

We use arrowheads to show the number line continues.

Example 1 Representing Addition on a Number Line

< Objective 1 >

Represent 3 + 4 on the number line.

To represent an addition, such as 3 + 4, on the number line, start by moving 3 spaces to the right of the origin. Then move 4 more spaces to the right to arrive at 7. The number 7 is called the *sum* of the addends.

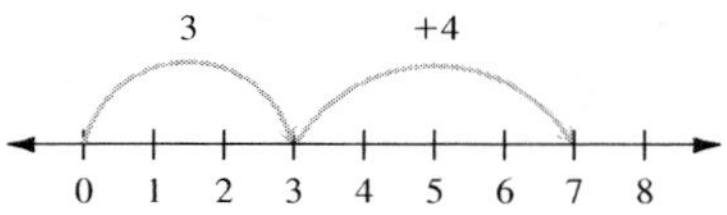

We can write 3 + 4 = 7

Addend Addend Sum

NOTE

Again, addition corresponds to combining groups of the same kind of objects.

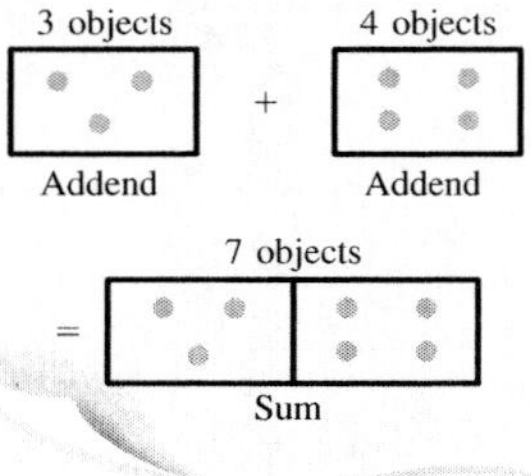

Check Yourself 1

Represent 5 + 6 on the number line.

A statement such as 3 + 4 = 7 is one of the **basic addition facts.** These facts include the sum of every possible pair of digits. Before you can add larger numbers correctly and quickly, you must memorize these basic facts.

Basic Addition Facts

+	0	1	2	3	4	5	6	7	8	9
0	0	1	2	3	4	5	6	7	8	9
1	1	2	3	4	5	6	7	8	9	10
2	2	3	4	5	6	7	8	9	10	11
3	3	4	5	6	7	8	9	10	11	12
4	4	5	6	7	8	9	10	11	12	13
5	5	6	7	8	9	10	11	12	13	14
6	6	7	8	9	10	11	12	13	14	15
7	7	8	9	10	11	12	13	14	15	16
8	8	9	10	11	12	13	14	15	16	17
9	9	10	11	12	13	14	15	16	17	18

NOTES

To find the sum $5 + 8$, start with the row labeled 5. Move along that row to the column headed 8 to find the sum, 13.

Commute means to move back and forth, as to school or work.

Examining the basic addition facts leads us to several important properties of addition on whole numbers. For instance, we know that the sum $3 + 4$ is 7. What about the sum $4 + 3$? It is also 7. This is an illustration of the fact that addition is a **commutative** operation.

Property

The Commutative Property of Addition

The order of two numbers around an addition sign *does not* affect the sum.

Example 2 Using the Commutative Property

< Objective 2 >

$8 + 5 = 13 = 5 + 8$

$6 + 9 = 15 = 9 + 6$

NOTE

The *order* does not affect the sum.

Check Yourself 2

Show that the sum on the left equals the sum on the right.

$7 + 8 = 8 + 7$

If we wish to add *more* than two numbers, we can group them and then add. In mathematics this grouping is indicated by a set of parentheses ( ). This symbol tells us to perform the operation inside the parentheses first.

Example 3 Using the Associative Property

NOTES

We add 3 and 4 as the first step and then add 5.

Here we add 4 and 5 as the first step and then add 3. Again the final sum is 12.

$(3 + 4) + 5 = 7 + 5 = 12$

We also have

$3 + (4 + 5) = 3 + 9 = 12$

This example suggests the following property of whole numbers.

Property

The Associative Property of Addition

The way in which several whole numbers are grouped *does not* affect the final sum when they are added.

NOTE

In Example 3, the addend 4 can be "associated" with the 3 or the 5.

Check Yourself 3

Find

(4 + 8) + 3 and 4 + (8 + 3)

The number 0 has a special property in addition.

Property

The Additive Identity Property

The sum of 0 and any whole number is just that whole number.

Because of this property, we call 0 the **identity** for the addition operation.

Example 4 Adding Zero

Find the sum of **(a)** 3 + 0 and **(b)** 0 + 8.

(a) $3 + 0 = 3$ **(b)** $0 + 8 = 8$

Check Yourself 4

Find each sum.

(a) 4 + 0 (b) 0 + 7

Next, we turn to the process of adding larger numbers. We apply the following rule.

Property

Adding Digits of the Same Place Value

We can add the digits of the same place value because they represent the same types of quantities.

NOTE

Remember that 25 means 2 tens and 5 ones; 34 means 3 tens and 4 ones.

Adding two numbers, such as 25 + 34, can be done in expanded form. Here we write out the place value for each digit.

$$\begin{aligned} 25 &= 2 \text{ tens} + 5 \text{ ones} \\ +\ 34 &= 3 \text{ tens} + 4 \text{ ones} \\ &= 5 \text{ tens} + 9 \text{ ones} \\ &= 59 \end{aligned}$$

Add down.

In actual practice, we use a more convenient short form to perform the addition.

Example 5 Adding Two Numbers

< Objective 3 >

NOTE

In using the short form, be very careful to line up the numbers correctly so that each column contains digits of the same place value.

Add 352 + 546.

Step 1 Add in the ones column.

$$\begin{array}{r} 352 \\ +\ 546 \\ \hline 8 \end{array}$$

Step 2 Add in the tens column.

$$\begin{array}{r} 352 \\ +\ 546 \\ \hline 98 \end{array}$$

Step 3 Add in the hundreds column.

$$\begin{array}{r} 352 \\ +\ 546 \\ \hline 898 \end{array}$$

Check Yourself 5

Add.

$$\begin{array}{r} 245 \\ +\ 632 \\ \hline \end{array}$$

You have already seen that the word *sum* indicates addition. There are other words that also tell you to use the addition operation.

The *total* of 12 and 5 is written as

12 + 5 or 17

8 *more than* 10 is written as

10 + 8 or 18

12 *increased by* 3 is written as

12 + 3 or 15

Example 6 Translating Words That Indicate Addition

< Objective 4 >

Find each of the following.

(a) 36 increased by 12.

36 increased by 12 is written as 36 + 12 = 48.

(b) The total of 18 and 31.

The total of 18 and 31 is written as 18 + 31 = 49.

NOTE

Get into the habit of writing down *all* your work, rather than just an answer.

Check Yourself 6

Find each of the following.

(a) **43 increased by 25** **(b)** **The total of 22 and 73**

Now we consider applications, or word problems, that will use the operation of addition. An organized approach is the key to successful problem solving, and we suggest the following strategy.

Step by Step

Solving Addition Applications

Step 1 Read the problem carefully to determine the given information and what you are being asked to find.

Step 2 Decide upon the operation (in this case, addition) to be used.

Step 3 Write down the complete statement necessary to solve the problem and do the calculations.

Step 4 Write your answer as a complete sentence. Check to make sure you have answered the question of the problem and that your answer seems reasonable.

We work through an example, using these steps.

Example 7 Setting Up a Word Problem

< Objective 5 >

Four sections of algebra were offered in the fall quarter, with enrollments of 33, 24, 20, and 22 students. What was the total number of students taking algebra?

Step 1 The given information is the number of students in each section. We want the total number.

Step 2 Since we are looking for a total, we use addition.

Step 3 Write 33 + 24 + 20 + 22 = 99 students.

Step 4 There were 99 students taking algebra.

NOTE

Remember to attach the proper unit (here "students") to your answer.

Check Yourself 7

Elva Ramos won an election for city council with 3,110 votes. Her two opponents had 1,022 and 1,211 votes. How many votes were cast in that election?

In the previous examples and exercises, the digits in each column added to 9 or less. We now look at the situation in which a column has a two-digit sum. This will involve the process of **carrying.** Look at the process in expanded form.

Example 8 Adding in Expanded Form When Regrouping Is Needed

< Objective 6 >

$$\begin{array}{rrcl} 67 & = & 60 & + 7 \\ +\ 28 & = & 20 & + 8 \\ \hline & & 80 & + 15 \end{array}$$

We have written 15 ones as 1 ten and 5 ones.

or $80 + 10 + 5$

The 1 ten is then combined with the 8 tens.

or $90 \quad + 5$

or 95

NOTE

Regrouping in addition is also called *carrying*. Of course, the name makes no difference as long as you understand the process.

The more convenient short form carries the excess units from one column to the next column to the left. Recall that the place value of the next column to the left is 10 times the value of the original column. It is this property of our decimal place-value system that makes carrying work. We work this problem again, this time using the short, or "carrying," form.

NOTE

This is true for any sized number. The place value thousands is 10 times the place value hundreds, and so on.

Step 1 **Step 2**

Carry 1 ten.

$$\begin{array}{r} ^{1}\ \ \\ 67 \\ +\ 28 \\ \hline 5 \end{array} \qquad \begin{array}{r} ^{1}\ \ \\ 67 \\ +\ 28 \\ \hline 95 \end{array}$$

Step 1: The sum of the digits in the ones column is 15, so write 5 and make the 10 ones a 1 in the tens column. **Step 2:** Now add in the tens column, being sure to include the carried 1.

Check Yourself 8

Add.

(a) $\begin{array}{r} 58 \\ +\ 36 \\ \hline \end{array}$ **(b)** $\begin{array}{r} 73 \\ +\ 18 \\ \hline \end{array}$ **(c)** $\begin{array}{r} 68 \\ +\ 25 \\ \hline \end{array}$

The addition process often requires more than one regrouping step, as is shown in Example 9.

Example 9 Adding in Short Form When Regrouping Is Needed

Add 285 and 378.

$$\begin{array}{r} {}^{1} \\ 285 \\ +\ 378 \\ \hline 3 \end{array}$$

← Write the 10 as 1 ten.

The sum of the digits in the ones column is 13, so write 3 and carry 1 to the tens column.

Carry → 1 hundred.

$$\begin{array}{r} {}^{1\,1} \\ 285 \\ +\ 378 \\ \hline 63 \end{array}$$

Now add in the tens column, being sure to include the carry. We have 16 tens, so write 6 in the tens place and carry 1 to the hundreds column.

$$\begin{array}{r} {}^{1\,1} \\ 285 \\ +\ 378 \\ \hline 663 \end{array}$$

Finally, add in the hundreds column.

Check Yourself 9

Add.

(a) $\begin{array}{r} 479 \\ +\ 287 \\ \hline \end{array}$

(b) $\begin{array}{r} 585 \\ +\ 368 \\ \hline \end{array}$

The regrouping process is the same if we want to add more than two numbers.

Example 10 Adding in Short Form with Multiple Regrouping Steps

Add 53, 2,678, 587, and 27,009.

$$\begin{array}{r} {}^{1\,1\ 2\,2} \\ 53 \\ 2{,}678 \\ 587 \\ +\ 27{,}009 \\ \hline 30{,}327 \end{array}$$

← Carries

Add in the ones column: 3 + 8 + 7 + 9 = 27. Write 7 in the sum and carry 2 to the tens column.

Now add in the tens column, being sure to include the carry. The sum is 22. Write 2 tens and carry 2 to the hundreds column. Complete the addition by adding in the hundreds column, the thousands column, and the ten thousands column.

Check Yourself 10

Add 46, 365, 7,254, and 24,006.

Finding the *perimeter* of a figure is one application of addition.

Definition

Perimeter

Perimeter is the distance around a closed figure.

If the figure has straight sides, the perimeter is the sum of the lengths of its sides.

Example 11 Finding the Perimeter

< Objective 7 >

NOTE

Make sure to include the unit with each number.

We wish to fence in the field shown in the figure. How much fencing, in feet (ft), will be needed?

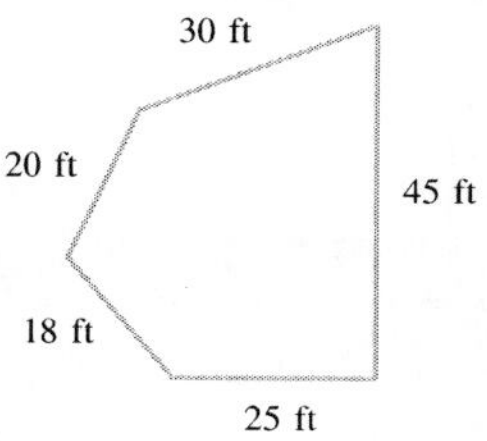

The fencing needed is the perimeter of (or the distance around) the field. We must add the lengths of the five sides.

20 ft + 30 ft + 45 ft + 25 ft + 18 ft = 138 ft

So the perimeter is 138 ft.

Check Yourself 11

What is the perimeter of the region shown?

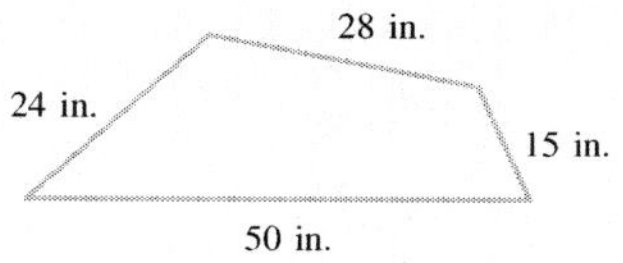

A **rectangle** is a figure, like a sheet of paper, with four equal corners. The perimeter of a rectangle is found by adding the lengths of the four sides.

Example 12 Finding the Perimeter of a Rectangle

Find the perimeter in inches (in.) of the rectangle pictured here.

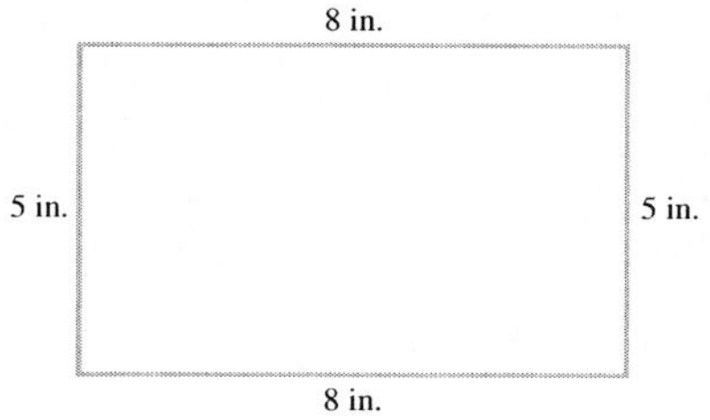

The perimeter is the sum of the lengths 8 in., 5 in., 8 in., and 5 in.

8 in. + 5 in. + 8 in. + 5 in. = 26 in.

The perimeter of the rectangle is 26 in.

Check Yourself 12

Find the perimeter of the rectangle pictured here.

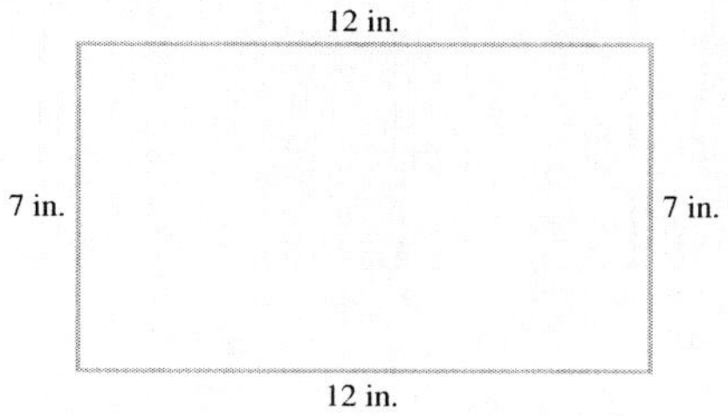

In general, we can find the perimeter of a rectangle by using a *formula*. A **formula** is a set of symbols that describe a general solution to a problem.

Look at a picture of a rectangle.

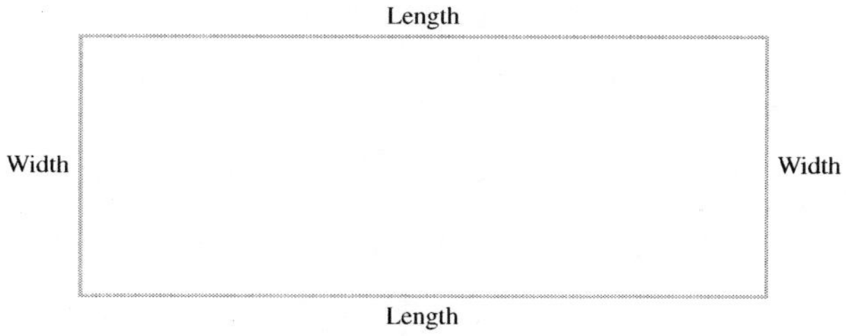

The perimeter can be found by adding the distances, so

Perimeter = length + width + length + width

To make this formula a little more readable, we abbreviate each of the words, using just the first letter.

Property

Formula for the Perimeter of a Rectangle

$$P = L + W + L + W \qquad (1)$$

There is another version of this formula that we can use. Because we add the length (L) twice, we could write that as $2 \cdot L$. Because we add the width (W) twice, we could write that as $2 \cdot W$. This gives us another version of the formula.

Property

Formula for the Perimeter of a Rectangle

$$P = 2 \cdot L + 2 \cdot W \qquad (2)$$

In words, we say that the perimeter of a rectangle is twice its length plus twice its width. Example 13 uses formula (1).

Example 13 Finding the Perimeter of a Rectangle

< Objective 8 >

NOTE

We say the rectangle is 8 in. by 11 in.

A rectangle has length 11 in. and width 8 in. What is its perimeter?

Start by drawing a picture of the problem.

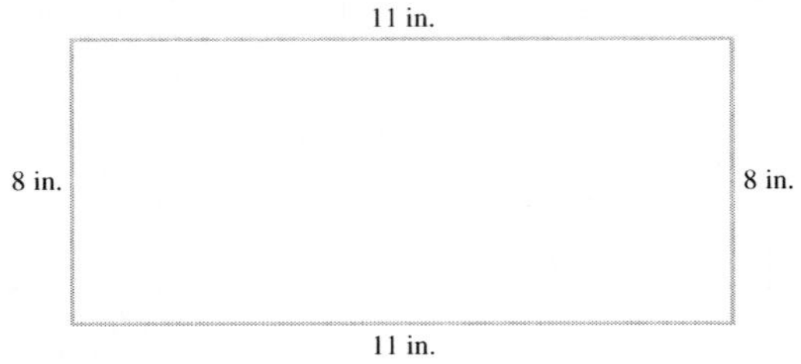

Now use formula (1).

$P = 11$ in. $+ 8$ in. $+ 11$ in. $+ 8$ in.

$= 38$ in.

The perimeter is 38 in.

Check Yourself 13

A bedroom is 9 ft by 12 ft. What is its perimeter?

Check Yourself ANSWERS

1. 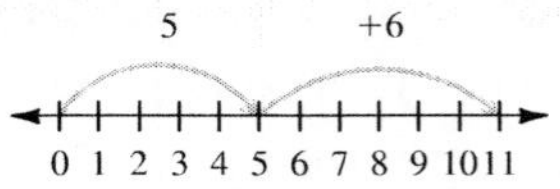

$5 + 6 = 11$

2. $7 + 8 = 15$ and $8 + 7 = 15$
3. $(4 + 8) + 3 = 12 + 3 = 15$; $4 + (8 + 3) = 4 + 11 = 15$
4. **(a)** 4; **(b)** 7 **5.** 877 **6.** **(a)** 68; **(b)** 95 **7.** 5,343 votes
8. **(a)** 94; **(b)** 91; **(c)** 93 **9.** **(a)** 766; **(b)** 953 **10.** 31,671
11. 117 in. **12.** 38 in. **13.** 42 ft

Reading Your Text

The following fill-in-the-blank exercises are designed to ensure that you understand some of the key vocabulary used in this section.

SECTION 1.2

(a) The ________ or counting numbers are the numbers used to count objects.

(b) A statement such as 3 + 4 = 7 is one of the basic ________ facts.

(c) The ________ of two numbers around an addition sign does not affect the sum.

(d) The first step in solving an addition application is to ________ the problem carefully.

1.2 exercises

Boost *your* GRADE at ALEKS.com!

Name ____________

Section ________ Date ________

Answers

1. ____
2. ____
3. ____
4. ____
5. ____
6. ____
7. ____
8. ____
9. ____ 10. ____
11. ____ 12. ____
13. ____ 14. ____
15. ____ 16. ____
17. ____ 18. ____
19. ____ 20. ____
21. ____ 22. ____
23. ____
24. ____
25. ____ 26. ____
27. ____ 28. ____

Basic Skills | Challenge Yourself | Calculator/Computer | Career Applications | Above and Beyond

< Objective 2 >

Name the property of addition that is illustrated. Explain your choice of property.

1. $5 + 8 = 8 + 5$

2. $2 + (7 + 9) = (2 + 7) + 9$

3. $(4 + 5) + 8 = 4 + (5 + 8)$

4. $9 + 7 = 7 + 9$

5. $4 + (7 + 6) = 4 + (6 + 7)$

6. $5 + 0 = 5$

7. $5 + (2 + 3) = (2 + 3) + 5$

8. $3 + (0 + 6) = (3 + 0) + 6$

< Objectives 3, 6 >

Perform the indicated addition.

9. $\begin{array}{r} 2{,}792 \\ +\ \ 205 \\ \hline \end{array}$

10. $\begin{array}{r} 5{,}463 \\ +\ \ 435 \\ \hline \end{array}$

11. $\begin{array}{r} 2{,}345 \\ +\ 6{,}053 \\ \hline \end{array}$

12. $\begin{array}{r} 3{,}271 \\ +\ 4{,}715 \\ \hline \end{array}$

13. $\begin{array}{r} 2{,}531 \\ +\ 5{,}354 \\ \hline \end{array}$

14. $\begin{array}{r} 5{,}003 \\ +\ 4{,}205 \\ \hline \end{array}$

15. $\begin{array}{r} 21{,}314 \\ +\ 43{,}042 \\ \hline \end{array}$

16. $\begin{array}{r} 12{,}325 \\ +\ 35{,}403 \\ \hline \end{array}$

17. $\begin{array}{r} 3{,}490 \\ 548 \\ +\ \ 25 \\ \hline \end{array}$

18. $\begin{array}{r} 678 \\ 4{,}533 \\ +\ \ 70 \\ \hline \end{array}$

19. $\begin{array}{r} 2{,}289 \\ 38 \\ 578 \\ +\ 3{,}489 \\ \hline \end{array}$

20. $\begin{array}{r} 3{,}678 \\ 259 \\ 27 \\ +\ 2{,}356 \\ \hline \end{array}$

21. $\begin{array}{r} 23{,}458 \\ +\ 32{,}623 \\ \hline \end{array}$

22. $\begin{array}{r} 52{,}591 \\ +\ 59{,}739 \\ \hline \end{array}$

< Objective 4 >

23. In the statement $5 + 4 = 9$
5 is called an ________.
4 is called an ________.
9 is called the ________.

24. In the statement $7 + 8 = 15$
7 is called an ________.
8 is called an ________.
15 is called the ________.

< Objectives 7, 8 >

Find the perimeter of each figure.

25.

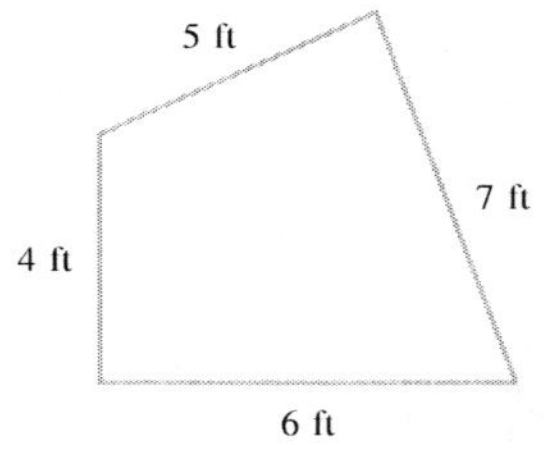

26.

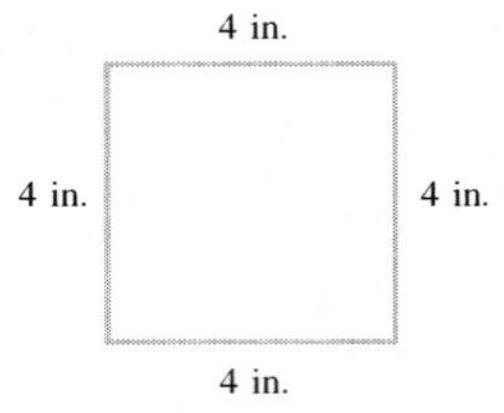

27.

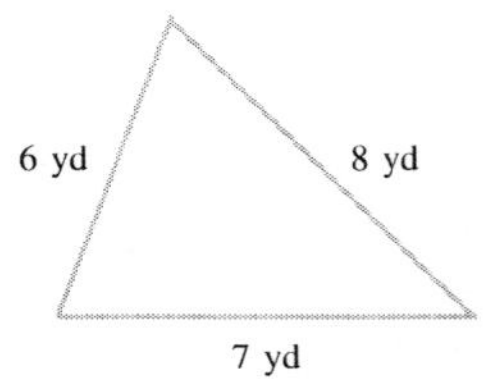

28.

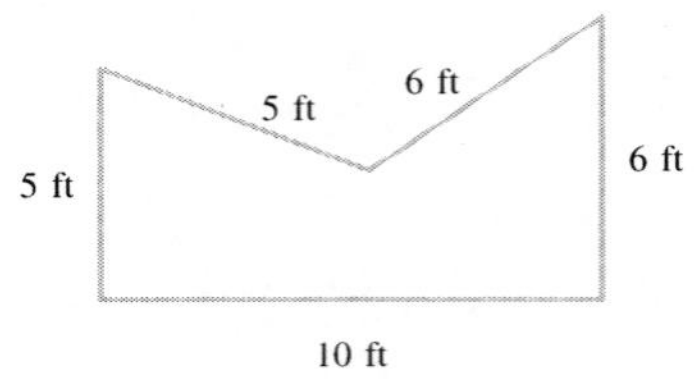

29.

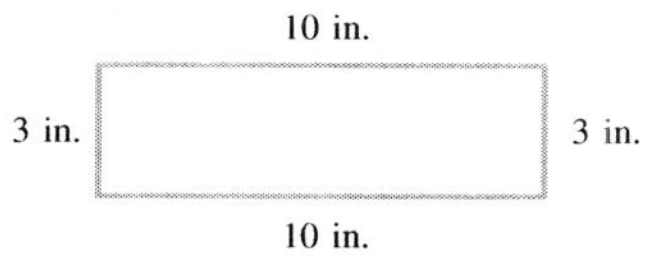

30.

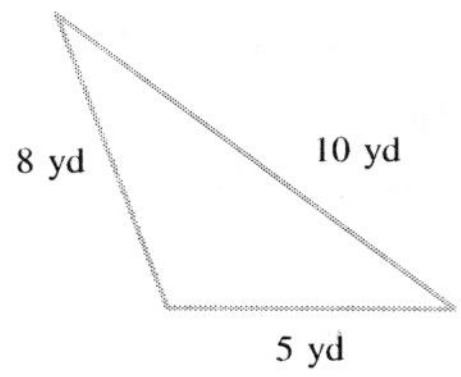

31. In each of the following exercises, find the appropriate sum.

(a) Find the number that is 356 more than 1,213.

(b) Add 23, 2,845, 5, and 589.

(c) What is the total of the five numbers 2,195, 348, 640, 59, and 23,785?

(d) Find the number that is 34 more than 125.

(e) What is 457 increased by 96?

32. In each of the following exercises, find the appropriate sum.

(a) Find the number that is 567 more than 2,322.

(b) Add 5,637, 78, 690, 28, and 35,589.

(c) What is the total of the five numbers 3,295, 9, 427, 56, and 11,100?

(d) Find the number that is 124 more than 2,351.

(e) What is 926 increased by 86?

33. **Business and Finance** Tral bought a 1931 Model A for $15,200, a 1964 Thunderbird convertible for $17,100, and a 1959 Austin Healy Mark I for $17,450. How much did he invest in the three cars?

34. **Business and Finance** The following chart shows Family Video's monthly rentals for the first 3 months of 2006 by category of film. Complete the totals.

Category of Film	Jan.	Feb.	Mar.	Category Totals
Comedy	4,568	3,269	2,189	______
Drama	5,612	4,129	3,879	______
Action/Adventure	2,654	3,178	1,984	______
Musical	897	623	528	______
Monthly Totals				

35. **Business and Finance** The following chart shows Regina's Dress Shop's expenses by department for the last 3 months of the year. Complete the totals.

Department	Oct.	Nov.	Dec.	Department Totals
Office	$31,714	$32,512	$30,826	______
Production	85,146	87,479	81,234	______
Sales	34,568	37,612	33,455	______
Warehouse	16,588	11,368	13,567	______
Monthly Totals				

Answers

29. ______

30. ______

31. ______

32. ______

33. ______

34. ______

35. ______

Answers

36. ______

37. ______

38. ______

36. Social Science The following table ranks the top 10 areas for women-owned firms in the United States.

Metro Area	Number of Firms	Employment	Sales (in millions)
Los Angeles–Long Beach, Calif.	360,300	1,056,600	$181,455,900
New York	282,000	1,077,900	193,572,200
Chicago	260,200	1,108,800	161,200,900
Washington, D.C.	193,600	440,000	56,644,000
Philadelphia	144,600	695,900	90,231,000
Atlanta	138,700	331,800	50,206,800
Houston	136,400	560,100	78,180,300
Dallas	123,900	431,900	63,114,900
Detroit	123,600	371,400	50,060,700
Minneapolis–St. Paul, Minn.	119,600	337,400	51,063,400

(a) How many firms in total are located in Washington, Philadelphia, and New York?

(b) What is the total number of employees in all 10 of the areas listed?

(c) What are the total sales for firms in Houston and Dallas?

(d) How many firms in total are located in Chicago and Detroit?

chapter 1 > Make the Connection

37. Number Problem The following sequences are called *arithmetic sequences*. Determine the pattern and write the next four numbers in each sequence.

(a) 5, 12, 19, 26, ____, ____, ____, ____

(b) 8, 14, 20, 26, ____, ____, ____, ____

(c) 7, 13, 19, 25, ____, ____, ____, ____

(d) 9, 17, 25, 33, ____, ____, ____, ____

38. Number Problem Fibonacci numbers occur in the sequence

1, 1, 2, 3, 5, 8, 13, 21, 34, 55, . . .

This sequence begins with the numbers 1 and 1 again, and each subsequent number is obtained by adding the two preceding numbers.

Find the next four numbers in the sequence.

Basic Skills | Challenge Yourself | **Calculator/Computer** | Career Applications | Above and Beyond

Although this text is designed to help you master the basic skills of arithmetic, it is occasionally preferable to perform complex calculations on a calculator. To that end, many of the exercise sets include a short explanation of how to use a calculator to do an operation described in the section. This explanation will be followed by a set of exercises for which the calculator might be the preferred tool. As indicated by the placement of the explanation, you should refrain from using a calculator on the exercises that precede it.

To perform the addition

2,473 + 258 + 35 + 5,823

Step 1	Press the clear key.	[C]
Step 2	Enter the first number.	2473
Step 3	Enter the plus key followed by the next number.	[+] 258
Step 4	Continue with the addition until the last number is entered.	[+] 35
		[+] 5823
Step 5	Press the equal-sign or enter key.	[=]
The desired sum should now be in the display.		8589

Use your calculator to find each sum.

39. 3,295,153 + 573,128 + 21,257 + 2,586,241 + 5,291

40. 23,563 + 5,638,487 + 385,005 + 27,345

Use your calculator to solve each application.

41. BUSINESS AND FINANCE The following table shows the number of customers using three branches of a bank during one week. Complete the table by finding the daily, weekly, and grand totals.

Branch	Mon.	Tues.	Wed.	Thurs.	Fri.	Weekly Totals
Downtown	487	356	429	278	834	______
Suburban	236	255	254	198	423	______
Westside	345	278	323	257	563	______
Daily Totals						______

42. STATISTICS The following table lists the number of possible types of poker hand. What is the total number of hands possible?

Royal flush	4
Straight flush	36
Four of a kind	624
Full house	3,744
Flush	5,108
Straight	10,200
Three of a kind	54,912
Two pairs	123,552
One pair	1,098,240
Nothing	1,302,540
Total Possible Hands	

Basic Skills | Challenge Yourself | Calculator/Computer | **Career Applications** | Above and Beyond

43. MANUFACTURING TECHNOLOGY An inventory of steel round stock shows 248 feet (ft) of $\frac{1}{4}$ inch (in.), 124 ft of $\frac{3}{8}$ in., 428 ft of $\frac{1}{2}$ in., and 162 ft of $\frac{5}{8}$ in. How many total feet of steel round stock are in inventory?

44. MANUFACTURING TECHNOLOGY B & L Industries produces three different products. Orders for today are for 351 of product A, 187 of product B, and 94 of product C. How many total products need to be produced today to fill the orders?

Answers

39. ______

40. ______

41. ______

42. ______

43. ______

44. ______

Answers

45. ______

46. ______

47. ______

48. ______

45. Allied Health The source-image receptor distance (SID) for radiographic images is the sum of the object-film distance (OFD) and the focus-object distance (FOD). Determine the SID if the distance from the object to the film is 8 inches (in.), and the distance from the object to the focus is 48 in.

46. Allied Health Total lung capacity, measured in milliliters (mL), is the sum of the vital capacity and the residual volume. Determine the total lung capacity for a patient whose vital capacity is 4,500 mL and whose residual volume is 1,800 mL.

Basic Skills | Challenge Yourself | Calculator/Computer | Career Applications | **Above and Beyond**

47. Number Problem A magic square is a square in which the sum along any row, column, or diagonal is the same. For example

35	10	15
0	20	40
25	30	5

Use the numbers 1 to 9 to form a magic square.

48. The following puzzle gives you a chance to practice some of your addition skills.

Across

1. 23 + 22
3. 103 + 42
6. 29 + 58 + 19
8. 3 + 3 + 4
9. 1,480 + 1,624
11. 568 + 730
13. 25 + 25
14. 131 + 132
16. The total of 121, 146, 119, and 132
17. The perimeter of a 4 × 6 rug

Down

1. The sum of 224,000, 155, and 186,000
2. 20 + 30
4. 210 + 200
5. 500,000 + 4,730
7. 130 + 509
10. 90 + 92
12. 100 + 101
15. The perimeter of a 15 × 16 room

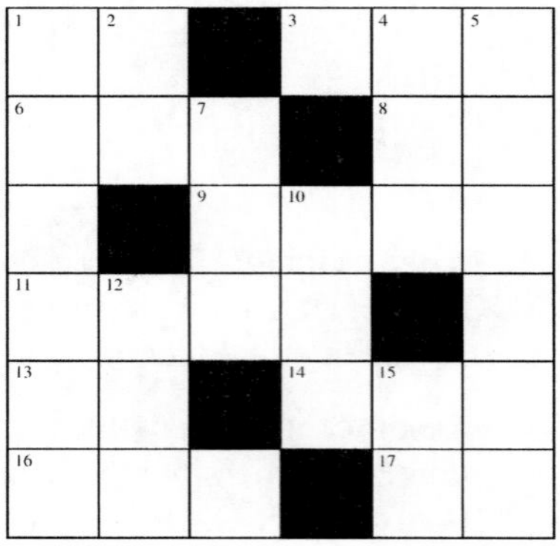

Answers

1. Commutative property of addition
3. Associative property of addition
5. Commutative property of addition
7. Commutative property of addition 9. 2,997 11. 8,398
13. 7,885 15. 64,356 17. 4,063 19. 6,394 21. 56,081
23. 5 is an addend, 4 is an addend, 9 is the sum 25. 22 ft 27. 21 yd
29. 26 in. 31. (a) 1,569; (b) 3,462; (c) 27,027; (d) 159; (e) 553
33. $49,750
35.

Department	Oct.	Nov.	Dec.	Department Totals
Office	$31,714	$32,512	$30,826	$95,052
Production	85,146	87,479	81,234	$253,859
Sales	34,568	37,612	33,455	$105,635
Warehouse	16,588	11,368	13,567	$41,523
Monthly Totals	$168,016	$168,971	$159,082	$496,069

37. (a) 33, 40, 47, 54; (b) 32, 38, 44, 50; (c) 31, 37, 43, 49; (d) 41, 49, 57, 65
39. 6,481,070
41.

Branch	Mon.	Tues.	Wed.	Thurs.	Fri.	Weekly Totals
Downtown	487	356	429	278	834	2,384
Suburban	236	255	254	198	423	1,366
Westside	345	278	323	257	563	1,766
Daily Totals	1,068	889	1,006	733	1,820	5,516
						Grand Total

43. 962 ft 45. 56 in.
47.

8	3	4
1	5	9
6	7	2

1.3 Subtraction

< 1.3 Objectives >

1 > Subtract whole numbers without borrowing

2 > Use the language of subtraction

3 > Solve applications of simple subtraction

4 > Use borrowing in subtracting whole numbers

5 > Solve applications that require borrowing

Tips for Student Success

Hint #3 Don't procrastinate!

1. Do your math homework while you're still fresh. If you wait until too late at night, your mind will be tired and have much more difficulty understanding the concepts.
2. Do your homework the day it is assigned. The more recent the explanation is, the easier it is to recall.
3. When you are finished with your homework, try reading the next section through once. This will give you a sense of direction when you next hear the material. This works whether you are in a lecture or lab setting.

Remember that, in a typical math class, you are expected to do two or three hours of homework for each weekly class hour. This means two or three hours per night. Schedule the time and stay on schedule.

NOTE

By *opposite operation* we mean that subtracting a number "undoes" an addition of that same number. Start with 1. Add 5 and then subtract 5. Where are you?

We are now ready to consider a second operation of arithmetic—subtraction. In Section 1.2, we described addition as the process of combining two or more groups of the same kind of objects. Subtraction can be thought of as the *opposite operation* to addition. Every arithmetic operation has its own notation. The symbol for subtraction, −, is called a **minus sign.**

When we write $8 - 5$, we wish to subtract 5 from 8. We call 5 the **subtrahend.** This is the number being subtracted. And 8 is the **minuend.** This is the number we are subtracting from. The **difference** is the result of the subtraction.

To find the *difference* of two numbers, we will assume that we wish to subtract the smaller number from the larger. Then we look for a number which, when added to the smaller number, will give us the larger number. For example,

$$8 - 5 = 3 \qquad \text{because} \qquad 3 + 5 = 8$$

This special relationship between addition and subtraction provides a method of checking subtraction.

Property

Relationship Between Addition and Subtraction

The sum of the difference and the subtrahend must be equal to the minuend.

Example 1 Subtracting a Single-Digit Number

< Objective 1 >

$12 - 5 = 7$

Check: $7 + 5 = 12$

Difference Subtrahend Minuend

Our check works because 12 − 5 asks for the number that must be added to 5 to get 12.

Check Yourself 1

Subtract and check your work.

13 − 9

The procedure for subtracting larger whole numbers is similar to the procedure for addition. We subtract digits of the same place value.

Example 2 Subtracting a Larger Number

Step 1 **Step 2** **Step 3**

$$\begin{array}{r} 789 \\ -\ 246 \\ \hline 3 \end{array} \qquad \begin{array}{r} 789 \\ -\ 246 \\ \hline 43 \end{array} \qquad \begin{array}{r} 789 \\ -\ 246 \\ \hline 543 \end{array}$$

We subtract in the ones column, then in the tens column, and finally in the hundreds column.

To check:

$$\begin{array}{r} 789 \\ -\ 246 \\ \hline 543 \end{array}$$

Add 543 + 246 = 789

The sum of the difference and the subtrahend must be the minuend.

Check Yourself 2

Subtract and check your work.

(a) $\begin{array}{r} 3{,}468 \\ -\ 2{,}248 \\ \hline \end{array}$ **(b)** $\begin{array}{r} 4{,}984 \\ -\ 1{,}081 \\ \hline \end{array}$

You know that the word *difference* indicates subtraction. There are other words that also tell you to use the subtraction operation. For instance, 5 *less than* 12 is written as

$12 - 5$ or 7

20 *decreased* by 8 is written as

$20 - 8$ or 12

Example 3 Translating Words That Indicate Subtraction

< Objective 2 >

Find each of the following.

(a) 4 less than 11

4 less than 11 is written $11 - 4 = 7$.

(b) 27 decreased by 6

27 decreased by 6 is written $27 - 6 = 21$.

Check Yourself 3

Find each of the following.

(a) 6 less than 19 **(b)** 18 decreased by 3

Units ANALYSIS

This is the first in a series of essays that are designed to help you solve applications using mathematics. Questions in the exercise sets will require the skills that you build by reading these essays.

A number with a unit attached (such as 7 **feet** or 26 **mi/gal**) is called a denominate number. Any genuine application of mathematics involves denominate numbers.

When adding or subtracting denominate numbers, the units must be identical for both numbers. The sum or difference will have those same units.

EXAMPLES:

$4 + $9 = $13 — Notice that, although we write the dollar sign first, we read it after the quantity, as in "four dollars."

7 feet + 9 feet = 16 feet

39 degrees − 12 degrees = 27 degrees

7 feet + 12 degrees yields no meaningful answer!

3 feet + 9 inches yields a meaningful result if 3 feet is converted into 36 inches. We will discuss conversion of units in later essays.

Now we consider subtraction word problems. The strategy is the same one presented in Section 1.2 for addition word problems. It is summarized with the following four basic steps.

Step by Step

Solving Subtraction Applications

Step 1 Read the problem carefully to determine the given information and what you are asked to find.

Step 2 Decide upon the operation (in this case, subtraction) to be used.

Step 3 Write down the complete statement necessary to solve the problem and do the calculations.

Step 4 Check to make sure you have answered the question of the problem and that your answer seems reasonable.

Here is an example using these steps.

Example 4 Setting Up a Subtraction Word Problem

< Objective 3 >

Tory has $37 in his wallet. He is thinking about buying a $24 pair of pants and a $10 shirt. If he buys them both, how much money will he have remaining?

First we must add the cost of the pants and the shirt.

$24 + $10 = $34

Now, that amount must be subtracted from the $37.

$37 − $34 = $3

He will have $3 left.

Check Yourself 4

Sonya has $97 left in her checking account. If she writes checks for $12, $32, and $21, how much will she have in the account?

Difficulties can arise in subtraction if one or more of the digits of the subtrahend are larger than the corresponding digits in the minuend. We will solve this problem by using another version of the regrouping process called **borrowing.**

First, we look at an example in expanded form.

Example 5 Subtracting When Regrouping Is Needed

< Objective 4 >

$$\begin{array}{r} 52 = 50 + 2 \\ -\ 27 = 20 + 7 \\ \hline \end{array}$$

Do you see that we cannot subtract in the ones column?

We regroup by borrowing 1 ten in the minuend and writing that ten as 10 ones:

$$\begin{array}{lr} & 50 \quad + 2 \\ \text{becomes} & 40 + 10 + 2 \\ \text{or} & 40 + \quad 12 \end{array}$$

We now have

$$\begin{array}{r} 52 = 40 + 12 \\ -\ 27 = 20 + \ \ 7 \\ \hline 20 + \ \ 5 \end{array}$$

or 25

We can now subtract as before.

In practice, we use a more convenient short form for the subtraction.

$$\begin{array}{r} 52 \\ -\ 27 \\ \hline \end{array} \qquad \begin{array}{r} {}^{4}\ {}^{1} \\ \not{5}2 \\ -\ 27 \\ \hline 25 \end{array}$$

We indicate the fact that we have borrowed 1 ten by putting a slash through the 5 and then writing 4 tens. Add 10 ones to the original 2 ones to get 12 ones. We can then subtract.

Check: 25 + 27 = 52

Check Yourself 5

Subtract and check your work.

$$\begin{array}{r} \mathbf{64} \\ -\ \mathbf{38} \\ \hline \end{array}$$

In Example 6, we work through a subtraction example that requires a number of regrouping steps. Here, zero appears as a digit in the minuend.

Example 6 Subtracting When Regrouping Is Needed

NOTE

Here we borrow 1 thousand; this is written as 10 hundreds.

Step 1

$$\begin{array}{r} {}^{4}\ {}^{1} \\ 4{,}0\not{5}3 \\ -\ 2{,}365 \\ \hline 8 \end{array}$$

In this first step we regroup by borrowing 1 ten. This is written as 10 ones and combined with the original 3 ones. We can then subtract in the ones column.

Step 2

$$\begin{array}{r} {}^{3}\ {}^{10}\ {}^{4}\ {}^{1} \\ \not{4}{,}\not{0}\not{5}3 \\ -\ 2{,}365 \\ \hline 8 \end{array}$$

We must regroup again to subtract in the tens column. There are no hundreds, and so we move to the thousands column.

NOTE

We now borrow 1 hundred; this is written as 10 tens and combined with the remaining 4 tens.

Step 3

$$\begin{array}{r} \overset{3\ 9\ 4\ 1}{\cancel{4},\cancel{0}\cancel{5}3} \\ -\ 2,365 \\ \hline 8 \end{array}$$

The minuend is now renamed as 3 thousands, 9 hundreds, 14 tens, and 13 ones.

Step 4

$$\begin{array}{r} \overset{3\ 9\ 14\ 1}{\cancel{4},\cancel{0}\cancel{5}3} \\ -\ 2,365 \\ \hline 1,688 \end{array}$$

The subtraction can now be completed.

To check our subtraction: 1,688 + 2,365 = 4,053

Check Yourself 6

Subtract and check your work.

$$\begin{array}{r} \mathbf{5,024} \\ -\ \mathbf{1,656} \\ \hline \end{array}$$

You need to use both addition and subtraction to solve some problems, as Example 7 illustrates.

Example 7 Solving a Subtraction Application

< Objective 5 >

Bernard wants to buy a new piece of stereo equipment. He has \$142 and can trade in his old amplifier for \$135. How much more does he need if the new equipment costs \$449?

First we must add to find out how much money Bernard has available. Then we subtract to find out how much more money he needs.

\$142 + \$135 = \$277 The money available to Bernard

\$449 − \$277 = \$172 The money Bernard still needs

Bernard will need \$172.

Check Yourself 7

Martina spent \$239 in airfare, \$174 for lodging, and \$108 for food on a business trip. Her company allowed her \$375 for the expenses. How much of these expenses will she have to pay herself?

Check Yourself ANSWERS

1. 13 − 9 = 4 Check: 4 + 9 = 13 **2.** **(a)** 1,220; **(b)** 3,903

3. **(a)** 13; **(b)** 15 **4.** Sonya will have \$32 left.

5. $\begin{array}{r} \overset{5\ 1}{\cancel{6}4} \\ -\ 38 \\ \hline 26 \end{array}$ To check: 26 + 38 = 64 **6.** 3,368 Check: 3,368 + 1,656 = 5,024

7. $\begin{array}{r} \$239 \\ 174 \\ +\ 108 \\ \hline \$521 \end{array}$ ← Total expenses

$\begin{array}{r} \$521 \\ -\ 375 \\ \hline \$146 \end{array}$ ← Total expenses; ← Amount allowed

Martina will have to pay \$146.

Reading Your Text

The following fill-in-the-blank exercises are designed to ensure that you understand some of the key vocabulary used in this section.

SECTION 1.3

(a) The ________ is the result of subtraction.

(b) 5 ________ than 12 is written as 12 − 5.

(c) The first step in solving a subtraction application is to ________ the problem carefully.

(d) The regrouping process used in subtraction is called ________.

1.3 exercises

Boost *your* GRADE at ALEKS.com!

ALEKS®

- Practice Problems
- Self-Tests
- NetTutor
- e-Professors
- Videos

Name ____________________

Section ________ Date ________

Answers

1. ________ 2. ________

3. ________ 4. ________

5. ________ 6. ________

7. ________ 8. ________

9. ________ 10. ________

11. ________ 12. ________

13. ________ 14. ________

15. ________ 16. ________

17. ________ 18. ________

19. ________ 20. ________

21. ____________________

22. ____________________

23. ________ 24. ________

25. ________ 26. ________

27. ________ 28. ________

29. ________ 30. ________

Basic Skills | Challenge Yourself | Calculator/Computer | Career Applications | Above and Beyond

< Objectives 1, 4 >

In exercises 1 to 20, do the indicated subtraction and check your results by addition.

1. $347 - 201$

2. $575 - 302$

3. $689 - 245$

4. $598 - 278$

5. $3{,}446 - 2{,}326$ > Videos

6. $5{,}896 - 3{,}862$

7. $64 - 27$

8. $73 - 36$

9. $627 - 358$

10. $642 - 367$

11. $6{,}423 - 3{,}678$

12. $5{,}352 - 2{,}577$

13. $6{,}034 - 2{,}569$ > Videos

14. $5{,}206 - 1{,}748$

15. $4{,}000 - 2{,}345$

16. $6{,}000 - 4{,}349$

17. $33{,}486 - 14{,}047$

18. $53{,}487 - 25{,}649$

19. $29{,}400 - 17{,}900$

20. $53{,}500 - 28{,}700$

< Objective 2 >

21. In the statement $9 - 6 = 3$
9 is called the ____________.
6 is called the ____________.
3 is called the ____________.
Write the related addition statement.

22. In the statement $7 - 5 = 2$
5 is called the ____________.
2 is called the ____________.
7 is called the ____________.
Write the related addition statement.

< Objective 3 >

23. Find the number that is 25 less than 76. > Videos

24. Find the number that results when 58 is decreased by 23.

25. Find the number that is the difference between 97 and 43.

26. Find the number that is 125 less than 265.

27. Find the number that results when 298 is decreased by 47.

28. Find the number that is the difference between 167 and 57.

Basic Skills | **Challenge Yourself** | Calculator/Computer | Career Applications | Above and Beyond

Based on units, determine if each operation produces a meaningful result.

29. 8 miles − 4 miles

30. \$560 + \$314

31. 7 feet + 11 meters

32. 18°F − 6°C

33. 17 yards − 10 yards

34. 4 mi/h + 6 ft/s

In exercises 35 to 38, for various treks by a hiker in a mountainous region, the starting elevations and various changes are given. Determine the final elevation of the hiker in each case.

35. Starting elevation 1,053 feet (ft), increase of 123 ft, decrease of 98 ft, increase of 63 ft.

36. Starting elevation 1,231 ft, increase of 213 ft, decrease of 112 ft, increase of 78 ft.

37. Starting elevation 7,302 ft, decrease of 623 ft, decrease of 123 ft, increase of 307 ft. Videos

38. Starting elevation 6,907 ft, decrease of 511 ft, decrease of 203 ft, increase of 419 ft.

< Objective 5 >

Solve each application.

39. **Social Science** Shaka's score on a math test was 87, and Tony's score was 23 points less than Shaka's. What was Tony's score on the test?

40. **Business and Finance** Duardo's monthly pay of $879 was decreased by $175 for withholding. What amount of pay did he receive? Videos

41. **Construction** The Sears Tower in Chicago is 1,454 ft tall. The Empire State Building is 1,250 ft tall. How much taller is the Sears Tower than the Empire State Building?

42. **Business and Finance** In one week, Margaret earned $278 in regular pay and $53 for overtime work, and $49 was deducted from her paycheck for income taxes and $18 for Social Security. What was her take-home pay?

43. **Business and Finance** Rafael opened a checking account and made deposits of $85 and $272. He wrote checks during the month for $35, $27, $89, and $178. What was his balance at the end of the month?

44. **Science and Medicine** Dalila is trying to limit herself to 1,500 calories per day (cal/day). Her breakfast was 270 cal, her lunch was 450 cal, and her dinner was 820 cal. By how much was she *under* or *over* her diet?

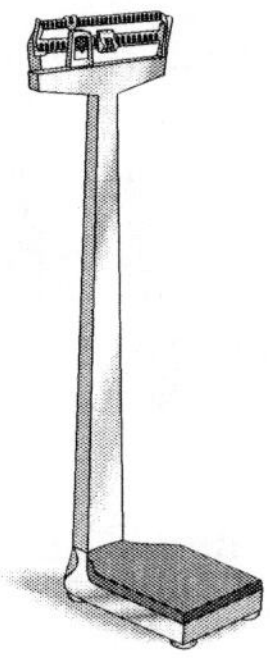

Answers

31. ______
32. ______
33. ______
34. ______
35. ______
36. ______
37. ______
38. ______
39. ______
40. ______
41. ______
42. ______
43. ______
44. ______

Answers

45. ______

46. ______

47. ______

48. ______

45. **Business and Finance** Complete the following record of a monthly expense account.

Monthly income	$1,620
Share of rent	343
Balance	
Car payment	183
Balance	
Food	312
Balance	
Clothing	89
Amount remaining	

46. **Business and Finance** To keep track of a checking account, you must subtract the amount of each check from the current balance. Complete the following statement.

Beginning balance	$351
Check #1	29
Balance	
Check #2	139
Balance	
Check #3	75
Ending balance	

47. **Business and Finance** Carmen's frequent-flyer program requires 30,000 miles (mi) for a free flight. During 2004 she accumulated 13,850 mi. In 2005 she took three more flights of 2,800, 1,475, and 4,280 mi. How much farther must she fly for her free trip?

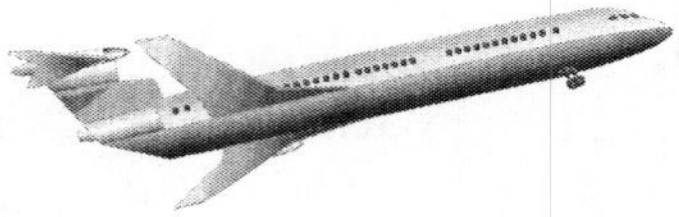

48. **Business and Finance** The value of all crops in the Salinas Valley in 2003 was nearly $3 billion. The top four crops are listed in the following table. **(a)** How much greater is the combined value of both types of lettuce than broccoli? **(b)** How much greater is the value of the lettuce and broccoli combined than that of the strawberries?

Crop	Crop value, in millions
Head lettuce	$361
Leaf lettuce	$277
Strawberries	$298
Broccoli	$259

Basic Skills | Challenge Yourself | **Calculator/Computer** | Career Applications | Above and Beyond

Now that you have reviewed the process of subtracting by hand, look at the use of the calculator in performing this operation.

Find

$23 - 13 + 56 - 29$

Enter the numbers and the operation signs exactly as they appear in the expression.

23 [−] 13 [+] 56 [−] 29 [ENTER]

Display 37

An alternative approach would be to add 23 and 56 first and then subtract 13 and 29. The result is the same in either case.

Do the indicated operations.

49. $\begin{array}{r} 5{,}830 \\ -\ 3{,}987 \\ \hline \end{array}$

50. $\begin{array}{r} 15{,}280 \\ -\ 7{,}595 \\ \hline \end{array}$

51. Subtract 235 from the sum of 534 and 678.

52. Subtract 476 from the sum of 306 and 572.

Solve each application.

53. Business and Finance Readings from Fast Service Station's storage tanks were taken at the beginning and end of a month. How much of each type of gas was sold? What was the total sold?

	Diesel	Unleaded	Super Unleaded	Total
Beginning reading	73,255	82,349	81,258	
End reading	28,387	19,653	8,654	
Gallons used				

The land areas, in square miles (mi^2), of three Pacific coast states are California, 155,959 mi^2; Oregon, 95,997 mi^2; and Washington, 66,544 mi^2.

54. Social Science How much larger is California than Oregon?

55. Social Science How much larger is California than Washington?

56. Social Science How much larger is Oregon than Washington?

Basic Skills | Challenge Yourself | Calculator/Computer | **Career Applications** | Above and Beyond

57. Allied Health A patient's anion gap is used to help evaluate her overall electrolyte balance. The anion gap is equal to the difference between the serum concentration [measured in milliequivalents per liter (mEq/L)] of sodium and the sum of the serum concentrations of chloride and bicarbonate. Determine the patient's anion gap if the concentration of sodium is 140 mEq/L, chloride is 93 mEq/L, and bicarbonate is 24 mEq/L.

58. Allied Health To increase the geometric sharpness of a radiographic image, it is easiest to set the focus-object distance (FOD), which is the difference between the source-image receptor distance (SID) and the object-film distance (OFD), to its maximum value. What is the maximum FOD possible if the distance between the object and the film is fixed at 8 inches and the maximum distance possible between the source-image and the receptor is 72 inches?

Answers

49. ______
50. ______
51. ______
52. ______
53. ______
54. ______
55. ______
56. ______
57. ______
58. ______

Answers

59. ______

60. ______

61. ______

62. ______

63. ______

64. ______

65. ______

66. ______

67. ______

59. **INFORMATION TECHNOLOGY** Sally's department needs a new printer. The old printer just died. Sally bought an ink-jet printer at a cost of \$150. For a growing department, the ink-jet printer is not appropriate. The problem is she really needs a laser printer at a cost of \$500. If she returns the ink-jet printer, how much extra money will she need to buy the laser printer?

60. **INFORMATION TECHNOLOGY** Max has a 20-foot roll of cable, and he needs to run the cable from a wiring closet to an outlet in a room that is adjacent to the closet. The distance from the wiring closet to the outlet is about 25 feet. How much cable will Max need to buy to be able to run the cable from the wiring closet to the outlet in the adjacent room?

61. **ELECTRONICS** Solder looks like flexible wire and typically comes wrapped on spools. When heated with a soldering iron or any other heat source, solder melts. It is used to connect an electronic component to wires, other components, or conductive traces. If a certain spool holds 10 pounds (lb) of solder, yet the shipping weight for the spool is 14 lb, how much does the empty spool and shipping materials weigh in pounds?

62. **MANUFACTURING TECHNOLOGY** Kinetics, Inc., sells an engine block for \$168. Production of the block is \$72 for materials, \$58 for labor, and \$19 for shipping and packaging. How much is the profit on the engine block?

Basic Skills | Challenge Yourself | Calculator/Computer | Career Applications | **Above and Beyond**

NUMBER PROBLEM Complete the magic squares.

63.

	7	2
	5	
8		

64.

4	3	
	5	
		6

65.

16	3		13
	10	11	
9	6	7	
			1

66.

7			14
2	13	8	11
16			
	6	15	

67. **SOCIAL SCIENCE** Use the Internet to find the population of Arizona, California, Oregon, and Pennsylvania in each of the last three censuses. chapter 1 > Make the Connection

(a) Find the total change in each state's population over this period.

(b) Which state shows the greatest change over the past three censuses?

(c) Write a brief essay describing the changes and any trends you see in these data. List any implications that they might have for future planning.

68. Think of any whole number.

Add 5.
Subtract 3.
Subtract 2 less than the original number.
What number do you end up with?
Check with other people. Does everyone have the same answer? Can you explain the results?

Answers

68. ______

Answers

1. 146 **3.** 444 **5.** 1,120 **7.** 37 **9.** 269 **11.** 2,745
13. 3,465 **15.** 1,655 **17.** 19,439 **19.** 11,500
21. 9 is the minuend, 6 is the subtrahend, and 3 is the difference; $3 + 6 = 9$
23. 51 **25.** 54 **27.** 251 **29.** Yes **31.** No **33.** Yes
35. 1,141 ft **37.** 6,863 ft **39.** 64 **41.** 204 ft **43.** \$28
45. \$1,277; \$1,094; \$782; \$693 **47.** 7,595 mi **49.** 1,843 **51.** 977
53. Diesel, 44,868 gal; unleaded, 62,696 gal; super unleaded, 72,604 gal; total, 180,168 gal **55.** 89,415 mi^2 **57.** 23 mEq/L **59.** \$350 **61.** 4 lb

63.

6	7	2
1	5	9
8	3	4

65.

16	3	2	13
5	10	11	8
9	6	7	12
4	15	14	1

67. Above and Beyond

Activity 1 ::
Population Changes

The following table gives the population for the United States and each of the six largest states from both the 1990 census and the 2000 census. Use this table to answer the questions that follow.

	1990 Population	2000 Population
United States	248,709,873	281,421,906
California	29,760,021	33,871,648
Texas	16,986,510	20,851,820
New York	17,990,455	18,976,457
Florida	12,937,926	15,982,378
Illinois	11,430,602	12,419,293
Pennsylvania	11,881,643	12,281,054

1. Which two pairs of states switched population ranking between the two censuses?
2. By how much did the population of the United States increase between 1990 and 2000?
3. Which state had the greatest increase in population from 1990 to 2000? What was that difference?
4. Which state had the smallest increase in population from 1990 to 2000? What was that difference?
5. What was the total population of the six largest states in 1990?
6. How many people living in the United States did not live in one of the six largest states in 1990?
7. What was the total population of the six largest states in 2000?
8. How many people living in the United States did not live in one of the six largest states in 2000?
9. What regional trends might be true based on what you see in this table?

1.4 Rounding, Estimation, and Order

< 1.4 Objectives >

1 > Round a whole number to a given place value

2 > Estimate sums and differences by rounding

3 > Use the inequality symbols

It is a common practice to express numbers to the nearest hundred, thousand, and so on. For instance, the distance from Los Angeles to New York along one route is 2,833 miles (mi). We might say that the distance is 2,800 mi. This is called **rounding,** because we have rounded the distance to the nearest hundred miles.

One way to picture this rounding process is with the use of a number line.

Example 1 Rounding to the Nearest Hundred

< Objective 1 >

To round 2,833 to the nearest hundred, we mark notations on a number line counting by hundreds: 2,800 and 2,900. (We only include those that "surround" 2,833.) Then we mark the spot halfway between these: 2,850. When we also mark 2,833 on the line, estimating its location, we must place the mark to the left of 2,850. This makes it clear that 2,833 is closer to 2,800 than it is to 2,900. So we round *down* to 2,800.

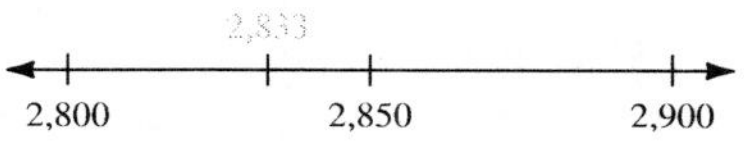

Check Yourself 1

Round 587 to the nearest hundred.

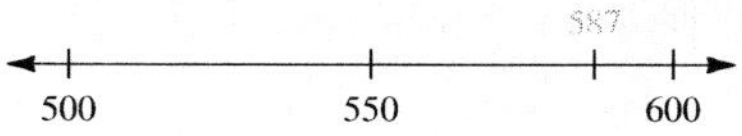

Example 2 Rounding to the Nearest Thousand

To round 28,734 to the nearest thousand:

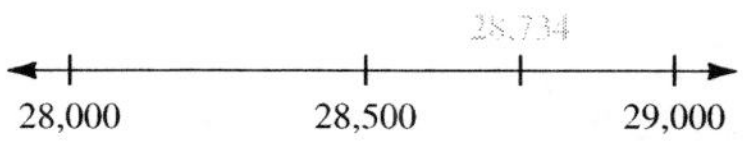

Because 28,734 is closer to 29,000 than it is to 28,000, we round *up* to 29,000.

Check Yourself 2

Locate 1,375 and round to the nearest hundred.

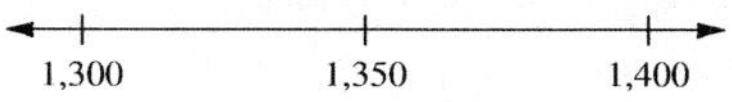

Instead of using a number line, we can apply the following rule.

Step by Step

Rounding Whole Numbers

Step 1 Identify the place of the digit to be rounded.

Step 2 Look at the digit to the right of that place.

Step 3 a. If that digit is 5 or more, that digit and all digits to the right become 0. The digit in the place you are rounding to is increased by 1.

b. If that digit is less than 5, that digit and all digits to the right become 0. The digit in the place you are rounding to remains the same.

Example 3 Rounding to the Nearest Ten

Round 587 to the nearest ten:

Tens
↓
5 8 7
↑
The digit to the right of the tens place
↓
5 8 7 is rounded to 590

We identify the tens digit. The digit to the right of the tens place, 7, is 5 or more. So round up.

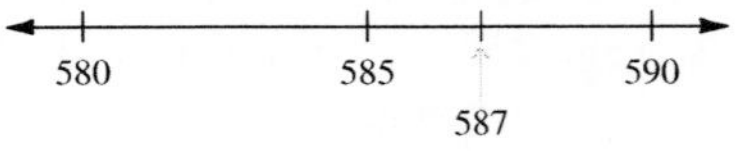

NOTE

587 is between 580 and 590. It is closer to 590, so it makes sense to round up.

Check Yourself 3

Round 847 to the nearest ten.

Example 4 Rounding to the Nearest Hundred

Round 2,638 to the nearest hundred:
↓
2, 6 38 is rounded to 2,600

We identify the hundreds digit. The digit to the right, 3, is less than 5. So round down.

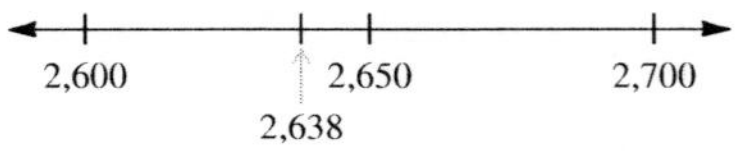

NOTE

2,638 is closer to 2,600 than to 2,700. So it makes sense to round down.

Check Yourself 4

Round 3,482 to the nearest hundred.

Here are some further examples of using the rounding rule.

Example 5 Rounding Whole Numbers

(a) Round 2,378 to the nearest hundred:
↓
2, 3 78 is rounded to 2,400

We identified the hundreds digit. The digit to the right is 7. Because this is 5 or more, the hundreds digit is increased by 1. The 7 and all digits to the right of 7 become 0.

(b) Round 53,258 to the nearest thousand:

↓

53,258 is rounded to 53,000

We identified the thousands digit. Because the digit to the right is less than 5, the thousands digit remains the same. The 2 and all digits to its right become 0.

(c) Round 685 to the nearest ten:

↓

685 is rounded to 690

The digit to the right of the tens place is 5 or more. Round up by our rule.

(d) Round 52,813,212 to the nearest million:

↓

52,813,212 is rounded to 53,000,000

Check Yourself 5

(a) Round 568 to the nearest ten.
(b) Round 5,446 to the nearest hundred.

Now, look at a case in which we round up a 9.

Example 6 Rounding to the Nearest Ten

NOTE

Which number is 397 closer to?

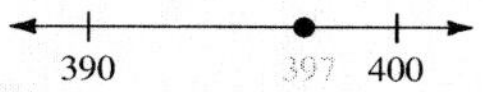

Suppose we want to round 397 to the nearest ten. We identify the tens digit and look at the next digit to the right.

↓

397

The digit to the right is 5 or more.
If this digit is 9, and it must be increased by 1, replace the 9 with 0 and increase the next digit to the *left* by 1.

So 397 is rounded to 400.

Check Yourself 6

Round 4,961 to the nearest hundred.

NOTE

An estimate is basically a good guess. If your answer is close to your estimate, then your answer is reasonable.

Whether you are doing an addition problem by hand or using a calculator, rounding numbers gives you a handy way of deciding whether an answer seems reasonable. The process is called **estimating,** which we illustrate with an example.

Example 7 Estimating a Sum

< Objective 2 >

NOTE

Placing an arrow above the column to be rounded can be helpful.

Begin by rounding to the nearest hundred.

456	500	
235	200	
976	1,000	
+ 344	+ 300	
2,011	2,000	← Estimate

By rounding to the nearest hundred and adding quickly, we get an estimate or guess of 2,000. Because this is close to the sum calculated, 2,011, the sum seems reasonable.

Check Yourself 7

Round each addend to the nearest hundred and estimate the sum. Then find the actual sum.

$287 + 526 + 311 + 378$

Estimation is a wonderful tool to use while you're shopping. Every time you go to the store, you should try to estimate the total bill by rounding the price of each item. If you do this regularly, both your addition skills and your rounding skills will improve. The same holds true when you eat in a restaurant. It is always a good idea to know approximately how much you are spending.

Example 8 Estimating a Sum in a Word Problem

Samantha has taken the family out to dinner, and she's now ready to pay the bill. The dinner check has no total, only the individual entries, as given below:

Soup	\$2.95
Soup	2.95
Salad	1.95
Salad	1.95
Salad	1.95
Lasagna	7.25
Spaghetti	4.95
Ravioli	5.95

What is the approximate cost of the dinner?

Rounding each entry to the nearest whole dollar, we can estimate the total by finding the sum

$3 + 3 + 2 + 2 + 2 + 7 + 5 + 6 = \$30$

Check Yourself 8

Jason is doing the weekly food shopping at FoodWay. So far his basket has items that cost \$3.99, \$7.98, \$2.95, \$1.15, \$2.99, and \$1.95. Approximate the total cost of these items.

Earlier in this section, we used the number line to illustrate the idea of rounding numbers. The number line also gives us an excellent way to picture the concept of **order** for whole numbers, which means that numbers become larger as we move from left to right on the number line.

For instance, we know that 3 is less than 5. On the number line

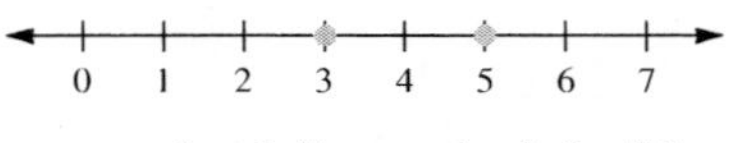

we see that 3 lies *to the left* of 5.

We also know that 4 is greater than 2. On the number line

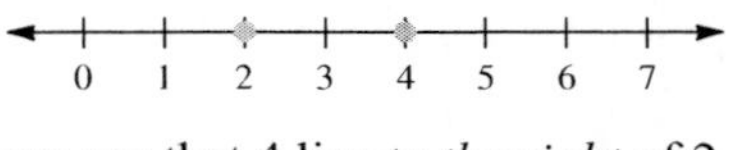

we see that 4 lies *to the right* of 2.

Two symbols, < for "less than" and > for "greater than," are used to indicate these relationships.

NOTE

The inequality symbol always "points at" the smaller number.

Definition

Inequalities

For whole numbers, we can write

1. $2 < 5$ (read "2 is less than 5") because 2 is *to the left* of 5 on the number line.
2. $8 > 3$ (read "8 is greater than 3") because 8 is *to the right* of 3 on the number line.

Example 9 illustrates the use of this notation.

Example 9 Indicating Order with < or >

< Objective 3 >

Use the symbol $<$ or $>$ to complete each statement.

(a) 7 _____ 10 **(b)** 25 _____ 20
(c) 200 _____ 300 **(d)** 8 _____ 0

(a) $7 < 10$ 7 lies to the left of 10 on the number line.
(b) $25 > 20$ 25 lies to the right of 20 on the number line.
(c) $200 < 300$
(d) $8 > 0$

Check Yourself 9

Use one of the symbols $<$ and $>$ to complete each of the following statements.

(a) 35 ___ 25 **(b)** 0 ___ 4
(c) 12 ___ 18 **(d)** 1,000 ___ 100

Check Yourself ANSWERS

1. 600 **2.** 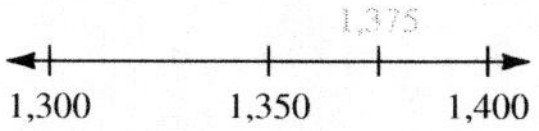

Round 1,375 *up* to 1,400.

3. 850 **4.** 3,500 **5.** **(a)** 570; **(b)** 5,400 **6.** 5,000 **7.** 1,500; 1,502
8. $21 **9.** **(a)** $35 > 25$; **(b)** $0 < 4$; **(c)** $12 < 18$; **(d)** $1{,}000 > 100$

Reading Your Text

The following fill-in-the-blank exercises are designed to ensure that you understand some of the key vocabulary used in this section.

SECTION 1.4

(a) The practice of expressing numbers to the nearest hundred, thousand, and so on is called __________.

(b) The first step in rounding is to identify the ____________ ____________ of the digit to be rounded.

(c) The number line gives us an excellent way to picture the concept of ______________ for whole numbers.

(d) The symbol $<$ is read as "______________ than."

1.4 exercises

Basic Skills | Challenge Yourself | Calculator/Computer | Career Applications | Above and Beyond

Name ______________________

Section ________ Date ________

Answers

1. ________ 2. ________
3. ________ 4. ________
5. ________ 6. ________
7. ________ 8. ________
9. ________ 10. ________
11. ________ 12. ________
13. ________ 14. ________
15. ________ 16. ________
17. ________ 18. ________
19. ______________________
20. ______________________
21. ______________________
22. ______________________
23. ______________________
24. ______________________
25. ______________________
26. ______________________

< Objective 1 >

Round each number to the indicated place.

1. 38, the nearest ten (Videos)
2. 72, the nearest ten
3. 253, the nearest ten
4. 578, the nearest ten
5. 696, the nearest ten
6. 683, the nearest hundred
7. 3,482, the nearest hundred (Videos)
8. 6,741, the nearest hundred
9. 5,962, the nearest hundred
10. 4,352, the nearest thousand
11. 4,927, the nearest thousand
12. 39,621, the nearest thousand
13. 23,429, the nearest thousand (Videos)
14. 38,589, the nearest thousand
15. 787,000, the nearest ten thousand
16. 582,000, the nearest hundred thousand
17. 21,800,000, the nearest million
18. 931,000, the nearest ten thousand

< Objective 2 >

In exercises 19 to 30, estimate each sum or difference by rounding to the indicated place. Then do the addition or subtraction and use your estimate to see if your actual sum or difference seems reasonable.

Round to the nearest ten.

19.

$$\begin{array}{r} 58 \\ 27 \\ +\ 33 \\ \hline \end{array}$$

20.

$$\begin{array}{r} 92 \\ 37 \\ 85 \\ +\ 64 \\ \hline \end{array}$$

21.

$$\begin{array}{r} 83 \\ -\ 27 \\ \hline \end{array}$$

22.

$$\begin{array}{r} 97 \\ -\ 31 \\ \hline \end{array}$$

Round to the nearest hundred.

23.

$$\begin{array}{r} 379 \\ 1{,}215 \\ +\ \ 528 \\ \hline \end{array}$$

24.

$$\begin{array}{r} 967 \\ 2{,}365 \\ 544 \\ +\ \ 738 \\ \hline \end{array}$$

25.

$$\begin{array}{r} 915 \\ -\ 411 \\ \hline \end{array}$$

26.

$$\begin{array}{r} 697 \\ -\ 539 \\ \hline \end{array}$$

Basic Skills | **Challenge Yourself** | Calculator/Computer | Career Applications | Above and Beyond

Round to the nearest thousand.

27.
$$\begin{array}{r} 2{,}238 \\ 3{,}925 \\ +\ 5{,}217 \\ \hline \end{array}$$

28.
$$\begin{array}{r} 3{,}678 \\ 4{,}215 \\ +\ 2{,}032 \\ \hline \end{array}$$

29.
$$\begin{array}{r} 4{,}822 \\ -\ 2{,}134 \\ \hline \end{array}$$

30.
$$\begin{array}{r} 6{,}120 \\ -\ 4{,}890 \\ \hline \end{array}$$

Solve each application.

31. **Business and Finance** Ed and Sharon go to lunch. The lunch check has no total but only lists individual items:

Soup \$1.95	Soup \$1.95
Salad \$1.80	Salad \$1.80
Salmon \$8.95	Flounder \$6.95
Pecan pie \$3.25	Vanilla ice cream \$2.25

Estimate the total amount of the lunch check.

32. **Business and Finance** Olivia will purchase several items at the stationery store. Thus far, the items she has collected cost \$2.99, \$6.97, \$3.90, \$2.15, \$9.95, and \$1.10. Approximate the total cost of these items.

33. **Statistics** Oscar scored 78, 91, 79, 67, and 100 on his arithmetic tests. Round each score to the nearest ten to estimate his total score.

34. **Business and Finance** Luigi's pizza parlor makes 293 pizzas on an average day. Estimate (to the nearest hundred) how many pizzas were made on a three-day holiday weekend.

35. **Business and Finance** Mrs. Gonzalez went shopping for clothes. She bought a sweater for \$32.95, a scarf for \$9.99, boots for \$68.29, a coat for \$125.90, and socks for \$18.15. Estimate the total amount of Mrs. Gonzalez's purchases.

36. **Business and Finance** Amir bought several items at the hardware store: hammer, \$8.95; screwdriver, \$3.15; pliers, \$6.90; wire cutters, \$4.25; and sandpaper; \$1.89. Estimate the total cost of Amir's bill.

< Objective 3 >

Use the symbol $<$ or $>$ to complete each statement.

37. 500 _____ 400

38. 20 _____ 15

39. 100 _____ 1,000

40. 3,000 _____ 2,000

Answers

27. ____________
28. ____________
29. ____________
30. ____________
31. ____________
32. ____________
33. ____________
34. ____________
35. ____________
36. ____________
37. ____________
38. ____________
39. ____________
40. ____________

Answers

41. ________

42. ________

43. ________

44. ________

45. ________

46. ________

47. ________

48. ________

Basic Skills | Challenge Yourself | Calculator/Computer | **Career Applications** | Above and Beyond

Use the following chart for exercises 41 and 42.

Appliance	Power Required (in Watts/hour [W/h])
Clock radio	10
Electric blanket	100
Clothes washer	500
Toaster oven	1,225
Laptop	50
Hair dryer	1,875
DVD player	25

41. **Electronics** Assuming all the appliances listed in the table are "on," estimate the total power required to the nearest hundred watts.

42. **Electronics** Which combination uses more power, the toaster oven and clothes washer or the hair dryer and DVD player?

43. **Manufacturing Technology** An inventory of machine screws shows that bin 1 contains 378 screws, bin 2 contains 192 screws, and bin 3 contains 267 screws. Estimate the total number of screws in the bins.

44. **Manufacturing Technology** A delivery truck must be loaded with the heaviest crates starting in the front to the lightest crates in the back. On Monday, crates weighing 378 pounds (lb), 221 lb, 413 lb, 231 lb, 208 lb, 911 lb, 97 lb, 188 lb, and 109 lb need to be shipped. In what order should the crates be loaded?

45. **Number Problem** A whole number rounded to the nearest ten is 60. **(a)** What is the smallest possible number? **(b)** What is the largest possible number?

46. **Number Problem** A whole number rounded to the nearest hundred is 7,700. **(a)** What is the smallest possible number? **(b)** What is the largest possible number?

Basic Skills | Challenge Yourself | Calculator/Computer | Career Applications | **Above and Beyond**

47. **Statistics** A bag contains 60 marbles. The number of blue marbles, rounded to the nearest 10, is 40, and the number of green marbles in the bag, rounded to the nearest 10, is 20. How many blue marbles are in the bag? (List all answers that satisfy the conditions of the problem.)

48. **Social Science** Describe some situations in which estimating and rounding would not produce a result that would be suitable or acceptable. Review the instructions for filing your federal income tax. What rounding rules are used in the preparation of your tax returns? Do the same rules apply to the filing of your state tax returns? If not, what are these rules?

49. The listed population of the United States on July 8, 2005, at 9:37 A.M. eastern standard time (EST) was 296,562,576 people. Round this number to the nearest ten million. chapter 1 > Make the Connection

50. According to the U.S. Census Bureau, the population of the world was believed to be 6,457,380,056 on August 1, 2005. Round this number to the nearest million. chapter 1 > Make the Connection

Answers

49. ______

50. ______

Answers

1. 40 **3.** 250 **5.** 700 **7.** 3,500 **9.** 6,000
11. 5,000 **13.** 23,000 **15.** 790,000 **17.** 22,000,000
19. Estimate: 120, actual sum: 118 **21.** Estimate: 50, actual difference: 56
23. Estimate: 2,100, actual sum: 2,122
25. Estimate: 500; actual difference: 504
27. Estimate: 11,000, actual sum: 11,380
29. Estimate: 3,000, actual difference: 2,688 **31.** $29 **33.** 420
35. $255 **37.** > **39.** < **41.** 3,800 W **43.** 900 screws
45. **(a)** 55; **(b)** 64 **47.** 36, 37, 38, 39, 40, 41, 42, 43, 44
49. 300,000,000 people

1.5 Multiplication

< 1.5 Objectives >

1 > Multiply whole numbers
2 > Use the properties of multiplication
3 > Solve applications of multiplication
4 > Estimate products
5 > Find area and volume using multiplication

NOTE

The use of the symbol × dates back to the 1600s.

Our work in this section deals with multiplication, another of the basic operations of arithmetic. Multiplication is closely related to addition. In fact, we can think of multiplication as a shorthand method for repeated addition. The symbol × is used to indicate multiplication.

3×4 can be interpreted as 3 rows of 4 objects. By counting we see that $3 \times 4 = 12$. Similarly, 4 rows of 3 means $4 \times 3 = 12$.

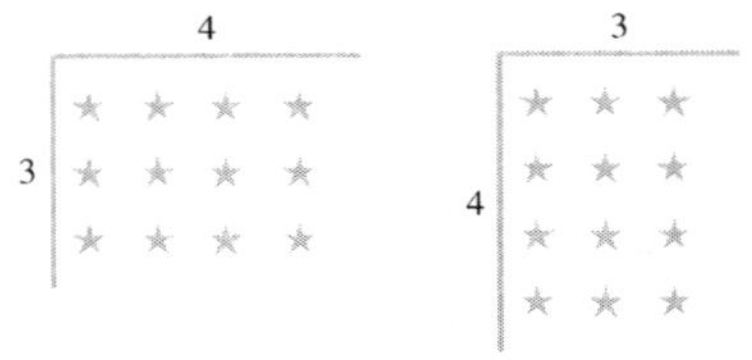

NOTE

A centered dot is used the same as the times sign (×). We use the centered dot when we are using letters to represent numbers, as we have done with *a* and *b* here. We do that so the times sign will not be confused with the letter *x*.

The fact that $3 \times 4 = 4 \times 3$ is an example of the **commutative property of multiplication,** which is given here.

Property

The Commutative Property of Multiplication

Given any two numbers, we can multiply them in either order and we get the same result.

In symbols, we say $a \cdot b = b \cdot a$.

Example 1 Multiplying Single-Digit Numbers

< Objective 1 >

3×5 means 5 multiplied by 3. It is read 3 *times* 5. To find 3×5, we can add 5 three times.

$3 \times 5 = 5 + 5 + 5 = 15$

In a multiplication problem such as $3 \times 5 = 15$, we call 3 and 5 the **factors.** The answer, 15, is the **product** of the factors, 3 and 5.

$3 \times 5 = 15$

Factor Factor Product

Check Yourself 1

Name the factors and the product in the following statement.

$2 \times 9 = 18$

Statements such as 3 × 4 = 12 and 3 × 5 = 15 are called the **basic multiplication facts.** If you have difficulty with multiplication, it may be that you do not know some of these facts. The following table will help you review before you go on. Notice that, because of the commutative property, you need memorize only half of these facts!

Basic Multiplication Facts Table

×	0	1	2	3	4	5	6	7	8	9
0	0	0	0	0	0	0	0	0	0	0
1	0	1	2	3	4	5	6	7	8	9
2	0	2	4	6	8	10	12	14	16	18
3	0	3	6	9	12	15	18	21	24	27
4	0	4	8	12	16	20	24	28	32	36
5	0	5	10	15	20	25	30	35	40	45
6	0	6	12	18	24	30	36	42	48	54
7	0	7	14	21	28	35	42	49	56	63
8	0	8	16	24	32	40	48	56	64	72
9	0	9	18	27	36	45	54	63	72	81

NOTE

To use the table to find the product of 7 × 6: Find the row labeled 7, and then move to the right in this row until you are in the column labeled 6 at the top. We see that 7 × 6 is 42.

Armed with these facts, you can become a better, and faster, problem solver. Take a look at Example 2.

Example 2 Multiplying Instead of Counting

NOTE

This checkerboard is an example of a rectangular array, a series of rows or columns that form a rectangle. When you see such an arrangement, multiply to find the total number of units.

Find the total number of squares on the checkerboard.

You could find the number of squares by counting them. If you counted one per second, it would take you just over a minute. You could make the job a little easier by simply counting the squares in one row (8), and then adding 8 + 8 + 8 + 8 + 8 + 8 + 8 + 8. Multiplication, which is simply repeated addition, allows you to find the total number of squares by multiplying 8 × 8. How long that takes depends on how well you know the basic multiplication facts! By now, you know that there are 64 squares on the checkerboard.

Check Yourself 2

Find the number of windows on the displayed side of the building.

The next property involves *both* multiplication and addition.

Example 3 Using the Distributive Property

< Objective 2 >

$2 \times (3 + 4) = 2 \times 7 = 14$ We have added 3 + 4 and then multiplied.

Also,

$2 \times (3 + 4) = (2 \times 3) + (2 \times 4)$ We have multiplied 2 × 3 and 2 × 4 as the first step.

$= 6 + 8$

$= 14$ The result is the same.

We see that $2 \times (3 + 4) = (2 \times 3) + (2 \times 4)$. This is an example of the **distributive property of multiplication over addition** because we distributed the multiplication (in this case by 2) over the "plus" sign.

NOTE

Multiplication can also be indicated by using parentheses. A number followed by parentheses or back-to-back parentheses represent multiplication.

$2 \times (3 + 4)$ could be written as $2(3 + 4)$ or $(2)(3 + 4)$.

Property

The Distributive Property of Multiplication over Addition

To multiply a factor by a sum of numbers, multiply the factor by each number inside the parentheses. Then add the products. (The result will be the same if we find the sum and then multiply.)

In symbols, we say $a \cdot (b + c) = a \cdot b + a \cdot c$

Check Yourself 3

Show that

$3 \times (5 + 2) = (3 \times 5) + (3 \times 2)$

Regrouping must often be used to multiply larger numbers. We see how regrouping works in multiplication by looking at an example in the expanded form. When regrouping results in changing a digit to the left we sometimes say we "carry" the units.

Example 4 Multiplying by a Single-Digit Number

$3 \times 25 = 3 \times (20 + 5)$ We use the distributive property again.

$= 3 \times 20 + 3 \times 5$

$= 60 \quad + 15$ Write the 15 as 10 + 5.

$= 60 + 10 + 5$ Carry 10 ones or 1 ten to the tens place.

$= 70 + 5$

$= 75$

NOTE

3×25

$3 \cdot 25$

$(3)(25)$

all mean the same thing.

Here is the same multiplication problem using the short form.

Step 1

$$\begin{array}{r} 1 \leftarrow \text{Carry} \\ 25 \\ \times\ 3 \\ \hline 5 \end{array}$$

Multiplying 3 × 5 gives us 15 ones. Write 5 ones and carry 1 ten.

Step 2

$$\begin{array}{r} 1 \\ 25 \\ \times\ 3 \\ \hline 75 \end{array}$$

Now multiply 3 × 2 tens and add the carry to get 7, the tens digit of the product.

Check Yourself 4

Multiply.

(a) $\begin{array}{r} 34 \\ \times\ 6 \\ \hline \end{array}$ **(b)** $\begin{array}{r} 43 \\ \times\ 7 \\ \hline \end{array}$

Units ANALYSIS

When you multiply a denominate number, such as 6 feet (ft), by an abstract number, such as 5, the result has the same units as the denominate number. Some examples are

$5 \times 6 \text{ ft} = 30 \text{ ft}$

$3 \times \$7 = \$21$

$9 \times 4 \text{ A's} = 36 \text{ A's}$

When you multiply two different denominate numbers, the units must also be multiplied. We will discuss this when we look at the area of geometric figures.

RECALL

It is best to write down the complete statement necessary for the solution of an application.

We briefly review our discussion of applications, or word problems.

As you will see, the process of solving applications is the same no matter which operation is required for the solution. In fact, the four-step procedure we suggested in Section 1.2 can be effectively applied here.

Step by Step

Solving Applications

Step 1 Read the problem carefully to determine the given information and what you are asked to find.

Step 2 Decide upon the operation or operations to be used.

Step 3 Write down the complete statement necessary to solve the problem and do the calculations.

Step 4 Check to make sure you have answered the question of the problem and that your answer seems reasonable.

Example 5 Solving an Application Involving Multiplication

< Objective 3 >

A car rental agency orders a fleet of 7 new subcompact cars at a cost of \$14,258 per automobile. What will the company pay for the entire order?

Step 1 We know the number of cars and the price per car. We want to find the total cost.

Step 2 Multiplication is the best approach to the solution.

Step 3 Write

$$7 \times \$14{,}258 = \$99{,}806$$

We could, of course, *add* \$14,258, the cost, 7 times, but multiplication is certainly more efficient.

Step 4 The total cost of the order is \$99,806.

Check Yourself 5

Tires sell for \$47 apiece. What is the total cost for 5 tires?

To multiply by numbers with more than one digit, we must multiply each digit of the first factor by each digit of the second. To do this, we form a series of partial products and then add them to arrive at the final product.

Example 6 Multiplying by a Two-Digit Number

Multiply 56×47.

Step 1

$$\begin{array}{r} {\scriptstyle 4} \\ 56 \\ \times\ 47 \\ \hline 392 \end{array}$$

The first partial product is 7×56, or 392. Note that we had to carry 4 to the tens column.

Step 2

$$\begin{array}{r} {\scriptstyle 2} \\ {\scriptstyle 4} \\ 56 \\ \times\ 47 \\ \hline 392 \\ 2240 \\ \hline \end{array}$$

The second partial product is 40×56, or 2,240. We must carry 2 during the process.

Step 3

$$\begin{array}{r} {\scriptstyle 2} \\ {\scriptstyle 4} \\ 56 \\ \times\ 47 \\ \hline 392 \\ 2240 \\ \hline 2{,}632 \end{array}$$

We add the partial products for our final result.

Check Yourself 6

Multiply.

$$\begin{array}{r} 38 \\ \times\ 76 \\ \hline \end{array}$$

If multiplication involves two three-digit numbers, another step is necessary. In this case we form three partial products. This will ensure that each digit of the first factor is multiplied by each digit of the second.

Example 7 Multiplying Two Three-Digit Numbers

Multiply.

$$\begin{array}{r} {\scriptstyle 22} \\ {\scriptstyle 33} \\ {\scriptstyle 22} \\ 278 \\ \times\ 343 \\ \hline 834 \\ 11120 \\ 83400 \\ \hline 95{,}354 \end{array}$$

In forming the third partial product, we must multiply by 300.

NOTE

The three partial products are formed when we multiply by the ones, tens, and then the hundreds digits.

Check Yourself 7

Multiply.

$$\begin{array}{r} 352 \\ \times\ 249 \\ \hline \end{array}$$

Next, look at an example of multiplying by a number involving 0 as a digit. There are several ways to arrange the work, as our example shows.

Example 8 Multiplying Larger Numbers

Multiply 573×205.

Method 1

$$\begin{array}{r} 1 \\ 31 \\ 573 \\ \times\ 205 \\ \hline 2865 \\ 0000 \\ 114600 \\ \hline 117{,}465 \end{array}$$

We can write the second partial product as 0000 to indicate the multiplication by 0 in the tens place.

Here is a second approach to the problem.

Method 2

$$\begin{array}{r} 1 \\ 31 \\ 573 \\ \times\ 205 \\ \hline 2865 \\ 114600 \\ \hline 117{,}465 \end{array}$$

We can write a double 0 as our second step. If we place the third partial product on the same line, that product will be shifted *two* places left, indicating that we are multiplying by 200.

Because this second method is more compact, it is usually used.

Check Yourself 8

Multiply.

$$\begin{array}{r} 489 \\ \times\ 304 \\ \hline \end{array}$$

Example 9 will lead us to another property of multiplication.

Example 9 Using the Associative Property

$(2 \times 3) \times 4 = 6 \times 4 = 24$

We do the multiplication in the parentheses first, $2 \times 3 = 6$. Then we multiply 6×4.

Also,

$2 \times (3 \times 4) = 2 \times 12 = 24$

Here we multiply 3×4 as the first step. Then we multiply 2×12.

We see that

$(2 \times 3) \times 4 = 2 \times (3 \times 4)$

The product is the same no matter which way we *group* the factors. This is called the **associative property** of multiplication.

Property

The Associative Property of Multiplication

Multiplication is an *associative* operation. The way in which you group numbers in multiplication does not affect the final product.

Check Yourself 9

Find the products.

(a) $(5 \times 3) \times 6$ **(b)** $5 \times (3 \times 6)$

There are some shortcuts that let you simplify your work when multiplying by a number that ends in 0. Let's see what we can discover by looking at some examples.

Example 10 Multiplying by 10

First we multiply by 10.

$$\begin{array}{r} 67 \\ \times\ 10 \\ \hline 670 \end{array} \quad 10 \times 67 = 670$$

Next we multiply by 100.

$$\begin{array}{r} 537 \\ \times\ 100 \\ \hline 53{,}700 \end{array} \quad 100 \times 537 = 53{,}700$$

Finally, we multiply by 1,000.

$$\begin{array}{r} 489 \\ \times\ 1{,}000 \\ \hline 489{,}000 \end{array} \quad 1{,}000 \times 489 = 489{,}000$$

Check Yourself 10

Multiply.

(a) $\begin{array}{r} 257 \\ \times\ 100 \\ \hline \end{array}$ **(b)** $\begin{array}{r} 2{,}436 \\ \times\ 1{,}000 \\ \hline \end{array}$

NOTE

We talk about powers of 10 in greater detail in Section 1.7.

Do you see a pattern? Rather than writing out the multiplication, there is an easier way! We call the numbers 10, 100, 1,000, and so on **powers of 10.**

Property

Multiplying by Powers of 10

When a natural number is multiplied by a power of 10, the product is just that number followed by as many zeros as there are in the power of 10.

Example 11 Multiplying by Numbers That End in Zero

Multiply 400×678.

Write

$$\begin{array}{r} 678 \\ \times\ \ 400 \\ \hline \end{array}$$

Shift 400 so that the two zeros are *to the right* of the digits above.

$$\begin{array}{r} {\scriptstyle 33}\ \ \\ 678 \\ \times\ \ 400 \\ \hline 271{,}200 \end{array}$$

Bring down the two zeros, then multiply 4×678 to find the product.

There is no mystery about why this works. We know that 400 is 4×100. In this method, we are multiplying 678 by 4 and then by 100, adding two zeros to the product by our earlier rule.

Check Yourself 11

Multiply.

300 × 574

Your work in this section, together with our earlier rounding techniques, provides a convenient means of using estimation to check the reasonableness of our results in multiplication, as Example 12 illustrates.

Example 12 Estimating a Product by Rounding

< Objective 4 >

Estimate the following product by rounding each factor to the nearest hundred.

		Rounded
512	⟶	500
× 289	⟶	× 300
		150,000

You might want to find the *actual* product and use our estimate to see if your result seems reasonable.

Check Yourself 12

Estimate the product by rounding each factor to the nearest hundred.

689
× 425

Rounding the factors can be a very useful way of estimating the solution to an application problem.

Example 13 Estimating the Solution to a Multiplication Application

Bart is thinking of running an ad in the local newspaper for an entire year. The ad costs \$19.95 per week. Approximate the annual cost of the ad.

Rounding the charge to \$20 and rounding the number of weeks in a year to 50, we get

$50 \times 20 = 1{,}000$

The ad would cost approximately \$1,000.

Check Yourself 13

Phyllis is debating whether to join the health club for \$400 per year or just pay \$9 per visit. If she goes about once a week, approximately how much would she spend at \$9 per visit?

Units ANALYSIS

What happens when we multiply two denominate numbers? The units of the result turn out to be the product of the units. This makes sense when we look at an example from geometry.

The area of a square is the square of one side. As a formula, we write that as

$A = s^2$

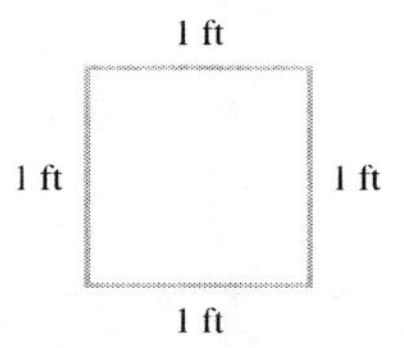

This tile is 1 ft by 1 ft.

$A = s^2 = (1\text{ ft})^2 = 1\text{ ft} \times 1\text{ ft} = 1\text{ (ft)} \times \text{(ft)} = 1\text{ ft}^2$

In other words, its area is one square foot (1 ft^2).

If we want to find the area of a room, we are actually finding how many of these square feet can be placed in the room.

NOTE

The small, raised 2 is called an *exponent* or *power.* This will be studied in Section 1.7. So in. × in. can be written in.^{2} and is read "square inches."

Now look at the idea of **area.** Area is a measure that we give to a surface. It is measured in terms of **square units.** The area is the number of square units that are needed to cover the surface.

One standard unit of area measure is the **square inch** (written in.^{2}). This is the measure of the surface contained in a square with sides of 1 in.

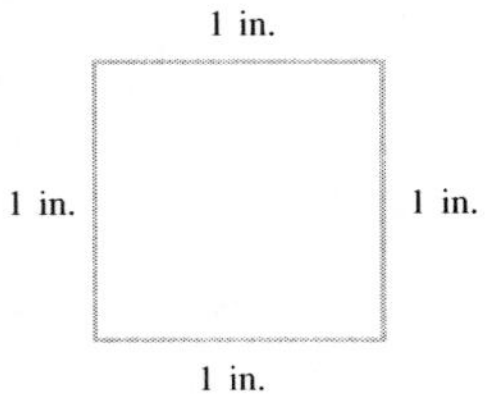

One square inch

Other units of area measure are the square foot (ft^2), the square yard (yd^2), the square centimeter (cm^2), and the square meter (m^2).

Finding the area of a figure means finding the number of square units it contains. One simple case is a rectangle.

NOTE

The length and width must be in terms of the same unit.

The figure to the right shows a rectangle. The length of the rectangle is 4 in., and the width is 3 in. The area of the rectangle is measured in terms of square inches. We can simply count to find the area, 12 square inches (in.^{2}). However, because each of the four vertical strips contains 3 in.^{2}, we can multiply:

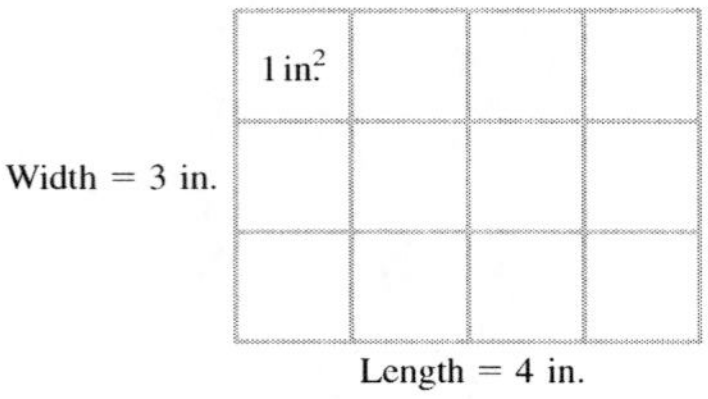

Area = 4 in. × 3 in. = 12 in.^{2}

Property

Formula for the Area of a Rectangle

In general, we can write the formula for the **area of a rectangle:** If the length of a rectangle is L units and the width is W units, then the formula for the area A of the rectangle can be written as

$A = L \cdot W$ (square units)

Example 14 **Find the Area of a Rectangle**

< Objective 5 >

A room has dimensions 12 ft by 15 ft. Find its area.

Use the area formula, with $L = 15$ ft and $W = 12$ ft.

$A = L \cdot W$

$= 15 \text{ ft} \times 12 \text{ ft} = 180 \text{ ft}^2$

The area of the room is 180 ft^2.

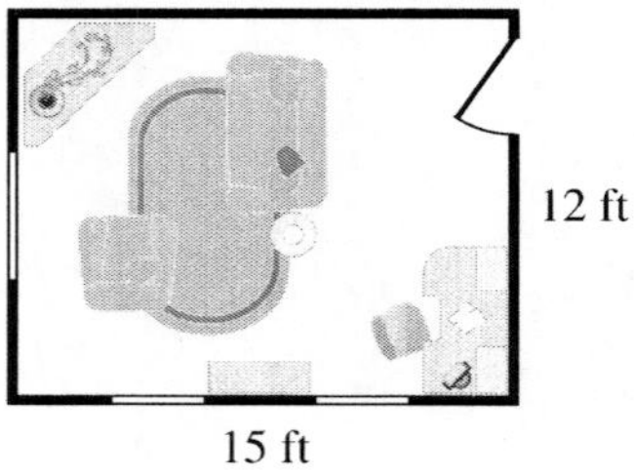

Check Yourself 14

A desktop has dimensions 50 in. by 25 in. What is the area of its surface?

NOTE

s^2 is read "s squared."

We can also write a convenient formula for the area of a square. If the sides of the square have length s, we can write

Property

Formula for the Area of a Square

$A = s \cdot s = s^2$

Example 15 Finding the Area

You wish to cover a square table with a plastic laminate that costs 60¢ a square foot. If each side of the table measures 3 ft, what will it cost to cover the table?

We first must find the area of the table. Use the area formula with $s = 3$ ft.

$$A = s^2$$
$$= (3\text{ ft})^2 = 3\text{ ft} \times 3\text{ ft} = 9\text{ ft}^2$$

Now, multiply by the cost per square foot.

Cost = 9 × 60¢ = 540¢ = $5.40

Check Yourself 15

You wish to carpet a room that is a square, 4 yd by 4 yd, with carpet that costs $12 per square yard. What will be the total cost of the carpeting?

Sometimes the total area of an oddly shaped figure is found by adding the smaller areas. Example 16 shows how this is done.

Example 16 Finding the Area of an Oddly Shaped Figure

Find the area of the figure.

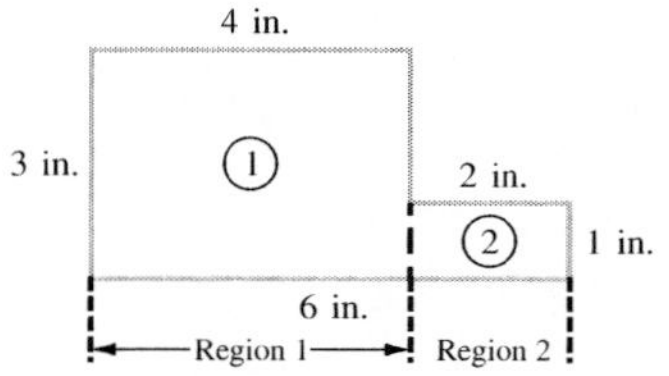

The area of the figure is found by adding the areas of regions 1 and 2. Region 1 is a 4 in. by 3 in. rectangle; the area of region 1 = 4 in. × 3 in. = 12 in.^{2}. Region 2 is a 2 in. by 1 in. rectangle; the area of region 2 = 2 in. × 1 in. = 2 in.^{2}.

The total area is the sum of the two areas:

Total area = 12 in.^{2} + 2 in.^{2} = 14 in.^{2}

Check Yourself 16

Find the area of the figure.

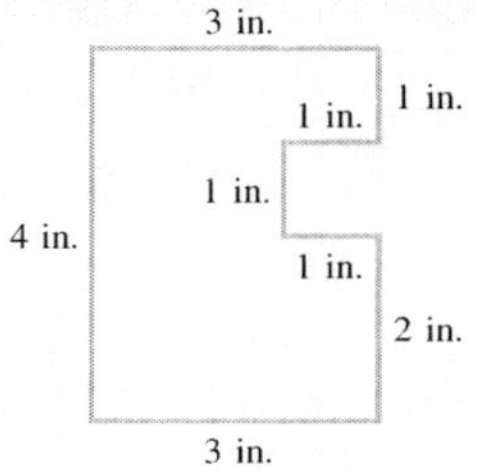

Hint: You can find the area by adding the areas of three rectangles, or by subtracting the area of the "missing" rectangle from the area of the "completed" larger rectangle.

Our next measurement deals with finding the **volume of a solid.** The volume of a solid measures the amount of space contained by the solid.

Definition

Solid — A **solid** is a three-dimensional figure. It has length, width, and height.

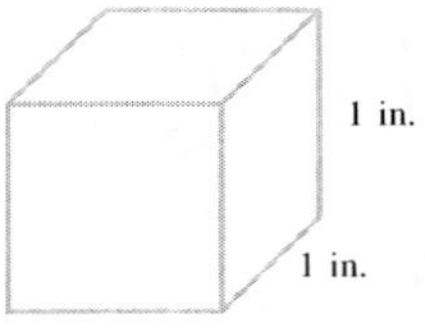

1 cubic inch

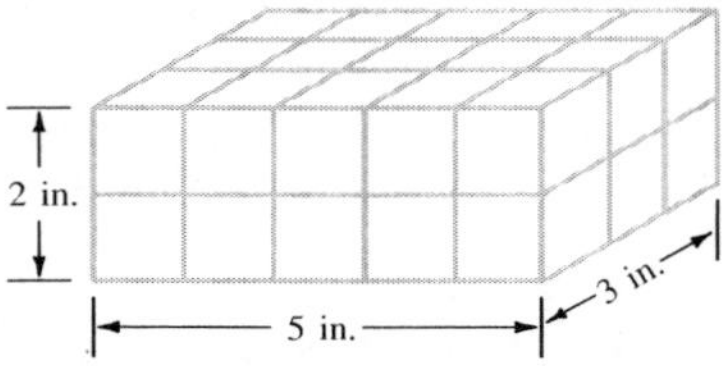

Volume is measured in **cubic units.** Examples include cubic inches ($in.^3$), cubic feet (ft^3), and cubic centimeters (cm^3). A cubic inch, for instance, is the measure of the space contained in a cube that is 1 in. on each edge. See the figure to the left.

In finding the volume of a figure, we want to know how many cubic units are contained in that figure. Let's start with a simple example, a **rectangular solid.** A rectangular solid is a very familiar figure. A box, a crate, and most rooms are rectangular solids. Say that the dimensions of the solid are 5 in. by 3 in. by 2 in. as pictured in the figure to the left. If we divide the solid into units of 1 $in.^3$, we have two layers, each containing 3 units by 5 units, or 15 $in.^3$ Because there are two layers, the volume is 30 $in.^3$

In general, we can see that the volume of a rectangular solid is the product of its length, width, and height.

Property

Formula for the Volume of a Rectangular Solid — The volume V of a rectangular solid with length L, width W, and height H is given by the product of the length, width, and height.

$$V = L \cdot W \cdot H$$

Volume is measured in cubic units.

Example 17 Finding the Volume

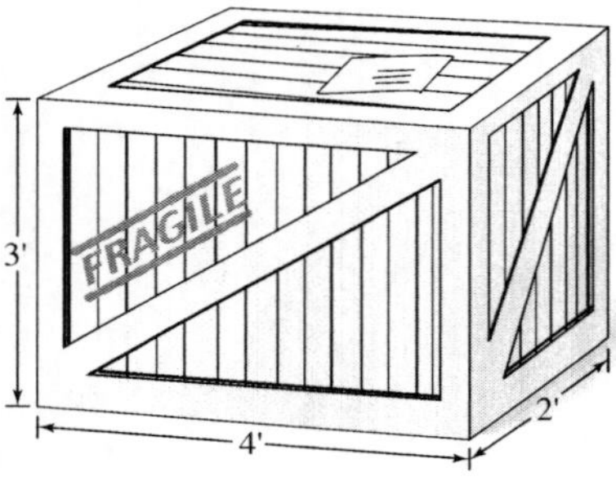

A crate has dimensions 4 ft by 2 ft by 3 ft. Find its volume.

We use the volume formula with $L = 4$ ft, $W = 2$ ft, and $H = 3$ ft.

$$V = L \cdot W \cdot H$$

$$= 4 \text{ ft} \times 2 \text{ ft} \times 3 \text{ ft}$$

$$= 24 \text{ ft}^3$$

The volume of the crate is 24 cubic feet.

Check Yourself 17

A room is 15 ft long, 10 ft wide, and 8 ft high. What is its volume?

Check Yourself ANSWERS

1. Factors 2, 9; product 18 **2.** 24 **3.** $3 \times 7 = 21$ and $15 + 6 = 21$ **4.** (a) 204; **(b)** 301 **5.** \$235 **6.** 2,888 **7.** 87,648 **8.** 148,656 **9. (a)** 90; **(b)** 90 **10. (a)** 25,700; **(b)** 2,436,000 **11.** 172,200 **12.** 280,000 **13.** \$500 **14.** 1,250 $in.^2$ **15.** \$192 **16.** 11 $in.^2$ **17.** 1,200 ft^3

Reading Your Text

The following fill-in-the-blank exercises are designed to ensure that you understand some of the key vocabulary used in this section.

SECTION 1.5

(a) The final step in solving an application is to make certain that the answer is ________.

(b) The way in which you group numbers in multiplication does not affect the final ____________.

(c) The numbers 10, 100, and 1,000 are called ____________ of 10.

(d) We can write the equation for the area of a ____________ as $A = L \cdot W$.

1.5 exercises

Basic Skills | Challenge Yourself | Calculator/Computer | Career Applications | Above and Beyond

Name ______________

Section ________ Date ________

Answers

1. ______ 2. ______
3. ______ 4. ______
5. ______ 6. ______
7. ______ 8. ______
9. ______ 10. ______
11. ______ 12. ______
13. ______ 14. ______
15. ______ 16. ______
17. ______ 18. ______
19. ______ 20. ______
21. ______ 22. ______
23. ______ 24. ______
25. ______ 26. ______
27. ______ 28. ______
29. ______ 30. ______
31. ______ 32. ______
33. ______ 34. ______
35. ______
36. ______
37. ______
38. ______

< Objective 1 >

Multiply.

1. 5×3

2. 7×4

3. $6 \cdot 0$

4. $6 \cdot 6$

5. 4×48

6. 5×53

7. 508×6

8. 903×9 > Videos

9. 75×68

10. 235×49

11. 327×59 > Videos

12. $2{,}364 \cdot 67$

13. $4{,}075 \cdot 84$

14. 315×243

15. 124×225

16. 345×267

17. 639×358

18. $547 \cdot 203$

19. $668 \cdot 305$

20. $2{,}458 \times 135$

21. $3{,}219 \times 207$

22. $2{,}534 \times 3{,}106$

23. $3{,}158 \times 2{,}034$

24. 43×70

25. 58×40

26. 562×400

27. 907×900

28. 345×230

29. 362×310

30. $157 \times 3{,}200$

31. Find the product of 304 and 7. > Videos

32. Find the product of 8 and 5,679.

33. What is 21 multiplied by 551?

34. What is 135 multiplied by 507?

< Objective 2 >

Name the property of addition and/or multiplication that is illustrated.

35. $5 \times 8 = 8 \times 5$ > Videos

36. $3 \times (4 + 9) = (3 \times 4) + (3 \times 9)$ > Videos

37. $2 \times (3 \times 5) = (2 \times 3) \times 5$

38. $5 \times (6 + 2) = 5 \times (2 + 6)$

Basic Skills | **Challenge Yourself** | Calculator/Computer | Career Applications | Above and Beyond

In exercises 39 and 40, complete the statement, using the given property.

39. $7 + (3 \times 8) =$ Commutative property of multiplication

40. $3 \times (2 + 7) =$ Distributive property

< Objective 3 >

Solve each application.

41. Business and Finance A convoy company can transport 8 new cars on one of its trucks. If 34 truck shipments were made in one week, how many cars were shipped?

42. Business and Finance A computer printer can print 40 mailing labels per minute. How many labels can be printed in 1 hour (h)?

43. Social Science A rectangular parking lot has 14 rows of parking spaces, and each row contains 24 spaces. How many cars can be parked in the lot?

44. Statistics A petition to get Tom on the ballot for treasurer of student council has 28 signatures on each of 43 pages. How many signatures were collected?

45. Business and Finance The manufacturer of wood-burning stoves can make 15 stoves in 1 day. How many stoves can be made in 28 days?

46. Business and Finance Each bundle of newspapers contains 25 papers. If 43 bundles are delivered to Jose's house, how many papers are delivered?

< Objective 5 >

Find the area of each figure.

47.

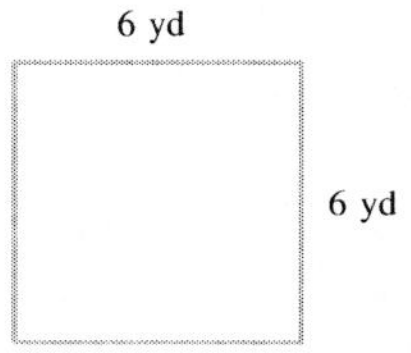

48.

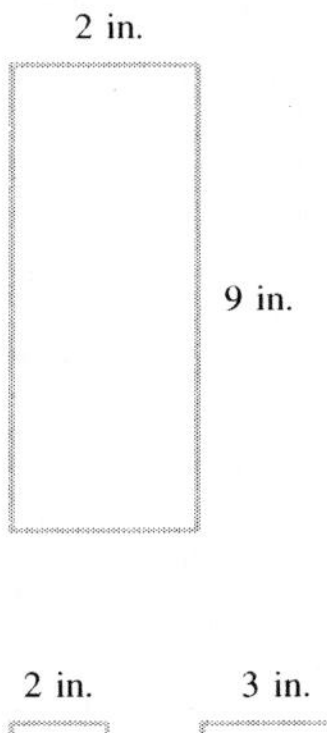

49.

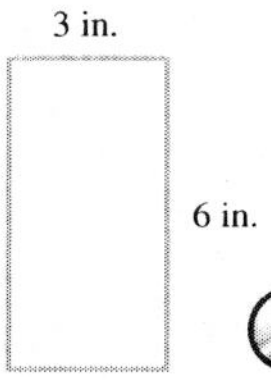

Videos

50.

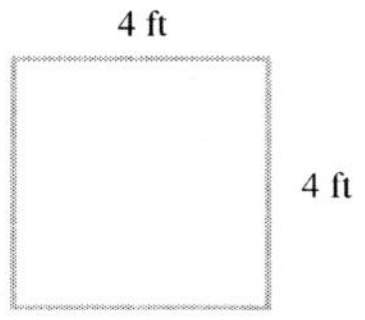

51.

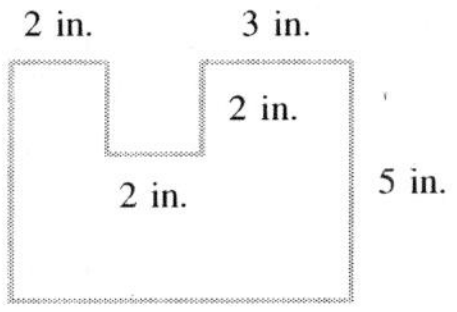

52.

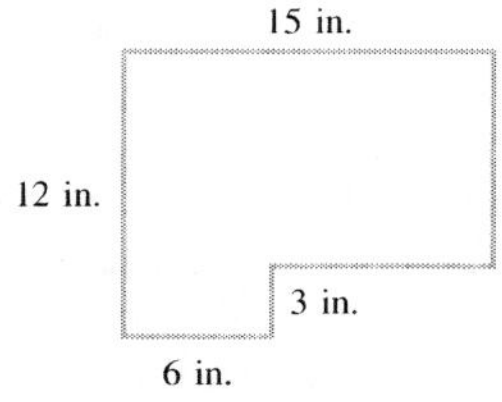

Answers

39. ______

40. ______

41. ______

42. ______

43. ______

44. ______

45. ______

46. ______

47. ______

48. ______

49. ______

50. ______

51. ______

52. ______

Answers

53. ______

54. ______

55. ______

56. ______

57. ______

58. ______

59. ______

60. ______

61. ______

62. ______

63. ______

64. ______

Find the volume of each figure.

53.

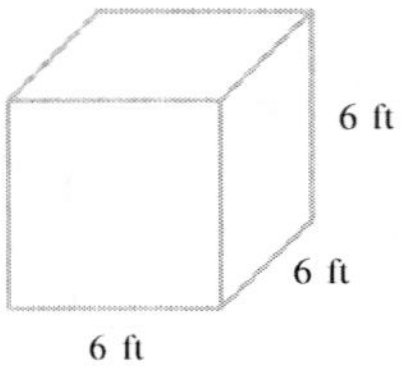

54.

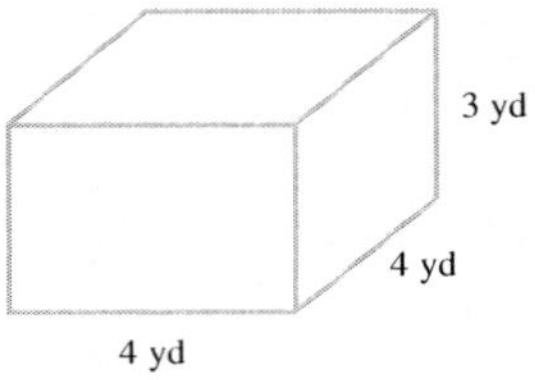

< Objective 4 >

Estimate each product by rounding the factors to the nearest hundred.

55. 391×531

56. 729×481

Solve each application.

57. Social Science A movie theater has its seats arranged so that there are 42 seats per row. The theater has 48 rows. Estimate the number of seats in the theater.

58. Statistics There are 52 mathematics classes with 28 students in each class. Estimate the total number of students in the mathematics classes.

59. Business and Finance A company can manufacture 45 sleds per day. Approximately how many can this company make in 128 days?

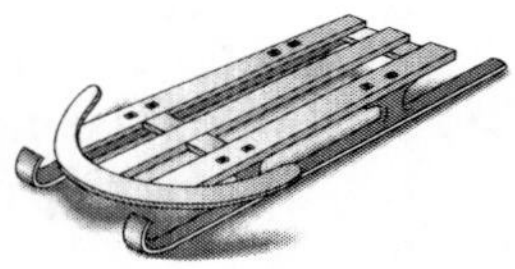

60. Business and Finance The attendance at a basketball game was 2,345. The cost of admission was $12 per person. Estimate the total gate receipts for the game.

Basic Skills | Challenge Yourself | Calculator/Computer | **Career Applications** | Above and Beyond

61. Allied Health A young male patient is to be administered an intravenous (IV) solution running on an infusion pump set for 125 milliliters (mL) per hour for 6 hours. What is the total volume of solution to be infused?

62. Allied Health To help assess breathing efficiency, respiratory therapists calculate the patient's alveolar minute ventilation, in milliliters per minute (mL/min), by taking the product of the patient's respiratory rate, in breaths per minute, and the difference between the patient's tidal volume and dead-space volume, both in milliliters. Calculate the alveolar minute ventilation for a male patient with lung disease given that his respiratory rate is 10 breaths per minute, his tidal volume is 575 mL, and his dead-space volume is 200 mL.

63. Information Technology Jack needs a thousand feet of twisted pair cable for a network installation project. He goes to a local electronics store. The store sells cable at 10¢ a foot. How much (in cents) will one thousand feet of cable cost? How much is that in dollars?

64. Information Technology Amber needs to buy 100 new computers for new employees that have been hired by ABC consulting. She finds the cost of a decent computer to be $655 from Dell Computers. How much will she spend to buy 100 new computers?

65. **Electronics** An electronics-component distributor sells resistors, small components that "resist" the flow of electric current, in presealed bags. Each bag contains 50 resistors. If you purchased 25 bags of resistors, how many resistors would you have?

66. **Electronics** Assume that is takes 4 hours to solder all the components on a given printed circuit board. If you are given 36 boards to solder, how many hours will the project take? If you worked nonstop, how many hours would the project take?

67. **Manufacturing Technology** A small shop has 6 machinists each earning \$14 per hour, 3 assembly workers earning \$8 per hour, and one supervisor-maintenance person earning \$18 per hour. What is the shop's payroll for a 40-hour week?

68. **Manufacturing Technology** What is the distance from the center of hole A to the center of hole B in the following diagram?

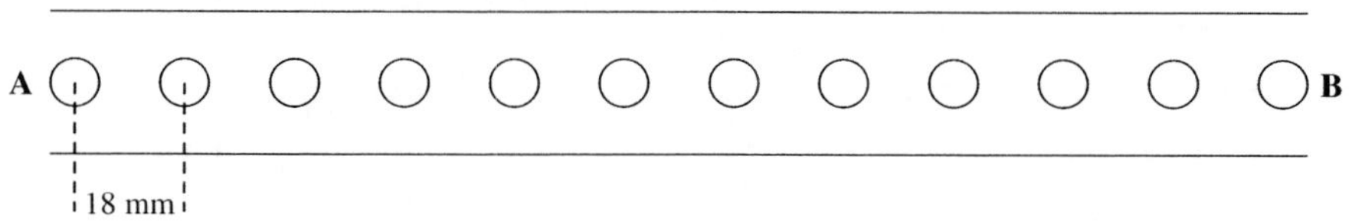

Basic Skills | Challenge Yourself | Calculator/Computer | Career Applications | **Above and Beyond**

69. **Social Science** We have seen that addition and multiplication are commutative operations. Decide which of the following activities are commutative.

(a) Taking a shower and eating breakfast

(b) Getting dressed and taking a shower

(c) Putting on your shoes and your socks

(d) Brushing your teeth and combing your hair

(e) Putting your key in the ignition and starting your car

70. **Social Science** The associative properties of addition and multiplication indicate that the result of the operation is the same regardless of where the grouping symbol is placed. This is not always the case in the use of the English language. Many phrases can have different meanings based on how the words are grouped. In each of the following, explain why the associative property would not hold.

(a) Cat fearing dog

(b) Hard test question

(c) Defective parts department

(d) Man eating animal

Write some phrases in which the associative property is satisfied.

71. **Construction** Suppose you wish to build a small, rectangular pen, and you have enough fencing for the pen's perimeter to be 36 ft. Assuming that the length and width are to be whole numbers, answer the following.

(a) List the possible dimensions that the pen could have. (*Note:* A square is a type of rectangle.)

(b) For each set of dimensions (length and width), find the area that the pen would enclose.

(c) Which dimensions give the greatest area?

(d) What is the greatest area?

Answers

65. ____________

66. ____________

67. ____________

68. ____________

69. ____________

70. ____________

71. ____________

Answers

72. ____________

73. ____________

74. ____________

72. Construction Suppose you wish to build a rectangular kennel that encloses 100 ft^2. Assuming that the length and width are to be whole numbers, answer the following.

(a) List the possible dimensions that the kennel could have. (*Note:* A square is a type of rectangle.)

(b) For each set of dimensions (length and width), find the perimeter that would surround the kennel.

(c) Which dimensions give the least perimeter?

(d) What is the least perimeter?

73. Social Science Most maps contain legends that allow you to convert the distance between two points on the map to actual miles. For instance, if a map uses a legend that equates 1 inch (in.) to 5 miles (mi) and the distance between two towns is 4 in. on the map, then the towns are actually 20 mi apart.

(a) Obtain a map of your state and determine the shortest distance between any two major cities.

(b) Could you actually travel the route you measured in part **(a)**?

(c) Plan a trip between the two cities you selected in part **(a)** over established roads. Determine the distance that you actually travel using this route.

74. Number Problem Complete the following number cross.

Across	Down
1. 6×551	**1.** 5×7
5. 7×8	**2.** 9×41
6. 27×27	**3.** 67×100
7. 19×50	**4.** $2 \times (49 + 100)$
10. 3×67	**8.** $4 \times 1{,}301$
12. 6×25	**9.** $100 + 10 + 1$
13. 9×8	**11.** 2×87
15. 16×303	**14.** $25 + 3$

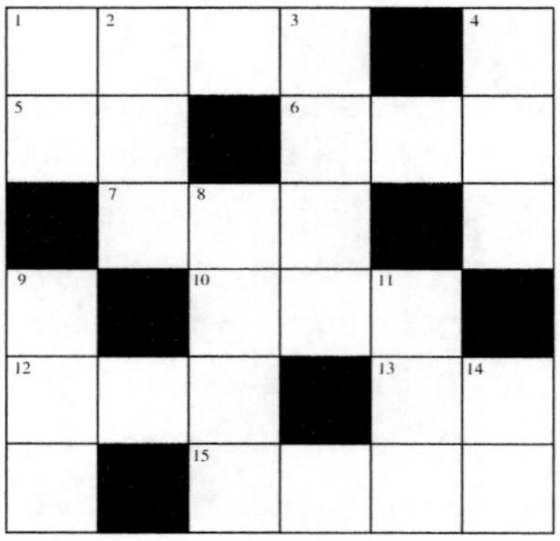

Answers

1. 15 3. 0 5. 192 7. 3,048 9. 5,100 11. 19,293
13. 342,300 15. 27,900 17. 228,762 19. 203,740
21. 666,333 23. 6,423,372 25. 2,320 27. 816,300
29. 112,220 31. 2,128 33. 11,571
35. Commutative property of multiplication
37. Associative property of multiplication
39. $7 + (8 \times 3)$ 41. 272 cars 43. 336 cars 45. 420 stoves
47. 36 yd^2 49. 18 $in.^2$ 51. 31 $in.^2$ 53. 216 ft^3
55. 200,000 57. 2,000 seats 59. 6,500 sleds 61. 750 mL
63. 10,000¢; \$100 65. 1,250 resistors 67. \$5,040
69. Above and Beyond 71. Above and Beyond 73. Above and Beyond

1.6 Division

< 1.6 Objectives >

1 > Write a division problem as repeated subtraction
2 > Use the language of division
3 > Divide whole numbers
4 > Estimate quotients
5 > Solve applications of division

Now we examine a fourth arithmetic operation, division. Just as multiplication is repeated addition, division is repeated subtraction. Division asks *how many times* one number is contained in another.

Example 1 Dividing by Using Subtraction

< Objective 1 >

NOTE

The 8 is subtracted six times.

Joel needs to set up 48 chairs in the student union for a concert. If there is room for 8 chairs per row, how many rows will it take to set up all 48 chairs?

This problem can be solved by subtraction. Each row subtracts another 8 chairs.

48	40	32	24	16	8
−8	−8	−8	−8	−8	−8
40	32	24	16	8	0

Because 8 can be subtracted from 48 six times, there will be 6 rows.

This can also be seen as a division problem.

Dividend, Divisor, Quotient: $48 \div 8 = 6$ or Divisor, Quotient, Dividend: $8\overline{)48}$ with quotient 6 or Dividend, Quotient, Divisor: $\frac{48}{8} = 6$

No matter which method we use, we call 48 the **dividend,** 8 the **divisor,** and 6 the **quotient.**

Check Yourself 1

Carlotta is creating a garden path made of bricks. She has 72 bricks. Each row will have 6 bricks in it. How many rows can she make?

Units ANALYSIS

When you divide a denominate number by an abstract number, the result will have the units of the denominate number. Here are a couple of examples:

76 trombones ÷ 4 = 19 trombones

\$55 ÷ 11 = \$5

When one denominate number is divided by another, the result will get the units of the dividend over the units of the divisor.

144 miles ÷ 6 gallons = 24 miles/gallon (which we read as "miles per gallon")

\$120 ÷ 8 hours = 15 dollars/hour ("dollars per hour")

To solve a problem requiring division, first set up the problem as a division statement. Example 2 illustrates this idea.

Example 2 Writing a Division Statement

< Objective 2 >

Write a division statement that corresponds to the following situation. You need not do the division.

The staff at the Wok Inn Restaurant splits all tips at the end of each shift. Yesterday's evening shift collected a total of \$224. How much should each of the 7 employees get in tips?

\$224 ÷ 7 employees (Note that the units for the answer will be "dollars per employee.")

Check Yourself 2

Write a division statement that corresponds to the following situation. You need not do the division.

All nine sections of basic math skills at SCC (Sum Community College) are full. There are a total of 315 students in the classes. How many students are in each class? What are the units for the answer?

In Section 1.5, we used a rectangular array of stars to represent multiplication. These same arrays can represent division. Just as $3 \times 4 = 12$ and $4 \times 3 = 12$, so is it true that $12 \div 3 = 4$ and $12 \div 4 = 3$.

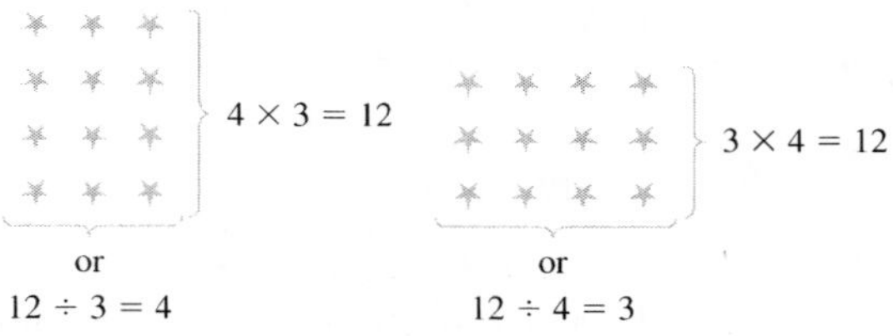

This relationship allows us to check our division results by doing multiplication.

Example 3 Checking Division by Using Multiplication

NOTE

For a division problem to check, the *product* of the divisor and the quotient *must equal the dividend.*

(a) $7\overline{)21}$ with quotient 3 Check: $7 \times 3 = 21$

(b) $48 \div 6 = 8$ Check: $6 \times 8 = 48$

Check Yourself 3

Complete the division statements and check your results.

(a) $9\overline{)45}$ **(b)** $28 \div 7$

NOTE

Because $36 \div 9 = 4$, we say that 36 is *exactly divisible* by 9.

In our examples so far, the product of the divisor and the quotient has been equal to the dividend. This means that the dividend is *exactly divisible* by the divisor. That is not always the case. Look at another example that uses repeated subtraction.

Example 4 Dividing by Using Subtraction, Leaving a Remainder

NOTE

The remainder must be smaller than the divisor or we could subtract again.

How many times is 5 contained in 23?

$$\begin{array}{r}23\\-\;5\\\hline 18\end{array}\qquad\begin{array}{r}18\\-\;5\\\hline 13\end{array}\qquad\begin{array}{r}13\\-\;5\\\hline 8\end{array}\qquad\begin{array}{r}8\\-5\\\hline 3\end{array}$$

We see that 5 is contained 4 times in 23, but 3 is "leftover."

The number 23 is not exactly divisible by 5. The "leftover" 3 is called the **remainder** in the division. To check the division operation when a remainder is involved, we have the following rule:

Definition

Remainder

Dividend = divisor × quotient + remainder

Check Yourself 4

How many times is 7 contained in 38?

Example 5 Checking Division by a Single-Digit Number

Using the work of Example 4, we can write

$5\overline{)23}$ with quotient 4   with remainder 3

NOTE

Another way to write the result is

$5\overline{)23}$ with 4 r3 above   The "r" stands for remainder.

To apply our previous rule, we have

Divisor   Quotient

$$\text{Dividend} \rightarrow 23 = 5 \times 4 + 3 \leftarrow \text{Remainder}$$
$$23 = 20 + 3$$
$$23 = 23$$

The division checks.

NOTE

The multiplication is done before the 3 is added.

Check Yourself 5

Evaluate $7\overline{)38}$. Check your answer.

We must be careful when 0 is involved in a division problem. There are two special cases.

Property

Division and Zero

1. Zero divided by any whole number (except 0) is 0.
2. Division by 0 is undefined.

The first case involving zero occurs when we are dividing into zero.

Example 6 Dividing into Zero

RECALL

There are three forms that are equivalent:

$0 \div 5 = 0$

$5\overline{)0} = 0$

$\frac{0}{5} = 0$

$0 \div 5 = 0$ because $0 = 5 \times 0$.

Check Yourself 6

(a) $0 \div 7$ (b) $9\overline{)0}$ (c) $\frac{0}{12}$

Our second case illustrates what happens when 0 is the *divisor*. Here we have a special problem.

Example 7 Dividing by Zero

$8 \div 0 = ?$ This means that $8 = 0 \times ?$

Can 0 times some number ever be 8? From our multiplication facts, the answer is *no!* There is no answer to this problem, so we say that $8 \div 0$ is undefined.

Check Yourself 7

Decide whether each problem results in 0 or is undefined.

(a) $\frac{9}{0}$ (b) $\frac{0}{9}$ (c) $15\overline{)0}$ (d) $0\overline{)15}$

It is easy to divide when small whole numbers are involved, because much of the work can be done mentally. In working with larger numbers, we turn to a process called **long division.** This is a shorthand method for performing the steps of repeated subtraction.

To start, look at an example in which we subtract multiples of the divisor.

Example 8 Dividing by a Single-Digit Number

< Objective 3 >

NOTE

With larger numbers, repeated subtraction is just too time-consuming to be practical.

Divide 176 by 8.

Because 20 eights are 160, we know that there are at least 20 eights in 176.

Step 1 Write

$$\begin{array}{r} 20 \\ 8\overline{)176} \\ \underline{160} \\ 16 \end{array}$$

20 eights → 160

Subtracting 160 is just a shortcut for subtracting eight 20 times.

After subtracting the 20 eights, or 160, we are left with 16. There are 2 eights in 16, and so we continue.

Step 2

```
      2 |
     20 | 22   Adding 20 and 2 gives us the quotient, 22.
  8)176
    160
     16
2 eights ⟶ 16
      0
```

Subtracting the 2 eights, we have a 0 remainder. So $176 \div 8 = 22$.

Check Yourself 8

Verify the result of Example 8, using multiplication.

The next step is to simplify this repeated-subtraction process one step further. The result will be the long-division method.

Example 9 Dividing by a Single-Digit Number

Divide 358 by 6.

The dividend is 358. We look at the first digit, 3. We cannot divide 6 into 3, and so we look at the *first two digits,* 35. There are 5 sixes in 35, and so we write 5 above the tens digit of the dividend.

```
   5     When we place 5 as the tens digit,
6)358    we really mean 5 tens, or 50.
```

Now multiply 5×6, place the product below 35, and subtract.

```
   5
6)358
  30     We have actually subtracted 50 sixes
   5     (300) from 358.
```

Because the remainder, 5, is smaller than the divisor, 6, we bring down 8, the ones digit of the dividend.

```
   5
6)358
  30↓
   58
```

Now divide 6 into 58. There are 9 sixes in 58, and so 9 is the ones digit of the quotient. Multiply 9×6 and subtract to complete the process.

```
   59    We now have:
6)358    358 ÷ 6 = 59 r4
  30↓
   58
   54
    4
```

To check: $358 = 6 \times 59 + 4$

NOTES

Because 4 is smaller than the divisor, we have a remainder of 4.

Verify that this is true and that the division checks.

Check Yourself 9

Divide $7\overline{)453}$.

Long division becomes a bit more complicated when we have a two-digit divisor. It is now a matter of trial and error. We round the divisor and dividend to form a *trial divisor and a trial dividend.* We then estimate the proper quotient and must determine whether our estimate was correct.

Example 10 Dividing by a Two-Digit Number

Divide.

$38\overline{)293}$

NOTE

Think: $4\overline{)29}$ = 7

Round the divisor and dividend to the nearest ten. So 38 is rounded to 40, and 293 is rounded to 290. The trial divisor is then 40, and the trial dividend is 290.

Now look at the nonzero digits in the trial divisor and dividend. They are 4 and 29. We know that there are 7 fours in 29, and so 7 is our first estimate of the quotient. Now let's see if 7 works.

$$\begin{array}{r} 7 \\ 38\overline{)293} \\ \underline{266} \\ 27 \end{array}$$

7 ← Your estimate

Multiply 7 × 38. The product, 266, is less than 293, so we can subtract.

The remainder, 27, is less than the divisor, 38, and so the process is complete.

$293 \div 38 = 7 \text{ r}27$

Check: $293 = 38 \times 7 + 27$ You should verify that this statement is true.

Check Yourself 10

Divide.

$57\overline{)482}$

Because this process is based on estimation, our first guess is often incorrect.

Example 11 Dividing by a Two-Digit Number

Divide.

$54\overline{)428}$

NOTE

Think: $5\overline{)43}$ = 8

Rounding to the nearest ten, we have a trial divisor of 50 and a trial dividend of 430.

If you look at the nonzero digits, how many fives are in 43? There are 8. This is our first estimate.

$$\begin{array}{r} 8 \\ 54\overline{)428} \\ \underline{432} \end{array}$$

432 ← Too large

We multiply 8 × 54. Do you see what's wrong? The product, 432, is too large. We can't subtract. Our estimate of the quotient must be adjusted *downward*.

We adjust the quotient downward to 7. We can now complete the division.

$$\begin{array}{r} 7 \\ 54\overline{)428} \\ \underline{378} \\ 50 \end{array}$$

We have

$428 \div 54 = 7 \text{ r}50$

Check: $428 = 54 \times 7 + 50$

Check Yourself 11

Divide.

$63\overline{)557}$

We must be careful when a 0 appears as a digit in the quotient. Here is an example in which this happens with a two-digit divisor.

Example 12 **Dividing with Large Dividends**

NOTE

Our divisor, 32, divides into 98, the first two digits of the dividend.

Divide.

$32\overline{)9{,}871}$

Rounding to the nearest ten, we have a trial divisor of 30 and a trial dividend of 100. Think, "How many threes are in 10?" There are 3, and this is our first estimate of the quotient.

$$\begin{array}{r} 3 \\ 32\overline{)9{,}871} \\ \underline{9\,6} \\ 2 \end{array}$$

Everything seems fine so far!

Bring down 7, the next digit of the dividend.

$$\begin{array}{r} 30 \\ 32\overline{)9{,}871} \\ \underline{9\,6} \\ 27 \end{array}$$

Now do you see the difficulty? We cannot divide 32 into 27, and so we place 0 in the tens place of the quotient to indicate this fact.

We continue by multiplying by 0. After subtraction, we bring down 1, the last digit of the dividend.

$$\begin{array}{r} 30 \\ 32\overline{)9{,}871} \\ \underline{9\,6} \\ 27 \\ \underline{00} \\ 271 \end{array}$$

Another problem develops here. We round 32 to 30 for our trial divisor, and we round 271 to 270, which is the trial dividend at this point. Our estimate of the last digit of the quotient must be 9.

$$\begin{array}{r} 309 \\ 32\overline{)9{,}871} \\ \underline{9\,6} \\ 27 \\ \underline{00} \\ 271 \\ \underline{288} \end{array}$$

288 ← Too large

We cannot subtract because 288 is larger than 271. The trial quotient must be adjusted downward to 8. We can now complete the division.

$$\begin{array}{r} 308 \\ 32\overline{)9{,}871} \\ \underline{9\,6} \\ 27 \\ \underline{00} \\ 271 \\ \underline{256} \\ 15 \end{array}$$

$9{,}871 \div 32 = 308 \text{ r}15$

Check: $9{,}871 = 32 \times 308 + 15$

Check Yourself 12

Divide.

$43\overline{)8,857}$

Because of the availability of calculators, it is rarely necessary that people find the exact answer when performing long division. On the other hand, it is frequently important that one be able to either estimate the result of long division or confirm that a given answer (particularly from a calculator) is reasonable. As a result, the emphasis in this section will be on improving your estimation skills in division.

Let's divide a four-digit number by a two-digit number. Generally, we will round the divisor to the nearest ten and the dividend to the nearest hundred.

Example 13 Estimating the Result of a Division Application

< Objective 4 >

The Ramirez family took a trip of 2,394 miles (mi) in their new car, using 77 gallons (gal) of gas. Estimate their gas mileage (mi/gal).

Our estimate will be based on dividing 2,400 by 80.

$$80\overset{\displaystyle 30}{\overline{)2,400}}$$

They got approximately 30 mi/gal.

Check Yourself 13

Troy flew a light plane on a trip of 2,844 mi that took 21 hours (h). What was his approximate speed in miles per hour (mi/h)?

As before, we may have to combine operations to solve an application of the mathematics you have learned.

Example 14 Estimating the Result of a Division Application

Charles purchases a used car for $8,574. Interest charges will be $978. He agrees to make payments for 4 years. Approximately what should his monthly payments be?

First, we find the amount that Charles owes:

$8,574 + $978 = $9,552

Now, to find the monthly payment, we divide that amount by 48 (months). To estimate the payment, we'll divide $9,600 by 50 months.

$$50\overset{\displaystyle 192}{\overline{)9,600}}$$

The payments will be approximately $192 per month.

Check Yourself 14

One $10 bag of fertilizer will cover 310 square feet (ft^2). Approximately what would it cost to cover 2,145 ft^2?

Check Yourself ANSWERS

1. 12 rows **2.** 315 students ÷ 9 classes; students per class
3. **(a)** 5; $9 \times 5 = 45$; **(b)** 4; $7 \times 4 = 28$ **4.** 5 **5.** 5 r3; $38 = 5 \times 7 + 3$
6. **(a)** 0; **(b)** 0; **(c)** 0 **7.** **(a)** Undefined; **(b)** 0; **(c)** 0; **(d)** undefined
8. $8 \times 22 = 176$ **9.** 64 r5 **10.** 8 r26 **11.** 8 r53 **12.** 205 r42
13. 140 mi/h **14.** $70

Reading Your Text

The following fill-in-the-blank exercises are designed to ensure that you understand some of the key vocabulary used in this section.

SECTION 1.6

(a) The result from division is called the ______________.

(b) The dividend is equal to the divisor times the quotient plus the ______________.

(c) Zero divided by any whole number (except ______________) is 0.

(d) Division is a shortened form for repeated ______________.

1.6 exercises

Boost *your* GRADE at ALEKS.com!

ALEKS

- Practice Problems
- Self-Tests
- NetTutor
- e-Professors
- Videos

Name ____________

Section ________ Date ________

Answers

1. ________
2. ________
3. ________ 4. ________
5. ________ 6. ________
7. ________ 8. ________
9. ________ 10. ________
11. ________ 12. ________
13. ________ 14. ________
15. ________ 16. ________
17. ________ 18. ________
19. ________ 20. ________
21. ________ 22. ________
23. ________ 24. ________
25. ________ 26. ________
27. ________ 28. ________
29. ________ 30. ________
31. ________ 32. ________

Basic Skills | Challenge Yourself | Calculator/Computer | Career Applications | Above and Beyond

< Objective 2 >

1. If $48 \div 8 = 6$, 8 is the ________, 48 is the ________, and 6 is the ________.

2. In the statement $5\overline{)45}$ with quotient 9, 9 is the ________, 5 is the ________, and 45 is the ________.

3. Find $36 \div 9$ by repeated subtraction.

4. Find $40 \div 8$ by repeated subtraction.

5. **CRAFTS** Stefanie is planting rows of tomato plants. She wants to plant 63 plants with 9 plants per row. How many rows will she have?

Videos

6. **CONSTRUCTION** Nick is designing a parking lot for a small office building. He must make room for 42 cars with 7 cars per row. How many rows should he plan for?

Divide. Identify the correct units for the quotient.

7. 36 pages $\div$ 4

8. \$96 $\div$ 8

9. 4,900 kilometers (km) $\div$ 7

10. 360 gal $\div$ 18

11. 160 miles $\div$ 4 hours

12. 264 ft $\div$ 3 s

13. 3,720 hours $\div$ 5 months

14. 560 calories $\div$ 7 grams

< Objective 3 >

Divide using long division, and check your work.

15. $54 \div 9$

16. $21 \div 3$

17. $6\overline{)42}$

18. $7\overline{)63}$

19. $4\overline{)32}$

20. $56 \div 8$

21. $5\overline{)43}$

22. $40 \div 9$

23. $9\overline{)65}$

24. $6\overline{)51}$

25. $57 \div 8$

26. $74 \div 8$

27. $0 \div 5$

28. $5 \div 0$

29. $4 \div 0$

30. $0 \div 12$

31. $0 \div 6$

32. $18 \div 0$

Divide.

33. $5\overline{)83}$ > Videos

34. $9\overline{)78}$

35. $162 \div 3$

36. $232 \div 4$

37. $\dfrac{293}{8}$

38. $\dfrac{346}{7}$

39. $8\overline{)3{,}136}$

40. $5\overline{)4{,}938}$

41. $5{,}438 \div 8$

42. $3{,}527 \div 9$

43. $\dfrac{22{,}153}{8}$

44. $\dfrac{43{,}287}{5}$

Basic Skills | **Challenge Yourself** | Calculator/Computer | Career Applications | Above and Beyond

45. $45\overline{)2{,}367}$

46. $53\overline{)3{,}480}$

47. $8{,}748 \div 34$ > Videos

48. $9{,}335 \div 27$

49. $\dfrac{7{,}902}{42}$ > Videos

50. $\dfrac{8{,}729}{53}$

< Objective 5 >

Solve each application.

51. Business and Finance There are 63 candy bars in 7 boxes. How many candy bars are in each box? > Videos

52. Business and Finance A total of 54 printers were shipped to 9 stores. How many printers were shipped to each store?

53. Social Science Joaquin is putting pictures in an album. He can fit 8 pictures on each page. If he has 77 pictures, how many will be left over after he has filled the last 8-picture page?

54. Statistics Kathy is separating a deck of 52 cards into 6 equal piles. How many cards will be left over?

55. Social Science The records of an office show that 1,702 calls were made in 1 day. If there are 37 phones in the office, how many calls were placed per phone?

56. Business and Finance A television dealer purchased 23 sets, each the same model, for $5,267. What was the cost of each set?

57. Business and Finance A computer printer can print 340 lines per minute (min). How long will it take to complete a report of 10,880 lines?

58. Statistics A train traveled 1,364 mi in 22 h. What was the speed of the train? (*Hint:* Speed is the distance traveled divided by the time.)

< Objective 4 >

Estimate the result in each division problem. (Remember to round divisors to the nearest ten and dividends to the nearest hundred.)

59. 810 divided by 38

60. 458 divided by 18

61. 4,967 divided by 96

62. 3,971 divided by 39

Answers

33. ______ 34. ______
35. ______ 36. ______
37. ______ 38. ______
39. ______ 40. ______
41. ______ 42. ______
43. ______ 44. ______
45. ______ 46. ______
47. ______ 48. ______
49. ______ 50. ______
51. ______ 52. ______
53. ______ 54. ______
55. ______ 56. ______
57. ______ 58. ______
59. ______ 60. ______
61. ______ 62. ______

Answers

63. ________ 64. ________

65. ________ 66. ________

67. ________ 68. ________

69. ________ 70. ________

71. ________ 72. ________

73. ________ 74. ________

75. ________ 76. ________

77. ________ 78. ________

79. ________ 80. ________

81. ________

82. ________

83. ________

84. ________

85. ________

86. ________

63. 8,971 divided by 91

64. 3,981 divided by 78

65. 3,879 divided by 126

66. 8,986 divided by 178

67. 3,812 divided by 188

68. 5,245 divided by 255

Basic Skills | Challenge Yourself | **Calculator/Computer** | Career Applications | Above and Beyond

Use your calculator to perform the indicated operations.

69. $583{,}467 \div 129$

70. $464{,}184 \div 189$

71. $6 + 9 \div 3$

72. $18 - 6 \div 3$

73. $24 \div 6 \times 4$

74. $32 \div 8 \times 4$

75. $4{,}368 \div 56 + 726 \div 33$

76. $1{,}176 \div 42 - 1{,}572 \div 524$

77. $3 \times 8 \times 8 \times 8 \div 12$

78. $5 \times 6 \times 6 \div 18$

Basic Skills | Challenge Yourself | Calculator/Computer | **Career Applications** | Above and Beyond

79. **ALLIED HEALTH** The doctor prescribes 525 milligrams (mg) of bexarotene to be given once daily to an adult female patient with lung cancer. How many pills should the nurse give her every day if each pill contains 75 mg of bexarotene?

80. **ALLIED HEALTH** Determine the flow rate, in milliliters per hour (mL/h), needed for an electronic infusion pump to administer 180 mL of a saline solution via intravenous (IV) infusion over the course of 12 hours (h).

81. **INFORMATION TECHNOLOGY** Marcela is in the process of building a new testing computer lab for ABC software. This lab has five rows of computers and nine computers per row. The distance from each computer to a switch is about 4 feet (ft). She has a 200-ft roll of cable for the job. How many 4-ft cables can she make with a 200-ft roll? Does she have enough cable on the roll for the job?

82. **INFORMATION TECHNOLOGY** Your modem on your computer typically transmits at 56,000 bits per second. How long will it take to transmit five hundred sixty thousand bits?

83. **ELECTRONICS** An electronics component distributor sells resistors in two package sizes. A small package contains 500 resistors. A large package contains 1,250 resistors. If 10,000 resistors are needed to make a batch of parts, how many packages would you need to buy if you bought all small packages? All large packages?

84. **ELECTRONICS** A vendor that makes small-quantity batches of printed circuit boards will sell 25 boards for $400. What is the cost per board?

85. **MANUFACTURING TECHNOLOGY** An order of 24 parts weighs 1,752 lb. Assuming that the parts are identical, how much does each part weigh?

86. **MANUFACTURING TECHNOLOGY** Triplet Precision Machining has a 3,000-gallon (gal) liquid petroleum (LP) tank. If the cutting line consumes 125 gal of LP each day, how many days will the LP supply last?

Basic Skills | Challenge Yourself | Calculator/Computer | Career Applications | **Above and Beyond**

87. CONSTRUCTION You are going to recarpet your living room. You have budgeted \$1,500 for the carpet and installation.

(a) Determine how much carpet you will need to do the job. Draw a sketch to support your measurements.

(b) What is the highest price per square yard you can pay and still stay within budget?

(c) Go to a local store and determine the total cost of doing the job for three different grades of carpet. Be sure to include padding, labor costs, and any other expenses.

(d) What considerations (other than cost) would affect your decision about what type of carpet to install?

(e) Write a brief paragraph indicating your final decision and give supporting reasons.

88. SOCIAL SCIENCE Division is the inverse operation of multiplication. Many daily activities have inverses. For each of the following activities, state the inverse activity.

(a) Spending money
(b) Going to sleep
(c) Turning down the volume on your CD player
(d) Getting dressed

89. If you have no money in your pocket and want to divide it equally among your four friends, how much does each person get? Use this situation to explain division of zero by a nonzero number.

90. NUMBER PROBLEM Complete the following number cross.

Across

1. $48 \div 4$
3. $1,296 \div 8$
6. $2,025 \div 5$
8. 4×5
9. 11×11
12. $15 \div 3 \times 111$
14. $144 \div (2 \times 6)$
16. $1,404 \div 6$
18. $2,500 \div 5$
19. 3×5

Down

1. $(12 + 16) \div 2$
2. 67×3
4. $744 \div 12$
5. $2,600 \div 13$
7. $6,300 \div 12$
10. $304 \div 2$
11. $5 \times (161 \div 7)$
13. $9,027 \div 17$
15. $400 \div 20$
17. 9×5

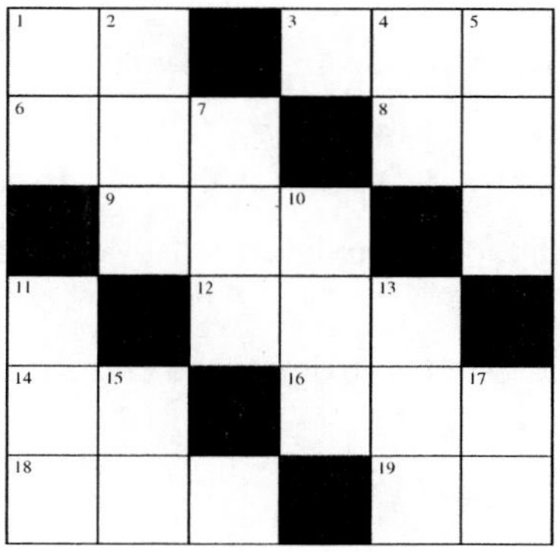

Answers

1. Divisor, dividend, quotient 3. 4 5. 7 7. 9 pages 9. 700 km 11. 40 mi/h 13. 744 h/month 15. 6 17. 7 19. 8 21. 8 r3 23. 7 r2 25. 7 r1 27. 0 29. Undefined 31. 0 33. 16 r3 35. 54 37. 36 r5 39. 392 41. 679 r6 43. 2,769 r1 45. 52 r27 47. 257 r10 49. 188 r6 51. 9 bars 53. 5 pictures 55. 46 calls 57. 32 min 59. 20 61. 50 63. 100 65. 30 67. 20 69. 4,523 71. 9 73. 16 75. 100 77. 128 79. 7 pills 81. Yes, 50 4-ft cables 83. 20 packages; 8 packages 85. 73 lb 87. Above and Beyond 89. Above and Beyond

Answers

87. ______

88. ______

89. ______

90. ______

Activity 2 :: Restaurant Management

In 2002 there were more than 30,000 McDonald's restaurants in the world. Of these, approximately 14,000 were in the United States. In Great Britain there were 1,116 McDonald's franchises. The following data are taken from those 1,116 McDonald's.

Total employees:	49,726
Office staff:	545
Management:	2,974
The rest are restaurant workers.	
Total employees 20 years old and under:	34,241
Total employees between 21 and 29 years old:	10,607
Total male employees:	27,546

Use these data to answer the questions that follow.

1. What is the total number of restaurant workers in McDonald's franchises in Great Britain?
2. How many of the employees mentioned are of age 30 or older?
3. How many of the employees were females?
4. Divide the total number of employees by the number of franchises to determine approximately how many employees are in each McDonald's in Great Britain.
5. Assume that each franchise decided to give each employee a $125 bonus. If you use your result from question 4, how much would that cost each franchise?
6. What would the total cost of the $125 bonus be for all the employees?
7. Assume that there are 45 employees in each of the U.S. McDonald's. Approximately how many people would be employed by McDonald's in the United States?
8. If health care costs $400 per month for one employee, what would the annual cost for health care be?
9. Use the results of questions 7 and 8 to approximate the cost to McDonald's of providing health care for all its workers.

1.7 Exponential Notation and the Order of Operations

< 1.7 Objectives >

1 > Use exponent notation

2 > Evaluate expressions containing powers of whole numbers

3 > Evaluate expressions that contain several operations

Tips for Student Success

Preparing for a Test

Preparation for a test really begins on the first day of class. Everything you do in class and at home is part of that preparation. However, there are a few things that you should focus on in the last few days before a scheduled test.

1. Plan your test preparation to end at least 24 hours before the test. The last 24 hours are too late, and besides, you need some rest before the test.
2. Go over your homework and class notes with pencil and paper in hand. Write down all the problem types, formulas, and definitions that you think might give you trouble on the test.
3. The day before the test, take the page(s) of notes from step 2, and transfer the most important ideas to a 3×5 card.
4. Just before the test, review the information on the card. You will be surprised at how much you remember about each concept.
5. Understand that, if you have been successful at completing your homework assignments, you can be successful on the test. This is an obstacle for many students, but it is an obstacle that can be overcome. Truly anxious students are often surprised that they scored as well as they did on a test. They tend to attribute this to blind luck. It is not. It is the first sign that you really do "get it." Enjoy the success.

Earlier we described multiplication as a shorthand for repeated addition. There is also a shorthand for repeated multiplication. It uses **powers of a whole number.**

Example 1 Writing Repeated Multiplication as a Power

< Objective 1.7 >

$3 \times 3 \times 3 \times 3$ can be written as 3^4.

This is read as "3 to the fourth power."

In this case, repeated multiplication is written as the power of a number.

In this example, 3 is the **base** of the expression, and the raised number, 4, is the **exponent,** or **power.**

Exponent or power

$$3^4 = \underbrace{3 \times 3 \times 3 \times 3}_{\text{4 factors}}$$

Base

We count the factors and make this the power (or exponent) of the base.

NOTE

Recall that

$3 + 3 + 3 + 3 = 4 \times 3$

Repeated addition was written as multiplication.

René Descartes, a French philosopher and mathematician, is generally credited with first introducing our modern exponent notation in about 1637.

Check Yourself 1

Write $2 \times 2 \times 2 \times 2 \times 2 \times 2$ as a power of 2.

Definition

Exponents — The *exponent* tells us the number of times the base is to be used as a factor.

Example 2 Evaluating a Number Raised to a Power

< Objective 2 >

2^5 is read "2 to the fifth power."

$$2^5 = \underbrace{2 \times 2 \times 2 \times 2 \times 2}_{\text{5 times}} = 32$$

2^5 tells us to use 2 as a factor 5 times. The result is 32.

Here 2 is the base, and 5 is the exponent.

Check Yourself 2

Read and evaluate 3^4.

Example 3 Evaluating a Number Raised to a Power

> CAUTION

5^3 is *entirely different* from 5×3. $5^3 = 125$ whereas $5 \times 3 = 15$.

Evaluate 5^3 and 8^2.

$5^3 = 5 \times 5 \times 5 = 125$ Use 3 factors of 5.

5^3 is read "5 to the third power" or "5 cubed."

$8^2 = 8 \times 8 = 64$ Use 2 factors of 8.

And 8^2 is read "8 to the second power" or "8 squared."

Check Yourself 3

Evaluate.

(a) 6^2 **(b)** 2^4

We need two special definitions for powers of whole numbers.

Definition

Raising a Number to the First Power — A number raised to the first power is just that number.

For example, $9^1 = 9$.

Definition

Raising a Number to the Zero Power — A number, other than 0, raised to the zero power is 1.

For example, $7^0 = 1$.

Example 4 Evaluating Numbers Raised to the Power of 0 or 1

(a) $8^0 = 1$ **(b)** $4^0 = 1$ **(c)** $5^1 = 5$ **(d)** $3^1 = 3$

Check Yourself 4

Evaluate.

(a) 7^0 **(b)** 7^1

NOTE

Notice that 10^3 is just a 1 followed by *three zeros*.

We talked about *powers of 10* earlier when we multiplied by numbers that end in 0. Because the powers of 10 have a special importance, we list some of them here.

$10^0 = 1$

$10^1 = 10$

$10^2 = 10 \times 10 = 100$

$10^3 = 10 \times 10 \times 10 = 1{,}000$

$10^4 = 10 \times 10 \times 10 \times 10 = 10{,}000$

$10^5 = 10 \times 10 \times 10 \times 10 \times 10 = 100{,}000$

NOTE

10^5 is a 1 followed by *five zeros*.

Do you see why the powers of 10 are so important?

Definition

Powers of 10

The powers of 10 correspond to the place values of our number system—ones, tens, hundreds, thousands, and so on.

NOTE

Archimedes (about 250 B.C.E.) reportedly estimated the number of grains of sand in the universe to be 10^{63}. This would be a 1 followed by 63 zeros!

This is what we meant earlier when we said that our number system was based on the number 10.

If multiplication is combined with addition or subtraction, you must know which operation to do first in finding the expression's value. We can easily illustrate this problem. How should we simplify the following statement?

$3 + 4 \times 5 = ?$

Both multiplication and addition are involved in this expression, and we must decide which to do first to find the answer.

1. Multiplying first gives us

   $3 + 20 = 23$

2. Adding first gives us

   $7 \times 5 = 35$

> CAUTION

The answers differ depending on which operation is done first!

Only one of these results can be correct, which is why mathematicians developed some rules to tell us the order in which the operations should be performed. The rules are as follows.

Step by Step

The Order of Operations

If multiplication, division, addition, and subtraction are involved in the same expression, do the operations in the following order:

Step 1 Do all multiplication and division in order from left to right.

Step 2 Do all addition and subtraction in order from left to right.

Example 5 Using the Order of Operations

< Objective 3 >

NOTE

By this rule, we see that strategy 1 from before was correct.

(a) $3 \times 4 + 5 = 12 + 5 = 17$ Multiply *first*, then add or subtract.

(b) $5 + 3 \times 6 = 5 + 18 = 23$

(c) $16 - 2 \times 3 = 16 - 6 = 10$

(d) $7 \times 8 - 20 = 56 - 20 = 36$

(e) $5 \times 6 + 4 \times 3 = 30 + 12 = 42$

NOTE

(See the "Step by Step" below.)

When learning the order of operations, students sometimes remember this order by relating each step to part of the phrase

"Please Excuse My Dear Aunt Sally."

P
E
MD
AS

Check Yourself 5

Evaluate.

(a) $8 + 3 \times 5$

(b) $15 \times 5 - 3$

(c) $4 \times 3 + 2 \times 6$

We now want to extend our rule for the order of operations to see what happens when parentheses or exponents are involved in an expression.

Step by Step

The Order of Operations

Mixed operations in an expression should be done in the following order:

Step 1 Do any operations inside ***p***arentheses.

Step 2 Apply any ***e***xponents.

Step 3 Do all ***m***ultiplication and ***d***ivision in order from left to right.

Step 4 Do all ***a***ddition and ***s***ubtraction in order from left to right.

Example 6 Evaluating an Expression

Evaluate 4×2^3.

Step 1 There are no parentheses.

Step 2 Apply exponents.

$4 \times 2^3 = 4 \times 8$

Step 3 Multiply or divide.

$4 \times 8 = 32$

Check Yourself 6

Evaluate.

3×3^2

Example 7 Evaluating an Expression

Evaluate $(2 + 3)^2 + 4 \times 3$.

Step 1 Do operations inside parentheses.

$(2 + 3)^2 + 4 \times 3 = (5)^2 + 4 \times 3$

Step 2 Apply exponents.

$5^2 + 4 \times 3 = 25 + 4 \times 3$

Step 3 Multiply or divide.

$25 + 4 \times 3 = 25 + 12$

Step 4 Add or subtract.

$25 + 12 = 37$

Check Yourself 7

Evaluate.

(a) $4 + (8 - 5)^2$ (b) $(6 - 4)^3 + 3 \cdot 2$

Example 8 Using the Order of Operations

(a) Evaluate $20 \div 2 \times 5$.

$$\begin{aligned} &\underbrace{20 \div 2} \times 5 \\ &= 10 \times 5 \\ &= 50 \end{aligned}$$

So $20 \div 2 \times 5 = 50$.

Because the multiplication and division appear next to each other, work in order from left to right. Try it the other way and see what happens!

(b) Evaluate $(5 + 13) \div 6$.

$$\begin{aligned} &\underbrace{(5 + 13)} \div 6 \\ &= (18) \div 6 \\ &= 3 \end{aligned}$$

So $(5 + 13) \div 6 = 3$.

Do the addition in the parentheses as the first step.

(c) Evaluate $(3 + 4)^2 \div (2^3 - 1)$.

$$\begin{aligned} &\underbrace{(3 + 4)^2} \div \underbrace{(2^3 - 1)} \\ &= (7)^2 \div (8 - 1) \\ &= 7^2 \div (7) \\ &= 49 \div 7 \\ &= 7 \end{aligned}$$

So $(3 + 4)^2 \div (2^3 - 1) = 7$.

Perform operations inside parentheses first.

Check Yourself 8

Evaluate.

(a) $36 \div 4 \times 2$ (b) $(2 + 4)^2 \div (3^2 - 3)$ (c) $15 \div 3 + (3 - 2)^2 \times 4 - 2$

Tips for Student Success

Taking a Test

Earlier in this section, we discussed test preparation. Now that you are thoroughly prepared for the test, you must learn how to take it.

There is much to the psychology of anxiety that we can't readily address. There is, however, a physical aspect to anxiety that can be addressed rather easily. When people are in a stressful situation, they frequently start to panic. One symptom of the panic is shallow breathing. In a test situation, this starts a vicious cycle. If you breathe too shallowly, then not enough oxygen reaches your brain. When that happens, you are unable to think clearly. In a test situation, being unable to think clearly can cause you to panic. Hence, we have a vicious cycle.

How do you break that cycle? It's pretty simple. Take a few deep breaths. We have seen students whose performance on math tests improved markedly after they got in the habit of writing "remember to breathe!" at the bottom of every test page. Try breathing; it will almost certainly improve your math test scores!

Check Yourself ANSWERS

1. 2^6 **2.** "Three to the fourth power" is 81 **3. (a)** 36; **(b)** 16
4. (a) 1; **(b)** 7 **5. (a)** 23; **(b)** 72; **(c)** 24 **6.** 27 **7. (a)** 13; **(b)** 14
8. (a) 18; **(b)** 6; **(c)** 7

Reading Your Text

The following fill-in-the-blank exercises are designed to ensure that you understand some of the key vocabulary used in this section.

SECTION 1.7

(a) Preparation for a test really begins on the ____________ day of class.

(b) Another name for a power is an ____________.

(c) The first step in the order of operations involves doing operations ____________ parentheses.

(d) A whole number (other than zero) raised to the zero power is always equal to ____________.

Basic Skills | Challenge Yourself | Calculator/Computer | Career Applications | Above and Beyond

1.7 exercises

Boost *your* GRADE at ALEKS.com!

ALEKS

- Practice Problems
- Self-Tests
- NetTutor
- e-Professors
- Videos

Name ____________

Section ________ Date ________

< Objectives 1–3 >

Evaluate.

1. 3^2
2. 2^3 > Videos
3. 5^1
4. 6^0
5. 10^3
6. 10^6
7. 2×4^3 > Videos
8. $(2 \times 4)^3$
9. $5 + 2^2$
10. $(5 + 2)^2$
11. $42 - 7 + 9$
12. $27 - 12 + 3$
13. $20 \div 5 \times 2$
14. $48 \div 3 \times 2$
15. $(3 + 2)^3 - 20$ > Videos
16. $5 + (9 - 5)^2$
17. $(7 - 4)^4 - 30$
18. $(5 + 2)^2 + 20$
19. $8^2 \div 4^2 + 2$
20. $3 \times 5^2 + 2^2$
21. $24 - 6 \div 3$ > Videos
22. $3 + 9 \div 3$
23. $(24 - 6) \div 3$
24. $(3 + 9) \div 3$
25. $12 + 3 \div (3^2 - 2 \cdot 3)$ > Videos
26. $(8^2 - 2^4) \div 2$
27. $8^2 - 2^4 \div 2$
28. $(5 - 3)^3 + (8 - 6)^2$
29. $30 \div 6 - 12 \div 3$
30. $5 + 8 \div 4 - 3$

Basic Skills | Challenge Yourself | Calculator/Computer | Career Applications | Above and Beyond

31. $16 - 12 \div 3 \cdot 2 + (16 - 12)^2 \cdot 3$
32. $3 \cdot 5 + 3 \cdot 4^2 \div (6 - 4)^2$
33. $6 + 3 \cdot 2^4 - (12 - 7)(10 - 7)$
34. $27 \div (2^2 + 5) - (35 - 33)(24 - 23)$

Answers

1. ________	2. ________
3. ________	4. ________
5. ________	6. ________
7. ________	8. ________
9. ________	10. ________
11. ________	12. ________
13. ________	14. ________
15. ________	16. ________
17. ________	18. ________
19. ________	20. ________
21. ________	22. ________
23. ________	24. ________
25. ________	26. ________
27. ________	28. ________
29. ________	30. ________
31. ________	32. ________
33. ________	34. ________

Answers

35. ____________

36. ____________

37. ____________

38. ____________

39. ____________

40. ____________

41. ____________

42. ____________

43. ____________

44. ____________

45. ____________

46. ____________

47. ____________

48. ____________

35. $3 \times [(7 - 5)^3 - 8] + 5 \times 2$

36. $[(3 + 1) + (7 - 2)] \times 4 - 5 \times 7$

Basic Skills | Challenge Yourself | **Calculator/Computer** | Career Applications | Above and Beyond

Use your calculator to evaluate each expression.

37. $4 \times 5 - 7$

38. $3 \times 7 + 8$

39. $9 + 3 \times 7$

40. $6 \times 0 + 3$

41. $4 + 5 \times 0$

42. $23 - 4 \times 5$

43. $5 \times (4 + 7)$

44. $8 \times (6 + 5)$

45. $5 \times 4 + 5 \times 7$

46. $8 \times 6 + 8 \times 5$

Solve each application, using a calculator.

47. **Business and Finance** A car dealer kept the following record of a month's sales. Complete the table.

Model	Number Sold	Profit per Sale	Monthly Profit
Subcompact	38	$528	______
Compact	33	647	______
Standard	19	912	______
		Monthly Total Profit	______

48. **Business and Finance** You take a job paying $1 the first day. On each following day your pay doubles. That is, on day 2 your pay is $2, on day 3 the pay is $4, and so on. Complete the table.

Day	Daily Pay	Total Pay
1	$1	$1
2	2	3
3	4	7
4	______	______
5	______	______
6	______	______
7	______	______
8	______	______
9	______	______
10	______	______

Basic Skills | Challenge Yourself | Calculator/Computer | **Career Applications** | Above and Beyond

Answers

49. ______

50. ______

51. ______

52. ______

49. Electronics Resistors are commonly identified by colored bands to indicate their approximate resistance, measured in ohms. Each band's color and position corresponds to a specific component of the overall value. In resistors with four colored bands, the third band is typically considered to be the exponent for a base 10. If the first two bands are decoded as 43 and the third band is decoded as 5, what is the total resistance in ohms?

$43 \times 10^5 = ?$

Which of the three bands is most important to read correctly? Why?

50. Manufacturing Technology The kinetic energy (KE) of an object (in Joules) is given by the formula:

$$KE = \frac{mv^2}{2}$$

Find the kinetic energy of an object that has a mass (m) of 46 kg and is moving at a velocity (v) of 16 meters per second.

51. Manufacturing Technology The power (P) of a circuit (in Watts) can be given by any of the following formulas:

$$P = IV$$

$$P = \frac{V^2}{R}$$

$$P = I^2 R$$

Find the power for each of the following circuits:

(a) Voltage (V) = 110 volts (V) and current (I) = 13 amperes (A).
(b) Voltage = 220 V and resistance (R) = 22 ohms.
(c) Current = 25 A and resistance = 9 ohms.

52. Manufacturing Technology A belt is used to connect two pulleys.

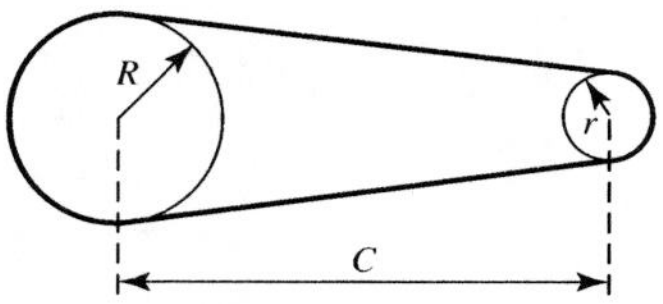

The length of the belt required is given by the formula:

$$\text{Belt length} = 2C + 3(R + r) + \frac{(2R + 2r)^2}{4C}$$

where C is the distance between the centers of the two pulleys.

Find the approximate belt length required to go around a 4-in. radius (r) pulley and a 6-in. radius (R) pulley that are 20 in. apart.

Basic Skills | Challenge Yourself | Calculator/Computer | Career Applications | **Above and Beyond**

Answers

53. ______
54. ______
55. ______
56. ______
57. ______
58. ______
59. ______
60. ______

*Numbers such as 3, 4, and 5 are called **Pythagorean triples,** after the Greek mathematician Pythagoras (sixth century B.C.), because*

$3^2 + 4^2 = 5^2$

Which sets of numbers are Pythagorean triples?

53. 6, 8, 10 **54.** 6, 11, 12 **55.** 5, 12, 13

56. 7, 24, 25 **57.** 8, 16, 18 **58.** 8, 15, 17

59. Is $(a + b)^P$ equal to $a^P + b^P$?

Try a few numbers and decide if you think this is true for all whole numbers, for some whole numbers, or never true. Write an explanation of your findings and give examples.

60. Does $(a \cdot b)^P = a^P \cdot b^P$?

Try a few numbers and decide if you think this is true for all whole numbers, for some whole numbers, or never true. Write an explanation of your findings and give examples.

Answers

1. 9 **3.** 5 **5.** 1,000 **7.** 128 **9.** 9 **11.** 44
13. 8 **15.** 105 **17.** 51 **19.** 6 **21.** 22 **23.** 6
25. 13 **27.** 56 **29.** 1 **31.** 56 **33.** 39 **35.** 10
37. 13 **39.** 30 **41.** 4 **43.** 55 **45.** 55
47. \$20,064 / 21,351 / 17,328 / \$58,743 **49.** 4,300,000 ohms; the third band; misreading it would lead to errors of powers of ten
51. (a) 1,430 W; (b) 2,200 W; (c) 5,625 W **53.** Yes **55.** Yes **57.** No
59. Above and Beyond

Activity 3 ::
Package Delivery

Read the following article and use the information you find there to answer the questions that follow.

> The 5-day workweek before Christmas is the busiest week of the year for package deliveries. In the year 2000, the U.S. Postal Service (USPS) averaged 750 million deliveries per day that week. In the same week, United Parcel Service (UPS) delivered about 18 million packages per day. Federal Express (Fed Ex) delivered nearly 5 million packages per day. Of the 5 million Federal Express deliveries, over 3 million of the orders were originated on the Internet.

1. Write out the number that represents the number of deliveries made by the USPS in the 5-day week before Christmas.
2. Write the word form for the answer to question 1.
3. Over the same 5 days, how many deliveries were made by UPS?
4. Over the same 5 days, how many deliveries were made by Fed Ex?
5. How many more deliveries were made by UPS than by Fed Ex that week?

Definition/Procedure	Example	Reference
The Decimal Place-Value System		Section 1.1
Digits Digits are the basic symbols of the system.	0, 1, 2, 3, 4, 5, 6, 7, 8, and 9 are digits.	p. 2
Place Value The value of a digit in a number depends on its position or place.	52,589 (5 — Ten thousands; 2 — Thousands; 5 — Hundreds; 8 — Tens; 9 — Ones)	p. 3
The value of a number is the sum of each digit multiplied by its place value.	$2{,}345 = (2 \times 1{,}000) + (3 \times 100) + (4 \times 10) + (5 \times 1)$	p. 3
Addition		Section 1.2
The Properties of Addition		
The Commutative Property The order in which you add two whole numbers does not affect the sum.	$5 + 4 = 4 + 5$	p. 12
The Associative Property The way in which you group whole numbers in addition does not affect the final sum.	$(2 + 7) + 8 = 2 + (7 + 8)$	p. 12
The Additive Identity The sum of 0 and any whole number is just that whole number.	$6 + 0 = 0 + 6 = 6$	p. 13
Measuring Perimeter		
The perimeter is the total distance around the outside edge of a shape. The perimeter of a rectangle is $P = 2 \cdot L + 2 \cdot W$.	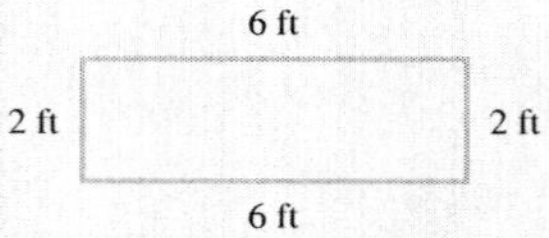 $P = 2 \times 6\text{ ft} + 2 \times 2\text{ ft} = 12\text{ ft} + 4\text{ ft} = 16\text{ ft}$	p. 18
Subtraction		Section 1.3
Minuend The number we are subtracting from. **Subtrahend** The number that is being subtracted. **Difference** The result of the subtraction.	15 ← Minuend − 9 ← Subtrahend 6 ← Difference	p. 26
Rounding, Estimation, and Order		Section 1.4
Step 1 To round a whole number to a certain decimal place, look at the digit to the right of that place.		p. 40
Step 2 **a.** If that digit is 5 or more, that digit and all digits to the right become 0. The digit in the place you are rounding to is increased by 1.	To the nearest hundred, 43,578 is rounded to 43,600.	
b. If that digit is less than 5, that digit and all digits to the right become 0. The digit in the place you are rounding to remains the same.	To the nearest thousand, 273,212 is rounded to 273,000.	
Multiplication		Section 1.5
Factors The numbers being multiplied. **Product** The result of the multiplication.	$7 \times 9 = 63$ ← Product (7 × 9: Factors)	p. 48

Definition/Procedure	Example	Reference
The Properties of Multiplication		
The Commutative Property The order in which you multiply two whole numbers does not affect the product.	$7 \times 9 = 9 \times 7$	*p.* 48
The Distributive Property To multiply a factor by a sum of numbers, multiply the factor by each number inside the parentheses. Then add the products.	$2 \times (3 + 7) = (2 \times 3) + (2 \times 7)$	*p.* 50
The Associative Property The way in which you group numbers in multiplication does not affect the final product.	$(3 \times 5) \times 6 = 3 \times (5 \times 6)$	*p.* 53
Finding Area and Volume		
The area of a rectangle is found using the formula $A = L \cdot W$. The volume of a rectangular solid is found using the formula $V = L \cdot W \cdot H$.	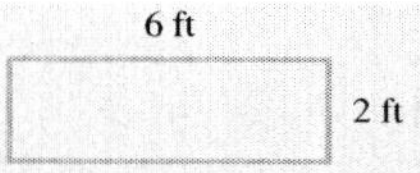 $A = L \times W = 6 \text{ ft} \times 2 \text{ ft} = 12 \text{ ft}^2$	*p.* 56
Division		**Section 1.6**
Divisor The number we are dividing by. **Dividend** The number being divided. **Quotient** The result of the division. **Remainder** The number "left over" after the division.	Divisor ↘ 7, Quotient ↙ 5 $7\overline{)38}$ ⟵ Dividend $\underline{35}$ 3 ⟵ Remainder	*pp.* 65–67
Dividend = divisor × quotient + remainder	$38 = 7 \times 5 + 3$	*p.* 67
Division by 0 is undefined.	$7 \div 0$ is undefined.	*p.* 68
Exponential Notation and the Order of Operations		**Section 1.7**
Using Exponents		
Base The number that is raised to a power. **Exponent** The exponent is written to the right and above the base. The exponent tells the number of times the base is to be used as a factor.	Exponent ↙ $5^3 = \underbrace{5 \times 5 \times 5}_{\text{Three factors}} = 125$ ↗ Base	*p.* 79
The Order of Operations		
Mixed operations in an expression should be done in the following order: **Step 1** Do any operations inside parentheses. **Step 2** Evaluate any exponents. **Step 3** Do all multiplication and division in order from left to right. **Step 4** Do all addition and subtraction in order from left to right. Remember *P*lease *E*xcuse *M*y *D*ear *A*unt *S*ally	$4 \times (2 + 3)^2 - 7$ $= 4 \times 5^2 - 7$ $= 4 \times 25 - 7$ $= 100 - 7$ $= 93$	*p.* 82

summary exercises :: chapter 1

This summary exercise set is provided to give you practice with each of the objectives of this chapter. Each exercise is keyed to the appropriate chapter section. When you are finished, you can check your answers to the odd-numbered exercises against those presented in the back of the text. If you have difficulty with any of these questions, go back and reread the examples from that section. The answers to the even-numbered exercises appear in the *Instructor's Solutions Manual*. Your instructor will give you guidelines on how to best use these exercises in your instructional setting.

1.1 *In exercises 1 and 2, give the place value of each of the indicated digits.*

1. 6 in the number 5,674

2. 5 in the number 543,400

In exercises 3 and 4, give word names of each number.

3. 27,428

4. 200,305

Write each number in standard form.

5. Thirty-seven thousand, five hundred eighty-three

6. Three hundred thousand, four hundred

1.2 *In exercises 7 and 8, name the property of addition illustrated.*

7. $4 + 9 = 9 + 4$

8. $(4 + 5) + 9 = 4 + (5 + 9)$

In exercises 9 to 13, perform the indicated operations.

9. $\begin{array}{r} 784 \\ 385 \\ +\ 247 \\ \hline \end{array}$

10. $\begin{array}{r} 2{,}570 \\ 498 \\ 21{,}456 \\ +\quad 28 \\ \hline \end{array}$

11. $\begin{array}{r} 367 \\ 289 \\ 1{,}463 \\ +\ 2{,}682 \\ \hline \end{array}$

12. $\begin{array}{r} 6{,}389 \\ 1{,}567 \\ 315 \\ +\ 113{,}602 \\ \hline \end{array}$

1.3 **13.** Find each value.

(a) 34 decreased by 7

(b) 7 more than 4

(c) The product of 9 and 5, divided by 3

Solve each application.

14. STATISTICS An airline had 173, 212, 185, 197, and 202 passengers on five morning flights between Washington, D.C. and New York. What was the total number of passengers?

15. BUSINESS AND FINANCE Future Stars summer camp employs five junior counselors. Their weekly salaries last week were \$108, \$135, \$81, \$135, and \$81. What was the total salary for the junior counselors?

1.3 *In exercises 16 to 20, perform the indicated operations.*

16. $\begin{array}{r} 5{,}325 \\ -\ 847 \\ \hline \end{array}$

17. $\begin{array}{r} 38{,}400 \\ -\ 19{,}600 \\ \hline \end{array}$

18. $\begin{array}{r} 86{,}000 \\ -\ 2{,}169 \\ \hline \end{array}$

19. $\begin{array}{r} 2{,}682 \\ -\ 108 \\ \hline \end{array}$

20. Find the difference of 7,342 and 5,579.

Solve each application.

21. BUSINESS AND FINANCE Chuck owes \$795 on a credit card after a trip. He makes payments of \$75, \$125, and \$90. Interest of \$31 is charged. How much remains to be paid on the account?

22. BUSINESS AND FINANCE Juan bought a new car for \$16,785. The manufacturer offers a cash rebate of \$987. What was the cost after rebate?

1.4 *Round the numbers to the indicated place.*

23. 6,975 to the nearest hundred

24. 15,897 to the nearest thousand

25. 548,239 to the nearest ten thousand

Complete the statements by using the symbol $<$ or $>$.

26. 60 ______ 70

27. 38 ______ 35

Find the perimeter of each figure.

28.

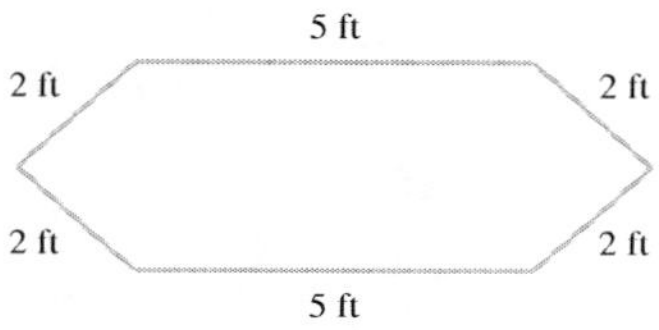

29.

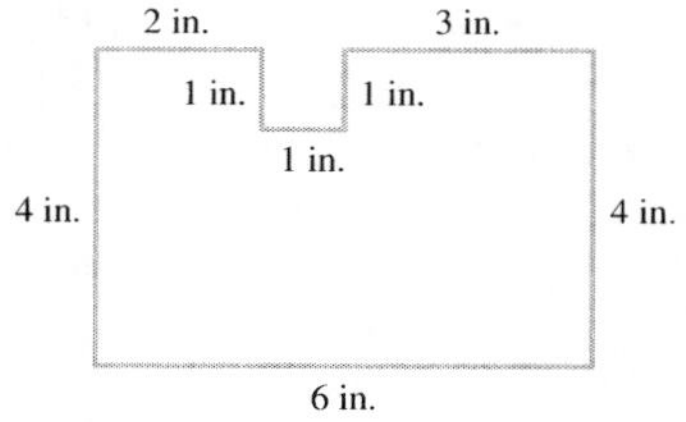

1.5 *In exercises 30 to 32, name the property of multiplication that is illustrated.*

30. $7 \times 8 = 8 \times 7$

31. $3 \times (4 + 7) = 3 \times 4 + 3 \times 7$

32. $(8 \times 9) \times 4 = 8 \times (9 \times 4)$

In exercises 33 to 35, perform the indicated operations.

33. $\begin{array}{r} 58 \\ \times\ 32 \\ \hline \end{array}$

34. $\begin{array}{r} 25 \\ \times\ 43 \\ \hline \end{array}$

35. $\begin{array}{r} 378 \\ \times\ 409 \\ \hline \end{array}$

36. *Find the area of the figure.*

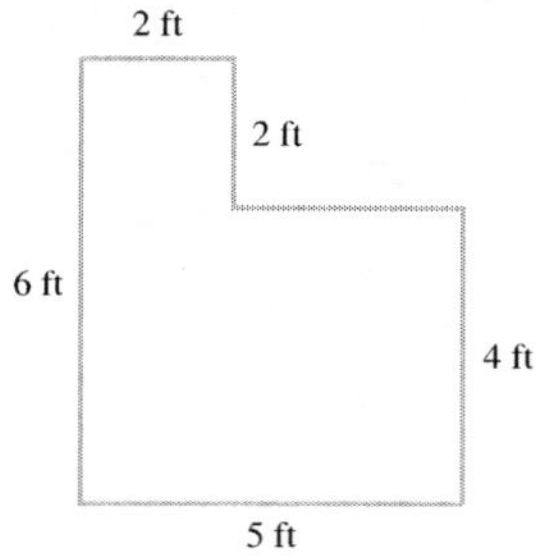

37. *Find the volume of the figure.*

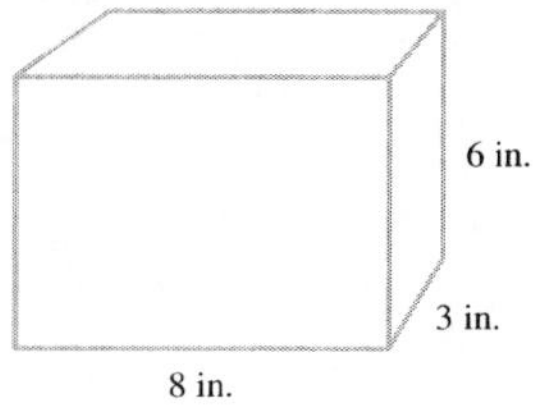

Solve the application.

38. CRAFTS You wish to carpet a room that is 5 yd by 7 yd. The carpet costs \$18 per square yard. What will be the total cost of the materials?

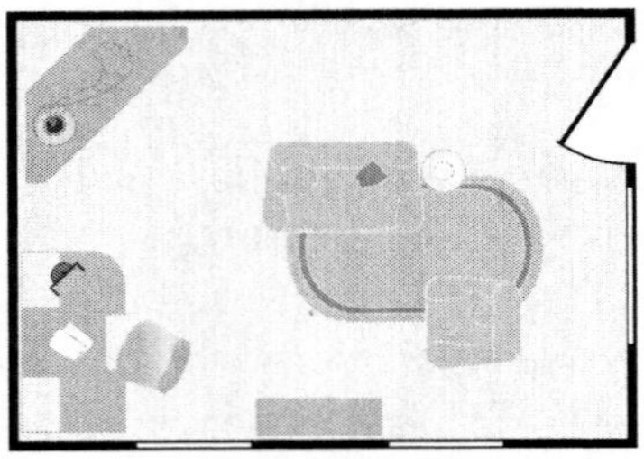

Perform the indicated operation.

39. $\begin{array}{r} 129 \\ \times\ 240 \\ \hline \end{array}$

Estimate the product by rounding each factor to the nearest hundred.

40. $\begin{array}{r} 1{,}217 \\ \times\ 494 \\ \hline \end{array}$

1.6 *Divide if possible.*

41. $0 \div 8$

42. $5 \div 0$

In exercises 43 to 46, divide.

43. $8\overline{)2{,}469}$

44. $39\overline{)2{,}157}$

45. $64\overline{)31{,}809}$

46. $362\overline{)86{,}915}$

Solve the application.

47. STATISTICS Hasina's odometer read 25,235 mi at the beginning of a trip and 26,215 mi at the end. If she used 35 gal of gas for the trip, what was her mileage (mi/gal)?

Estimate.

48. 356 divided by 37

49. 2,125 divided by 123

1.7 *In exercises 50 to 59, evaluate each expression.*

50. 5×2^3

51. $(5 \times 2)^3$

52. $4 + 8 \times 3$

53. $48 \div (2^3 + 4)$

54. $(4 + 8) \times 3$

55. $4 \times 3 + 8 \times 3$

56. $8 \div 4 \times 2 - 2 + 1$

57. $63 \times 2 \div 3 - 54 \div (12 \times 2 \div 4)$

58. $(3 \times 4)^2 - 100 \div 5 \times 6$

59. $(16 \times 2) \div 8 - (6 \div 3 \times 2)$

self-test 1

Name ________________

Section ________ Date ________

The purpose of this self-test is to help you assess your progress so that you can find concepts that you need to review before the next exam. Allow yourself about an hour to take this test. At the end of that hour, check your answers against those given in the back of this text. If you miss any, go back to the appropriate section to reread the examples until you have mastered that particular concept.

Perform the indicated operations.

1. $\begin{array}{r} 489 \\ 562 \\ 613 \\ +254 \\ \hline \end{array}$

2. $\begin{array}{r} 13 \\ 2,543 \\ +10,547 \\ \hline \end{array}$

3. $\begin{array}{r} 89 \\ \times 56 \\ \hline \end{array}$

4. $\begin{array}{r} 538 \\ \times 103 \\ \hline \end{array}$

5. Give the word name for 302,525.

Find the perimeter of the figure shown.

6.

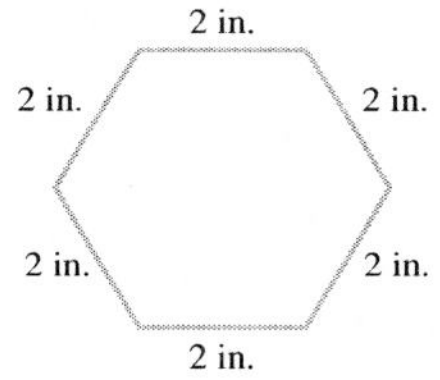

Complete the statements by using the symbol < or >.

7. 49 ______ 47

8. 80 ______ 90

9. Give the place value of 7 in 3,738,500.

Name the property that is illustrated.

10. $4 \times (3 + 6) = (4 \times 3) + (4 \times 6)$

11. $(7 + 3) + 8 = 7 + (3 + 8)$

12. $3 \times (2 \times 7) = (3 \times 2) \times 7$

13. $5 + 12 = 12 + 5$

Divide, using long division.

14. $28\overline{)2,135}$

15. $293\overline{)61,382}$

16. Write two million, four hundred thirty thousand as a number.

17. What is the total of 392, 95, 9,237, and 11,972?

Answers

1. ________
2. ________
3. ________
4. ________
5. ________
6. ________
7. ________
8. ________
9. ________
10. ________
11. ________
12. ________
13. ________
14. ________
15. ________
16. ________
17. ________

Answers

18. ______

19. ______

20. ______

21. ______

22. ______

23. ______

24. ______

25. ______

26. ______

27. ______

28. ______

29. ______

30. ______

18. **Business and Finance** A truck rental firm has ordered 25 new vans at a cost of $22,350 per van. What will be the total cost of the order?

19. **Business and Finance** Eight people estimate that the total expenses for a trip they are planning will be $1,784. If each person pays an equal amount, what will be each person's share?

Find the area of the given figure.

20.

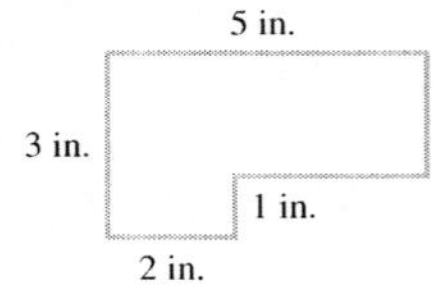

Find the volume of the given figure.

21.

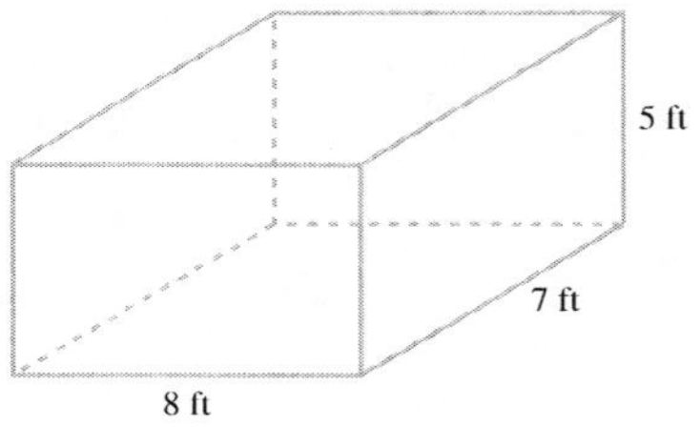

22. **Statistics** The attendance for the games of a playoff series in basketball was 12,438, 14,325, 14,581, and 14,634. What was the total attendance for the series?

In exercises 23 to 26, subtract.

23. $289 - 54$

24. $55,342 - 14,787$

25. $32,345 - 1,575$

26. $53,294 - 41,074$

27. **Social Science** The maximum load for a light plane with full gas tanks is 500 pounds (lb). Mr. Whitney weighs 215 lb; his wife, 135 lb; and their daughter, 78 lb. How much luggage can they take on a trip without exceeding the load limit?

28. Evaluate the expression $(3 + 4)^2 - (2 + 3^2 - 1)$.

29. Evaluate the expression $15 - 12 \div 2^2 \times 3 + (12 \div 4 \times 3)$.

Estimate the sum by rounding each addend to the nearest hundred.

30.

$$\begin{array}{r} 943 \\ 3,281 \\ 778 \\ 2,112 \\ +570 \\ \hline \end{array}$$

CHAPTER

2

Multiplying and Dividing Fractions

INTRODUCTION

Rebecca got tired of working nine to five as a paralegal in a busy law office in Philadelphia. On many occasions, she had to stay at work until 6:00 or 6:30, and the commute back and forth was exhausting. She wanted a more flexible schedule and started looking for an opportunity to be her own boss.

Rebecca loved to cook and often made delicious meals when she had the time. After investigating certain job opportunities, Rebecca decided to become a personal chef. She read somewhere that personal chefs can make between $50,000 and $70,000 a year. She knew of many busy families in her area that did not have the time to cook meals at night, and she thought this might be a good opportunity. She quit her job and started making meals for some of the people in the law firm where she had previously worked. She planned menus, did the grocery shopping, and cooked the meals right in her clients' kitchens. Sometimes, she cooked enough meals for an entire week and left the meals in containers in the freezer with instructions on how to reheat. She had to adjust her recipes for larger or smaller amounts, depending on whom she was cooking for.

Before long, Rebecca's clients started referring her to friends and relatives and her business began to grow. She was very happy with her new schedule and the free time that she had.

CHAPTER 2 OUTLINE

2 prerequisite test

Name ______________________

Section ________ Date ________

This prerequisite test provides some exercises requiring skills that you will need to be successful in the coming chapter. The answers for these exercises can be found in the back of this text. This prerequisite test can help you identify topics that you will need to review before beginning the chapter.

Answers

1. ______________________
2. ______________________
3. ______________________
4. ______________________
5. ______________________
6. ______________________
7. ______________________
8. ______________________
9. ______________________
10. ______________________

1. Does 4 divide exactly into 30 (that is, with no remainder)?

2. Does 5 divide exactly into 29?

3. Does 6 divide exactly into 72?

4. Does 3 divide exactly into 412?

5. Does 2 divide exactly into 238?

6. List all the whole numbers that can divide exactly into 9.

7. List all the whole numbers that can divide exactly into 10.

8. List all the whole numbers that can divide exactly into 17.

9. List all the whole numbers that can divide exactly into 48.

10. List all the whole numbers that can divide exactly into 60.

2.1 Prime Numbers and Divisibility

< 2.1 Objectives >

1 > Find the factors of a number

2 > Determine whether a number is prime, composite, or neither

3 > Determine whether a number is divisible by 2, 3, 4, 5, 6, or 9

Tips for Student Success

Working Together

How many of your classmates do you know? Whether you are by nature gregarious or shy, you have much to gain by getting to know your classmates.

1. It is important to have someone to call when you miss class or if you are unclear on an assignment.
2. Working with another person is almost always beneficial to both people. If you don't understand something, it helps to have someone to ask about it. If you do understand something, nothing will cement that understanding more than explaining the idea to another person.
3. Sometimes we need to commiserate. If an assignment is particularly frustrating, it is reassuring to find that it is also frustrating for other students.
4. Have you ever thought you had the right answer, but it didn't match the answer in the text? Frequently the answers are equivalent, but that's not always easy to see. A different perspective can help you see that. Occasionally there is an error in a textbook (here, we are talking about *other* textbooks). In such cases it is wonderfully reassuring to find that someone else has the same answer as you do.

NOTE

Also, 2 and 5 can be called *divisors* of 10. They divide 10 exactly.

In Section 1.5 we said that because $2 \times 5 = 10$, we call 2 and 5 **factors** of 10.

Definition

Factor A **factor** of a whole number is another whole number that *divides exactly* into the original number. This means that the division has a remainder of 0.

Example 1 Finding Factors

< Objective 1 >

List all the factors of 18.

When finding all the factors for any number, we always start with division by 1 because 1 is a factor of every number.

$1 \times 18 = 18$ Our list of factors starts with 1 and 18.

We continue with division by 2.

$2 \times 9 = 18$ Our list now contains 1, 2, 9, 18.

We check divisibility by each subsequent whole number until we get to a number that is already in the factor list.

$3 \times 6 = 18$ The list is now 1, 2, 3, 6, 9, 18.

Our number, 18, is not divisible by either 4 or 5. It is divisible by 6, but 6 is already in the list. The factor list is complete.

NOTE

This is a complete list of the factors. There are no other whole numbers that divide 18 exactly. Note that the factors of 18, except for 18 itself, are *smaller* than 18.

Check Yourself 1

List all the factors of 24.

Listing factors leads us to an important classification of whole numbers. Any whole number larger than 1 is either a *prime* or a *composite* number.

A whole number greater than 1 always has itself and 1 as factors. Sometimes these are the *only* factors. For instance, 1 and 3 are the only factors of 3.

Definition

Prime Number

A **prime number** is any whole number that has exactly two factors, 1 and itself.

As examples, 2, 3, 5, and 7 are prime numbers. Their only factors are 1 and themselves.

To check whether a number is prime, one approach is simply to divide the smaller primes—2, 3, 5, 7, and so on—into the given number. If no factors other than 1 and the given number are found, the number is prime.

Here is the method known as the **sieve of Eratosthenes** for identifying prime numbers.

NOTE

How large can a prime number be? There is no largest prime number. To date, the largest known prime is $2^{43,112,609} - 1$. This is a number with 12,978,189 digits. Of course, computers have to be used to verify that a number of this size is prime. If this number were printed out in 12-point type, it would be 30 miles long. By the time you read this, someone may very well have found an even larger prime number.

1. Write down a series of counting numbers, starting with the number 2. In this example, we stop at 50.
2. Start at the number 2. Delete every second number after 2.
3. Move to the number 3. Delete every third number after 3 (some numbers will be deleted twice).
4. Continue this process, deleting every fourth number after 4, every fifth number after 5, and so on.
5. When you have finished, the undeleted numbers are the prime numbers.

	2	3	~~4~~	5	~~6~~	7	~~8~~	~~9~~	~~10~~
11	~~12~~	13	~~14~~	~~15~~	~~16~~	17	~~18~~	19	~~20~~
~~21~~	~~22~~	23	~~24~~	~~25~~	~~26~~	~~27~~	~~28~~	29	~~30~~
31	~~32~~	~~33~~	~~34~~	~~35~~	~~36~~	37	~~38~~	~~39~~	~~40~~
41	~~42~~	43	~~44~~	~~45~~	~~46~~	47	~~48~~	~~49~~	~~50~~

The prime numbers less than 50 are 2, 3, 5, 7, 11, 13, 17, 19, 23, 29, 31, 37, 41, 43, 47.

Example 2 Identifying Prime Numbers

< Objective 2 >

Which of the numbers 17, 29, and 33 are prime?

17 is a prime number. 1 and 17 are the only factors.

29 is a prime number. 1 and 29 are the only factors.

33 is *not* prime. 1, 3, 11, and 33 are all factors of 33.

Note: For two-digit numbers, if the number is *not* a prime, it has one or more of the numbers 2, 3, 5, or 7 as factors.

Check Yourself 2

Which of the following numbers are prime numbers?

2, 6, 9, 11, 15, 19, 23, 35, 41

We can now define a second class of whole numbers.

Definition

Composite Number

A **composite number** is any whole number greater than 1 that is not prime. Every composite number has more than two factors.

Example 3 Identifying Composite Numbers

Which of the numbers 18, 23, 25, and 38 are composite?

18 is a composite number. — 1, 2, 3, 6, 9, and 18 are all factors of 18.

23 is *not* a composite number. — 1 and 23 are the only factors. This means that 23 is a *prime number*.

25 is a composite number. — 1, 5, and 25 are factors.

38 is a composite number. — 1, 2, 19, and 38 are factors.

Check Yourself 3

Which of the following numbers are composite numbers?

2, 6, 10, 13, 16, 17, 22, 27, 31, 35

By the definitions of prime and composite numbers:

Definition

Zero and One

The whole numbers 0 and 1 are neither prime nor composite.

NOTE

Divisibility by 2 indicates that a number is *even*.

This is simply a matter of the way in which prime and composite numbers are defined in mathematics. The numbers 0 and 1 are the *only* two whole numbers that cannot be classified as one or the other.

For our work in this and the following sections, it is very useful to be able to tell whether a given number is divisible by 2, 3, or 5. The tests that follow will give you some tools to check divisibility without actually having to divide.

Tests for divisibility by other numbers are also available. However, we have limited this section to those tests involving 2, 3, 4, 5, 6, 9, and 10 because they are very easy to use and occur frequently in our work.

Property

Divisibility by 2

A whole number is divisible by 2 if its last digit is 0, 2, 4, 6, or 8.

Example 4 Determining If a Number Is Divisible by 2

< Objective 3 >

Which of the numbers 2,346, 13,254, 23,573, and 57,085 are divisible by 2?

2,346 is divisible by 2. — The final digit is 6.

13,254 is divisible by 2. — The final digit is 4.

23,573 is *not* divisible by 2. — The final digit is not 0, 2, 4, 6, or 8.

57,085 is *not* divisible by 2.

Check Yourself 4

Which of the following are divisible by 2?

274 3,587 7,548 13,593

Property

Divisibility by 3

A whole number is divisible by 3 if the sum of its digits is divisible by 3.

Example 5 Determining If a Number Is Divisible by 3

Which of the numbers 345, 1,243, and 25,368 are divisible by 3?

345 is divisible by 3. The sum of the digits, 3 + 4 + 5, is 12, and 12 is divisible by 3.

1,243 is *not* divisible by 3. The sum of the digits, 1 + 2 + 4 + 3, is 10, and 10 is not divisible by 3.

25,368 is divisible by 3. The sum of the digits, 2 + 5 + 3 + 6 + 8, is 24, and 24 is divisible by 3. Note that 25,368 is also divisible by 2.

Check Yourself 5

(a) Is 372 divisible by 2? By 3? (b) Is 5,493 divisible by 2? By 3?

Property

Divisibility by 5

A whole number is divisible by 5 if its last digit is 0 or 5.

Example 6 Determining If a Number Is Divisible by 5

Determine which of the following are divisible by 5.

2,435 is divisible by 5. Its last digit is 5.

23,123 is *not* divisible by 5. Its last digit is 3.

123,240 is divisible by 5. Its last digit is 0. Do you see that 123,240 is also divisible by 2 and 3?

Check Yourself 6

(a) Is 12,585 divisible by 5? By 2? By 3?

(b) Is 5,890 divisible by 5? By 2? By 3?

Combining some of the techniques we have developed in this section, we can come up with divisibility tests for composite numbers as well.

Property

Divisibility by 4

A whole number is divisible by 4 if its final two digits are divisible by 4.

Example 7 Determining If a Number Is Divisible by 4

Determine if the numbers 1,464 and 2,434 are divisible by 4.

1,464 is divisible by 4. 64 is divisible by 4.

2,434 is *not* divisible by 4. 34 is not divisible by 4.

Check Yourself 7

Determine if each number is divisible by 4.

(a) 6,456 **(b)** 242 **(c)** 22,100

Property

Divisibility by 6 A whole number is divisible by 6 if it is an even number that is divisible by 3.

Example 8 Determining If a Number Is Divisible by 6

Determine if the numbers 1,464 and 2,434 are divisible by 6.

1,464 is divisible by 6. It is an even number, and the sum of the digits, 15, indicates that it is divisible by 3.

2,434 is *not* divisible by 6. Although it is an even number, the sum of the digits, 13, indicates that it is not divisible by 3.

Check Yourself 8

Determine if each number is divisible by 6.

(a) 6,456 **(b)** 242 **(c)** 22,100

Property

Divisibility by 9 A whole number is divisible by 9 if the sum of its digits is divisible by 9.

Example 9 Determining If a Number Is Divisible by 9

Determine if the numbers 1,494 and 2,634 are divisible by 9.

1,494 is divisible by 9. The sum of the digits, 18, indicates that it is divisible by 9.

2,634 is *not* divisible by 9. The sum of the digits, 15, indicates that it is not divisible by 9.

Check Yourself 9

Determine if each number is divisible by 9.

(a) 3,456 **(b)** 243,000 **(c)** 22,200

Property

Divisibility by 10 A whole number is divisible by 10 if it ends with a zero.

Example 10 Determining If a Number Is Divisible by 10

Determine if the numbers 4,390,005 and 6,420 are divisible by 10.

4,390,005 is *not* divisible by 10. The number does not end with a zero.

6,420 is divisible by 10. The number does end with a zero.

Check Yourself 10

Determine whether each number is divisible by 10.

(a) 2,000,020 **(b)** 2,000,002 **(c)** 3,571,110

Check Yourself ANSWERS

1. 1, 2, 3, 4, 6, 8, 12, and 24 **2.** 2, 11, 19, 23, and 41 are prime numbers
3. 6, 10, 16, 22, 27, and 35 are composite numbers **4.** 274 and 7,548
5. **(a)** Yes in both cases; **(b)** only by 3 **6.** **(a)** By 5 and by 3; **(b)** by 5 and by 2
7. **(a)** Yes; **(b)** no; **(c)** yes **8.** **(a)** Yes; **(b)** no; **(c)** no
9. **(a)** Yes; **(b)** yes; **(c)** no **10.** **(a)** Yes; **(b)** no; **(c)** yes

Reading Your Text

The following fill-in-the-blank exercises are designed to ensure that you understand some of the key vocabulary used in this section.

SECTION 2.1

(a) _______________ is a factor of every number.

(b) A _______________ number is any whole number that has exactly two factors, 1 and itself.

(c) A __________ number is any whole number greater than 1 that is not prime.

(d) When a whole number is divisible by 2, we call it an _______________ number.

2.1 exercises

Name ____________

Section ________ Date ________

< Objective 1 >

List the factors of each number.

1. 4

2. 6

3. 10

4. 12

5. 15

6. 21

7. 24 > Videos

8. 32

9. 64

10. 66

11. 11 > Videos

12. 37

13. 135

14. 236

15. 256

16. 512

< Objective 2 >

Use the list of numbers for exercises 17 and 18.

0, 1, 15, 19, 23, 31, 49, 55, 59, 87, 91, 97, 103, 105

17. Which of the given numbers are prime?

18. Which of the given numbers are composite?

19. List all the prime numbers between 30 and 50.

20. List all the prime numbers between 55 and 75.

Answers

1. ________ 2. ________
3. ________
4. ________
5. ________ 6. ________
7. ________
8. ________
9. ________
10. ________
11. ________ 12. ________
13. ________
14. ________
15. ________
16. ________
17. ________
18. ________
19. ________
20. ________

Answers

21. ______

22. ______

23. ______

24. ______

25. ______

26. ______

27. ______

28. ______

29. ______

30. ______

31. ______

< Objective 3 >

Use the list of numbers for exercises 21 through 26.

45, 72, 158, 260, 378, 569, 570, 585, 3,541, 4,530, 8,300

21. Which of the given numbers are divisible by 2? > Videos

22. Which of the given numbers are divisible by 3?

23. Which of the given numbers are divisible by 6? > Videos

24. Which of the given numbers are divisible by 9?

25. Which of the given numbers are divisible by 4?

26. Which of the given numbers are divisible by 10?

27. NUMBER PROBLEM A school auditorium is to have 350 seats. The principal wants to arrange them in rows with the same number of seats in each row. Use divisibility tests to determine if it is possible to have rows of 10 seats each. Are 15 rows of seats possible?

28. SOCIAL SCIENCE Dr. Mento has a class of 80 students. For a group project, she wants to divide the students into groups of 6, 8, or 10. Is this possible? Explain your answer.

Basic Skills | Challenge Yourself | Calculator/Computer | Career Applications | **Above and Beyond**

29. NUMBER PROBLEM Use the *sieve of Eratosthenes* to determine all the prime numbers less than 100.

	2	3	4	5	6	7	8	9	10
11	12	13	14	15	16	17	18	19	20
21	22	23	24	25	26	27	28	29	30
31	32	33	34	35	36	37	38	39	40
41	42	43	44	45	46	47	48	49	50
51	52	53	54	55	56	57	58	59	60
61	62	63	64	65	66	67	68	69	70
71	72	73	74	75	76	77	78	79	80
81	82	83	84	85	86	87	88	89	90
91	92	93	94	95	96	97	98	99	100

30. Why is the statement not a valid divisibility test for 8?

"A number is divisible by 8 if it is divisible by 2 and 4."

Support your answer with an example. Give a valid divisibility test for 8.

31. Prime numbers that differ by 2 are called *twin primes*. Examples are 3 and 5, 5 and 7, and so on. Find one pair of twin primes between 85 and 105.

32. The following questions refer to *twin primes* (see exercise 31).

(a) Search for, and make a list of, several pairs of twin primes in which the primes are greater than 3.

(b) What do you notice about each number that lies *between* a pair of twin primes?

(c) Write an explanation for your observation in part **(b)**.

33. Obtain (or imagine that you have) a quantity of square tiles. Six tiles can be arranged in the shape of a rectangle in two different ways:

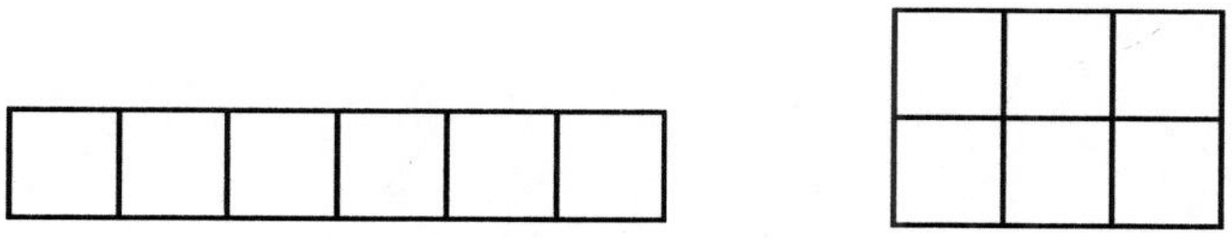

(a) Record the dimensions of the rectangles shown.

(b) If you use 7 tiles, how many different rectangles can you form?

(c) If you use 10 tiles, how many different rectangles can you form?

(d) What kind of number (of tiles) permits *only one* arrangement into a rectangle? *More than one* arrangement?

34. The number 10 has 4 factors: 1, 2, 5, and 10. We can say that 10 has an even number of factors. Investigate several numbers to determine which numbers have an *even number* of factors and which numbers have an *odd number* of factors.

35. **Number Problem** Suppose that a school has 1,000 lockers and that they are all closed. A person passes through, opening every other locker, beginning with locker 2. Then another person passes through, changing every third locker (closing it if it is open, opening it if it is closed), starting with locker 3. Yet another person passes through, changing every fourth locker, beginning with locker 4. This process continues until 1,000 people pass through.

(a) At the end of this process, which locker numbers are closed?

(b) Write an explanation for your answer to part **(a)**. (*Hint:* It may help to attempt exercise 34 first.)

Answers

32. ______

33. ______

34. ______

35. ______

Answers

1. 1, 2, 4 **3.** 1, 2, 5, 10 **5.** 1, 3, 5, 15 **7.** 1, 2, 3, 4, 6, 8, 12, 24
9. 1, 2, 4, 8, 16, 32, 64 **11.** 1, 11 **13.** 1, 3, 5, 9, 15, 27, 45, 135
15. 1, 2, 4, 8, 16, 32, 64, 128, 256 **17.** 19, 23, 31, 59, 97, 103
19. 31, 37, 41, 43, 47 **21.** 72, 158, 260, 378, 570, 4,530, 8,300
23. 72, 378, 570, 4,530 **25.** 72, 260, 8,300 **27.** Yes; no
29. Above and Beyond **31.** Above and Beyond **33.** Above and Beyond
35. Above and Beyond

2.2 Factoring Whole Numbers

< 2.2 Objectives >

1 > Find the factors of a whole number

2 > Find the prime factorization for any number

3 > Find the greatest common factor (GCF) of two numbers

4 > Find the GCF for a group of numbers

To **factor a number** means to write the number as a product of its whole-number factors.

Example 1 Factoring a Composite Number

< Objective 1 >

Factor the number 10.

$10 = 2 \times 5$ The order in which you write the factors does not matter, so $10 = 5 \times 2$ would also be correct.

Of course, $10 = 10 \times 1$ is also a correct statement. However, in this section we are interested in factors other than 1 and the given number.

Factor the number 21.

$21 = 3 \times 7$

Check Yourself 1

Factor 35.

In writing composite numbers as a product of factors, there are a number of different possible factorizations.

Example 2 Factoring a Composite Number

NOTE

There have to be at least two different factorizations, because a composite number has factors other than 1 and itself.

Find three different factorizations of 72.

$72 = 8 \times 9 \quad (1)$

$= 6 \times 12 \quad (2)$

$= 3 \times 24 \quad (3)$

Check Yourself 2

Find three different factorizations of 42.

We now want to write composite numbers as a product of their **prime factors.** Look again at the first factored line of Example 2. The process of factoring can be continued until all the factors are prime numbers.

Example 3 Factoring a Composite Number

< Objective 3 >

NOTES

This is often called a **factor tree.**

Finding the prime factorization of a number will be important in our later work in adding fractions.

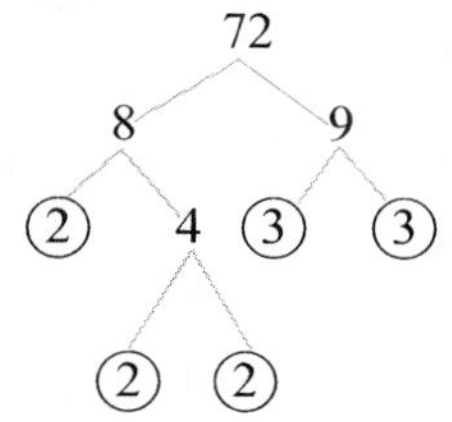

4 is still not prime, and so we continue by factoring 4.

72 is now written as a product of prime factors.

When we write 72 as $2 \times 2 \times 2 \times 3 \times 3$, no further factorization is possible. This is called the *prime factorization* of 72.

Now, what if we start with a different factored line from the same example, $72 = 6 \times 12$?

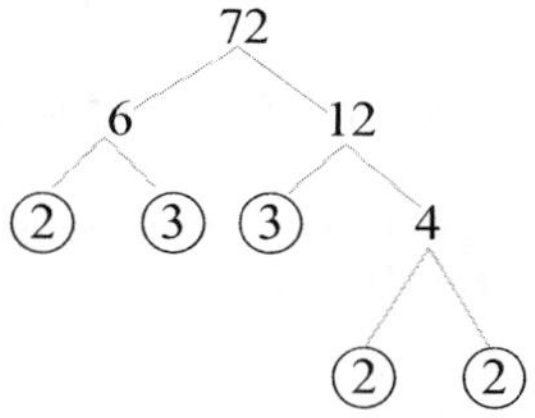

Continue to factor 6 and 12.

Continue again to factor 4. Other choices for the factors of 12 are possible. As we shall see, the end result will be the same.

No matter which pair of factors you start with, you will find the same prime factorization. In this case, there are three factors of 2 and two factors of 3. Because **multiplication is commutative,** the order in which we write the factors does not matter.

Check Yourself 3

We could also begin

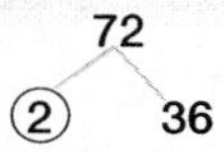

Continue the factorization.

Property

The Fundamental Theorem of Arithmetic

There is exactly one prime factorization for any composite number.

The method of Example 3 always works. However, another method for factoring composite numbers exists. This method is particularly useful when numbers get large, in which case a factor tree becomes unwieldy.

Property

Factoring by Division

To find the prime factorization of a number, divide the number by a series of primes until the final quotient is a prime number.

The prime factorization is then the product of all the prime divisors and the final quotient, as we see in Example 4.

Example 4 Finding the Prime Factorization

< Objective 2 >

NOTE

Do you see how the divisibility tests are used here? 60 is divisible by 2, 30 is divisible by 2, and 15 is divisible by 3.

To write 60 as a product of prime factors, divide 2 into 60 for a quotient of 30. Continue to divide by 2 again for the quotient of 15. Because 2 won't divide evenly into 15, we try 3. Because the quotient 5 is prime, we are done.

$2\overline{)60}$ → 30; $2\overline{)30}$ → 15; $3\overline{)15}$ → 5 Prime

Our factors are the prime divisors and the final quotient. We have

$60 = 2 \times 2 \times 3 \times 5$

Check Yourself 4

Complete the process to find the prime factorization of 90.

$2\overline{)90}$ → 45; $?\overline{)45}$ → ?

Remember to continue until the final quotient is prime.

Writing composite numbers in their completely factored form can be simplified if we use a format called **continued division.**

Example 5 Finding Prime Factors Using Continued Division

NOTE

In each short division, we write the quotient *below* rather than above the dividend. This is just a convenience for the next division.

Use the continued-division method to divide 60 by a series of prime numbers.

$$\begin{array}{r} 2\overline{)60} \\ 2\overline{)30} \\ 3\overline{)15} \\ 5 \end{array}$$

Primes (2, 2, 3)

Stop when the final quotient is prime.

To write the factorization of 60, we list each divisor used and the final prime quotient. In our example, we have

$60 = 2 \times 2 \times 3 \times 5$

Check Yourself 5

Find the prime factorization of 234.

NOTE

The factors of 20, other than 20 itself, are less than 20.

We know that a factor or a divisor of a whole number divides that number exactly. The factors or divisors of 20 are

1, 2, 4, 5, 10, 20

Each of these numbers divides 20 exactly; that is, with no remainder.

Our work in this section involves common factors or divisors. A **common factor** or **divisor** for two numbers is any factor that divides both numbers exactly.

Example 6 Finding Common Factors

< Objective 3 >

Look at the numbers 20 and 30. Is there a common factor for the two numbers?

First, we list the factors. Then we circle the ones that appear in both lists.

Factors

20: (1), (2), 4, (5), (10), 20

30: (1), (2), 3, (5), 6, (10), 15, 30

We see that 1, 2, 5, and 10 are common factors of 20 and 30. Each of these numbers divides both 20 and 30 exactly.

Our later work with fractions will require that we find the greatest common factor of a group of numbers.

Definition

Greatest Common Factor

The **greatest common factor** (GCF) of a group of numbers is the *largest* number that divides each of the given numbers exactly.

Example 6 (Continued) Finding the Greatest Common Factor

In the first part of Example 6, the common factors of the numbers 20 and 30 were listed as

1, 2, 5, 10 Common factors of 20 and 30

The greatest common factor of the two numbers is then 10, because 10 is the *largest* of the four common factors.

Check Yourself 6

List the factors of 30 and 36 and then find the greatest common factor.

The method of Example 6 also works in finding the greatest common factor of a group of more than two numbers.

Example 7 Finding the Greatest Common Factor by Listing Factors

< Objective 4 >

Find the GCF of 24, 30, and 36. We list the factors of each of the three numbers.

24: (1), (2), (3), 4, (6), 8, 12, 24

30: (1), (2), (3), 5, (6), 10, 15, 30

36: (1), (2), (3), 4, (6), 9, 12, 18, 36

So 6 is the greatest common factor of 24, 30, and 36.

NOTE

Looking at the three lists, we see that 1, 2, 3, and 6 are common factors.

Check Yourself 7

Find the greatest common factor of 16, 24, and 32.

NOTE

If there are no common prime factors, the GCF is 1.

The process shown in Example 7 is very time-consuming when larger numbers are involved. A better approach to the problem of finding the GCF of a group of numbers uses the prime factorization of each number. We outline the process here.

Step by Step

Finding the Greatest Common Factor

Step 1 Write the prime factorization for each of the numbers in the group.

Step 2 Locate the prime factors that are *common* to all the numbers.

Step 3 The greatest common factor (GCF) is the *product* of all the common prime factors.

Example 8 Finding the Greatest Common Factor

Find the GCF of 20 and 30.

Step 1 Write the prime factorization of 20 and 30.

$20 = 2 \times 2 \times 5$

$30 = 2 \times 3 \times 5$

Step 2 Find the prime factors common to each number.

$20 = \textcircled{2} \times 2 \times \textcircled{5}$

$30 = \textcircled{2} \times 3 \times \textcircled{5}$

2 and 5 are the common prime factors.

Step 3 Form the product of the common prime factors.

$2 \times 5 = 10$

So 10 is the greatest common factor.

Check Yourself 8

Find the GCF of 30 and 36.

To find the greatest common factor of a group of more than two numbers, we use the same process.

Example 9 Finding the Greatest Common Factor

Find the GCF of 24, 30, and 36.

$24 = \textcircled{2} \times 2 \times 2 \times \textcircled{3}$

$30 = \textcircled{2} \times \textcircled{3} \times 5$

$36 = \textcircled{2} \times 2 \times \textcircled{3} \times 3$

So 2 and 3 are the prime factors common to *all three numbers.*

And $2 \times 3 = 6$ is the GCF.

Check Yourself 9

Find the GCF of 15, 30, and 45.

Example 10 Finding the Greatest Common Factor

NOTE

If two numbers, such as 15 and 28, have no common factor other than 1, they are called **relatively prime.**

Find the greatest common factor of 15 and 28.

$15 = 3 \times 5$

$28 = 2 \times 2 \times 7$

There are no common prime factors listed. But remember that 1 is a factor of every whole number.

The greatest common factor of 15 and 28 is 1.

Check Yourself 10

Find the greatest common factor of 30 and 49.

Check Yourself ANSWERS

1. 5×7 **2.** $2 \times 21, 3 \times 14, 6 \times 7$ **3.** $2 \times 2 \times 2 \times 3 \times 3$

4. $\begin{array}{r} 45 \\ 2\overline{)90} \end{array} \rightarrow \begin{array}{r} 15 \\ 3\overline{)45} \end{array} \rightarrow \begin{array}{r} 5 \\ 3\overline{)15} \end{array}$ **5.** $2 \times 3 \times 3 \times 13$

$90 = 2 \times 3 \times 3 \times 5$

6. 30: $\textcircled{1}, \textcircled{2}, \textcircled{3}, 5, \textcircled{6}, 10, 15, 30$

36: $\textcircled{1}, \textcircled{2}, \textcircled{3}, 4, \textcircled{6}, 9, 12, 18, 36$

6 is the greatest common factor.

7. 16: $\textcircled{1}, \textcircled{2}, \textcircled{4}, \textcircled{8}, 16$

24: $\textcircled{1}, \textcircled{2}, 3, \textcircled{4}, 6, \textcircled{8}, 12, 24$

32: $\textcircled{1}, \textcircled{2}, \textcircled{4}, \textcircled{8}, 16, 32$

The GCF is 8.

8. $30 = \textcircled{2} \times \textcircled{3} \times 5$

$36 = \textcircled{2} \times 2 \times \textcircled{3} \times 3$

The GCF is $2 \times 3 = 6$.

9. $15 = \textcircled{3} \times \textcircled{5}$

$30 = 2 \times \textcircled{3} \times \textcircled{5}$

$45 = \textcircled{3} \times 3 \times \textcircled{5}$

The GCF is 15.

10. GCF is 1; 30 and 49 are relatively prime

Reading Your Text

The following fill-in-the-blank exercises are designed to ensure that you understand some of the key vocabulary used in this section.

SECTION 2.2

(a) Because multiplication is ______________, the order in which we write factors does not matter.

(b) There is exactly one ____________ factorization for any whole number.

(c) A ______________ factor for two numbers is any factor that divides both numbers exactly.

(d) GCF is an abbreviation for ______________ common factor.

2.2 exercises

Basic Skills | Challenge Yourself | Calculator/Computer | Career Applications | Above and Beyond

Boost *your* GRADE at ALEKS.com!

ALEKS®

- Practice Problems
- Self-Tests
- NetTutor
- e-Professors
- Videos

Name ____________________

Section ________ Date ________

Answers

1. ______ 2. ______
3. ______ 4. ______
5. ______ 6. ______
7. ______
8. ______
9. ______
10. ______
11. ______
12. ______
13. ______
14. ______
15. ______
16. ______
17. ______ 18. ______
19. ______ 20. ______
21. ______ 22. ______
23. ______ 24. ______

< Objectives 1 and 2 >

Find the prime factorization of each number.

1. 18

2. 22

3. 30

4. 35

5. 51

6. 42

7. 66 > Videos

8. 100

9. 130

10. 88

11. 315

12. 400

13. 225

14. 132

15. 189 > Videos

16. 330

In later mathematics courses, you sometimes want to find factors of a number with a given sum or difference. These exercises use this technique.

17. Find two factors of 48 with a sum of 14.

6 x 8 = 48
6 + 8 = 14

18. Find two factors of 48 with a sum of 26.

19. Find two factors of 48 with a difference of 8.

20. Find two factors of 48 with a difference of 2.

21. Find two factors of 24 with a sum of 10. > Videos

22. Find two factors of 15 with a difference of 2.

23. Find two factors of 30 with a difference of 1.

24. Find two factors of 28 with a sum of 11.

< Objective 3 >

Find the greatest common factor for each group of numbers.

25. 4 and 6 > Videos

26. 6 and 9

27. 10 and 15

28. 12 and 14

29. 21 and 24

30. 22 and 33

31. 20 and 21

32. 28 and 42

33. 18 and 24

34. 35 and 36

35. 18 and 54 > Videos

36. 12 and 48

Basic Skills | **Challenge Yourself** | Calculator/Computer | Career Applications | Above and Beyond

< Objective 4 >

Find the GCF for each group of numbers.

37. 12, 36, and 60

38. 15, 45, and 90

39. 105, 140, and 175

40. 17, 19, and 31

41. 25, 75, and 150 > Videos

42. 36, 72, and 144

For exercises 43 to 46 fill in each blank with either **always, sometimes,** *or* **never.**

43. Factors of a composite number ____________ include 1 and the number itself.

44. Factors of a prime number ____________ include 1 and the number itself.

45. A number with a repeated factor is ____________ a prime number.

46. Factors of an even number are ________________ even numbers.

Answers

25. ____________

26. ____________

27. ____________

28. ____________

29. ____________

30. ____________

31. ____________

32. ____________

33. ____________

34. ____________

35. ____________

36. ____________

37. ____________

38. ____________

39. ____________

40. ____________

41. ____________

42. ____________

43. ____________

44. ____________

45. ____________

46. ____________

Basic Skills | Challenge Yourself | Calculator/Computer | Career Applications | **Above and Beyond**

Answers

47. ______

48. ______

49. ______

50. ______

47. A natural number is said to be *perfect* if it is equal to the sum of its factors, except itself.

(a) Show that 28 is a perfect number.

(b) Identify another perfect number less than 28.

48. Find the smallest natural number that is divisible by all the following: 2, 3, 4, 6, 8, 9.

49. SOCIAL SCIENCE Tom and Dick both work the night shift at the steel mill. Tom has every sixth night off, and Dick has every eighth night off. If they both have August 1 off, when will they both be off together again?

50. SCIENCE AND MEDICINE Mercury, Venus, and Earth revolve around the sun once every 3, 7, and 12 months, respectively. If the three planets are now in the same straight line, what is the smallest number of months that must pass before they line up again?

Answers

1. $2 \times 3 \times 3$ 3. $2 \times 3 \times 5$ 5. 3×17 7. $2 \times 3 \times 11$ 9. $2 \times 5 \times 13$ 11. $3 \times 3 \times 5 \times 7$ 13. $3 \times 3 \times 5 \times 5$ 15. $3 \times 3 \times 3 \times 7$ 17. 6, 8 19. 4, 12 21. 4, 6 23. 5, 6 25. 2 27. 5 29. 3 31. 1 33. 6 35. 18 37. 12 39. 35 41. 25 43. always 45. never 47. (a) $1 + 2 + 4 + 7 + 14 = 28$; (b) 6 49. August 25

2.3

Fraction Basics

< 2.3 Objectives >

1 > Identify the numerator and denominator of a fraction

2 > Use fractions to name parts of a whole

3 > Identify proper and improper fractions

4 > Write improper fractions as mixed numbers

5 > Write mixed numbers as improper fractions

Previous sections dealt with whole numbers and the operations that are performed on them. We are now ready to consider a new kind of number, a **fraction.**

Definition

Fraction — Whenever a unit or a whole quantity is divided into parts, we call those parts **fractions** of the unit.

NOTE

Our word *fraction* comes from the Latin stem *fractio,* which means "breaking into pieces."

In this figure, the whole has been divided into five equal parts. We use the symbol $\frac{2}{5}$ to represent the shaded portion of the whole.

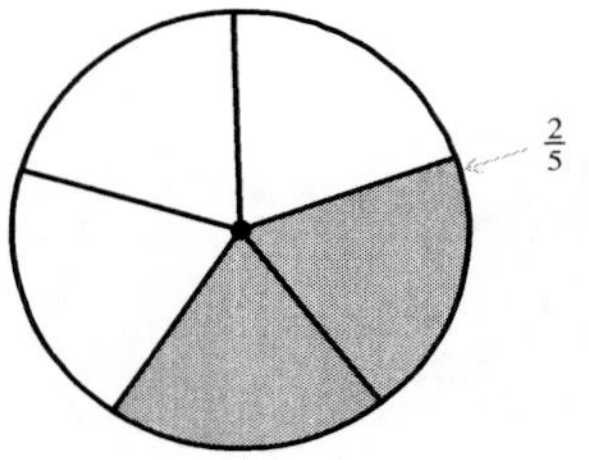

The symbol $\frac{2}{5}$ is called a **common fraction,** or more simply a fraction. A fraction is written in the form $\frac{a}{b}$, in which a and b represent whole numbers and b cannot be equal to 0.

NOTE

Common fraction is technically the correct term. We just use *fraction* in these materials.

We give the numbers a and b special names. The **denominator,** b, is the number on the bottom. This tells us into how many equal parts the unit or whole has been divided. The **numerator,** a, is the number on the top. This tells us how many parts of the unit are used.

In the fraction $\frac{2}{5}$, the *denominator* is 5; the unit or whole (the circle) has been divided into five equal parts. The *numerator* is 2. We have shaded two parts of the unit.

$\frac{2}{5}$ ← Numerator (2), ← Denominator (5)

Example 1 — **Labeling Fraction Components**

< Objectives 1, 2 >

The fraction $\frac{4}{7}$ names the shaded part of the rectangle in the figure.

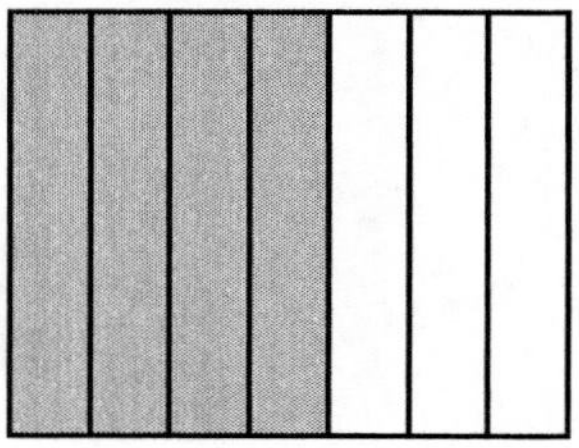

The unit or whole is divided into seven equal parts, so the denominator is 7. We have shaded four of those parts, and so we have a numerator of 4.

Check Yourself 1

What fraction names the shaded part of this diagram? Identify the numerator and denominator.

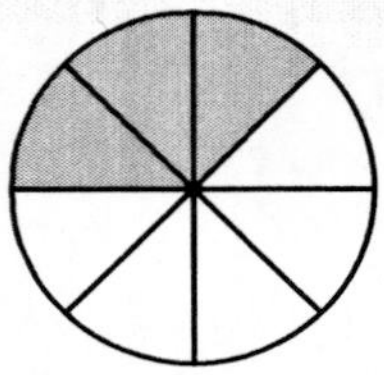

Fractions can also be used to name a part of a collection or a set of identical objects.

Example 2 Naming a Fractional Part

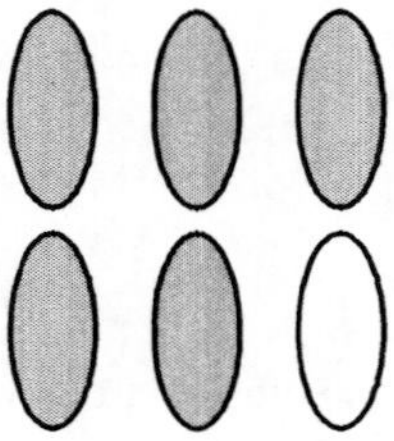

The fraction $\frac{5}{6}$ names the shaded part of the figure to the left. We have shaded five of the six identical objects.

Check Yourself 2

What fraction names the shaded part of this diagram?

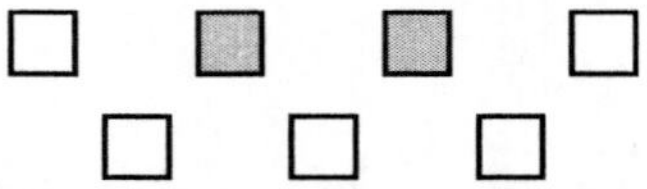

Example 3 Naming a Fractional Part

NOTES

The fraction $\frac{8}{23}$ names the part of the class that is not women.

$\frac{a}{b}$ names the *quotient* when *a* is divided by *b*. Of course, *b* cannot be 0.

In a class of 23 students, 15 are women. We can name the part of the class that is women as $\frac{15}{23}$.

Check Yourself 3

Seven replacement parts out of a shipment of 50 were faulty. What fraction names the portion of the shipment that was faulty?

A fraction can also be thought of as indicating division. The symbol $\frac{a}{b}$ also means $a \div b$.

Example 4 Interpreting a Fraction as Division

The fraction $\frac{2}{3}$ names the quotient when 2 is divided by 3. So $\frac{2}{3} = 2 \div 3$.

Note: $\frac{2}{3}$ can be read as "two-thirds" or as "2 divided by 3."

Check Yourself 4

Write $\frac{5}{9}$ using division.

We can use the relative size of the numerator and denominator of a fraction to separate fractions into two different categories.

Definition

Proper Fraction

If the numerator is *less than* the denominator, the fraction names a number less than 1 and is called a **proper fraction.**

Definition

Improper Fraction

If the numerator is *greater than or equal to* the denominator, the fraction names a number greater than or equal to 1 and is called an **improper fraction.**

Example 5 Categorizing Fractions

< Objective 3 >

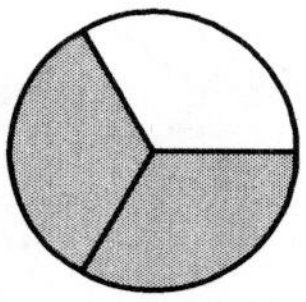

$\frac{2}{3}$ names less than 1 unit and $2 < 3$.
Numerator Denominator

(a) $\frac{2}{3}$ is a proper fraction because the numerator is less than the denominator.

(b) $\frac{4}{3}$ is an improper fraction because the numerator is larger than the denominator.

(c) Also, $\frac{6}{6}$ is an improper fraction because it names exactly 1 unit; the numerator is equal to the denominator.

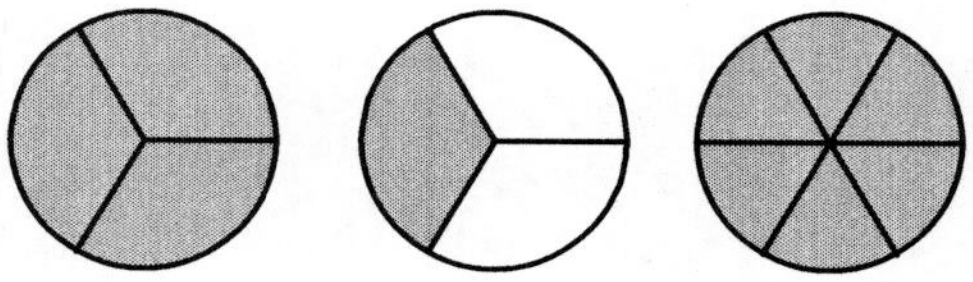

$\frac{4}{3}$ names more than 1 unit and $4 > 3$.
Numerator Denominator

$\frac{6}{6} = 1$

NOTE

In Figure 5, the circle on the left is divided into 3 parts, so it represents $\frac{3}{3}$.

Check Yourself 5

List the proper fractions and the improper fractions in the following list:

$$\frac{5}{4}, \frac{10}{11}, \frac{3}{4}, \frac{8}{5}, \frac{6}{6}, \frac{13}{10}, \frac{7}{8}, \frac{15}{8}$$

Another way to write a fraction that is larger than 1 is as a **mixed number.**

Definition

Mixed Number

A **mixed number** is the sum of a whole number and a proper fraction.

Example 6 Identifying a Mixed Number

NOTE

$2\frac{3}{4}$ means $2 + \frac{3}{4}$. In fact, we read the mixed number as "two *and* three-fourths." The plus sign is usually not written.

The number $2\frac{3}{4}$ is a mixed number. It represents the sum of the whole number 2 and the fraction $\frac{3}{4}$. Look at the following diagram, which represents $2\frac{3}{4}$.

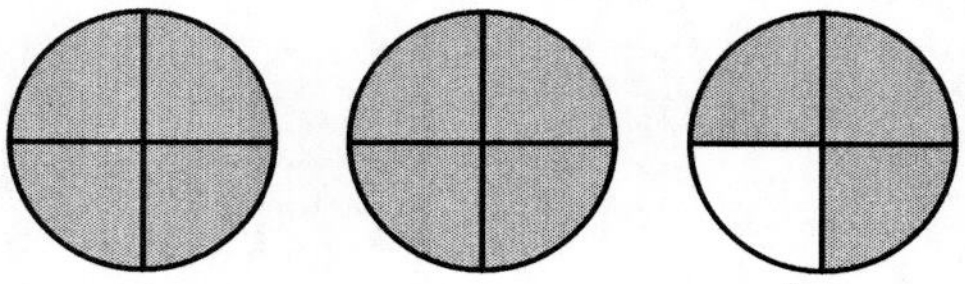

1 unit + 1 unit + $\frac{3}{4}$ unit

Check Yourself 6

Give the mixed number that names the shaded portion of the given diagram.

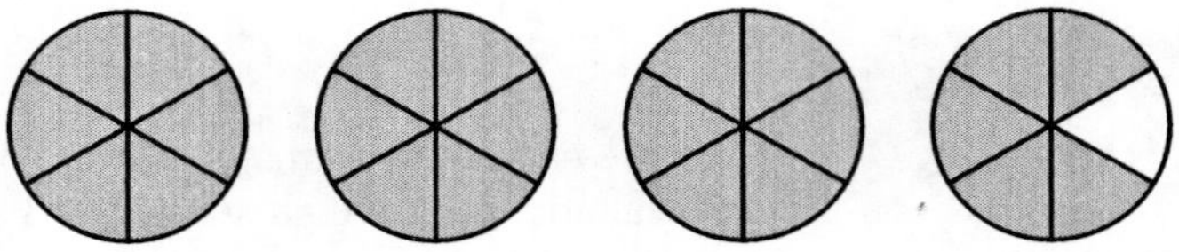

NOTE

In subsequent courses, you will find that improper fractions are preferred to mixed numbers.

For our later work it will be important to be able to change back and forth between improper fractions and mixed numbers. Because an improper fraction represents a number that is greater than or equal to 1, we have the following property:

Property

Improper Fractions to Mixed Numbers

An improper fraction can always be written as either a mixed number or a whole number.

To do this, remember that you can think of a fraction as indicating division. The numerator is divided by the denominator. This leads us to the following process:

Step by Step

To Change an Improper Fraction to a Mixed Number

Step 1 Divide the numerator by the denominator.

Step 2 If there is a remainder, write the remainder over the original denominator.

Example 7 Converting a Fraction to a Mixed Number

< Objective 4 >

Convert $\frac{17}{5}$ to a mixed number.

Divide 17 by 5.

$$5\overline{)17} \quad 3 \quad \frac{15}{2} \qquad \frac{17}{5} = 3\frac{2}{5}$$

Remainder (2); Original denominator (5); Quotient (3)

NOTES

You can write the fraction $\frac{17}{5}$ as $17 \div 5$. We divide the numerator by the denominator.

In step 1, the quotient gives the whole-number portion of the mixed number.
Step 2 gives the fractional portion of the mixed number.

In diagram form:

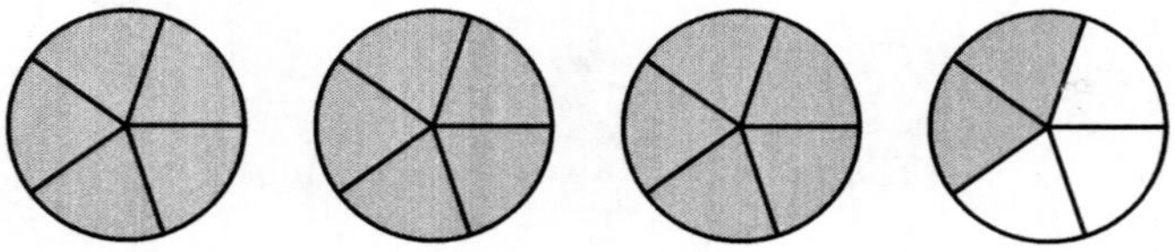

$$\frac{17}{5} = 3\frac{2}{5}$$

Check Yourself 7

Convert $\frac{32}{5}$ to a mixed number.

Example 8 Converting a Fraction to a Mixed Number

NOTE

If there is *no* remainder, the improper fraction is equal to some whole number, in this case 3.

Convert $\frac{21}{7}$ to a mixed or a whole number.

Divide 21 by 7.

$$7\overline{)21} = 3 \quad \begin{array}{r} 21 \\ \underline{21} \\ 0 \end{array} \qquad \frac{21}{7} = 3$$

Check Yourself 8

Convert $\frac{48}{6}$ to a mixed or a whole number.

You may also need to convert mixed numbers to improper fractions. Just use the following rule:

Step by Step

To Change a Mixed Number to an Improper Fraction

Step 1 Multiply the denominator of the fraction by the whole-number portion of the mixed number.

Step 2 Add the numerator of the fraction to that product.

Step 3 Write that sum over the original denominator to form the improper fraction.

Example 9 Converting Mixed Numbers to Improper Fractions

< Objective 5 >

(a) Convert $3\frac{2}{5}$ to an improper fraction.

Denominator × Whole number; Numerator

$$3\frac{2}{5} = \frac{(5 \times 3) + 2}{5}$$

Denominator

$$= \frac{17}{5}$$

Multiply the denominator by the whole number (5 × 3 = 15). Add the numerator. We now have 17.

Write 17 over the original denominator.

In diagram form:

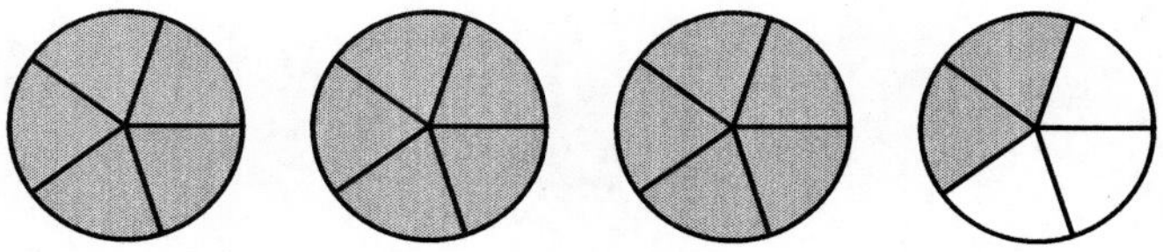

Each of the three units has 5 fifths, so the whole-number portion is 5 × 3, or 15, fifths. Then add the $\frac{2}{5}$ from the fractional portion for $\frac{17}{5}$.

NOTE

Multiply the denominator, 7, by the whole number, 4, and add the numerator, 5.

(b) Convert $4\frac{5}{7}$ to an improper fraction.

$$4\frac{5}{7} = \frac{(7 \times 4) + 5}{7} = \frac{33}{7}$$

Check Yourself 9

Convert $5\frac{3}{8}$ to an improper fraction.

One special kind of improper fraction should be mentioned at this point: a fraction with a denominator of 1.

Definition

Fractions with a Denominator of 1

Any fraction with a denominator of 1 is equal to the numerator alone. For example,

$\frac{5}{1} = 5$ and $\frac{12}{1} = 12$

You probably do many conversions between mixed and whole numbers without even thinking about the process that you follow, as Example 10 illustrates.

Example 10 Converting Quarter-Dollars to Dollars

Maritza has 53 quarters in her bank. How many dollars does she have?

Because there are 4 quarters in each dollar, 53 quarters can be written as

$$\frac{53}{4}$$

Converting the amount to dollars is the same as rewriting it as a mixed number.

$$\frac{53}{4} = 13\frac{1}{4}$$

She has $13\frac{1}{4}$ dollars, which you would probably write as \$13.25. (*Note:* We will discuss decimal point usage later in this text.)

Check Yourself 10

Kevin is doing the inventory in the convenience store in which he works. He finds there are 11 half-gallons (gal) of milk. Write the amount of milk as a mixed number of gallons.

Check Yourself ANSWERS

1. $\frac{3}{8}$ ← Numerator, ← Denominator

2. $\frac{2}{7}$ **3.** $\frac{7}{50}$ **4.** $5 \div 9$

5. Proper fractions: $\frac{10}{11}, \frac{3}{4}, \frac{7}{8}$ Improper fractions: $\frac{5}{4}, \frac{8}{5}, \frac{6}{6}, \frac{13}{10}, \frac{15}{8}$ **6.** $3\frac{5}{6}$ **7.** $6\frac{2}{5}$ **8.** 8

9. $\frac{43}{8}$ **10.** $5\frac{1}{2}$ gal

Reading Your Text

The following fill-in-the-blank exercises are designed to ensure that you understand some of the key vocabulary used in this section.

SECTION 2.3

(a) Given a fraction like $\frac{3}{4}$, we call 4 the ______________ of the fraction.

(b) If the numerator is less than the denominator, the fraction names a number less than 1 and is called a ______________ fraction.

(c) An improper fraction can always be written as either a ______________ number or a whole number.

(d) Any fraction with a denominator of 1 is equal to the ______________ alone.

2.3 exercises

Basic Skills | Challenge Yourself | Calculator/Computer | Career Applications | Above and Beyond

Name ____________________

Section ________ Date ________

Answers

1. ____________________
2. ____________________
3. ____________________
4. ____________________
5. ____________________
6. ____________________
7. ____________________
8. ____________________
9. ____________________
10. ____________________
11. ____________________
12. ____________________
13. ____________________
14. ____________________

< Objective 1 >

Identify the numerator and denominator of each fraction.

1. $\frac{6}{11}$

2. $\frac{5}{12}$

3. $\frac{3}{11}$

4. $\frac{9}{14}$

< Objective 2 >

What fraction names the shaded part of each figure?

5.

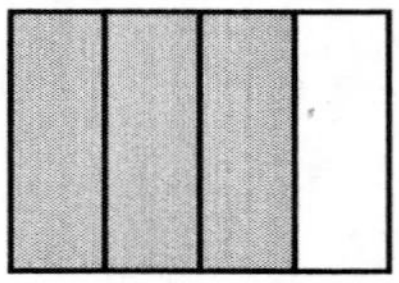

6.

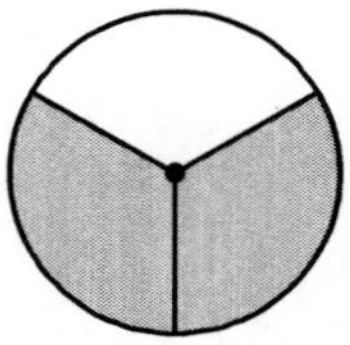

7.

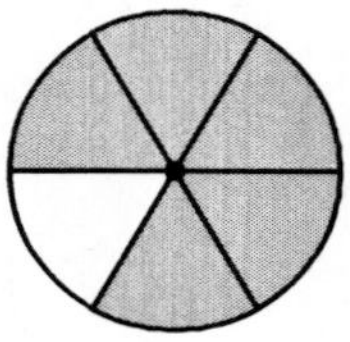

8.

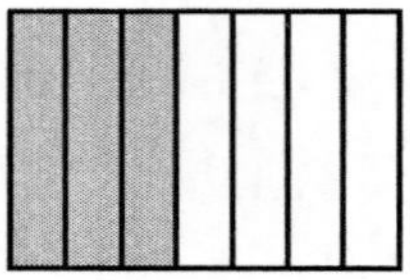

9.

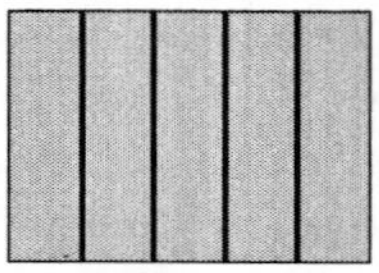

10.

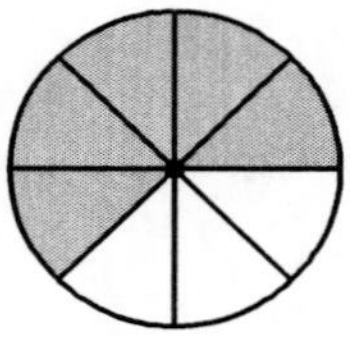

11.

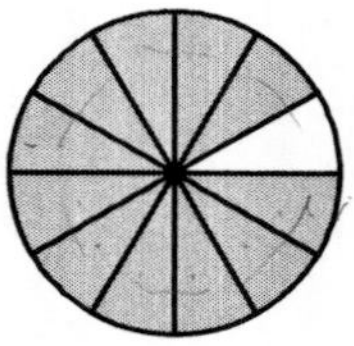

12.

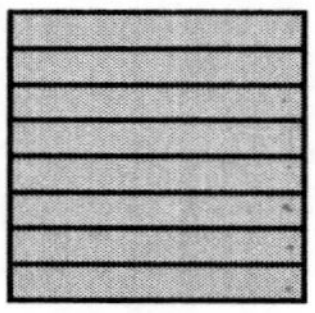

13.

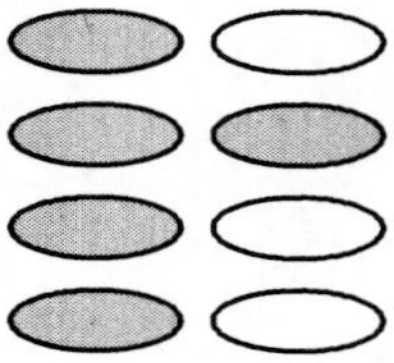

> Videos

14.

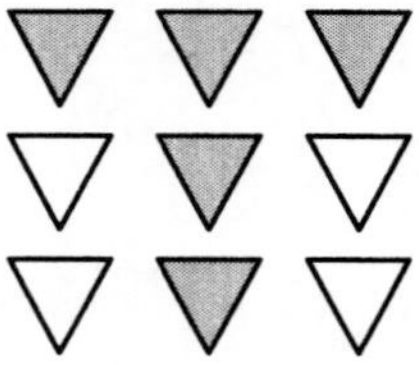

Solve each application.

15. Statistics You missed 7 questions on a 20-question test. What fraction names the part you got correct? The part you got wrong?

Videos

16. Statistics Of the 5 starters on a basketball team, 2 fouled out of a game. What fraction names the part of the starting team that fouled out?

17. Business and Finance A used-car dealer sold 11 of the 17 cars in stock. What fraction names the portion sold? What fraction names the portion *not* sold?

18. Business and Finance At lunch, 5 people out of a group of 9 had hamburgers. What fraction names the part of the group who had hamburgers? What fraction names the part who did *not* have hamburgers?

19. Use division to show another way of writing $\frac{2}{5}$.

20. Use division to show another way of writing $\frac{4}{5}$.

< Objective 3 >

Identify each number as a proper fraction, an improper fraction, or a mixed number.

21. $\frac{3}{5}$ **22.** $\frac{9}{5}$ **23.** $2\frac{3}{5}$

24. $\frac{7}{9}$ **25.** $\frac{6}{6}$ **26.** $1\frac{1}{5}$

27. $\frac{13}{17}$ **28.** $\frac{16}{15}$

Give the mixed number that names the shaded portion of each diagram. Also write each as an improper fraction.

29.

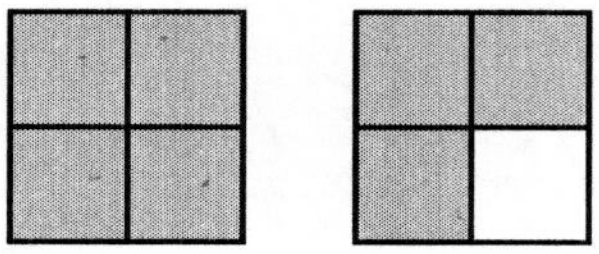

30.

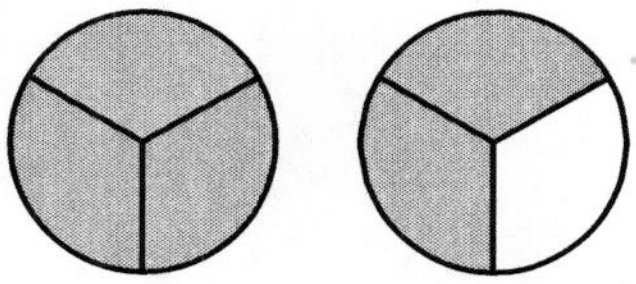

31.

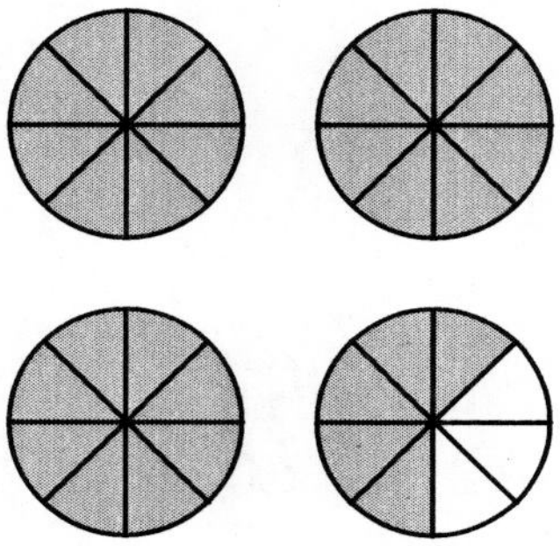

32.

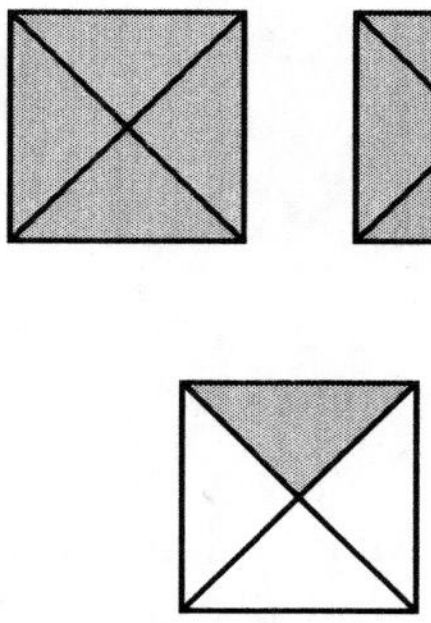

Answers

15. ____

16. ____

17. ____

18. ____

19. ____

20. ____

21. ____

22. ____

23. ____

24. ____

25. ____

26. ____

27. ____

28. ____

29. ____

30. ____

31. ____

32. ____

Answers

33. ______ 34. ______

35. ______ 36. ______

37. ______ 38. ______

39. ______ 40. ______

41. ______ 42. ______

43. ______ 44. ______

45. ______ 46. ______

47. ______ 48. ______

49. ______ 50. ______

51. ______ 52. ______

53. ______ 54. ______

55. ______ 56. ______

57. ______

Solve each application.

33. Business and Finance Clayton has 64 quarters in his bank. How many dollars does he have?

34. Business and Finance Amy has 19 quarters in her purse. How many dollars does she have?

35. Business and Finance Manuel counted 35 half-gallons of orange juice in his store. Write the amount of orange juice as a mixed number of gallons.

36. Business and Finance Sarah has 19 half-gallons of turpentine in her paint store. Write the amount of turpentine as a mixed number of gallons.

< Objective 4 >

Change to a mixed or whole number.

37. $\frac{22}{5}$ Videos

38. $\frac{27}{8}$

39. $\frac{34}{5}$

40. $\frac{25}{6}$

41. $\frac{73}{8}$

42. $\frac{151}{12}$

43. $\frac{24}{6}$

44. $\frac{160}{8}$

45. $\frac{9}{1}$

46. $\frac{8}{1}$

< Objective 5 >

Change to an improper fraction.

47. $4\frac{2}{3}$

48. $2\frac{5}{6}$

49. 8

50. $4\frac{5}{8}$

51. $7\frac{6}{13}$

52. $7\frac{3}{10}$

53. $10\frac{2}{5}$

54. $13\frac{2}{5}$

55. $118\frac{3}{4}$

56. $250\frac{3}{4}$

Basic Skills | Challenge Yourself | Calculator/Computer | **Career Applications** | Above and Beyond

57. Allied Health A dilution contains 3 parts blood serum out of a total of 10 parts. Write this number as a fraction.

58. **ELECTRONICS** Write all the fractional values described in the following paragraph as fractions.

Betsy ordered electronic components from her favorite supplier. She bought two dozen, one-quarter watt resistors, 10 light-emitting diodes (LEDs) that require ten-thirds of a volt (forward voltage) to illuminate, and one, three-eighths henry inductor.

59. **MANUFACTURING TECHNOLOGY** In the packaging division of Early Enterprises, there are 36 packaging machines. At any given time, five of the machines are shut down for scheduled maintenance and service. What is the fraction of machines that are operating at one time?

60. **INFORMATION TECHNOLOGY** On a visit to a wiring closet, Joseph finds a rack of servers that has eight slots. He wants to know what fraction names the two already in the slots. Also, if he buys five more servers, what fraction names the total servers installed in the slots? If he has to remove two servers because of failure, what fraction names the total servers installed in the slots?

Basic Skills | Challenge Yourself | Calculator/Computer | Career Applications | **Above and Beyond**

61. **SOCIAL SCIENCE** The U.S. Census information can be found in your library, or on the Web, at www.census.gov. Use the 2000 census to determine the following:
(a) Fraction of the population of the United States contained in your state
(b) Fraction of the population of the United States 65 years of age or older
(c) Fraction of the United States that is female

62. **SOCIAL SCIENCE** Suppose the national debt had to be paid by individuals.
(a) How would the amount each individual owed be determined?
(b) Would this be a proper or an improper fraction?

Answers

58. ______
59. ______
60. ______
61. ______
62. ______

Answers

1. 6 is the numerator; 11 is the denominator
3. 3 is the numerator; 11 is the denominator
5. $\frac{3}{4}$
7. $\frac{5}{6}$
9. $\frac{5}{5}$
11. $\frac{11}{12}$
13. $\frac{5}{8}$
15. Correct: $\frac{13}{20}$; wrong: $\frac{7}{20}$
17. Sold: $\frac{11}{17}$; not sold: $\frac{6}{17}$
19. $2 \div 5$
21. Proper
23. Mixed number
25. Improper
27. Proper
29. $1\frac{3}{4}$ or $\frac{7}{4}$
31. $3\frac{5}{8}$ or $\frac{29}{8}$
33. \$16
35. $17\frac{1}{2}$ gal
37. $4\frac{2}{5}$
39. $6\frac{4}{5}$
41. $9\frac{1}{8}$
43. 4
45. 9
47. $\frac{14}{3}$
49. $\frac{8}{1}$
51. $\frac{97}{13}$
53. $10\frac{2}{5} = \frac{(5 \times 10) + 2}{5} = \frac{52}{5}$
55. $\frac{475}{4}$
57. $\frac{3}{10}$
59. $\frac{31}{36}$
61. Above and Beyond

2.4 Simplifying Fractions

< 2.4 Objectives >

1 > Determine whether two fractions are equivalent

2 > Use the fundamental principle to simplify fractions

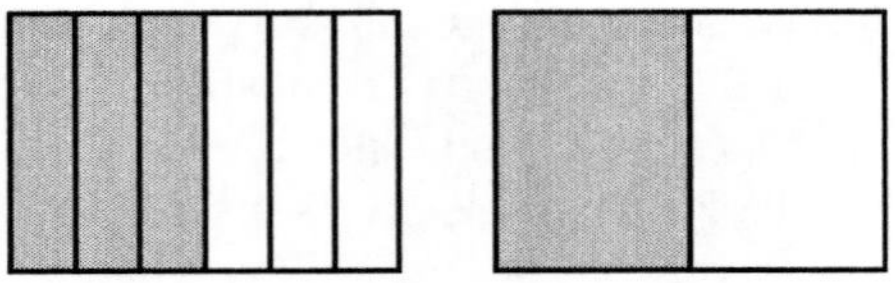

It is possible to represent the same portion of a whole by different fractions. Look at the figure, representing $\frac{3}{6}$ and $\frac{1}{2}$. The two fractions are simply different names for the same amount. They are called **equivalent fractions** for this reason.

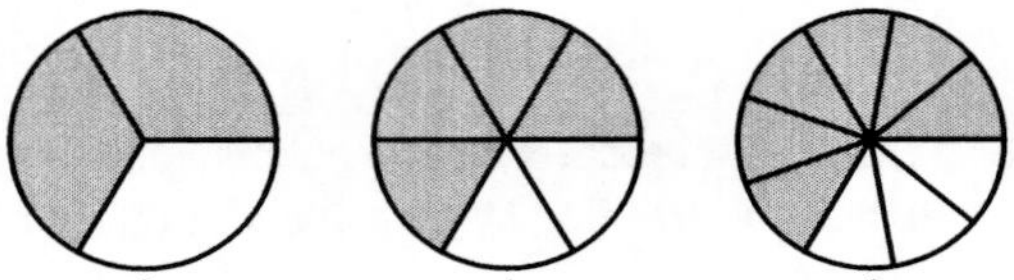

$\frac{2}{3}$ $\frac{4}{6}$ $\frac{6}{9}$

Any fraction has many equivalent fractions. For instance, $\frac{2}{3}, \frac{4}{6},$ and $\frac{6}{9}$ are all equivalent fractions because they name the same part of a unit.

Many more fractions are equivalent to $\frac{2}{3}$. All these fractions can be used interchangeably. An easy way to find out if two fractions are equivalent is to use cross products.

$\frac{a}{b} \quad \frac{c}{d}$

We call $a \times d$ and $b \times c$ the cross products.

Property

Testing for Equivalence If the **cross products** for two fractions are equal, the two fractions are equivalent.

Example 1 Identifying Equivalent Fractions Using Cross Products

< Objective 1 >

(a) Are $\frac{3}{24}$ and $\frac{4}{32}$ equivalent fractions?

The cross products are 3×32, or 96, and 24×4, or 96. Because the cross products are equal, the fractions are equivalent.

(b) Are $\frac{2}{5}$ and $\frac{3}{7}$ equivalent fractions?

The cross products are 2×7 and 5×3.

$2 \times 7 = 14 \qquad \text{and} \qquad 5 \times 3 = 15$

Because $14 \neq 15$, the fractions are *not* equivalent.

Check Yourself 1

(a) Are $\frac{3}{8}$ and $\frac{9}{24}$ equivalent fractions?

(b) Are $\frac{7}{8}$ and $\frac{8}{9}$ equivalent fractions?

In writing equivalent fractions, we use the following important principle.

Property

The Fundamental Principle of Fractions

For the fraction $\frac{a}{b}$ and any nonzero number c,

$$\frac{a}{b} = \frac{a \div c}{b \div c}$$

The Fundamental Principle of Fractions tells us that we can divide the numerator and denominator by the same nonzero number. The result is an equivalent fraction. For instance,

$$\frac{2}{4} = \frac{2 \div 2}{4 \div 2} = \frac{1}{2} \qquad \frac{3}{6} = \frac{3 \div 3}{6 \div 3} = \frac{1}{2} \qquad \frac{4}{8} = \frac{4 \div 4}{8 \div 4} = \frac{1}{2}$$

$$\frac{5}{10} = \frac{5 \div 5}{10 \div 5} = \frac{1}{2} \qquad \frac{6}{12} = \frac{6 \div 6}{12 \div 6} = \frac{1}{2} \qquad \frac{7}{14} = \frac{7 \div 7}{14 \div 7} = \frac{1}{2}$$

Simplifying a fraction or *reducing a fraction to lower terms* means finding an equivalent fraction with a *smaller* numerator and denominator than those of the original fraction. Dividing the numerator and denominator by the same nonzero number does exactly that.

Consider Example 2.

Example 2 Simplifying Fractions

< Objective 2 >

Simplify each fraction.

NOTES

We apply the fundamental principle to divide the numerator and denominator by 5.

We divide the numerator and denominator by 2.

(a) $\frac{5}{15} = \frac{5 \div 5}{15 \div 5} = \frac{1}{3}$

$\frac{5}{15}$ and $\frac{1}{3}$ are equivalent fractions.

Check this by finding the cross products.

(b) $\frac{4}{8} = \frac{4 \div 2}{8 \div 2} = \frac{2}{4}$

$\frac{4}{8}$ and $\frac{2}{4}$ are equivalent fractions.

Check Yourself 2

Write two fractions that are equivalent to $\frac{30}{45}$.

(a) Divide the numerator and denominator by 5.
(b) Divide the numerator and denominator by 15.

We say that a fraction is in **simplest form,** or in **lowest terms,** if the numerator and denominator have no common factors other than 1. This means that the fraction has the smallest possible numerator and denominator.

In Example 2, $\frac{1}{3}$ is in simplest form because the numerator and denominator have no common factors other than 1. The fraction is in lowest terms.

NOTE

In this case, the numerator and denominator are *not* as small as possible. The numerator and denominator have a common factor of 2.

$\frac{2}{4}$ is *not* in simplest form. Do you see that $\frac{2}{4}$ can also be written as $\frac{1}{2}$?

To write a fraction in simplest form or to *reduce a fraction to lowest terms,* divide the numerator and denominator by their greatest common factor (GCF).

Example 3 Simplifying Fractions

Write $\frac{10}{15}$ in simplest form.

From our work earlier in this chapter, we know that the greatest common factor of 10 and 15 is 5. To write $\frac{10}{15}$ in simplest form, divide the numerator and denominator by 5.

$$\frac{10}{15} = \frac{10 \div 5}{15 \div 5} = \frac{2}{3}$$

The resulting fraction, $\frac{2}{3}$, is in lowest terms.

Check Yourself 3

Write $\frac{12}{18}$ in simplest form by dividing the numerator and denominator by the GCF.

Many students prefer to simplify fractions by using the prime factorizations of the numerator and denominator. Example 4 uses this method.

Example 4 Factoring to Simplify a Fraction

(a) Simplify $\frac{24}{42}$.

To simplify $\frac{24}{42}$, factor.

NOTE

From the prime factorization of 24 and 42, we divide by the common factors of 2 and 3.

$$\frac{24}{42} = \frac{\overset{1}{\cancel{2}} \times 2 \times 2 \times \overset{1}{\cancel{3}}}{\underset{1}{\cancel{2}} \times \underset{1}{\cancel{3}} \times 7} = \frac{4}{7}$$

Note: The numerator of the simplified fraction is the *product* of the prime factors remaining in the numerator after the division by 2 and 3.

(b) Simplify $\frac{120}{180}$.

To reduce $\frac{120}{180}$ to lowest terms, write the prime factorizations of the numerator and denominator. Then divide by any common factors.

$$\frac{120}{180} = \frac{\cancel{2} \times \cancel{2} \times 2 \times \cancel{3} \times \cancel{5}}{\cancel{2} \times \cancel{2} \times \cancel{3} \times 3 \times \cancel{5}} = \frac{2}{3}$$

Check Yourself 4

Write each fraction in simplest form.

(a) $\frac{60}{75}$ **(b)** $\frac{210}{252}$

There is another way to organize your work in simplifying fractions. It again uses the fundamental principle to divide the numerator and denominator by any common factors. We illustrate this with the fractions considered in Example 4.

Example 5 Using Common Factors to Simplify Fractions

(a) Simplify $\frac{24}{42}$.

$$\frac{24}{42} = \frac{\overset{12}{\cancel{24}}}{\underset{21}{\cancel{42}}} = \frac{\overset{4}{\cancel{12}}}{\underset{7}{\cancel{21}}} = \frac{4}{7}$$

Divide by the common factor of 2.

Divide by the common factor of 3.

The original numerator and denominator are divisible by 2, and so we divide by that factor to arrive at $\frac{12}{21}$. Our divisibility tests tell us that a common factor of 3 still exists. (Do you remember why?) Divide again for the result $\frac{4}{7}$, which is in lowest terms.

Note: If we had seen the GCF of 6 at first, we could have divided by 6 and arrived at the same result in one step.

(b) Simplify $\frac{120}{180}$.

$$\frac{120}{180} = \frac{\overset{\overset{2}{\cancel{20}}}{\cancel{120}}}{\underset{\underset{3}{\cancel{30}}}{\cancel{180}}} = \frac{2}{3}$$

Our first step is to divide by the common factor of 6. We then have $\frac{20}{30}$. There is still a common factor of 10, so we again divide.

Again, we could have divided by the GCF of 60 in one step if we had recognized it.

Check Yourself 5

Using the method of Example 5, write each fraction in simplest form.

(a) $\frac{60}{75}$ **(b)** $\frac{84}{196}$

Check Yourself ANSWERS

1. **(a)** Yes; **(b)** no **2.** **(a)** $\frac{6}{9}$; **(b)** $\frac{2}{3}$

3. 6 is the GCF of 12 and 18, so $\frac{12}{18} = \frac{12 \div 6}{18 \div 6} = \frac{2}{3}$

4. **(a)** $\frac{60}{75} = \frac{2 \times 2 \times \cancel{3} \times \cancel{5}}{\cancel{3} \times \cancel{5} \times 5} = \frac{4}{5}$; **(b)** $\frac{210}{252} = \frac{\cancel{2} \times \cancel{3} \times 5 \times \cancel{7}}{\cancel{2} \times 2 \times 3 \times \cancel{3} \times \cancel{7}} = \frac{5}{6}$

5. **(a)** Divide by the common factors of 3 and 5, $\frac{60}{75} = \frac{4}{5}$

(b) Divide by the common factors of 4 and 7, $\frac{84}{196} = \frac{3}{7}$

Reading Your Text

The following fill-in-the-blank exercises are designed to ensure that you understand some of the key vocabulary used in this section.

SECTION 2.4

(a) If the _______________ products of two fractions are equal, the two fractions are equivalent.

(b) Two fractions that are simply different names for the same fraction are called _______________ fractions.

(c) In writing equivalent fractions, we use the _______________ Principle of Fractions.

(d) We say that a fraction is in simplest form if the numerator and denominator have no _______________ factors other than 1.

Basic Skills | Challenge Yourself | Calculator/Computer | Career Applications | Above and Beyond

2.4 exercises

Boost *your* GRADE at ALEKS.com!

ALEKS

- Practice Problems
- Self-Tests
- NetTutor
- e-Professors
- Videos

Name ______________

Section ________ Date ________

< Objective 1 >

Are the pairs of fractions equivalent?

1. $\frac{1}{3}, \frac{3}{5}$

2. $\frac{3}{5}, \frac{9}{15}$

3. $\frac{1}{7}, \frac{4}{28}$

4. $\frac{2}{3}, \frac{3}{5}$

5. $\frac{5}{6}, \frac{15}{18}$ > Videos

6. $\frac{3}{4}, \frac{16}{20}$

7. $\frac{2}{21}, \frac{4}{25}$

8. $\frac{20}{24}, \frac{5}{6}$

9. $\frac{2}{7}, \frac{3}{11}$ > Videos

10. $\frac{12}{15}, \frac{36}{45}$

11. $\frac{16}{24}, \frac{40}{60}$

12. $\frac{15}{20}, \frac{20}{25}$

< Objective 2 >

Write each fraction in simplest form.

13. $\frac{15}{30}$

14. $\frac{100}{200}$

15. $\frac{8}{12}$

16. $\frac{12}{15}$

17. $\frac{10}{14}$

18. $\frac{15}{50}$

19. $\frac{12}{18}$ > Videos

20. $\frac{28}{35}$

21. $\frac{35}{40}$

22. $\frac{21}{24}$

23. $\frac{11}{44}$

24. $\frac{10}{25}$

25. $\frac{12}{36}$ > Videos

26. $\frac{18}{48}$

27. $\frac{24}{27}$

28. $\frac{30}{50}$

Answers

1. ________ 2. ________
3. ________ 4. ________
5. ________ 6. ________
7. ________ 8. ________
9. ________ 10. ________
11. ________ 12. ________
13. ________ 14. ________
15. ________ 16. ________
17. ________ 18. ________
19. ________ 20. ________
21. ________ 22. ________
23. ________ 24. ________
25. ________ 26. ________
27. ________ 28. ________

Answers

29. ______

30. ______

31. ______

32. ______

33. ______

34. ______

35. ______

36. ______

37. ______

38. ______

39. ______

40. ______

41. ______

42. ______

43. ______

44. ______

29. $\frac{32}{40}$

30. $\frac{17}{51}$

31. Statistics On a test of 72 questions, Sam answered 54 correctly. On another test, Sam answered 66 correctly out of 88. Did Sam get the same portion of each test correct?

32. Statistics Chipper Jones of the Atlanta Braves had 112 hits in 320 times at bat. Albert Pujols of the St. Louis Cardinals had 91 hits in 260 times at bat. Did they have the same batting average?

Solve each application.

33. Number Problem A quarter is what fractional part of a dollar? Simplify your result. Videos

34. Number Problem A dime is what fractional part of a dollar? Simplify your result.

Basic Skills | **Challenge Yourself** | Calculator/Computer | Career Applications | Above and Beyond

35. Statistics What fractional part of an hour is 15 minutes (min)? Simplify your result. Videos

36. Statistics What fractional part of a day is 6 hours (h)? Simplify your result.

37. Science and Medicine One meter is equal to 100 centimeters (cm). What fractional part of a meter is 70 cm? Simplify your result.

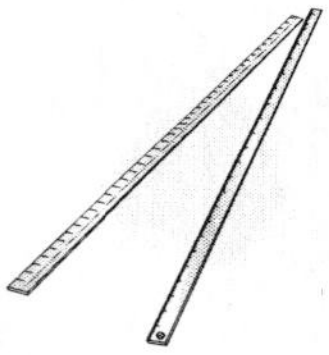

38. Science and Medicine One kilometer is equal to 1,000 meters (m). What fractional part of a kilometer is 300 m? Simplify your result.

39. Technology Susan did a tune-up on her automobile. She found that two of her eight spark plugs were fouled. What fraction represents the number of fouled plugs? Reduce to lowest terms.

40. Statistics Samantha answered 18 of 20 problems correctly on a test. What fractional part did she answer correctly? Reduce your answer to lowest terms.

Write each fraction in simplest form.

41. $\frac{75}{105}$

42. $\frac{62}{93}$

43. $\frac{48}{60}$

44. $\frac{48}{66}$

45. $\frac{105}{135}$ **46.** $\frac{54}{126}$ **47.** $\frac{66}{110}$

48. $\frac{280}{320}$ **49.** $\frac{16}{21}$ **50.** $\frac{21}{32}$

51. $\frac{31}{52}$ **52.** $\frac{42}{55}$ **53.** $\frac{96}{132}$

54. $\frac{33}{121}$ **55.** $\frac{85}{102}$ **56.** $\frac{133}{152}$

Answers

45. ______
46. ______
47. ______
48. ______
49. ______
50. ______
51. ______
52. ______
53. ______
54. ______
55. ______
56. ______

Basic Skills | Challenge Yourself | **Calculator/Computer** | Career Applications | Above and Beyond

Using Your Calculator to Simplify Fractions

If you have a calculator that supports fraction arithmetic, you should learn to use it to check your work. Here we look at two different types of these calculators.

Scientific Calculator

Before doing the following example, find the button on your scientific calculator that is labeled **a b/c**. This is the button that will be used to enter fractions.

Simplify the fraction $\frac{24}{68}$.

There are four steps in simplifying fractions using a scientific calculator.

(a) Enter the numerator, 24.
(b) Press the **a b/c** key.
(c) Enter the denominator, 68.
(d) Press =.

The calculator will display the simplified fraction, $\frac{6}{17}$.

Graphing Calculator

We can simplify the same fraction, $\frac{24}{68}$, using a graphing calculator, such as the TI-84 Plus.

(a) Enter the fraction as a division problem: 24 ÷ 68. The calculator will display $\frac{24}{68}$ as 24/68.
(b) Press the **MATH** key.
(c) Select **1: ▶ Frac**.
(d) Press Enter.

The calculator displays the simplified fraction, $\frac{6}{17}$.

The graphing calculator is particularly useful for simplifying fractions with large values in the numerator and denominator. Some scientific calculators cannot handle denominators larger than 999.

Answers

57. ________

58. ________

59. ________

60. ________

61. ________

62. ________

63. ________

64. ________

65. ________

66. ________

67. ________

68. ________

Use your calculator to simplify each fraction.

57. $\frac{28}{40}$ **58.** $\frac{121}{132}$ **59.** $\frac{96}{144}$

60. $\frac{445}{623}$ **61.** $\frac{299}{391}$ **62.** $\frac{289}{459}$

Basic Skills | Challenge Yourself | Calculator/Computer | **Career Applications** | Above and Beyond

63. Allied Health Pepto-Bismol tablets contain 300 milligrams (mg) of medication; however, children 6 to 8 years of age should only take 200 mg at a time. What fractional part of a tablet should a 6-year-old child be given?

64. Allied Health The recommended adult dose of the laxative docusate is 500 milligrams (mg) per day, and the recommended dose for children 3 to 5 years old is 40 mg per day. The dose for a 4-year-old child is what fractional part of the adult dose?

65. Manufacturing Technology Express the width of the piece shown in the figure as a fraction of the length.

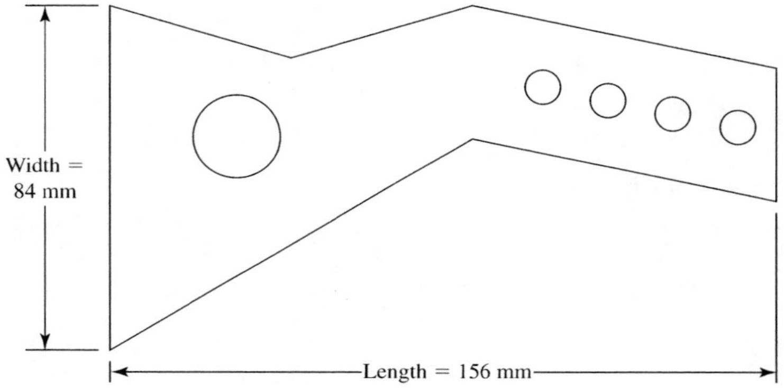

66. Manufacturing Technology In the packaging division of Early Enterprises, there are 36 packaging machines. At any given time, 4 of the machines are shut down for scheduled maintenance and service. What is the fraction of machines that are operating at one time?

67. Information Technology Jo, an executive vice president of information technology, has 10 people on staff, and she needs to hire two more people. What fraction names the new people of the total staff? Simplify your answer.

68. Information Technology Jason is responsible for the administration of the servers at his company. He measures that the average arrival rate of requests to the server is 50,000 requests per second, and he also finds out the servers can service 100,000 requests per second. The intensity of the traffic is measured by x, which is the quotient of the average arrival rate and the service rate. The intensity also shows how busy the servers are. What is the fraction that names this situation? Simplify your answer.

Basic Skills | Challenge Yourself | Calculator/Computer | Career Applications | **Above and Beyond**

69. Can any of the following fractions be simplified?

(a) $\dfrac{824}{73}$ **(b)** $\dfrac{59}{11}$ **(c)** $\dfrac{135}{17}$

What characteristic do you notice about the denominator of each fraction? What rule would you make up based on your observations?

70. Consider the given figures.

(a) Give the fraction that represents the shaded region.

(a)

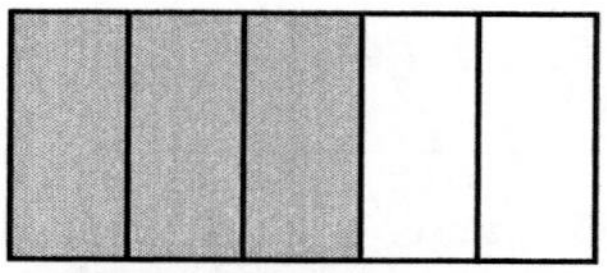

(b) Draw a horizontal line through the figure, as shown. Now give the fraction representing the shaded region.

(b)

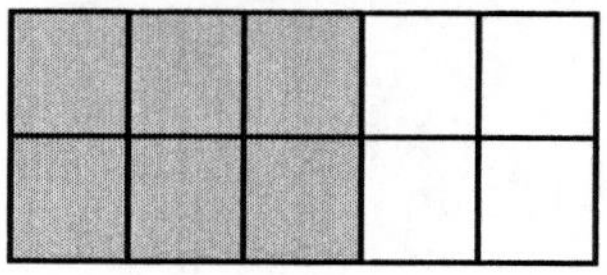

71. Repeat exercise 70, using these figures.

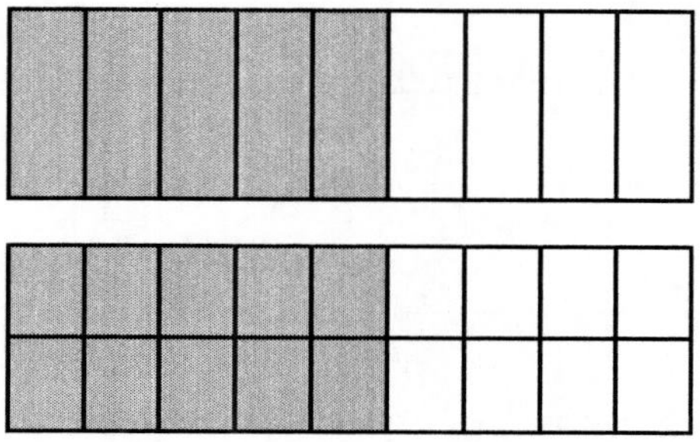

72. A student is attempting to reduce the fraction $\dfrac{8}{12}$ to lowest terms. He produces the following argument:

$$\frac{8}{12} = \frac{4+4}{8+4} = \frac{4}{8} = \frac{1}{2}$$

What is the fallacy in this argument? What is the correct answer?

Answers

69. ______

70. ______

71. ______

72. ______

Answers

1. $1 \times 5 = 5$; $3 \times 3 = 9$. The fractions are not equivalent.
3. Yes 5. Yes 7. No 9. No
11. $16 \times 60 = 960$, and $24 \times 40 = 960$. The fractions are equivalent.

13. $\frac{1}{2}$ 15. $\frac{2}{3}$ 17. $\frac{5}{7}$ 19. $\frac{2}{3}$ 21. $\frac{7}{8}$ 23. $\frac{1}{4}$ 25. $\frac{1}{3}$

27. $\frac{8}{9}$ 29. $\frac{4}{5}$ 31. Yes 33. $\frac{1}{4}$ 35. $\frac{1}{4}$ 37. $\frac{7}{10}$ 39. $\frac{1}{4}$

41. $\frac{5}{7}$ 43. $\frac{4}{5}$ 45. $\frac{7}{9}$ 47. $\frac{3}{5}$ 49. $\frac{16}{21}$ 51. $\frac{31}{52}$ 53. $\frac{8}{11}$

55. $\frac{5}{6}$ 57. $\frac{7}{10}$ 59. $\frac{2}{3}$ 61. $\frac{13}{17}$ 63. $\frac{2}{3}$ 65. $\frac{7}{13}$ 67. $\frac{1}{6}$

69. Above and Beyond 71. (a) $\frac{5}{9}$; (b) $\frac{10}{18}$

Activity 4 ::
Daily Reference Values

According to the Food and Drug Administration (FDA) in 2003, the following table represents the daily reference values (DRV) for each dietary element, based on a 2,000-calorie diet.

	DRV
Total fat	65 grams
Saturated fat	20 grams
Cholesterol	300 milligrams
Sodium	2,400 milligrams
Carbohydrates	300 grams
Dietary fiber	25 grams (minimum)

A high-performance energy bar made by PowerBar has the following amounts of each food type.

	DRV
Total fat	3 grams
Saturated fat	1 gram
Cholesterol	0 milligrams
Sodium	1,000 milligrams
Carbohydrates	45 grams
Dietary fiber	3 grams

Use the tables to answer each of the following questions.

1. What fraction of the DRV for sodium is contained in the PowerBar?
2. What fraction of the DRV for carbohydrates is contained in the PowerBar?
3. What fraction of the DRV for dietary fiber is contained in the PowerBar?
4. What fraction of the DRV for total fat is contained in the PowerBar?
5. What fraction of the DRV for saturated fat is contained in the PowerBar?

2.5 Multiplying Fractions

< 2.5 Objectives >

1 > Multiply two fractions
2 > Multiply mixed numbers and fractions
3 > Simplify before multiplying fractions
4 > Estimate products by rounding
5 > Solve applications involving multiplication of fractions

Multiplication is the easiest of the four operations with fractions. We can illustrate multiplication by picturing fractions as parts of a whole or unit. Using this idea, we show the fractions $\frac{4}{5}$ and $\frac{2}{3}$.

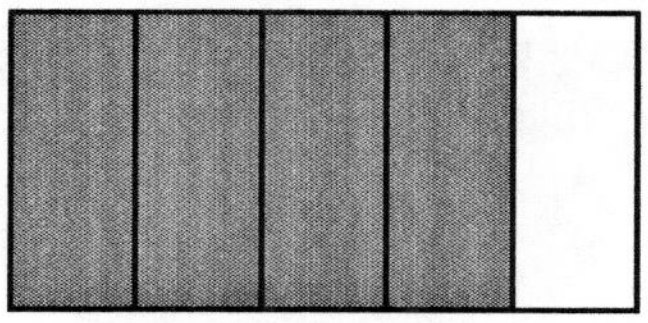

$\frac{4}{5}$

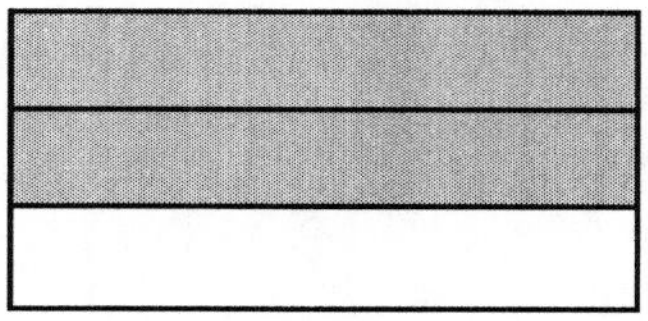

$\frac{2}{3}$

NOTE

A fraction followed by the word *of* means that we want to multiply by that fraction.

Suppose now that we wish to find $\frac{2}{3}$ of $\frac{4}{5}$. We can combine the diagrams as shown below. The part of the whole representing the product $\frac{2}{3} \times \frac{4}{5}$ is the purple region. The unit has been divided into 15 parts, and 8 of those parts are purple, so $\frac{2}{3} \times \frac{4}{5}$ must be $\frac{8}{15}$.

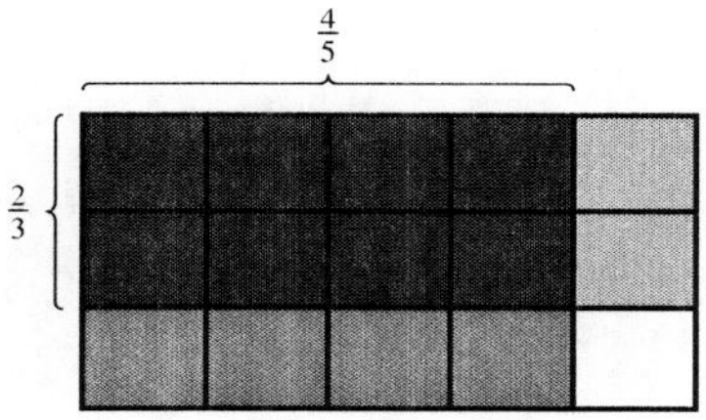

$\frac{2}{3} \times \frac{4}{5} = \frac{8}{15}$

The purple parts represent $\frac{2}{3}$ of the red area, or $\frac{2}{3} \times \frac{4}{5}$.

The following rule is suggested by the diagrams.

Step by Step

To Multiply Fractions

Step 1 Multiply the numerators to find the numerator of the product.
Step 2 Multiply the denominators to find the denominator of the product.
Step 3 Simplify the resulting fraction if possible.

We need only use the first two steps in Example 1.

Example 1 Multiplying Two Fractions

< Objective 1 >

Multiply.

(a) $\frac{2}{3} \times \frac{4}{5} = \frac{2 \times 4}{3 \times 5} = \frac{8}{15}$

(b) $\frac{5}{8} \times \frac{7}{9} = \frac{5 \times 7}{8 \times 9} = \frac{35}{72}$

(c) $\left(\frac{2}{3}\right)^2 = \frac{2}{3} \times \frac{2}{3} = \frac{2 \times 2}{3 \times 3} = \frac{4}{9}$

NOTE

We multiply fractions in this way *not* because it is easy, but because it works!

Check Yourself 1

Multiply.

(a) $\frac{7}{8} \times \frac{3}{10}$ (b) $\frac{5}{7} \times \frac{3}{4}$ (c) $\left(\frac{3}{4}\right)^2$

Step 3 indicates that the product of fractions should always be simplified to lowest terms. Consider the following.

Example 2 Multiplying Two Fractions

Multiply and write the result in lowest terms.

$\frac{3}{4} \times \frac{2}{9} = \frac{3 \times 2}{4 \times 9} = \frac{6}{36} = \frac{1}{6}$

Noting that $\frac{6}{36}$ is not in simplest form, we divide numerator and denominator by 6 to write the product in lowest terms.

Check Yourself 2

Multiply and write the result in lowest terms.

$\frac{5}{7} \times \frac{3}{10}$

To find the product of a fraction and a whole number, write the whole number as a fraction (the whole number divided by 1) and apply the multiplication rule as before. Example 3 illustrates this approach.

Example 3 Multiplying a Whole Number and a Fraction

Do the indicated multiplication.

Remember that $5 = \frac{5}{1}$.

(a) $5 \times \frac{3}{4} = \frac{5}{1} \times \frac{3}{4} = \frac{5 \times 3}{1 \times 4}$

$= \frac{15}{4} = 3\frac{3}{4}$

NOTES

We have written the resulting improper fraction as a mixed number.

Write the product as a mixed number, and then write the fraction part in simplest form.

Alternatively, simplify $\frac{30}{12}$ to $\frac{5}{2}$, and then write this as $2\frac{1}{2}$.

(b) $\frac{5}{12} \times 6 = \frac{5}{12} \times \frac{6}{1}$

$$= \frac{5 \times 6}{12 \times 1}$$

$$= \frac{30}{12} = 2\frac{6}{12}$$

$$= 2\frac{1}{2}$$

Check Yourself 3

Multiply.

(a) $\frac{3}{16} \times 8$ **(b)** $4 \times \frac{5}{7}$

When mixed numbers are involved in multiplication, the problem requires an additional step. First change any mixed numbers to improper fractions. Then apply our multiplication rule for fractions.

Example 4 Multiplying a Mixed Number and a Fraction

< Objective 2 >

$$1\frac{1}{2} \times \frac{3}{4} = \frac{3}{2} \times \frac{3}{4}$$ Change the mixed number to an improper fraction.

Here $1\frac{1}{2} = \frac{3}{2}$.

$$= \frac{3 \times 3}{2 \times 4}$$ Multiply as before.

$$= \frac{9}{8} = 1\frac{1}{8}$$ The product is usually written in mixed-number form.

Check Yourself 4

Multiply.

$\frac{5}{8} \times 3\frac{1}{2}$

If two mixed numbers are involved, change both of the mixed numbers to improper fractions. Example 5 illustrates this.

Example 5 Multiplying Two Mixed Numbers

Multiply.

$$3\frac{2}{3} \times 2\frac{1}{2} = \frac{11}{3} \times \frac{5}{2}$$ Change the mixed numbers to improper fractions.

$$= \frac{11 \times 5}{3 \times 2} = \frac{55}{6} = 9\frac{1}{6}$$

> CAUTION

Be Careful! Students sometimes think of

$$3\frac{2}{3} \times 2\frac{1}{2} \quad \text{as} \quad (3 \times 2) + \left(\frac{2}{3} \times \frac{1}{2}\right)$$

This is *not* the correct multiplication pattern. You must first change the mixed numbers to improper fractions.

Check Yourself 5

Multiply.

$$2\frac{1}{3} \times 3\frac{1}{2}$$

When you multiply fractions, it is usually easier to simplify, that is, remove any common factors in the numerator and denominator, *before multiplying.* Remember that to simplify means to *divide* by the same common factor.

Example 6 Simplifying Before Multiplying Two Fractions

< Objective 3 >

NOTE

Once again we are applying the fundamental principle to divide the numerator and denominator by 3.

Simplify and then multiply.

$$\frac{3}{5} \times \frac{4}{9} = \frac{\overset{1}{\not{3}} \times 4}{5 \times \underset{3}{\not{9}}}$$

To simplify, we divide the *numerator* and *denominator* by the common factor 3. Remember that $\overset{1}{\not{3}}$ means $3 \div 3 = 1$, and $\underset{3}{\not{9}}$ means $9 \div 3 = 3$.

$$= \frac{1 \times 4}{5 \times 3}$$

$$= \frac{4}{15}$$

Because we divide by any common factors before we multiply, the resulting product is *in simplest form.*

Check Yourself 6

Simplify and then multiply.

$$\frac{7}{8} \times \frac{5}{21}$$

Our work in Example 6 leads to the following general rule about simplifying fractions in multiplication.

Property

Simplifying Fractions Before Multiplying

In multiplying two or more fractions, we can divide any factor of the numerator and any factor of the denominator by the same nonzero number to simplify the product.

When mixed numbers are involved, the process is similar. Consider Example 7.

Example 7 Simplifying Before Multiplying Two Mixed Numbers

Multiply.

$$2\frac{2}{3} \times 2\frac{1}{4} = \frac{8}{3} \times \frac{9}{4}$$

First, convert the mixed numbers to improper fractions.

$$= \frac{\overset{2}{\not{8}} \times \overset{3}{\not{9}}}{\underset{1}{\not{3}} \times \underset{1}{\not{4}}}$$

To simplify, divide by the common factors of 3 and 4.

$$= \frac{2 \times 3}{1 \times 1}$$

Multiply as before.

$$= \frac{6}{1} = 6$$

Check Yourself 7

Simplify and then multiply.

$3\frac{1}{3} \times 2\frac{2}{5}$

The ideas of our previous examples also allow us to find the product of more than two fractions.

Example 8 Simplifying Before Multiplying Three Numbers

RECALL

We can divide *any* factor of the numerator and *any* factor of the denominator by the same nonzero number.

Simplify and then multiply.

$\frac{2}{3} \times 1\frac{4}{5} \times \frac{5}{8} = \frac{2}{3} \times \frac{9}{5} \times \frac{5}{8}$ Write any mixed or whole numbers as improper fractions.

$= \frac{\overset{1}{\cancel{2}} \times \overset{3}{\cancel{9}} \times \overset{1}{\cancel{5}}}{\underset{1}{\cancel{3}} \times \underset{1}{\cancel{5}} \times \underset{4}{\cancel{8}}}$ To simplify, divide by the common factors in the numerator and denominator.

$= \frac{3}{4}$

Check Yourself 8

Simplify and then multiply.

$\frac{5}{8} \times 4\frac{4}{5} \times \frac{1}{6}$

We encountered estimation by rounding in our earlier work with whole numbers. Estimation can also be used to check the "reasonableness" of an answer when working with fractions or mixed numbers.

Example 9 Estimating the Product of Two Mixed Numbers

< Objective 4 >

Estimate the product of

$3\frac{1}{8} \times 5\frac{5}{6}$

Round each mixed number to the nearest whole number.

$3\frac{1}{8} \rightarrow 3$

$5\frac{5}{6} \rightarrow 6$

Our estimate of the product is then

$3 \times 6 = 18$

Note: The actual product in this case is $18\frac{11}{48}$, which certainly seems reasonable in view of our estimate.

Check Yourself 9

Estimate the product.

$2\frac{7}{8} \times 8\frac{1}{3}$

Units ANALYSIS

When you divide two denominate numbers, the units are also divided. This yields a unit in fraction form.

EXAMPLES:

$$250 \text{ mi} \div 10 \text{ gal} = \frac{250 \text{ mi}}{10 \text{ gal}} = \frac{25 \text{ mi}}{1 \text{ gal}} = 25 \text{ mi/gal (read "miles per gallon")}$$

$$360 \text{ ft} \div 30 \text{ s} = \frac{360 \text{ ft}}{30 \text{ s}} = 12 \text{ ft/s ("feet per second")}$$

When we multiply denominate numbers that have these units in fraction form, they behave just as fractions do.

EXAMPLES:

$$25 \text{ mi/gal} \times 12 \text{ gal} = \frac{25 \text{ mi}}{1 \cancel{\text{gal}}} \times \frac{12 \cancel{\text{gal}}}{1} = 300 \text{ mi}$$

(If we look at the units, we see that the gallons essentially "cancel" when one is in the numerator and the other in the denominator.)

$$12 \text{ ft/s} \times 60 \text{ s/min} = \frac{12 \text{ ft}}{1 \cancel{\text{s}}} \times \frac{60 \cancel{\text{s}}}{1 \text{ min}} = \frac{720 \text{ ft}}{1 \text{ min}} = 720 \text{ ft/min}$$

(Again, the seconds cancel, leaving feet in the numerator and minutes in the denominator.)

Now we can look at some applications of fractions that involve multiplication. In solving these word problems, we use the same approach we used earlier with whole numbers. Let's review the four-step process introduced in Section 1.2.

Step by Step

Solving Applications Involving the Multiplication of Fractions

Step 1 Read the problem carefully to determine the given information and what you are asked to find.

Step 2 Decide upon the operation or operations to be used.

Step 3 Write down the complete statement necessary to solve the problem and do the calculations.

Step 4 Check to make sure that you have answered the question of the problem and that your answer seems reasonable.

We can work through some examples, using these steps.

Example 10 An Application Involving Multiplication

< Objective 5 >

Lisa worked $10\frac{1}{4}$ hours per day $\left(\frac{\text{h}}{\text{day}}\right)$ for 5 days. How many hours did she work?

Step 1 We are looking for the total hours Lisa worked.

Step 2 We will multiply the hours per day by the days.

Step 3 $10\frac{1}{4}\frac{\text{h}}{\text{day}} \times 5 \text{ days} = \frac{41}{4}\frac{\text{h}}{\text{day}} \times 5 \text{ days} = \frac{205}{4}\text{ h} = 51\frac{1}{4}\text{ h}$

Step 4 Note the days cancel, leaving only the unit of hours. The units should always be compared to the desired units from step 1. The answer also seems reasonable. An answer such as 5 h or 500 h would not seem reasonable.

Check Yourself 10

Carlos gets 30 mi/gal in his Miata. How far should he be able to drive with an 11-gal tank of gas?

In Example 11, we follow the four steps for solving applications, but do not label the steps. You should still think about these steps as we solve the problem.

Example 11 An Application Involving the Multiplication of Mixed Numbers

A sheet of notepaper is $6\frac{3}{4}$ inches (in.) wide and $8\frac{2}{3}$ in. long. Find the area of the paper.

Multiply the given length by the width. This gives the desired area. First, we will estimate the area.

9 in. × 7 in. = 63 in.^{2}

Now, we find the exact area.

RECALL

The area of a rectangle is the product of its length and its width.

$$8\frac{2}{3}\text{ in.} \times 6\frac{3}{4}\text{ in.} = \frac{26}{3}\text{ in.} \times \frac{27}{4}\text{ in.}$$
$$= \frac{117}{2}\text{ in.}^2$$
$$= 58\frac{1}{2}\text{ in.}^2$$

The units (square inches) are units of area. Note that from our estimate the result is reasonable.

Check Yourself 11

A window is $4\frac{1}{2}$ feet (ft) high by $2\frac{1}{3}$ ft wide. What is its area?

Example 12 reminds us that an abstract number multiplied by a denominate number yields the units of the denominate number.

Example 12 An Application Involving the Multiplication of a Mixed Number and a Fraction

A state park contains $38\frac{2}{3}$ acres. According to the plan for the park, $\frac{3}{4}$ of the park is to be left as a wildlife preserve. How many acres is this?

We want to find $\frac{3}{4}$ of $38\frac{2}{3}$ acres. We then multiply as shown:

RECALL

The word *of* usually indicates multiplication.

$$\frac{3}{4} \times 38\frac{2}{3} = \frac{3}{4} \times \frac{116}{3} = \frac{\overset{1}{\cancel{3}} \times \overset{29}{\cancel{116}}}{\underset{1}{\cancel{4}} \times \underset{1}{\cancel{3}}}\text{ acres} = 29\text{ acres}$$

Check Yourself 12

A backyard has $25\frac{3}{4}$ square yards (yd^2) of open space. If Patrick wants to build a vegetable garden covering $\frac{2}{3}$ of the open space, how many square yards is this?

We have mentioned the word *of* usually indicates multiplication. You should also note that it indicates that the fraction preceding it is an abstract number (it has no units attached). There are even occasions, as in Example 13, when we are looking at the product of two abstract numbers.

Example 13 An Application Involving the Multiplication of Fractions

A grocery store survey shows that $\frac{2}{3}$ of the customers buy meat. Of these, $\frac{3}{4}$ will buy at least one package of beef. What portion of the store's customers buy beef?

Step 1 We know that $\frac{2}{3}$ of the customers buy meat and that $\frac{3}{4}$ of these customers buy beef.

Step 2 We wish to know $\frac{3}{4}$ of $\frac{2}{3}$. The operation here is multiplication.

NOTE

In this problem, *of* means to multiply.

Step 3 Multiplying, we have

$$\frac{3}{4} \times \frac{2}{3} = \frac{\overset{1}{\cancel{3}} \times \overset{1}{\cancel{2}}}{\underset{2}{\cancel{4}} \times \underset{1}{\cancel{3}}} = \frac{1}{2}$$

Step 4 From step 3 we have the result: $\frac{1}{2}$ of the store's customers buy beef.

Check Yourself 13

A supermarket survey shows that $\frac{2}{5}$ of the customers buy lunch meat. Of these, $\frac{3}{4}$ buy boiled ham. What portion of the store's customers buy boiled ham?

Example 14 An Application Involving the Multiplication of Mixed Numbers

Shirley drives at an average speed of 52 miles per hour (mi/h) for $3\frac{1}{4}$ h. How far has she traveled at the end of $3\frac{1}{4}$ h?

NOTE

Distance is the product of speed and time.

$$\underset{\text{Speed}}{52\,\frac{\text{mi}}{\text{h}}} \times \underset{\text{Time}}{3\frac{1}{4}\,\text{h}} = \frac{52}{1}\,\frac{\text{mi}}{\cancel{\text{h}}} \times \frac{13}{4}\,\cancel{\text{h}}$$

$$= \frac{\overset{13}{\cancel{52}} \times 13}{1 \times \underset{1}{\cancel{4}}}\,\text{mi}$$

$$= 169\text{ mi}$$

Check Yourself 14

(a) The scale on a map is 1 inch (in.) = 60 miles (mi). What is the distance in miles between two towns that are $3\frac{1}{2}$ in. apart on the map?

(b) Maria is ordering concrete for a new sidewalk that is to be $\frac{1}{9}$ yd thick, $22\frac{1}{2}$ yd long, and $1\frac{1}{3}$ yd wide. How much concrete should she order if she must order a whole number of cubic yards?

Check Yourself ANSWERS

1. **(a)** $\frac{7}{8} \times \frac{3}{10} = \frac{7 \times 3}{8 \times 10} = \frac{21}{80}$; **(b)** $\frac{5}{7} \times \frac{3}{4} = \frac{5 \times 3}{7 \times 4} = \frac{15}{28}$; **(c)** $\frac{9}{16}$

2. $\frac{5}{7} \times \frac{3}{10} = \frac{5 \times 3}{7 \times 10} = \frac{15}{70} = \frac{3}{14}$ **3.** **(a)** $1\frac{1}{2}$; **(b)** $2\frac{6}{7}$

4. $\frac{5}{8} \times 3\frac{1}{2} = \frac{5}{8} \times \frac{7}{2} = \frac{35}{16} = 2\frac{3}{16}$ **5.** $8\frac{1}{6}$

6. $\frac{7}{8} \times \frac{5}{21} = \frac{\overset{1}{\cancel{7}} \times 5}{8 \times \underset{3}{\cancel{21}}} = \frac{5}{24}$

7. $3\frac{1}{3} \times 2\frac{2}{5} = \frac{10}{3} \times \frac{12}{5} = \frac{\overset{2}{\cancel{10}} \times \overset{4}{\cancel{12}}}{\underset{1}{\cancel{3}} \times \underset{1}{\cancel{5}}} = \frac{8}{1} = 8$ **8.** $\frac{1}{2}$ **9.** 24

10. 330 mi **11.** $10\frac{1}{2}$ ft^2 **12.** $17\frac{1}{6}$ yd^2 **13.** $\frac{3}{10}$

14. **(a)** 210 mi; **(b)** the answer, $3\frac{1}{3}$ yd^3, is rounded up to 4 yd^3.

Reading Your Text

The following fill-in-the-blank exercises are designed to ensure that you understand some of the key vocabulary used in this section.

SECTION 2.5

(a) The product of fractions should always be expressed in ____________ terms.

(b) When multiplying fractions, it is usually easier to ____________ before multiplying.

(c) Estimation can be used to check the ______________ of an answer when working with fractions or mixed numbers.

(d) The final step in solving an application is to make sure that your answer seems ______________.

2.5 exercises

Basic Skills | Challenge Yourself | Calculator/Computer | Career Applications | Above and Beyond

Boost *your* GRADE at ALEKS.com!

ALEKS

- Practice Problems
- Self-Tests
- NetTutor
- e-Professors
- Videos

Name ____________________

Section __________ Date __________

Answers

1.	2.
3.	4.
5.	6.
7.	8.
9.	10.
11.	12.
13.	14.
15.	16.
17.	18.
19.	20.
21.	22.
23.	24.
25.	26.
27.	28.
29.	30.

< Objective 1 >

Multiply. Be sure to write each answer in simplest form.

1. $\frac{3}{4} \times \frac{5}{11}$

2. $\frac{2}{7} \times \frac{5}{9}$

3. $\frac{3}{4} \times \frac{7}{11}$ > Videos

4. $\frac{2}{5} \times \frac{3}{7}$

5. $\frac{3}{5} \cdot \frac{5}{7}$

6. $\frac{6}{11} \cdot \frac{8}{6}$

7. $\left(\frac{4}{9}\right)^2$

8. $\left(\frac{5}{6}\right)^2$

9. $\frac{3}{11} \cdot \frac{7}{9}$

10. $\frac{7}{9} \cdot \frac{3}{5}$

11. $\frac{3}{10} \times \frac{5}{9}$

12. $\frac{5}{21} \times \frac{14}{25}$

13. $\frac{7}{9} \cdot \frac{6}{5}$

14. $\frac{48}{63} \cdot \frac{81}{60}$

15. $\frac{24}{33} \cdot \frac{55}{40}$ > Videos

< Objectives 2–3 >

16. $3\frac{1}{3} \times \frac{9}{11}$

17. $\left(\frac{2}{3}\right)\left(2\frac{2}{5}\right)$ > Videos

18. $\left(3\frac{1}{3}\right)\left(\frac{3}{7}\right)$

19. $\frac{2}{5} \times 3\frac{1}{4}$

20. $2\frac{1}{3} \times 2\frac{1}{6}$

21. $2\frac{1}{3} \cdot 2\frac{1}{2}$

22. $\frac{3}{7} \cdot 14$

23. $\left(\frac{5}{6}\right)^3$ > Videos

24. $\left(\frac{4}{5}\right)^3$

25. $\frac{12}{25} \times \frac{11}{18}$

26. $\frac{10}{12} \times \frac{16}{25}$

27. $\frac{14}{15} \cdot \frac{10}{21}$

28. $\frac{21}{25} \cdot \frac{30}{7}$

29. $\left(\frac{18}{28}\right)\left(\frac{35}{22}\right)$

30. $\left(3\frac{2}{3}\right)\left(\frac{9}{10}\right)$

Basic Skills | **Challenge Yourself** | Calculator/Computer | Career Applications | Above and Beyond

< Objective 5 >

Evaluate. Be sure to use the proper units.

31. 36 mi/h × 4 h

32. 80 cal/g × 5 g

33. 55 joules/s × 11 s

34. 5 lb/ft × 3 ft

35. 88 ft/s × 1 mi/5,280 ft × 3,600 s/h

36. 24 h/day × 3,600 s/h × 365 days/yr

Solve each application.

37. Business and Finance Maria earns $11 per hour. Last week, she worked 9 hours/day for 6 days. What was her gross pay?

38. Statistics The gas tank in Luigi's Toyota Camry holds 17 gal when full. The car gets 21 mi/gal. How far can he travel on 3 full tanks?

39. Crafts A recipe calls for $\frac{2}{3}$ cup of sugar for each serving. How much sugar is needed for 6 servings? chapter 2 > Make the Connection

40. Crafts Mom-Mom's French toast requires $\frac{3}{4}$ cup of batter for each serving. If 5 people are expected for breakfast, how much batter is needed? chapter 2 > Make the Connection

Multiply and simplify.

41. $\frac{4}{9} \times 3\frac{3}{5}$

42. $5\frac{1}{3} \times \frac{7}{8}$

43. $\frac{10}{27} \times 3\frac{3}{5}$

44. $1\frac{1}{3} \times 1\frac{1}{5}$

45. $2\frac{2}{5} \cdot 3\frac{3}{4}$

46. $2\frac{2}{7} \cdot 2\frac{1}{3}$

47. $4\frac{1}{5} \times \frac{10}{21} \times \frac{9}{20}$ > Videos

48. $\frac{7}{8} \times 5\frac{1}{3} \times \frac{5}{14}$

49. $3\frac{1}{3} \cdot \frac{4}{5} \cdot 1\frac{1}{8}$

50. $4\frac{1}{2} \cdot 5\frac{5}{6} \cdot \frac{8}{15}$

51. Find $\frac{2}{3}$ of $\frac{3}{7}$.

52. What is $\frac{5}{6}$ of $\frac{9}{10}$?

< Objective 4 >

Estimate each product.

53. $3\frac{1}{5} \times 4\frac{2}{3}$

54. $5\frac{1}{7} \times 2\frac{2}{13}$

55. $11\frac{3}{4} \times 5\frac{1}{4}$

Answers

31. ______ 32. ______
33. ______ 34. ______
35. ______
36. ______
37. ______ 38. ______
39. ______ 40. ______
41. ______ 42. ______
43. ______ 44. ______
45. ______ 46. ______
47. ______ 48. ______
49. ______ 50. ______
51. ______ 52. ______
53. ______ 54. ______
55. ______

$$56.\ 3\frac{4}{5} \times 5\frac{6}{7} \qquad 57.\ 8\frac{2}{9} \cdot 7\frac{11}{12} \qquad 58.\ \frac{9}{10} \cdot 2\frac{2}{7}$$

< Objective 5 >

59. **Science and Medicine** A jet flew at an average speed of 540 mi/h on a $4\frac{2}{3}$-h flight. What was the distance flown?

60. **Construction** A piece of land that has $11\frac{2}{3}$ acres is being subdivided for home lots. It is estimated that $\frac{2}{7}$ of the area will be used for roads. What amount remains to be used for lots?

61. **Geometry** Find the volume of a box that measures $2\frac{1}{4}$ in. by $3\frac{7}{8}$ in. by $4\frac{5}{6}$ in.

62. **Construction** Nico wishes to purchase mulch to cover his garden. The garden measures $7\frac{7}{8}$ ft by $10\frac{1}{8}$ ft. He wants the mulch to be $\frac{1}{3}$ ft deep. How much mulch should Nico order if he must order a whole number of cubic feet?

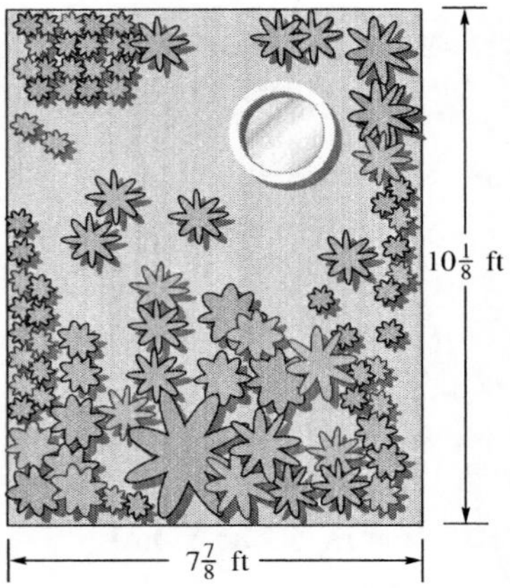

Basic Skills | Challenge Yourself | **Calculator/Computer** | Career Applications | Above and Beyond

Using Your Calculator to Multiply Fractions

Scientific Calculator

To multiply fractions on a scientific calculator, you enter the first fraction, using the [a b/c] key, then press the multiplication sign, next enter the second fraction, and then press the equal sign. It is always a good idea to separate the fractions by using parentheses. Note that we do that in the example below.

Graphing Calculator

When using a graphing calculator, you must choose the fraction option [1:► Frac] from the [MATH] menu before pressing [Enter].

For the fraction problem $\frac{7}{15} \times \frac{5}{21}$, the keystroke sequence is

[(] 7 [÷] 15 [)] [×] [(] 5 [÷] 21 [)] [1:► Frac] [Enter]

The result is $\frac{1}{9}$.

Find each product, using your calculator.

$$63.\ \frac{7}{12} \times \frac{36}{63} \qquad 64.\ \frac{8}{27} \times \frac{45}{64} \qquad 65.\ \frac{12}{45} \times \frac{27}{72}$$

Answers

56. ____
57. ____
58. ____
59. ____
60. ____
61. ____
62. ____
63. ____
64. ____
65. ____

66. $\frac{18}{132} \times \frac{36}{63}$

67. $\frac{27}{72} \cdot \frac{24}{45}$

68. $\frac{81}{136} \cdot \frac{84}{135}$

Basic Skills | Challenge Yourself | Calculator/Computer | **Career Applications** | Above and Beyond

69. **Manufacturing Technology** Calculate the distance from the center of hole A to the center of hole B.

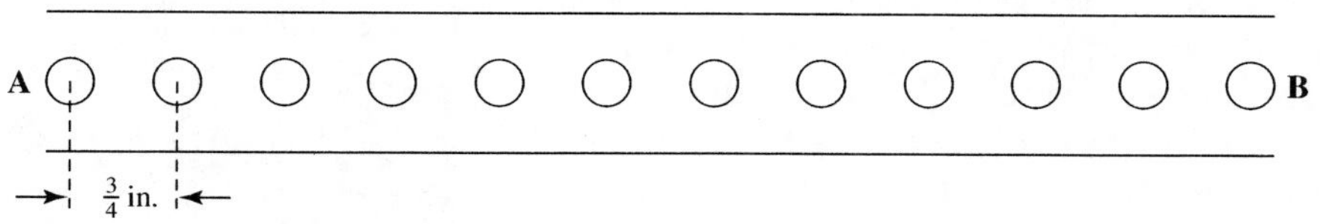

70. **Manufacturing Technology** A cut $3\frac{3}{8}$ in. long needs to be made in a piece of material. The cut rate is $\frac{3}{4}$ minute per in. How many minutes does it take to make the cut?

71. **Manufacturing Technology** A custom order requires $14\frac{3}{4}$ ounces of material that costs $7\frac{1}{2}$¢ per ounce. Find the total cost of the material.

72. **Manufacturing Technology** A customer order requires $8\frac{5}{8}$ ounces of material that costs $10\frac{1}{2}$¢ per ounce. Find the total cost of the material.

Answers

66. ______

67. ______

68. ______

69. ______

70. ______

71. ______

72. ______

Answers

1. $\frac{15}{44}$ 3. $\frac{3}{4} \times \frac{7}{11} = \frac{21}{44}$ 5. $\frac{3}{7}$ 7. $\frac{16}{81}$ 9. $\frac{7}{33}$ 11. $\frac{3}{10} \times \frac{5}{9} = \frac{15}{90} = \frac{1}{6}$ 13. $\frac{14}{15}$ 15. 1 17. $1\frac{3}{5}$ 19. $1\frac{3}{10}$ 21. $5\frac{5}{6}$ 23. $\frac{125}{216}$ 25. $\frac{22}{75}$ 27. $\frac{4}{9}$ 29. $1\frac{1}{44}$ 31. 144 mi 33. 605 joules 35. 60 mi/h 37. $594 39. 4 cups 41. $1\frac{3}{5}$ 43. $1\frac{1}{3}$ 45. 9 47. $\frac{9}{10}$ 49. 3 51. $\frac{2}{7}$ 53. 15 55. 60 57. 64 59. 2,520 mi 61. $42\frac{9}{64}$ in.^{3} 63. $\frac{1}{3}$ 65. $\frac{1}{10}$ 67. $\frac{1}{5}$ 69. $8\frac{1}{4}$ in. 71. $110\frac{5}{8}$¢ or $1.11

Activity 5 :: Overriding a Presidential Veto

Read the following article and use the information you find there to answer the questions that follow.

A bill is sent to the President of the United States when it has passed both houses of Congress. A majority vote in both the House of Representatives (218 of 435 members) and the Senate (51 of 100 members) is needed for the bill to be passed on to the President. The majority vote is a majority of the members present, as long as more than one-half of all the members are present. More than one-half of the members makes up what is called a quorum.

Once the bill comes to him, the President may either sign the bill, making it a law, or he can veto the bill. His veto sends the bill back to Congress.

Congress can still make the bill a law by overriding the Presidential veto. To override the veto, $\frac{2}{3}$ of the members of each legislative body must vote to override it. Again, this is $\frac{2}{3}$ of a quorum of members.

1. Assume that 420 members of the House are available to vote. How many votes are necessary to make up a majority, which is anything over $\frac{1}{2}$?

2. If 90 members of the Senate are available to vote, how many votes would constitute a majority?

3. How many votes from a group of 420 members of the House would be necessary to overturn a veto?

4. How many votes from a group of 90 members of the Senate would be necessary to overturn a veto?

2.6 Dividing Fractions

< 2.6 Objectives >

1 > Find the reciprocal of a fraction
2 > Divide fractions
3 > Divide mixed numbers
4 > Solve applications involving division of fractions

We are now ready to look at the operation of division on fractions. First we need a new concept, the **reciprocal** of a fraction.

Property

The Reciprocal of a Fraction

We invert, or turn over, a fraction to write its **reciprocal.**

Example 1 Finding the Reciprocal of a Fraction

< Objective 1 >

Find the reciprocal of **(a)** $\frac{3}{4}$, **(b)** 5, and **(c)** $1\frac{2}{3}$.

NOTE

In general, the reciprocal of the fraction $\frac{a}{b}$ is $\frac{b}{a}$. Neither a nor b can be 0.

(a) The reciprocal of $\frac{3}{4}$ is $\frac{4}{3}$.

Just invert, or turn over, the fraction.

(b) The reciprocal of 5, or $\frac{5}{1}$, is $\frac{1}{5}$.

Write 5 as $\frac{5}{1}$ and then turn over the fraction.

(c) The reciprocal of $1\frac{2}{3}$, or $\frac{5}{3}$, is $\frac{3}{5}$.

Write $1\frac{2}{3}$ as $\frac{5}{3}$ and then invert.

Check Yourself 1

Find the reciprocal of (a) $\frac{5}{8}$ and (b) $3\frac{1}{4}$.

An important property relating a number and its reciprocal follows.

Property

Reciprocal Products

The product of any number and its reciprocal is 1. (Every number except zero has a reciprocal.)

We are now ready to use the reciprocal to find a rule for dividing fractions. Recall that we can represent the operation of division in several ways. We used the symbol ÷ earlier. Remember that a fraction also indicates division. For instance,

NOTE

$3 \div 5$ and $\frac{3}{5}$ both mean "3 divided by 5."

$$3 \div 5 = \frac{3}{5}$$

In this statement, 5 is called the *divisor*. It follows the division sign ÷ and is written *below* the fraction bar.

Using this information, we can write a statement involving fractions and division as a *complex fraction,* which has a fraction as both its numerator and its denominator, as Example 2 illustrates.

Example 2 Writing a Quotient as a Complex Fraction

Write $\frac{2}{3} \div \frac{4}{5}$ as a complex fraction.

$$\frac{\frac{2}{3}}{\frac{4}{5}}$$

The numerator is $\frac{2}{3}$.

A *complex fraction* is written by placing the dividend in the numerator and the divisor in the denominator.

The denominator is $\frac{4}{5}$.

Check Yourself 2

Write $\frac{2}{5} \div \frac{3}{4}$ as a complex fraction.

Let's continue with the same division problem you looked at in Check Yourself 2.

Example 3 Rewriting a Division Problem

$$\textbf{(I)}\quad \frac{2}{5} \div \frac{3}{4} = \frac{\frac{2}{5}}{\frac{3}{4}}$$

Write the original quotient as a complex fraction.

$$= \frac{\frac{2}{5} \times \frac{4}{3}}{\frac{3}{4} \times \frac{4}{3}}$$

Multiply the numerator and denominator by $\frac{4}{3}$, the reciprocal of the denominator. This does *not* change the value of the fraction.

$$= \frac{\frac{2}{5} \times \frac{4}{3}}{1}$$

The denominator becomes 1.

$$\textbf{(II)}\quad = \frac{2}{5} \times \frac{4}{3}$$

Recall that a number divided by 1 is just that number.

We see from **(I)** and **(II)** that

$$\frac{2}{5} \div \frac{3}{4} = \frac{2}{5} \times \frac{4}{3}$$

NOTE

Do you see a rule suggested?

We would certainly like to be able to divide fractions easily without all the work of this example. Look carefully at the calculations. The following rule is suggested.

Property

To Divide Fractions

To divide one fraction by another, invert the divisor (the fraction after the division sign) and multiply.

Check Yourself 3

Write $\frac{3}{5} \div \frac{7}{8}$ as a multiplication problem.

Example 4 applies the rule for dividing fractions.

Example 4 Dividing Two Fractions

< Objective 2 >

RECALL

The number inverted is the divisor. It *follows* the division sign.

Divide.

(a) $\dfrac{\frac{1}{3}}{\frac{4}{7}}$

$$\dfrac{\frac{1}{3}}{\frac{4}{7}} = \frac{1}{3} \div \frac{4}{7} = \frac{1}{3} \times \frac{7}{4}$$ We invert the divisor, $\frac{4}{7}$, and then multiply.

$$= \frac{1 \times 7}{3 \times 4} = \frac{7}{12}$$

(b) $\dfrac{\frac{3}{4}}{6}$

$$\dfrac{\frac{3}{4}}{6} = \frac{3}{4} \div 6 = \frac{\overset{1}{\cancel{3}}}{4} \times \frac{1}{\underset{2}{\cancel{6}}}$$

$$= \frac{1}{8}$$

Check Yourself 4

Divide.

(a) $\dfrac{\frac{2}{5}}{\frac{3}{4}}$ (b) $\dfrac{\frac{2}{7}}{4}$

Here is a similar example.

Example 5 Dividing Two Fractions

Divide.

$$\frac{5}{8} \div \frac{3}{5} = \frac{5}{8} \times \frac{5}{3} = \frac{5 \times 5}{8 \times 3}$$

$$= \frac{25}{24} = 1\frac{1}{24}$$

Check Yourself 5

Divide.

$\frac{5}{6} \div \frac{3}{7}$

Simplifying will also be useful in dividing fractions. Consider Example 6.

Example 6 Dividing Two Fractions

> CAUTION

NOTE

Be careful! We must invert the divisor *before simplifying.*

Divide.

$$\frac{3}{5} \div \frac{6}{7} = \frac{3}{5} \times \frac{7}{6}$$

Invert the divisor *first!* Then you can divide by the common factor of 3.

$$= \frac{\overset{1}{\cancel{3}} \times 7}{5 \times \underset{2}{\cancel{6}}} = \frac{7}{10}$$

Check Yourself 6

Divide.

$$\frac{4}{9} \div \frac{8}{15}$$

When mixed or whole numbers are involved, the process is similar. Simply change the mixed or whole numbers to improper fractions as the first step. Then proceed with the division rule. Example 7 illustrates this approach.

Example 7 Dividing Two Mixed Numbers

< Objective 3 >

Divide.

$$2\frac{3}{8} \div 1\frac{3}{4} = \frac{19}{8} \div \frac{7}{4}$$

Write the mixed numbers as improper fractions.

$$\frac{19}{8} \times \frac{4}{7} = \frac{19 \times \overset{1}{\cancel{4}}}{\underset{2}{\cancel{8}} \times 7}$$

Invert the divisor and multiply as before.

$$= \frac{19}{14} = 1\frac{5}{14}$$

Check Yourself 7

Divide.

$$3\frac{1}{5} \div 2\frac{2}{5}$$

Example 8 illustrates the division process when a whole number is involved.

Example 8 Dividing a Mixed Number and a Whole Number

NOTE

Write the whole number 6 as $\frac{6}{1}$.

Divide and simplify.

$$1\frac{4}{5} \div 6 = \frac{9}{5} \div \frac{6}{1}$$

$$\frac{9}{5} \times \frac{1}{6} = \frac{\overset{3}{\cancel{9}} \times 1}{5 \times \underset{2}{\cancel{6}}}$$

Invert the divisor, and then divide by the common factor of 3.

$$= \frac{3}{10}$$

Check Yourself 8

Divide.

$$8 \div 4\frac{4}{5}$$

Units ANALYSIS

When dividing by denominate numbers that have fractional units, we multiply by the reciprocal of the number *and its units.*

EXAMPLES:

$$500 \text{ mi} \div \frac{25 \text{ mi}}{1 \text{ gal}} = \frac{500 \text{ mi}}{1} \times \frac{1 \text{ gal}}{25 \text{ mi}} = 20 \text{ gal}$$

$$\$24{,}000 \div \frac{\$400}{1 \text{ yr}} = \frac{24{,}000 \text{ dol}}{1} \div \frac{400 \text{ dol}}{1 \text{ yr}} = \frac{24{,}000 \cancel{\text{dol}}}{1} \times \frac{1 \text{ yr}}{400 \cancel{\text{dol}}} = 60 \text{ yr}$$

(As always, note that in each case, the arithmetic of the units produces the final units.)

As was the case with multiplication, dividing fractions can be used in the solution of a variety of applications. The steps of the problem-solving process remain the same.

Example 9 An Application Involving the Division of Mixed Numbers

< Objective 4 >

NOTES

One kilometer, abbreviated km, is a metric unit of distance. It is about $\frac{6}{10}$ mi.

The important formula is Speed = distance ÷ time.

Jack traveled 140 kilometers (km) in $2\frac{1}{3}$ hours (h). What was his average speed?

Distance ↓ Time ↓

$$\text{Speed} = 140 \text{ km} \div 2\frac{1}{3} \text{ h}$$

$$= \frac{140}{1} \text{ km} \div \frac{7}{3} \text{ h}$$

We know the distance traveled and the time for that travel. To find the *average* speed, we must use division. Do you remember why?

$$\frac{140}{1} \times \frac{3}{7} = \frac{\overset{20}{\cancel{140}} \times 3}{1 \times \underset{1}{\cancel{7}}} \frac{\text{km}}{\text{h}}$$

$$= 60 \text{ km/h}$$

$\frac{\text{km}}{\text{h}}$ is read "kilometers per hour." This is a unit of speed.

Check Yourself 9

A light plane flew 280 mi in $1\frac{3}{4}$ h. What was its average speed?

Example 10 An Application Involving the Division of Mixed Numbers

NOTE

We must divide the length of the longer piece by the desired length of the shorter piece.

An electrician needs pieces of wire $2\frac{3}{5}$ in. long. If she has a $20\frac{4}{5}$-in. piece of wire, how many of the shorter pieces can she cut?

$$20\frac{4}{5} \text{ in.} \div 2\frac{3}{5} \frac{\text{in.}}{\text{piece}} = \frac{104}{5} \text{ in.} \div \frac{13}{5} \frac{\text{in.}}{\text{piece}}$$

$$\frac{104}{5} \text{ in.} \times \frac{5}{13} \frac{\text{pieces}}{\text{in.}} = \frac{\overset{8}{\cancel{104}} \times \overset{1}{\cancel{5}}}{\underset{1}{\cancel{5}} \times \underset{1}{\cancel{13}}} \text{ pieces}$$

$$= 8 \text{ pieces}$$

Check Yourself 10

A piece of plastic water pipe 63 in. long is to be cut into lengths of $3\frac{1}{2}$ in. How many of the shorter pieces can be cut?

Units ANALYSIS

When you convert units, it is important, and helpful, to carry out all unit arithmetic.

EXAMPLES:

Convert $1\frac{1}{2}$ years into minutes.

To accomplish this, we must recall that there are $365\ \frac{\text{days}}{\text{yr}}$, $24\ \frac{\text{h}}{\text{day}}$, and $60\ \frac{\text{min}}{\text{h}}$. This allows us to set up the following expression.

$$1\frac{1}{2}\ \text{yr} \times 365\ \frac{\text{days}}{\text{yr}} \times 24\ \frac{\text{h}}{\text{day}} \times 60\ \frac{\text{min}}{\text{h}}$$

Before we work with the numbers, we should check the units to make certain that our result will be in "min(utes)."

Because the years, days, and hours all cancel, we are left with only minutes, so we can go ahead with the computation.

$$\frac{3}{2}\ \text{yr} \times 365\ \frac{\text{days}}{\text{yr}} \times 24\ \frac{\text{h}}{\text{day}} \times 60\ \frac{\text{min}}{\text{h}} = 788{,}400\ \text{min}$$

There are 788,400 min in $1\frac{1}{2}$ yr.

Some applications require both multiplication and division. Example 11 is such an application.

Example 11 An Application Involving the Division of Mixed Numbers

A parcel of land that is $2\frac{1}{2}$ mi long and $1\frac{1}{3}$ mi wide is to be divided into tracts that are each $\frac{1}{3}$ square mile (mi^2). How many of these tracts will the parcel make?

The area of the parcel is its length times its width:

$$\begin{aligned}\text{Area} &= 2\frac{1}{2}\ \text{mi} \times 1\frac{1}{3}\ \text{mi}\\ &= \frac{5}{2}\ \text{mi} \times \frac{4}{3}\ \text{mi}\\ &= \frac{10}{3}\ \text{mi}^2\end{aligned}$$

We need to divide the total area of the parcel into $\frac{1}{3}$-mi² tracts.

$$\frac{10}{3}\text{ mi}^2 \div \frac{1}{3}\text{ mi}^2 = \frac{10}{3}\text{ mi}^2 \times \frac{3}{1\text{ mi}^2} = 10$$

The land will provide 10 tracts, each with an area of $\frac{1}{3}$ mi².

Check Yourself 11

A parcel of land that is $3\frac{1}{3}$ mi long and $2\frac{1}{2}$ mi wide is to be divided into $\frac{1}{3}$-mi² tracts. How many of these tracts will the parcel make?

In our final example, we look at a case in which the divisor has fractional units.

Example 12 An Application Involving Mixed Numbers

NOTE

We are using the gardener/contractor definition of a "yard" of mulch. It is actually 1 yd × 1 yd × 1 yd, *or* 1 yd³.

Jackson has $6\frac{1}{2}$ yards of mulch. His garden needs $\frac{2}{3}$ yards per row. How many rows can he cover with the mulch?

We have $6\frac{1}{2}$ yards and $\frac{2}{3}\frac{\text{yards}}{\text{row}}$. Even if you don't immediately see how to solve the problem, units analysis can help. The units of the answer will be "rows." To get there, we need to have the yards units cancel. That will happen if we divide $6\frac{1}{2}$ by $\frac{2}{3}$!

$$6\frac{1}{2}\text{ yards} \div \frac{2}{3}\frac{\text{yards}}{\text{row}} = \frac{13}{2}\text{ yards} \div \frac{2}{3}\frac{\text{yards}}{\text{row}}$$
$$= \frac{13}{2}\text{ yards} \times \frac{3}{2}\frac{\text{rows}}{\text{yard}} = \frac{39}{4}\text{ rows} = 9\frac{3}{4}\text{ rows}$$

He can cover all of 9 rows and part $\left(\frac{3}{4}\right)$ of the tenth row.

Check Yourself 12

Tangela has $4,100 to invest in a certain stock. If the stock is selling at $\$25\frac{5}{8}$ per share, how many shares can she buy?

Check Yourself ANSWERS

1. **(a)** $\frac{8}{5}$; **(b)** $3\frac{1}{4}$ is $\frac{13}{4}$, so the reciprocal is $\frac{4}{13}$ **2.** $\dfrac{\frac{2}{5}}{\frac{3}{4}}$ **3.** $\frac{3}{5} \times \frac{8}{7}$

4. **(a)** $\frac{8}{15}$; **(b)** $\frac{1}{14}$ **5.** $1\frac{17}{18}$ **6.** $\frac{4}{9} \div \frac{8}{15} = \frac{4}{9} \times \frac{15}{8} = \frac{\overset{1}{\cancel{4}} \times \overset{5}{\cancel{15}}}{\underset{3}{\cancel{9}} \times \underset{2}{\cancel{8}}} = \frac{5}{6}$

7. $3\frac{1}{5} \div 2\frac{2}{5} = \frac{16}{5} \div \frac{12}{5} = \frac{16}{5} \times \frac{5}{12} = \frac{\overset{4}{\cancel{16}} \times \overset{1}{\cancel{5}}}{\underset{1}{\cancel{5}} \times \underset{3}{\cancel{12}}} = \frac{4}{3} = 1\frac{1}{3}$ **8.** $1\frac{2}{3}$

9. 160 mi/h **10.** 18 pieces **11.** 25 tracts **12.** 160 shares

Reading Your Text

The following fill-in-the-blank exercises are designed to ensure that you understand some of the key vocabulary used in this section.

SECTION 2.6

(a) The product of any number and its ______________ is 1.

(b) An expression that has a fraction as both its numerator and denominator is called a ______________ fraction.

(c) To divide one fraction by another, invert the ______________ and multiply.

(d) When dividing by denominate numbers that have fractional units, we multiply by the reciprocal of the number and its ______________.

Basic Skills | Challenge Yourself | Calculator/Computer | Career Applications | Above and Beyond

2.6 exercises

Name ______________

Section ________ Date ________

< Objective 1 >

Find the reciprocal of each number.

1. $\frac{7}{8}$ > Videos

2. $\frac{9}{5}$

3. $\frac{1}{2}$

4. 6

5. $2\frac{1}{3}$ > Videos

6. $4\frac{3}{5}$

7. $9\frac{3}{4}$

8. $\frac{1}{8}$

< Objective 2 >

Divide. Write each result in simplest form.

9. $\frac{1}{5} \div \frac{3}{4}$ > Videos

10. $\frac{2}{5} \div \frac{1}{3}$

11. $\dfrac{\frac{2}{5}}{\frac{3}{4}}$

12. $\dfrac{\frac{5}{8}}{\frac{3}{4}}$

13. $\frac{8}{9} \div \frac{4}{3}$

14. $\frac{5}{9} \div \frac{8}{11}$

15. $\frac{7}{10} \div \frac{5}{9}$

16. $\frac{8}{9} \div \frac{11}{15}$

17. $\frac{8}{15} \div \frac{2}{5}$

18. $\frac{5}{27} \div \frac{15}{54}$

19. $\dfrac{\frac{5}{27}}{\frac{25}{36}}$

20. $\dfrac{\frac{9}{28}}{\frac{27}{35}}$

21. $\frac{4}{5} \div 4$

22. $27 \div \frac{3}{7}$

23. $12 \div \frac{2}{3}$

24. $\frac{5}{8} \div 5$

25. $\dfrac{\frac{12}{17}}{\frac{6}{7}}$

26. $\dfrac{\frac{3}{4}}{\frac{9}{10}}$

Answers

1. ________ 2. ________
3. ________ 4. ________
5. ________ 6. ________
7. ________ 8. ________
9. ________ 10. ________
11. ________ 12. ________
13. ________ 14. ________
15. ________ 16. ________
17. ________ 18. ________
19. ________ 20. ________
21. ________ 22. ________
23. ________ 24. ________
25. ________ 26. ________

Answers

27. ______
28. ______
29. ______
30. ______
31. ______
32. ______
33. ______
34. ______
35. ______
36. ______
37. ______
38. ______
39. ______
40. ______
41. ______
42. ______
43. ______
44. ______
45. ______
46. ______

< Objective 3 >

27. $15 \div 3\frac{1}{3}$

28. $2\frac{4}{7} \div 12$

29. $1\frac{3}{5} \div \frac{4}{15}$

30. $\frac{9}{14} \div 2\frac{4}{7}$

31. $\frac{7}{12} \div 2\frac{1}{3}$

32. $1\frac{3}{8} \div \frac{5}{12}$

33. $5\frac{3}{5} \div \frac{7}{15}$

34. $\frac{7}{18} \div 5\frac{5}{6}$

Basic Skills | **Challenge Yourself** | Calculator/Computer | Career Applications | Above and Beyond

35. $\left(\frac{2}{3}\right)^3 \div 4$

36. $\left(\frac{3}{5}\right)^3 \div 9$

37. $\frac{3}{5} \div \left(\frac{3}{10}\right)^2$ > Videos

38. $\left(\frac{2}{7}\right)^2 \div \frac{3}{14}$

< Objective 4 >

Divide. Be sure to attach the proper units.

39. $900 \text{ mi} \div 15 \frac{\text{mi}}{\text{gal}}$

40. $1{,}500 \text{ joules} \div 75 \frac{\text{joules}}{\text{s}}$

41. $8{,}750 \text{ watts} \div 350 \frac{\text{watts}}{\text{s}}$

42. $\$75{,}744 \div \frac{\$3{,}156}{\text{month}}$

Solve each application.

43. **Construction** A $5\frac{1}{4}$ ft long wire is to be cut into 7 pieces of the same length. How long is each piece? > Videos

44. **Crafts** A potter uses $\frac{2}{3}$ pound (lb) of clay in making a bowl. How many bowls can be made from 16 lb of clay?

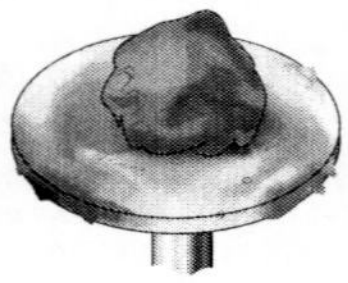

45. **Statistics** Virginia made a trip of 95 mi in $1\frac{1}{4}$ h. What was her average speed?

46. **Business and Finance** A piece of land measures $3\frac{3}{4}$ acres and is for sale at \$60,000. What is the price per acre?

47. CRAFTS A roast weighs $3\frac{1}{4}$ lb. How many $\frac{1}{4}$-lb servings will the roast provide?

chapter 2 > Make the Connection

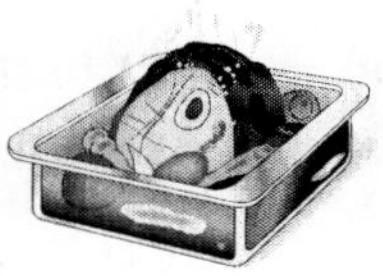

48. CONSTRUCTION A bookshelf is 55 in. long. If the books have an average thickness of $1\frac{1}{4}$ in., how many books can be put on the shelf?

Basic Skills | Challenge Yourself | **Calculator/Computer** | Career Applications | Above and Beyond

Using Your Calculator to Divide Fractions

Dividing fractions on your calculator is almost exactly the same as multiplying them. You simply press the [÷] key instead of the [×] key. Again, parentheses are important when using a calculator to work with fractions.

Scientific Calculator

Dividing fractions on a scientific calculator requires only that you enter the problem followed by the equal sign. Recall that fractions are entered using the [a b/c] key.

Graphing Calculator

When using a graphing calculator, you must choose the fraction option [1:► Frac] from the [MATH] menu before pressing [Enter].

Find each quotient, using your calculator.

49. $\frac{1}{5} \div \frac{2}{15}$

50. $\frac{13}{17} \div \frac{39}{34}$

51. $\frac{5}{7} \div \frac{15}{28}$

52. $\frac{3}{7} \div \frac{9}{28}$

53. $\frac{15}{18} \div \frac{45}{27}$

54. $\frac{19}{63} \div \frac{38}{9}$

55. $\frac{25}{45} \div \frac{100}{135}$

56. $\frac{86}{24} \div \frac{258}{96}$

Basic Skills | Challenge Yourself | Calculator/Computer | **Career Applications** | Above and Beyond

57. MANUFACTURING TECHNOLOGY Calculate the distance from the center of hole A to the center of hole B.

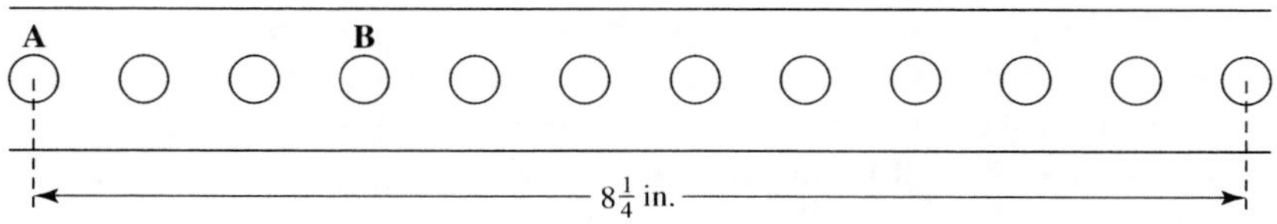

Answers

47. ______

48. ______

49. ______

50. ______

51. ______

52. ______

53. ______

54. ______

55. ______

56. ______

57. ______

Answers

58. ______

59. ______

60. ______

61. ______

62. ______

63. ______

64. ______

58. Manufacturing Technology A staircase is $95\frac{7}{8}$ in. tall and has 13 risers. What is the height of each riser? (*Hint:* Convert $95\frac{7}{8}$ into an improper fraction and divide by $\frac{13}{1}$.)

59. Manufacturing Technology A part that is $\frac{3}{4}$ in. wide is to be magnified for a detailed drawing. The scale is 1 in. $= \frac{3}{8}$ in. What is the width of the part in the drawing? (*Hint:* Divide the width by $\frac{3}{8}$.)

60. Manufacturing Technology A typical unified threaded bolt has one thread every $\frac{1}{20}$ in. How many threads are in $\frac{1}{4}$ in.?

61. Crafts Manuel has $7\frac{1}{2}$ yd of cloth. He wants to cut it into strips $1\frac{3}{4}$ yd long. How many strips will he have? How much cloth remains, if any?

62. Crafts Evette has $41\frac{1}{2}$ ft of string. She wants to cut it into pieces $3\frac{3}{4}$ ft long. How many pieces of string will she have? How much string remains, if any?

Basic Skills | Challenge Yourself | Calculator/Computer | Career Applications | **Above and Beyond**

63. Crafts In squeezing oranges for fresh juice, 3 oranges yield about $\frac{1}{3}$ of a cup.

chapter 2 > Make the Connection

(a) How much juice could you expect to obtain from a bag containing 24 oranges?

(b) If you needed 8 cups of orange juice, how many bags of oranges should you buy?

64. Number Problem A farmer died and left 17 cows to be divided among three workers. The first worker was to receive $\frac{1}{2}$ of the cows, the second worker was to receive $\frac{1}{3}$ of the cows, and the third worker was to receive $\frac{1}{9}$ of the cows. The executor of the farmer's estate realized that 17 cows could not be divided into halves, thirds, or ninths and so added a neighbor's cow to the farmer's. With 18 cows, the executor gave 9 cows to the first worker, 6 cows to the second worker, and 2 cows to the third worker. This accounted for the 17 cows, so the executor returned the borrowed cow to the neighbor. Explain why this works.

65. In general division of fractions is not commutative.

For example, $\frac{3}{4} \div \frac{5}{6} \neq \frac{5}{6} \div \frac{3}{4}$.

There could be an exception. Can you think of a situation in which division of fractions would be commutative?

66. Josephine's boss tells her that her salary is to be divided by $\frac{1}{3}$. Should she quit?

67. Compare the English phrases "divide in half" and "divide by one-half." Do they say the same thing? Create examples to support your answer.

68. **(a)** Compute: $5 \div \frac{1}{10}$; $5 \div \frac{1}{100}$; $5 \div \frac{1}{1{,}000}$; $5 \div \frac{1}{10{,}000}$.

(b) As the divisor gets smaller (approaches 0), what happens to the quotient?

(c) What does this say about the answer to $5 \div 0$?

Answers

65. ____

66. ____

67. ____

68. ____

Answers

1. $\frac{8}{7}$ **3.** 2 **5.** $\frac{3}{7}$ **7.** $\frac{4}{39}$ **9.** $\frac{4}{15}$ **11.** $\frac{8}{15}$ **13.** $\frac{2}{3}$ **15.** $1\frac{13}{50}$ **17.** $1\frac{1}{3}$ **19.** $\frac{4}{15}$ **21.** $\frac{1}{5}$ **23.** 18 **25.** $\frac{14}{17}$ **27.** $4\frac{1}{2}$ **29.** 6 **31.** $\frac{1}{4}$ **33.** 12 **35.** $\frac{2}{27}$ **37.** $6\frac{2}{3}$ **39.** 60 gal **41.** 25 s **43.** $\frac{3}{4}$ ft **45.** 76 $\frac{\text{mi}}{\text{h}}$ **47.** 13 servings **49.** $\frac{3}{2}$ **51.** $\frac{4}{3}$ or $1\frac{1}{3}$ **53.** $\frac{1}{2}$ **55.** $\frac{3}{4}$ **57.** $2\frac{1}{4}$ in. **59.** 2 in. **61.** 4 strips; $\frac{1}{2}$ yd **63.** $2\frac{2}{3}$ cups; 3 bags **65.** Above and Beyond **67.** Above and Beyond

Activity 6 :: Adapting a Recipe

Tom and Susan like eating in ethnic restaurants, so they were thrilled when Marco's Cafe, an Indian restaurant, opened in their neighborhood. The first time they ate there, Susan had a bowl of Mulligatawny soup and she loved it. She decided that it would be a great soup to serve her friends, so she asked Marco for the recipe. Marco said that was no problem. He had already had so many requests for the recipe that he had made up a handout. A copy of it is reproduced here (try it if you are adventurous):

Mulligatawny Soup

This recipe makes 10 gal; recommended serving size is a 12-ounce (12-oz) bowl. Sauté the following in a steam kettle until the onions are translucent:

10 lb	diced onion
10 lb	diced celery
$\frac{1}{2}$ cup	garlic puree
1 cup	madras curry
2 cups	mild curry

Add the following and bring to a boil:

4 cups	white wine
$\frac{1}{3}$ cup	sugar
1 #10 can	diced tomato
1 gal	fresh apple juice
$\frac{1}{3}$ cup	lemon juice
2 gal	water
1 #10 can	diced carrots
16 oz	chicken stock

Finish with:

Roux (1 lb butter and 1 lb flour) and 8 quarts cream (temper into hot liquid). Season to taste with salt, pepper, celery seed, basil, and garlic.

How many servings does this recipe make?

Visit local grocery stores to find out how much each item costs. Calculate the total cost for 10 gal of soup. What is the cost for each 12-oz serving? (This is called the *marginal cost*—it does not include the overhead for running the restaurant.)

What is roux? Call another restaurant to find out whether it would use the same definition.

Susan does want to make this soup for a dinner party she is having. Rewrite the recipe so that it will serve six 12-oz bowls. Use reasonable measures, such as teaspoons and cups. Answering the following questions will help. For some items you may have to experiment.

How many ounces in a #10 can?
How many cups in a gallon?
How many ounces in a pound?
How many teaspoons in a cup?
How many cups in a pound of diced onion?

Definition/Procedure	Example	Reference
Prime Numbers and Divisibility		**Section 2.1**
Prime Number Any whole number that has exactly two factors, 1 and itself.	7, 13, 29, and 73 are prime numbers.	*p.* 100
Composite Number Any whole number greater than 1 that is not prime.	8, 15, 42, and 65 are composite numbers.	*p.* 101
Zero and One Zero and one are neither classified as prime nor composite numbers.		*p.* 101
Divisibility Tests		
By 2 A whole number is divisible by 2 if its last digit is 0, 2, 4, 6, or 8.	932 is divisible by 2; 1,347 is not.	*p.* 101
By 3 A whole number is divisible by 3 if the sum of its digits is divisible by 3.	546 is divisible by 3; 2,357 is not.	*p.* 102
By 5 A whole number is divisible by 5 if its last digit is 0 or 5.	865 is divisible by 5; 23,456 is not.	*p.* 102
Factoring Whole Numbers		**Section 2.2**
Prime Factorization		
To find the prime factorization of a number, divide the number by a series of primes until the final quotient is a prime number. The prime factors include each prime divisor and the final quotient.	$2\overline{)630}$ $3\overline{)315}$ $3\overline{)105}$ $5\overline{)35}$ 7 So $630 = 2 \times 3 \times 3 \times 5 \times 7$.	*p.* 110
Greatest Common Factor (GCF) The GCF is the *largest* number that is a factor of each of a group of numbers.		*p.* 111

Continued

Definition/Procedure	Example	Reference
To Find the GCF		
Step 1 Write the prime factorization for each of the numbers in the group. **Step 2** Locate the prime factors that are *common* to all the numbers. **Step 3** The greatest common factor is the *product* of all of the common prime factors. If there are no common prime factors, the GCF is 1.	To find the GCF of 24, 30, and 36: $24 = \textcircled{2} \times 2 \times 2 \times \textcircled{3}$ $30 = \textcircled{2} \times \textcircled{3} \times 5$ $36 = \textcircled{2} \times 2 \times \textcircled{3} \times 3$ The GCF is $2 \times 3 = 6$.	*p.* 111
Fraction Basics		Section 2.3
Fraction Fractions name a number of equal parts of a unit or whole. A fraction is written in the form $\frac{a}{b}$, in which a and b are whole numbers and b cannot be zero.	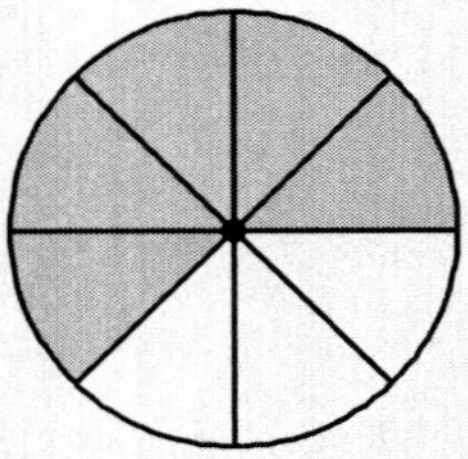	*p.* 117
Denominator The number of equal parts into which the whole is divided. **Numerator** The number of parts of the whole that are used.	$\frac{5}{8}$ ← Numerator (5), Denominator (8)	*p.* 117
Proper Fraction A fraction whose numerator *is less than* its denominator. It names a number less than 1.	$\frac{2}{3}$ and $\frac{11}{15}$ are proper fractions.	*p.* 119
Improper Fraction A fraction whose numerator *is greater than* or equal to its denominator. It names a number greater than or equal to 1.	$\frac{7}{5}$, $\frac{21}{20}$, and $\frac{8}{8}$ are improper fractions.	*p.* 119
Mixed Number The sum of a whole number and a proper fraction.	$2\frac{1}{3}$ and $5\frac{7}{8}$ are mixed numbers. Note that $2\frac{1}{3}$ means $2 + \frac{1}{3}$.	*p.* 119

Definition/Procedure	Example	Reference
To Change an Improper Fraction into a Mixed Number		
Step 1 Divide the numerator by the denominator. The quotient is the whole-number portion of the mixed number. **Step 2** If there is a remainder, write the remainder over the original denominator. This gives the fractional portion of the mixed number.	To change $\frac{22}{5}$ to a mixed number: $5\overline{)22}$ with quotient 4 (Quotient); -20; remainder 2 (Remainder) $\frac{22}{5} = 4\frac{2}{5}$	p. 120
To Change a Mixed Number to an Improper Fraction		
Step 1 Multiply the denominator of the fraction by the whole-number portion of the mixed number. **Step 2** Add the numerator of the fraction to that product. **Step 3** Write that sum over the original denominator to form the improper fraction.	Denominator, Whole number, Numerator $5\frac{3}{4} = \frac{(4 \times 5) + 3}{4} = \frac{23}{4}$ Denominator	p. 121
Simplifying Fractions		**Section 2.4**
Equivalent Fractions Two fractions that are equivalent (have equal value) are different names for the same number.		p. 128
Cross Products $\frac{a}{b} \times \frac{c}{d}$ $a \times d$ and $b \times c$ are called the *cross products.* If the cross products for two fractions are equal, the two fractions are equivalent.	$\frac{2}{3} = \frac{4}{6}$ because $2 \times 6 = 3 \times 4$	p. 128
The Fundamental Principle of Fractions For the fraction $\frac{a}{b}$, and any nonzero number c, $\frac{a}{b} = \frac{a \div c}{b \div c}$ **In words:** We can divide the numerator and denominator of a fraction by the same nonzero number. The result is an equivalent fraction.	$\frac{8}{12} = \frac{8 \div 4}{12 \div 4} = \frac{2}{3}$ $\frac{8}{12}$ and $\frac{2}{3}$ are equivalent fractions.	p. 129

Continued

Definition/Procedure	Example	Reference
Simplest Form A fraction is in simplest form, or in lowest terms, if the numerator and denominator have no common factors other than 1. This means that the fraction has the smallest possible numerator and denominator.	$\frac{2}{3}$ is in simplest form. $\frac{12}{18}$ is *not* in simplest form. The numerator and denominator have the common factor 6.	*p.* 130
To Write a Fraction in Simplest Form		
Divide the numerator and denominator by their greatest common factor.	$\frac{10}{15} = \frac{10 \div 5}{15 \div 5} = \frac{2}{3}$	*p.* 130
Multiplying Fractions		**Section 2.5**
To Multiply Two Fractions		
Step 1 Multiply numerator by numerator. This gives the numerator of the product. **Step 2** Multiply denominator by denominator. This gives the denominator of the product. **Step 3** Simplify the resulting fraction if possible. In multiplying fractions it is usually easiest to divide by any common factors in the numerator and denominator *before* multiplying.	$\frac{5}{8} \times \frac{3}{7} = \frac{5 \times 3}{8 \times 7} = \frac{15}{56}$ $\frac{5}{9} \times \frac{3}{10} = \frac{\overset{1}{\cancel{5}} \times \overset{1}{\cancel{3}}}{\underset{3}{\cancel{9}} \times \underset{2}{\cancel{10}}} = \frac{1}{6}$	*p.* 139
Dividing Fractions		**Section 2.6**
To Divide Two Fractions		
Invert the divisor and multiply.	$\frac{3}{7} \div \frac{4}{5} = \frac{3}{7} \times \frac{5}{4} = \frac{15}{28}$	*p.* 154
Multiplying or Dividing Mixed Numbers		
Convert any mixed or whole numbers to improper fractions. Then multiply or divide the fractions as before.	$6\frac{2}{3} \times 3\frac{1}{5} = \frac{\overset{4}{\cancel{20}} \times 16}{3 \times \underset{1}{\cancel{5}}}$ $= \frac{64}{3} = 21\frac{1}{3}$	*p.* 156

This summary exercise set is provided to give you practice with each of the objectives of this chapter. Each exercise is keyed to the appropriate chapter section. When you are finished, you can check your answers to the odd-numbered exercises against those presented in the back of the text. If you have difficulty with any of these questions, go back and reread the examples from that section. The answers to the even-numbered exercises appear in the *Instructor's Solutions Manual.* Your instructor will give you guidelines on how to best use these exercises in your instructional setting.

2.1 *List all the factors of the given numbers.*

1. 52

2. 41

Use the group of numbers 2, 5, 7, 11, 14, 17, 21, 23, 27, 39, and 43.

3. List the prime numbers; then list the composite numbers.

Use the divisibility tests to determine which, if any, of the numbers 2, 3, and 5 are factors of each number.

4. 2,350

5. 33,451

2.2 *Find the prime factorization for the given numbers.*

6. 48

7. 420

8. 2,640

9. 2,250

Find the greatest common factor (GCF).

10. 15 and 20

11. 30 and 31

12. 24 and 40

13. 39 and 65

14. 49, 84, and 119

15. 77, 121, and 253

2.3 *Identify the numerator and denominator of each fraction.*

16. $\frac{5}{9}$

17. $\frac{17}{23}$

Give the fractions that name the shaded portions in each diagram. Identify the numerator and the denominator.

18.

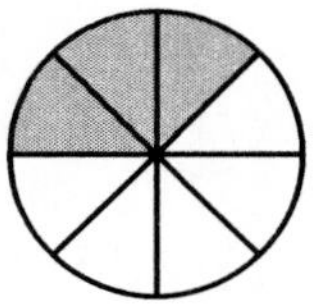

Fraction ________

Numerator ________

Denominator ________

19. 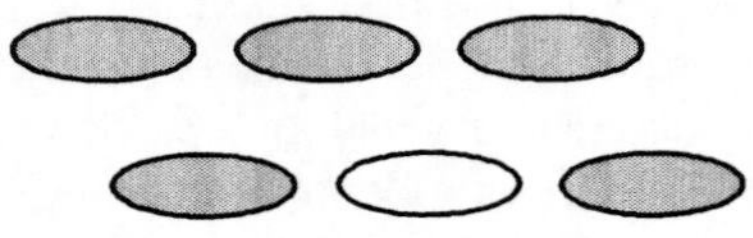

Fraction: __________

Numerator: __________

Denominator: __________

20. From the group of numbers:

$\frac{2}{3}, \frac{5}{4}, 2\frac{3}{7}, \frac{45}{8}, \frac{7}{7}, 3\frac{4}{5}, \frac{9}{1}, \frac{7}{10}, \frac{12}{5}, 5\frac{2}{9}$

List the proper fractions. __________

List the improper fractions. __________

List the mixed numbers. __________

Convert to mixed or whole numbers.

21. $\frac{41}{6}$ **22.** $\frac{32}{8}$ **23.** $\frac{23}{3}$ **24.** $\frac{47}{4}$

Convert to improper fractions.

25. $7\frac{5}{8}$ **26.** $4\frac{3}{10}$ **27.** $5\frac{2}{7}$ **28.** $12\frac{8}{13}$

2.4 *Determine whether each pair of fractions is equivalent.*

29. $\frac{5}{8}, \frac{7}{12}$ **30.** $\frac{8}{15}, \frac{32}{60}$

Write each fraction in simplest form.

31. $\frac{24}{36}$ **32.** $\frac{45}{75}$ **33.** $\frac{140}{180}$ **34.** $\frac{16}{21}$

Decide whether each is a true statement.

35. $\frac{15}{25} = \frac{3}{5}$ **36.** $\frac{36}{40} = \frac{4}{5}$

2.5 *Multiply.*

37. $\frac{7}{15} \times \frac{5}{21}$ **38.** $\frac{10}{27} \times \frac{9}{20}$ **39.** $4 \cdot \frac{3}{8}$ **40.** $3\frac{2}{5} \cdot \frac{5}{8}$

41. $5\frac{1}{3} \times 1\frac{4}{5}$

42. $1\frac{5}{12} \times 8$

43. $3\frac{1}{5} \times \frac{7}{8} \times 2\frac{6}{7}$

Solve each application.

44. **Social Science** The scale on a map is 1 inch (in.) = 80 miles (mi). If two cities are $2\frac{3}{4}$ in. apart on the map, what is the actual distance between the cities?

45. **Construction** A kitchen measures $5\frac{1}{3}$ yards (yd) by $4\frac{1}{4}$ yd. If you purchase linoleum costing \$9 per square yard (yd^2), what will it cost to cover the floor?

46. **Construction** Your living room measures $6\frac{2}{3}$ yd by $4\frac{1}{2}$ yd. If you purchase carpeting at \$18 per square yard (yd^2), what will it cost to carpet the room?

47. **Business and Finance** Maria earns \$72 per day. If she works $\frac{5}{8}$ of a day, how much will she earn?

48. **Science and Medicine** David drove at an average speed of 65 mi/h for $2\frac{2}{5}$ h. How many miles did he travel?

49. **Social Science** The scale on a map is 1 in. = 120 mi. What actual distance, in miles, does $3\frac{2}{5}$ in. on the map represent?

50. **Social Science** At a college, $\frac{2}{5}$ of the students take a science course. Of the students taking science, $\frac{1}{4}$ take biology. What fraction of the students take biology?

51. **Social Science** A student survey found that $\frac{3}{4}$ of the students have jobs while going to school. Of those who have jobs, $\frac{5}{6}$ work more than 20 h/week. What fraction of those surveyed work more than 20 h/week?

52. **Construction** A living room has dimensions $5\frac{2}{3}$ yd by $4\frac{1}{2}$ yd. How much carpeting must be purchased to cover the room?

2.6 *Divide.*

53. $\frac{5}{12} \div \frac{5}{8}$

54. $\dfrac{\frac{7}{15}}{\frac{14}{25}}$

55. $\dfrac{\frac{9}{20}}{\frac{12}{5}}$

56. $3\frac{3}{8} \div 2\frac{1}{4}$

57. $3\frac{3}{7} \div 8$

58. $6\frac{1}{7} \div \frac{3}{14}$

Solve each application.

59. **CONSTRUCTION** A piece of wire $3\frac{3}{4}$ ft long is to be cut into 5 pieces of the same length. How long will each piece be?

60. **CRAFTS** A blouse pattern requires $1\frac{3}{4}$ yd of fabric. How many blouses can be made from a piece of silk that is 28 yd long?

61. **SCIENCE AND MEDICINE** If you drive 126 mi in $2\frac{1}{4}$ h, what is your average speed?

62. **SCIENCE AND MEDICINE** If you drive 117 mi in $2\frac{1}{4}$ h, what is your average speed?

63. **CONSTRUCTION** An 18-acre piece of land is to be subdivided into home lots that are each $\frac{3}{8}$ acre. How many lots can be formed?

self-test 2

Name ____________

Section ________ Date ________

The purpose of this self-test is to help you assess your progress so that you can find concepts that you need to review before the next exam. Allow yourself about an hour to take this test. At the end of that hour, check your answers against those given in the back of this text. If you miss any, go back to the appropriate section to reread the examples until you have mastered that particular concept.

Find the greatest common factor (GCF) for the given numbers.

1. 36 and 84

2. 16, 24, and 72

3. Give the mixed number that names the shaded part of the following diagram.

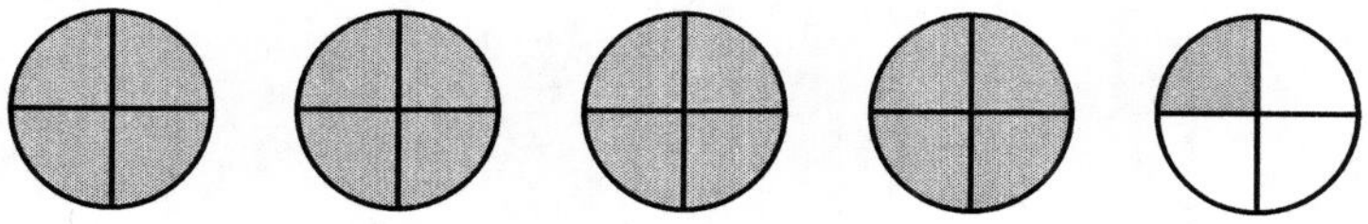

Write the fractions in simplest form.

4. $\frac{21}{27}$

5. $\frac{36}{84}$

6. $\frac{8}{23}$

Perform the indicated operations.

7. $\frac{2}{3} \times \frac{5}{7}$

8. $5\frac{1}{3} \times \frac{3}{4}$

9. $\frac{7}{12} \div \frac{14}{15}$

10. $2\frac{2}{3} \times 1\frac{2}{7}$

11. $\frac{16}{35} \times \frac{14}{24}$

12. $5\frac{3}{5} \div 2\frac{1}{10}$

13. $\frac{9}{10} \times \frac{5}{8}$

14. $\frac{6}{7} \div \frac{3}{4}$

15. $3\frac{5}{6} \times 2\frac{2}{5}$

16. $1\frac{3}{4} \div 1\frac{3}{8}$

17. Which of the numbers 5, 9, 13, 17, 22, 27, 31, and 45 are prime numbers? Which are composite numbers?

What fraction names the shaded part of each diagram? Identify the numerator and denominator.

18.

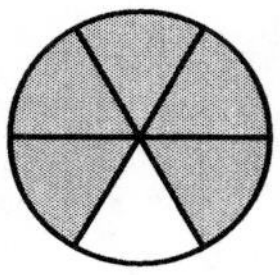

19.

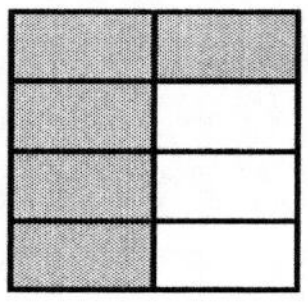

20.

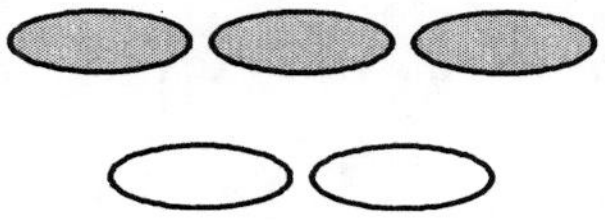

Answers

1. ____________
2. ____________
3. ____________
4. ____________
5. ____________
6. ____________
7. ____________
8. ____________
9. ____________
10. ____________
11. ____________
12. ____________
13. ____________
14. ____________
15. ____________
16. ____________
17. ____________
18. ____________
19. ____________
20. ____________

Answers

21. ______
22. ______
23. ______
24. ______
25. ______
26. ______
27. ______
28. ______
29. ______
30. ______
31. ______
32. ______
33. ______
34. ______
35. ______
36. ______
37. ______
38. ______

Solve each application.

21. Business and Finance What is the cost of $2\frac{3}{4}$ pounds (lb) of apples if the price per pound is 48 cents?

22. Crafts A bookshelf is 66 in. long. If the thickness of each book on the shelf is $1\frac{3}{8}$ in., how many books can be placed on the shelf?

Convert the fractions to mixed or whole numbers.

23. $\frac{17}{4}$

24. $\frac{15}{1}$

25. $\frac{74}{8}$

26. $\frac{18}{6}$

27. Find the prime factorization for 264.

28. Identify the proper fractions, improper fractions, and mixed numbers in the following group.

$\frac{10}{11}, \frac{9}{5}, \frac{7}{7}, \frac{8}{1}, 2\frac{3}{5}, \frac{1}{8}$

Solve each application.

29. Construction A $31\frac{1}{3}$-acre piece of land is subdivided into home lots. Each home lot is to be $\frac{2}{3}$ acre. How many homes can be built?

30. Construction A room measures $5\frac{1}{3}$ yd by $3\frac{3}{4}$ yd. How many square yards (yd^2) of linoleum must be purchased to cover the floor?

31. Social Science The scale on a map is 1 inch (in.) = 80 miles (mi). If two towns are $2\frac{3}{8}$ in. apart on the map, what is the actual distance in miles between the towns?

32. Use the divisibility tests to determine which, if any, of the numbers 2, 3, and 5 are factors of 54,204.

Use the cross-product method to find out whether the pair of fractions is equivalent.

33. $\frac{2}{7}, \frac{8}{28}$

34. $\frac{8}{20}, \frac{12}{30}$

35. $\frac{3}{20}, \frac{2}{15}$

Convert the mixed numbers to improper fractions.

36. $5\frac{2}{7}$

37. $4\frac{3}{8}$

38. $8\frac{2}{9}$

The following exercises are presented to help you review concepts from earlier chapters. This is meant as review material and not as a comprehensive exam. The answers are presented in the back of the text. Beside each answer is a section reference for the concept. If you have difficulty with any of these exercises, be certain to at least read through the summary related to that section.

Name ________________

Section ________ Date ________

1. Give the place value of 7 in 3,738,500.

2. Give the word name for 302,525.

3. Write two million, four hundred thirty thousand as a numeral.

Name the property of addition that is illustrated.

4. $5 + 12 = 12 + 5$

5. $9 + 0 = 9$

6. $(7 + 3) + 8 = 7 + (3 + 8)$

Perform the indicated operations.

7.
$$\begin{array}{r} 593 \\ 275 \\ +\ 98 \\ \hline \end{array}$$

8. Find the sum of 58, 673, 5,325, and 17,295.

Round each number to the indicated place value.

9. 5,873 to the nearest hundred

10. 953,150 to the nearest ten thousand

Estimate the sum by rounding each addend to the nearest hundred.

11.
$$\begin{array}{r} 943 \\ 3{,}281 \\ 778 \\ 2{,}112 \\ +\ 570 \\ \hline \end{array}$$

Complete each statement by using the symbol $<$ or $>$.

12. 49 ______ 47

13. 80 ______ 90

Answers

1. ________________
2. ________________
3. ________________
4. ________________
5. ________________
6. ________________
7. ________________
8. ________________
9. ________________
10. ________________
11. ________________
12. ________________
13. ________________

Answers

14. ______

15. ______

16. ______

17. ______

18. ______

19. ______

20. ______

21. ______

22. ______

23. ______

24. ______

25. ______

26. ______

27. ______

28. ______

29. ______

Perform the indicated operations.

14. $\begin{array}{r} 4{,}834 \\ -\ 973 \\ \hline \end{array}$

15. Find the difference of 25,000 and 7,535.

Solve each application.

16. STATISTICS Attendance for five performances of a play was 172, 153, 205, 193, and 182. How many people in total attended those performances?

17. BUSINESS AND FINANCE Alan bought a Volkswagen with a list price of \$18,975. He added stereo equipment for \$439 and an air conditioner for \$615. If he made a down payment of \$2,450, what balance remained on the car?

Name the property of addition and/or multiplication that is illustrated.

18. $3 \times (4 \times 7) = (3 \times 4) \times 7$

19. $3 \times 4 = 4 \times 3$

20. $5 \times (2 + 4) = 5 \times 2 + 5 \times 4$

Perform the indicated operations.

21. $\begin{array}{r} 538 \\ \times\ 703 \\ \hline \end{array}$

22. $\begin{array}{r} 1{,}372 \\ \times\ 500 \\ \hline \end{array}$

Solve the application.

23. CONSTRUCTION A classroom is 8 yards (yd) wide by 9 yd long. If the room is to be recarpeted with material costing \$14 per square yard, find the cost of the carpeting.

Divide, using long division.

24. $48\overline{)3{,}259}$

25. $458\overline{)47{,}350}$

Evaluate each expression.

26. $3 + 5 \times 7$

27. $(3 + 5) \times 7$

28. 4×3^2

29. $2 + 8 \times 3 \div 4$

Solve each application.

30. Business and Finance William bought a washer-dryer combination that, with interest charges, cost \$841. He paid \$145 down and agreed to pay the balance in 12 monthly payments. Find the amount of each payment.

31. Number Problem Which of the numbers 5, 9, 13, 17, 22, 27, 31, and 45 are prime numbers? Which are composite numbers?

32. Use the divisibility tests to determine which, if any, of the numbers 2, 3, and 5 are factors of 54,204.

33. Find the prime factorization for 264.

Find the greatest common factor (GCF) for the given numbers.

34. 36 and 96

35. 16, 40, and 72

Identify the proper fractions, improper fractions, and mixed numbers from the following group.

$\frac{7}{12}, \frac{10}{8}, 3\frac{1}{5}, \frac{9}{9}, \frac{7}{1}, \frac{3}{7}, 2\frac{2}{3}$

36. Proper: __________ Improper: __________

Mixed numbers: __________

Convert to mixed or whole numbers.

37. $\frac{14}{5}$

38. $\frac{28}{7}$

Convert to improper fractions.

39. $4\frac{1}{3}$

40. $7\frac{7}{8}$

Determine whether each pair of fractions is equivalent.

41. $\frac{7}{21}, \frac{8}{24}$

42. $\frac{7}{12}, \frac{8}{15}$

Answers

30. __________
31. __________
32. __________
33. __________
34. __________
35. __________
36. __________
37. __________
38. __________
39. __________
40. __________
41. __________
42. __________

Answers

43. ______
44. ______
45. ______
46. ______
47. ______
48. ______
49. ______
50. ______
51. ______
52. ______
53. ______
54. ______
55. ______

Write each fraction in simplest form.

43. $\frac{28}{42}$

44. $\frac{36}{96}$

Multiply.

45. $\frac{5}{9} \times \frac{8}{15}$

46. $\frac{20}{21} \cdot \frac{7}{25}$

47. $1\frac{1}{8} \cdot 4\frac{4}{5}$

48. $8 \times 2\frac{5}{6}$

49. $\frac{2}{3} \times 1\frac{4}{5} \times \frac{5}{8}$

Divide.

50. $\frac{5}{8} \div \frac{15}{32}$

51. $2\frac{5}{8} \div \frac{7}{12}$

52. $4\frac{1}{6} \div 5$

53. $2\frac{2}{7} \div 1\frac{11}{21}$

Solve each application.

54. CONSTRUCTION Your living room measures $6\frac{2}{3}$ yd by $4\frac{1}{2}$ yd. If you purchase carpeting at \$18 per square yard (yd^2), what will it cost to carpet the room?

55. CONSTRUCTION If a stack of $\frac{5}{8}$-in. plywood measures 55 in. high, how many sheets of plywood are in the stack?

CHAPTER

3

Adding and Subtracting Fractions

INTRODUCTION

Carpentry is one of the oldest and most important of all trades. It dates back to ancient times and the earliest use of primitive tools. It includes large-scale work such as architecture and smaller-scale work such as cabinetry and furniture making. Carpenters mostly work with wood, but they also use ceramic, metal, and plastic. Sometimes carpenters also do roofing, refinishing, remodeling, restoration, and flooring.

Carpenters need to have a vast knowledge of scale drawing and an understanding of blueprints. They have to be able to use a substantial amount of math for measuring and making scale drawings and drafts. They work with models that are hundreds of times smaller than the actual construction. Sometimes these are actual models, and sometimes they are drawings. Carpenters have to be extremely precise in their measuring, sometimes to tiny fractions of an inch. Errors in measurement can have dire consequences such as warping or cracking of materials later on.

Carpenters learn their trades from vocational schools or by serving as apprentices to a more experienced carpenter. Some carpenters are highly skilled and looked upon as artists, whereas others just do handy work.

CHAPTER 3 OUTLINE

Name ______________________

Section ________ Date ________

Answers

1. ______________________
2. ______________________
3. ______________________
4. ______________________
5. ______________________
6. ______________________
7. ______________________
8. ______________________
9. ______________________
10. ______________________

This prerequisite test provides some exercises requiring skills that you will need to be successful in the coming chapter. The answers for these exercises can be found in the back of this text. This prerequisite test can help you identify topics that you will need to review before beginning the chapter.

Write the prime factorization for each number.

1. 24

2. 36

3. 90

Change each mixed number to an improper fraction.

4. $4\frac{2}{3}$

5. $6\frac{2}{5}$

6. $9\frac{1}{10}$

Change each improper fraction to a mixed or whole number.

7. $\frac{29}{4}$

8. $\frac{42}{6}$

9. $\frac{8}{8}$

Evaluate.

10. $7 \times 11 - 2 \times (2 + 3)^2$

3.1 Adding and Subtracting Fractions with Like Denominators

< 3.1 Objectives >

1 > Add two like fractions

2 > Add a group of like fractions

3 > Subtract two like fractions

Recall from our work in Chapter 1 that adding can be thought of as combining groups of the *same kind* of objects. This is also true when you think about adding fractions.

Fractions can be added only if they name a number of the *same parts* of a whole. This means that we can add fractions only when they are **like fractions,** that is, when they have the *same* (*a common*) denominator. For instance, we can add two nickels and three nickels to get five nickels. We *cannot* directly add two nickels and three dimes!

As long as we are dealing with like fractions, addition is an easy matter. Just use the following rule.

Step by Step

To Add Like Fractions

Step 1 Add the numerators.

Step 2 Place the sum over the common denominator.

Step 3 Simplify the resulting fraction when necessary.

Example 1 illustrates the use of this rule.

Example 1 Adding Like Fractions

< Objective 1 >

Add.

$$\frac{1}{5} + \frac{3}{5}$$

Step 1 Add the numerators.

$1 + 3 = 4$

Step 2 Write that sum over the common denominator, 5. We are done at this point because the answer, $\frac{4}{5}$, is in the simplest possible form.

Step 1 Step 2

$$\frac{1}{5} + \frac{3}{5} = \frac{1+3}{5} = \frac{4}{5}$$

We illustrate this addition with a diagram.

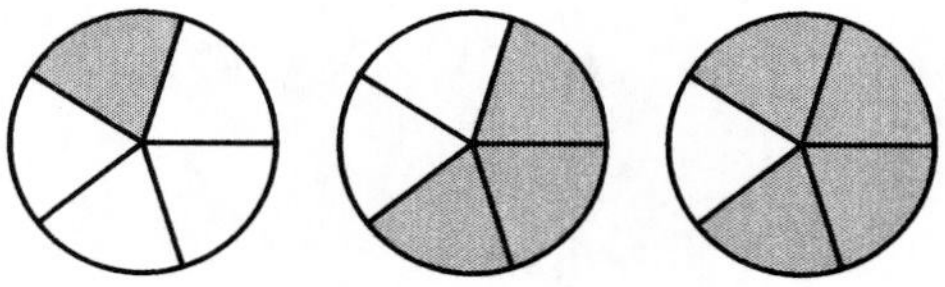

$\frac{1}{5}$ + $\frac{3}{5}$ = $\frac{4}{5}$

NOTE

Combining 1 of the 5 parts with 3 of the 5 parts gives a total of 4 of the 5 equal parts.

Check Yourself 1

Add.

$$\frac{2}{9} + \frac{5}{9}$$

> CAUTION

Be Careful! In adding fractions, *do not* follow the rule for multiplying fractions. To multiply $\frac{1}{5} \times \frac{3}{5}$, you would multiply both the numerators and the denominators:

$$\frac{1}{5} \times \frac{3}{5} = \frac{3}{25}$$

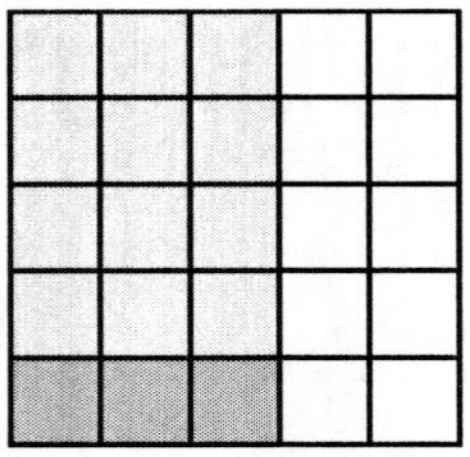

$\frac{1}{5}$ of $\frac{3}{5} = \frac{3}{25}$

However, when you add two fractions, the sum will have the same like denominator. So, you **do not** add the denominators.

$$\frac{1}{5} + \frac{3}{5} \neq \frac{4}{10}$$

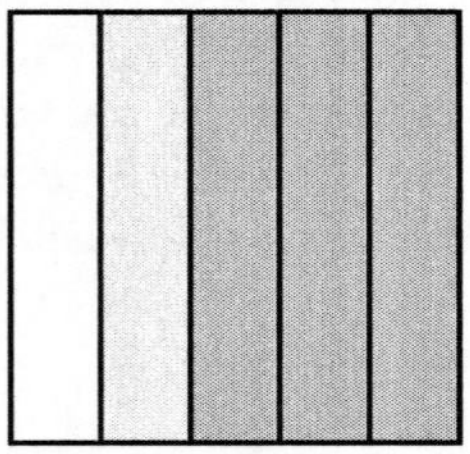

$\frac{1}{5} + \frac{3}{5} = \frac{4}{5}$

Step 3 of the addition rule for like fractions tells us to *simplify* the sum. Fractions should always be written in lowest terms. Consider Example 2.

Example 2 Adding Like Fractions That Require Simplifying

Add and simplify.

$$\frac{3}{12} + \frac{5}{12} = \frac{8}{12} = \frac{2}{3}$$

Step 3

The sum $\frac{8}{12}$ is *not* in lowest terms.

Divide the numerator and denominator by 4 to simplify the result.

Check Yourself 2

Add.

$$\frac{4}{15} + \frac{6}{15}$$

If the sum of two fractions is an improper fraction, we usually write that sum as a mixed number.

Example 3 Adding Like Fractions That Result in Mixed Numbers

NOTE

Add as before. Then convert the sum to a mixed number.

Add.

$$\frac{5}{9} + \frac{8}{9} = \frac{13}{9} = 1\frac{4}{9}$$

Write the sum $\frac{13}{9}$ as a mixed number.

Check Yourself 3

Add.

$$\frac{7}{12} + \frac{10}{12}$$

We can easily extend our addition rule to find the sum of more than two fractions as long as they all have the same denominator. This is shown in Example 4.

Example 4 Adding a Group of Like Fractions

< Objective 2 >

Add.

$$\frac{2}{7} + \frac{3}{7} + \frac{6}{7} = \frac{11}{7}$$ Add the numerators: 2 + 3 + 6 = 11.

$$= 1\frac{4}{7}$$

Check Yourself 4

Add.

$$\frac{1}{8} + \frac{3}{8} + \frac{5}{8}$$

Many applications can be solved by adding fractions.

Example 5 An Application Involving the Adding of Like Fractions

Noel walked $\frac{9}{10}$ miles (mi) to Jensen's house and then walked $\frac{7}{10}$ mi to school. How far did Noel walk?

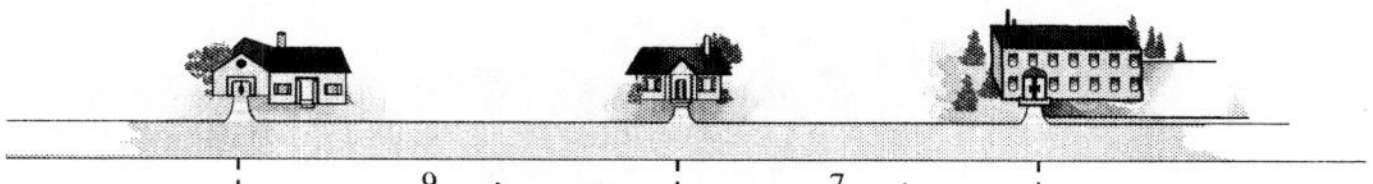

To find the total distance Noel walked, add the two distances.

$$\frac{9}{10} + \frac{7}{10} = \frac{16}{10} = 1\frac{6}{10} = 1\frac{3}{5}$$

Noel walked $1\frac{3}{5}$ mi.

NOTE

Like fractions have the same denominator.

Check Yourself 5

Emir bought $\frac{7}{16}$ pounds (lb) of candy at one store and $\frac{11}{16}$ lb at another store. How much candy did Emir buy?

If a problem involves like fractions, then subtraction, like addition, is not difficult.

Step by Step

To Subtract Like Fractions

Step 1 Subtract the numerators.
Step 2 Place the difference over the common denominator.
Step 3 Simplify the resulting fraction when necessary.

Example 6 Subtracting Like Fractions

< Objective 3 >

Subtract.

(a) $\frac{4}{5} - \frac{2}{5} = \frac{4 - 2}{5} = \frac{2}{5}$

Step 1: $\frac{4-2}{5}$; Step 2: $\frac{2}{5}$

Subtract the numerators: 4 − 2 = 2. Write the difference over the common denominator, 5. Step 3 is not necessary because the difference is in simplest form.

NOTE

Subtracting 2 of the 5 parts from 4 of the 5 parts leaves 2 of the 5 parts.

Illustrating with a diagram:

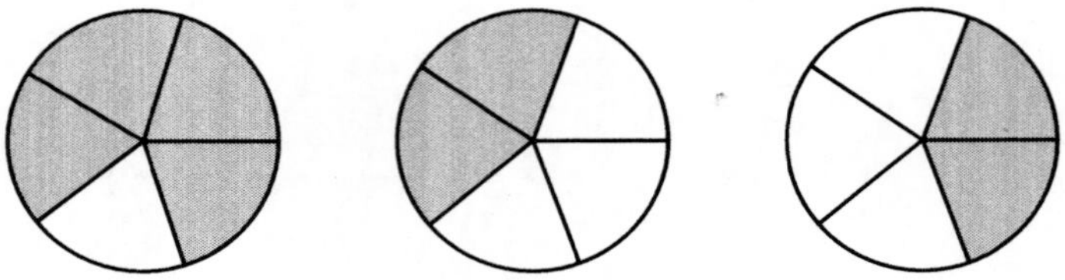

$\frac{4}{5} - \frac{2}{5} = \frac{2}{5}$

NOTE

Always write the result in simplest terms.

(b) $\frac{5}{8} - \frac{3}{8} = \frac{5 - 3}{8} = \frac{2}{8} = \frac{1}{4}$

Check Yourself 6

Subtract.

$\frac{11}{12} - \frac{5}{12}$

Check Yourself ANSWERS

1. $\frac{7}{9}$ 2. $\frac{2}{3}$ 3. $1\frac{5}{12}$ 4. $1\frac{1}{8}$ 5. $1\frac{1}{8}$ lb 6. $\frac{1}{2}$

Reading Your Text

The following fill-in-the-blank exercises are designed to ensure that you understand some of the key vocabulary used in this section.

SECTION 3.1

(a) Fractions with the same (common) denominator are called ____________ fractions.

(b) When adding like fractions, add the ____________.

(c) After adding two fractions, ____________ the result when necessary.

(d) The result of subtraction is called the ____________.

Basic Skills | Challenge Yourself | Calculator/Computer | Career Applications | Above and Beyond

3.1 exercises

< Objective 1 >

Add. Write all answers in simplest terms.

1. $\frac{3}{5} + \frac{1}{5}$

2. $\frac{4}{7} + \frac{1}{7}$

3. $\frac{4}{11} + \frac{6}{11}$

4. $\frac{5}{16} + \frac{4}{16}$

5. $\frac{2}{10} + \frac{3}{10}$ > Videos

6. $\frac{5}{12} + \frac{1}{12}$

7. $\frac{3}{7} + \frac{4}{7}$

8. $\frac{13}{20} + \frac{17}{20}$

9. $\frac{29}{30} + \frac{11}{30}$

10. $\frac{4}{9} + \frac{5}{9}$

11. $\frac{13}{48} + \frac{23}{48}$

12. $\frac{17}{60} + \frac{31}{60}$

13. $\frac{3}{7} + \frac{6}{7}$

14. $\frac{3}{5} + \frac{4}{5}$

15. $\frac{7}{10} + \frac{9}{10}$

16. $\frac{5}{8} + \frac{7}{8}$

17. $\frac{11}{12} + \frac{10}{12}$

18. $\frac{13}{18} + \frac{11}{18}$

< Objective 2 >

19. $\frac{1}{8} + \frac{1}{8} + \frac{3}{8}$

20. $\frac{1}{10} + \frac{3}{10} + \frac{3}{10}$

21. $\frac{1}{9} + \frac{4}{9} + \frac{5}{9}$ > Videos

22. $\frac{7}{12} + \frac{11}{12} + \frac{1}{12}$

< Objective 3 >

Subtract. Write all answers in simplest terms.

23. $\frac{3}{5} - \frac{1}{5}$

24. $\frac{5}{7} - \frac{2}{7}$

Boost *your* GRADE at ALEKS.com!

ALEKS®

- Practice Problems
- Self-Tests
- NetTutor
- e-Professors
- Videos

Name ______________

Section ________ Date ________

Answers

1. ________ 2. ________
3. ________ 4. ________
5. ________ 6. ________
7. ________ 8. ________
9. ________ 10. ________
11. ________ 12. ________
13. ________ 14. ________
15. ________ 16. ________
17. ________ 18. ________
19. ________ 20. ________
21. ________ 22. ________
23. ________ 24. ________

Answers

25. ______
26. ______
27. ______
28. ______
29. ______
30. ______
31. ______
32. ______
33. ______
34. ______
35. ______
36. ______
37. ______
38. ______
39. ______
40. ______

25. $\frac{7}{9} - \frac{4}{9}$

26. $\frac{7}{10} - \frac{3}{10}$

27. $\frac{13}{20} - \frac{3}{20}$ > Videos

28. $\frac{19}{30} - \frac{17}{30}$

29. $\frac{19}{24} - \frac{5}{24}$

30. $\frac{25}{36} - \frac{13}{36}$

31. $\frac{11}{12} - \frac{7}{12}$

32. $\frac{9}{10} - \frac{6}{10}$

33. $\frac{8}{9} - \frac{3}{9}$

34. $\frac{5}{8} - \frac{1}{8}$

Solve each application. Write each answer in simplest terms.

35. **Number Problem** You work 7 hours (h) one day, 5 h the second day, and 6 h the third day. How long did you work, as a fraction of a 24-h day?

> Videos

36. **Number Problem** One task took 7 minutes (min), a second task took 12 min, and a third task took 21 min. How long did the three tasks take, as a fraction of an hour?

37. **Geometry** What is the perimeter of a rectangle if the length is $\frac{7}{10}$ inches (in.) and the width is $\frac{2}{10}$ in.?

38. **Geometry** Find the perimeter of a rectangular picture if the width is $\frac{7}{9}$ yd and the length is $\frac{5}{9}$ yd.

39. **Statistics** Patrick spent $\frac{4}{9}$ of an hour (h) in the batting cages on Friday and $\frac{7}{9}$ of an hour on Saturday. He wants to spend 2 h total on the weekend. How much time should he spend on Sunday to accomplish this goal?

40. **Business and Finance** Maria, a road inspector, must inspect $\frac{17}{30}$ of a mile of road. If she has already inspected $\frac{11}{30}$ of a mile, how much more does she need to inspect?

Basic Skills | **Challenge Yourself** | Calculator/Computer | Career Applications | Above and Beyond

GEOMETRY *Find the perimeter of each triangle.*

41.

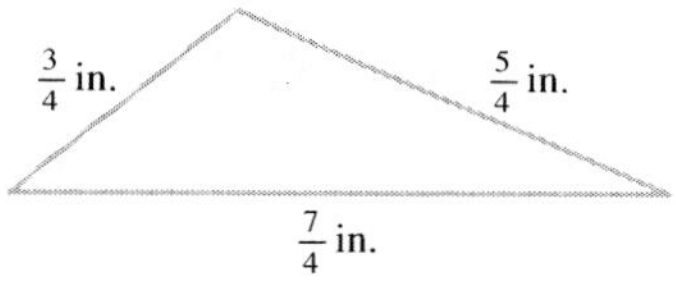

42.

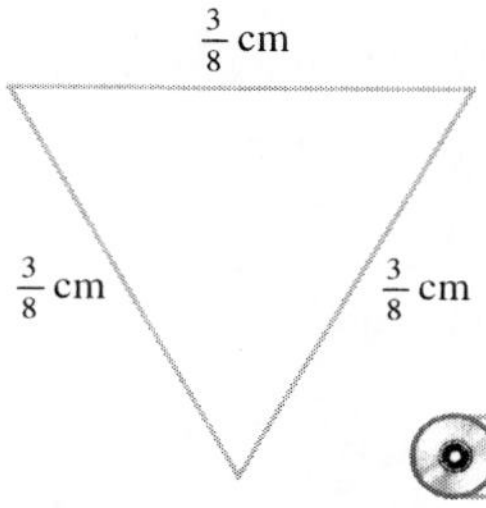

Videos

43.

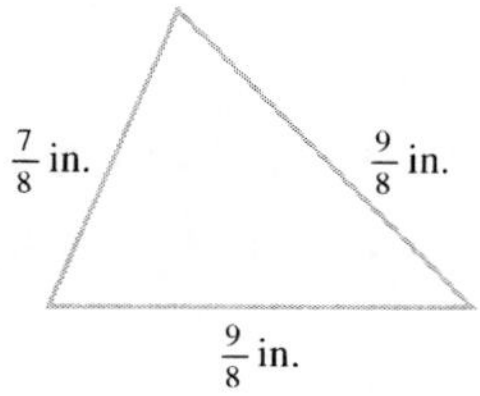

44.

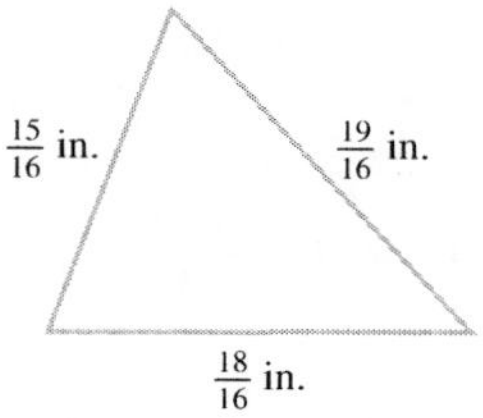

GEOMETRY *Find the perimeter of each polygon.*

45.

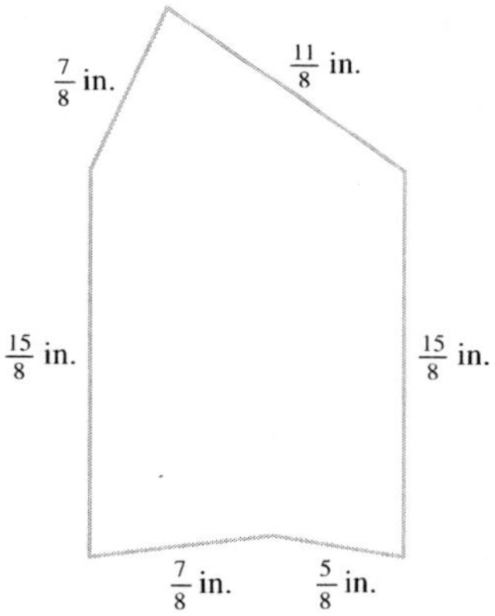

46.

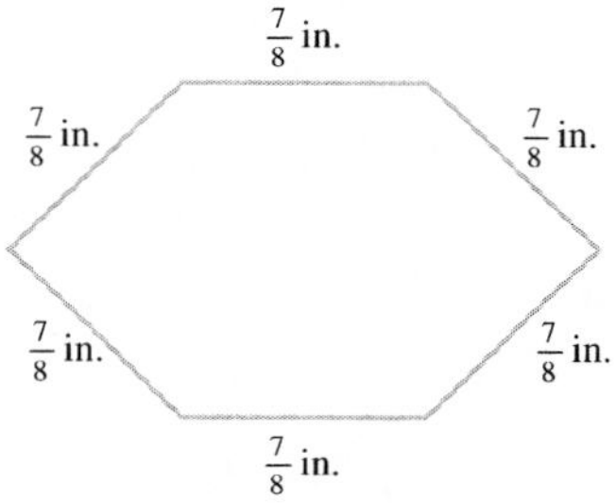

Evaluate. Write all answers in simplest terms.

47. $\frac{7}{12} - \frac{4}{12} + \frac{3}{12}$ Videos

48. $\frac{8}{9} + \frac{3}{9} - \frac{5}{9}$

49. $\frac{6}{13} - \frac{3}{13} + \frac{11}{13}$

50. $\frac{9}{11} - \frac{3}{11} + \frac{7}{11}$

51. $\frac{18}{23} - \frac{13}{23} - \frac{3}{23}$

52. $\frac{17}{18} - \frac{11}{18} - \frac{5}{18}$

Answers

41. ____________
42. ____________
43. ____________
44. ____________
45. ____________
46. ____________
47. ____________
48. ____________
49. ____________
50. ____________
51. ____________
52. ____________

Basic Skills | Challenge Yourself | Calculator/Computer | **Career Applications** | Above and Beyond

Answers

53. ______

54. ______

55. ______

56. ______

53. ALLIED HEALTH Carla is to be given $\frac{1}{8}$ gram (g) of medication in the morning, $\frac{1}{8}$ g at 3 P.M. in the afternoon, and $\frac{3}{8}$ g before she goes to bed. How many grams of medication will she receive in one day?

54. ALLIED HEALTH Prior to chemotherapy, a patient's malignant tumor weighed $\frac{7}{8}$ pound (lb). After the initial round of chemotherapy, the tumor's weight had been reduced by $\frac{3}{8}$ lb. How much did the tumor weigh after the chemotherapy treatment?

55. MANUFACTURING TECHNOLOGY Triplet Precision Machine has ordered $\frac{5}{8}$ ton of steel. The first truck arrived with $\frac{1}{8}$ ton of the steel. How much is yet to arrive?

56. MANUFACTURING TECHNOLOGY A sidewalk will require $\frac{15}{16}$ yard (yd) of concrete. The concrete mixer is capable of mixing $\frac{3}{16}$ yd at a time. How much concrete is still needed after one mixer load is used?

chapter 3 > Make the Connection

Answers

1. $\frac{4}{5}$ 3. $\frac{10}{11}$ 5. $\frac{1}{2}$ 7. 1 9. $\frac{4}{3} = 1\frac{1}{3}$ 11. $\frac{3}{4}$ 13. $1\frac{2}{7}$

15. $1\frac{3}{5}$ 17. $1\frac{3}{4}$ 19. $\frac{5}{8}$ 21. $1\frac{1}{9}$ 23. $\frac{2}{5}$ 25. $\frac{1}{3}$ 27. $\frac{1}{2}$

29. $\frac{7}{12}$ 31. $\frac{1}{3}$ 33. $\frac{5}{9}$ 35. $\frac{3}{4}$ day 37. $\frac{9}{5}$ in. $= 1\frac{4}{5}$ in.

39. $\frac{7}{9}$ h 41. $\frac{15}{4}$ in. $= 3\frac{3}{4}$ in. 43. $\frac{25}{8}$ in. $= 3\frac{1}{8}$ in.

45. $\frac{15}{2}$ in. $= 7\frac{1}{2}$ in. 47. $\frac{1}{2}$ 49. $\frac{14}{13} = 1\frac{1}{13}$ 51. $\frac{2}{23}$

53. $\frac{5}{8}$ g 55. $\frac{1}{2}$ ton

3.2 Common Multiples

< 3.2 Objectives >

1 > Find the least common multiple (LCM) of two numbers

2 > Find the LCM of a group of numbers

3 > Compare the size of two fractions

In this chapter, we discuss the process used for adding or subtracting fractions. One of the most important concepts we use when we add or subtract fractions is that of **multiples.**

Definition

Multiples The *multiples* of a number are the product of that number with the natural numbers 1, 2, 3, 4, 5, . . .

Example 1 Listing Multiples

List the multiples of 3.

The multiples of 3 are

$3 \times 1, 3 \times 2, 3 \times 3, 3 \times 4, \ldots$

or

3, 6, 9, 12, . . . The three dots indicate that the list continues without stopping.

NOTE

Notice that the multiples, except for 3 itself, are *larger* than 3.

An easy way of listing the multiples of 3 is to think of *counting by threes.*

Check Yourself 1

List the first seven multiples of 4.

Sometimes we need to find common multiples of two or more numbers.

Definition

Common Multiples If a number is a multiple of each of a group of numbers, it is called a *common multiple* of the numbers; that is, it is a number that is exactly divisible by each of the numbers in the group.

Example 2 Finding Common Multiples

Find four common multiples of 3 and 5.

Some common multiples of 3 and 5 are

15, 30, 45, 60

NOTE

15, 30, 45, and 60 are multiples of *both* 3 and 5.

Check Yourself 2

List the first six multiples of 6. Then look at your list from Check Yourself 1 and list some common multiples of 4 and 6.

For our later work, we will use the *least common multiple* of a group of numbers.

Definition

Least Common Multiple

The **least common multiple** (LCM) of a group of numbers is the *smallest* number that is divisible by each number in the group.

It is possible to simply list the multiples of each number and then find the LCM by inspection.

Example 3 Finding the Least Common Multiple (LCM)

< Objective 1 >

NOTE

48 is also a common multiple of 6 and 8, but we are looking for the *smallest* such number.

Find the least common multiple of 6 and 8.

Multiples

6: 6, 12, 18, (24), 30, 36, 42, 48, . . .

8: 8, 16, (24), 32, 40, 48, . . .

We see that 24 is the smallest number common to both lists. So 24 is the LCM of 6 and 8.

Check Yourself 3

Find the least common multiple of 20 and 30 by listing the multiples of each number.

The technique used in Example 3 will work for any group of numbers. However, it becomes tedious for larger numbers. Let's outline a different approach.

Step by Step

Finding the Least Common Multiple

Step 1 Write the prime factorization for each of the numbers in the group.

Step 2 Find all the prime factors that appear in any one of the prime factorizations.

Step 3 Form the product of those prime factors, using each factor the greatest number of times it occurs in any one factorization.

For instance, if a number appears three times in the factorization of a number, it must be included at least three times in forming the least common multiple.

This method is illustrated in Example 4.

Example 4 Finding the Least Common Multiple (LCM)

NOTE

Line up the *like* factors vertically.

To find the LCM of 10 and 18, factor:

$$10 = 2 \qquad\qquad \times 5$$
$$18 = 2 \times 3 \times 3$$
$$2 \times 3 \times 3 \times 5 \quad \text{Bring down the factors.}$$

The numbers 2 and 5 appear, at most, one time in any one factorization. And 3 appears two times in one factorization.

$2 \times 3 \times 3 \times 5 = 90$

So 90 is the LCM of 10 and 18.

Check Yourself 4

Use the method of Example 4 to find the LCM of 24 and 36.

The procedure is the same for a group of more than two numbers.

Example 5 Finding the Least Common Multiple (LCM)

< Objective 2 >

NOTE

The different factors that appear are 2, 3, and 5.

To find the LCM of 12, 18, and 20, we factor:

$$\begin{aligned} 12 &= 2 \times 2 \times 3 \\ 18 &= 2 \quad\quad \times 3 \times 3 \\ 20 &= \underline{2 \times 2 \quad\quad\quad\quad \times 5} \\ &\quad 2 \times 2 \times 3 \times 3 \times 5 \end{aligned}$$

The numbers 2 and 3 appear twice in one factorization, and 5 appears just once.

$2 \times 2 \times 3 \times 3 \times 5 = 180$

So 180 is the LCM of 12, 18, and 20.

Check Yourself 5

Find the LCM of 3, 4, and 6.

The process of finding the least common multiple is very useful when we are adding, subtracting, or comparing unlike fractions (fractions with different denominators).

Suppose you are asked to compare the sizes of the fractions $\frac{3}{7}$ and $\frac{4}{7}$. Because each unit in the diagram is divided into seven parts, it is easy to see that $\frac{4}{7}$ is larger than $\frac{3}{7}$.

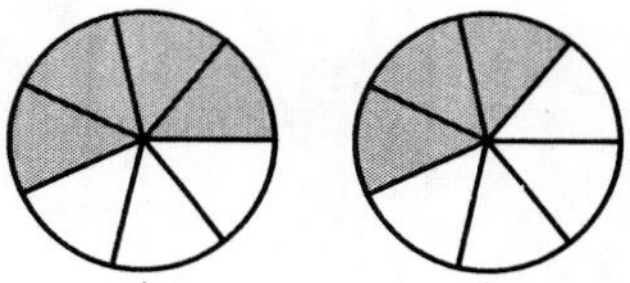

$\frac{4}{7}$ $\frac{3}{7}$

Four parts of seven are a greater portion than three parts. Now compare the size of the fractions $\frac{2}{5}$ and $\frac{3}{7}$.

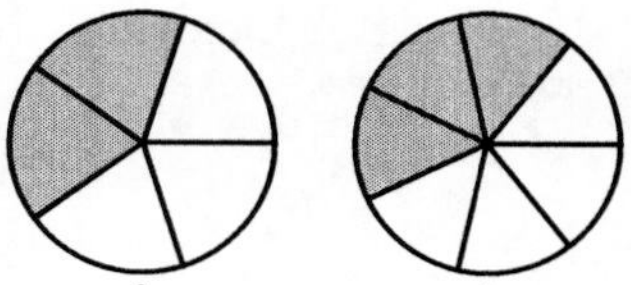

$\frac{2}{5}$ $\frac{3}{7}$

We *cannot* compare fifths with sevenths! The fractions $\frac{2}{5}$ and $\frac{3}{7}$ are *not* like fractions. Because they name different ways of dividing the whole, deciding which fraction is larger is not nearly so easy.

To compare the sizes of fractions, we change them to equivalent fractions having a *common denominator.* This common denominator must be a common multiple of the original denominators.

We will use the following property to form such fractions.

Property

The Fundamental Principle of Fractions

$$\frac{a}{b} = \frac{a \times c}{b \times c}$$

Example 6 Comparing the Size of Fractions

< Objective 3 >

RECALL

$\frac{2}{5}$ and $\frac{14}{35}$ are **equivalent fractions.** They name the same part of a whole.

Compare the sizes of $\frac{2}{5}$ and $\frac{3}{7}$.

The original denominators are 5 and 7. Because 35 is a common multiple of 5 and 7, let's use 35 as our common denominator.

$$\frac{2}{5} \overset{\times 7}{=} \frac{14}{35}$$

Think, "What must we multiply 5 by to get 35?" The answer is 7. Multiply the numerator and denominator by that number.

$$\frac{3}{7} \overset{\times 5}{=} \frac{15}{35}$$

Multiply the numerator and denominator by 5.

NOTE

15 of 35 parts represents a greater portion of the whole than 14 parts.

Because $\frac{2}{5} = \frac{14}{35}$ and $\frac{3}{7} = \frac{15}{35}$, we see that $\frac{3}{7}$ is larger than $\frac{2}{5}$.

Check Yourself 6

Which is larger, $\frac{5}{9}$ or $\frac{4}{7}$?

Now, consider an example that uses inequality notation.

Example 7 Using an Inequality Symbol with Two Fractions

RECALL

The inequality symbols "point" to the smaller quantity.

Use the inequality symbols $<$ or $>$ to complete the statement.

$$\frac{5}{8} \square \frac{3}{5}$$

Once again we must compare the sizes of the two fractions, and we do this by converting the fractions to equivalent fractions with a common denominator. Here we use 40 as that denominator.

NOTE

We use the Fundamental Principle of Fractions to convert these fractions.

$$\frac{5}{8} \xrightarrow{\times 5} \frac{25}{40} \qquad \frac{3}{5} \xrightarrow{\times 8} \frac{24}{40}$$

Because $\frac{5}{8}\left(\text{or } \frac{25}{40}\right)$ is larger than $\frac{3}{5}\left(\text{or } \frac{24}{40}\right)$, we write

$$\frac{5}{8} > \frac{3}{5}$$

Check Yourself 7

Use the symbols < or > to complete the statement.

$\frac{5}{9} \square \frac{6}{11}$

Check Yourself ANSWERS

1. The first seven multiples of 4 are 4, 8, 12, 16, 20, 24, and 28.
2. 6, 12, 18, 24, 30, 36; some common multiples of 4 and 6 are 12 and 24.
3. The multiples of 20 are 20, 40, 60, 80, 100, 120, . . . ; the multiples of 30 are 30, 60, 90, 120, 150, . . . ; the least common multiple of 20 and 30 is 60, the smallest number common to both lists.
4. $2 \times 2 \times 2 \times 3 \times 3 = 72$ **5.** 12 **6.** $\frac{4}{7}$ is larger **7.** $\frac{5}{9} > \frac{6}{11}$

Reading Your Text

The following fill-in-the-blank exercises are designed to ensure that you understand some of the key vocabulary used in this section.

SECTION 3.2

(a) The ______________ of a number are the products of that number with the natural numbers.

(b) The LCM of a group of numbers is the ______________ number that is divisible by each number in that group.

(c) To compare the sizes of fractions, we change them to equivalent fractions having a common ______________.

(d) The statement $\frac{5}{8} > \frac{3}{5}$ is read "$\frac{5}{8}$ is ______________ than $\frac{3}{5}$."

3.2 exercises

Basic Skills | Challenge Yourself | Calculator/Computer | Career Applications | Above and Beyond

Boost *your* GRADE at ALEKS.com!

ALEKS®

- Practice Problems
- Self-Tests
- NetTutor
- e-Professors
- Videos

Name ____________

Section ________ Date ________

Answers

1. ______ 2. ______
3. ______ 4. ______
5. ______ 6. ______
7. ______ 8. ______
9. ______ 10. ______
11. ______ 12. ______
13. ______ 14. ______
15. ______ 16. ______
17. ______ 18. ______
19. ______ 20. ______
21. ______ 22. ______
23. ______
24. ______
25. ______
26. ______

< Objective 1 >

Find the least common multiple (LCM) for each group of numbers. Use whichever methods you wish.

1. 2 and 3

2. 3 and 5

3. 4 and 6

4. 6 and 9

5. 10 and 20

6. 12 and 36

7. 9 and 12

8. 20 and 30

9. 12 and 16

10. 10 and 15

11. 12 and 15 > Videos

12. 12 and 21

13. 18 and 36 > Videos

14. 25 and 50

15. 25 and 40

16. 10 and 14

< Objective 2 >

17. 3, 5, and 6

18. 2, 8, and 10

19. 18, 21, and 28

20. 8, 15, and 20

21. 20, 30, and 45

22. 12, 20, and 35

< Objective 3 >

Arrange the fractions from smallest to largest.

23. $\frac{12}{17}, \frac{9}{10}$

24. $\frac{4}{9}, \frac{5}{11}$

25. $\frac{5}{8}, \frac{3}{5}$

26. $\frac{9}{10}, \frac{8}{9}$

27. $\frac{3}{8}, \frac{1}{3}, \frac{1}{4}$ > Videos

28. $\frac{7}{12}, \frac{5}{18}, \frac{1}{3}$

29. $\frac{11}{12}, \frac{4}{5}, \frac{5}{6}$

30. $\frac{5}{8}, \frac{9}{16}, \frac{13}{32}$

Complete the statements, using the symbols < or >.

31. $\frac{5}{6} \square \frac{2}{5}$ > Videos

32. $\frac{3}{4} \square \frac{10}{11}$

33. $\frac{4}{9} \square \frac{3}{7}$

34. $\frac{7}{10} \square \frac{11}{15}$

35. $\frac{7}{20} \square \frac{9}{25}$

36. $\frac{5}{12} \square \frac{7}{18}$

37. $\frac{5}{16} \square \frac{7}{20}$

38. $\frac{7}{12} \square \frac{9}{15}$

Complete each equivalent fraction.

39. $\frac{4}{5} = \frac{\quad}{25}$ > Videos

40. $\frac{6}{13} = \frac{\quad}{26}$

41. $\frac{5}{6} = \frac{25}{\quad}$

42. $\frac{2}{5} = \frac{14}{\quad}$

43. $\frac{11}{37} = \frac{\quad}{111}$

44. $\frac{9}{31} = \frac{\quad}{248}$

Basic Skills | **Challenge Yourself** | Calculator/Computer | Career Applications | Above and Beyond

Solve each application.

45. **CRAFTS** Three drill bits are marked $\frac{3}{8}, \frac{5}{16}$, and $\frac{11}{32}$. Which drill bit is largest?

chapter 3 > Make the Connection

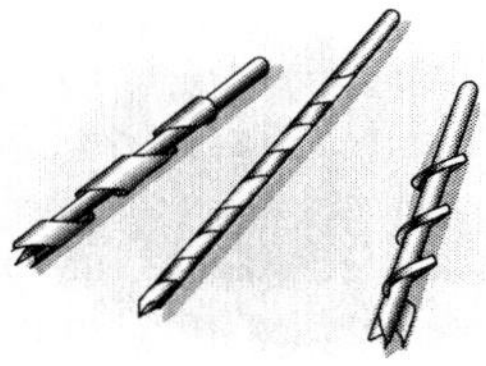

46. **CRAFTS** Bolts can be purchased with diameters of $\frac{3}{8}, \frac{1}{4}$, or $\frac{3}{16}$ inches (in.). Which is smallest?

chapter 3 > Make the Connection

47. **CONSTRUCTION** Plywood comes in thicknesses of $\frac{5}{8}, \frac{3}{4}, \frac{1}{2}$, and $\frac{3}{8}$ in. Which size is thickest?

chapter 3 > Make the Connection

48. **CONSTRUCTION** Dowels are sold with diameters of $\frac{1}{2}, \frac{9}{16}, \frac{5}{8}$, and $\frac{3}{8}$ in. Which size is smallest?

chapter 3 > Make the Connection

Answers

27. ______
28. ______
29. ______
30. ______
31. ______
32. ______
33. ______
34. ______
35. ______
36. ______
37. ______
38. ______
39. ______
40. ______
41. ______
42. ______
43. ______
44. ______
45. ______
46. ______
47. ______
48. ______

Answers

49. ____________

50. ____________

51. ____________

52. ____________

49. Elian is asked to create a fraction equivalent to $\frac{1}{4}$. His answer is $\frac{4}{7}$. What did he do wrong? What would be a correct answer?

50. A sign on a busy highway says Exit 5A is $\frac{3}{4}$ mile away and Exit 5B is $\frac{5}{8}$ mile away. Which exit is first?

Basic Skills | Challenge Yourself | Calculator/Computer | **Career Applications** | Above and Beyond

51. **ELECTRONICS** Imagine a guitar string vibrating back and forth. Each back-and-forth vibration is called a *cycle.* The number of times that a string vibrates back and forth per second is called the *frequency.* Accordingly, frequency is measured in cycles per second [CPS or hertz (Hz)]. If you had a camera that could zoom in on a vibrating guitar string, you'd see that it doesn't simply vibrate back and forth but actually vibrates differently in different sections of the string. The loudest vibration is called the fundamental frequency; quieter vibrations are called harmonics, which are multiples of the fundamental frequency.

I. If a note's fundamental frequency is 440 Hz, 1,760 Hz is a harmonic.

II. If a note's fundamental frequency is 440 Hz, 771.76 Hz is a harmonic.

Which of the following conclusions is valid?

(a) I is true and II is true. **(b)** I is true and II is false.
(c) I is false and II is true. **(d)** I is false and II is false.
(e) None of the above.

52. **ELECTRONICS** Music producers know that, when mixing tracks containing instruments and vocals, it is usually necessary to add some reverb and/or delay (echo) from each track into the mix. For a good mix, every instrument or vocal track usually has different degrees of reverb and delay. Delay, measured in milliseconds (ms), is the time it takes to hear the "echo," which can be quiet or sometimes quite loud. It is usually desirable to have the delay times be "in beat." If we let BPM denote the number of beats per minute the drum machine is set at, then the delay time is a multiple of $\frac{60{,}000}{\text{BPM}}$.

I. If the drum machine is set at 120 BPM, then 1,200 ms will produce an in-beat delay.

II. If the drum machine is set at 120 BPM, then 1,000 ms will produce an in-beat delay.

Which of the following conclusions is valid?

(a) I is true and II is true. **(b)** I is true and II is false.
(c) I is false and II is true. **(d)** I is false and II is false.
(e) None of the above.

Basic Skills | Challenge Yourself | Calculator/Computer | Career Applications | **Above and Beyond**

53. Business and Finance A company uses two types of boxes, 8 cm and 10 cm long. They are packed in larger cartons to be shipped. What is the shortest length of a container that will accommodate boxes of either size without any room left over? (Each container can contain only boxes of one size—no mixing allowed.)

54. There is an alternate approach to finding the least common multiple of two numbers. The LCM of two numbers can be found by dividing the product of the two numbers by the greatest common factor (GCF) of those two numbers. For example, the GCF of 24 and 36 is 12. If we use the given formula, we obtain

$$\text{LCM of 24 and 36} = \frac{24 \cdot 36}{12} = 72$$

(a) Use the given formula to find the LCM of 150 and 480.

(b) Verify the result by finding the LCM using the method of prime factorization.

55. Complete the crossword puzzle.

Across

2. The LCM of 11 and 13

4. The GCF of 120 and 300

7. The GCF of 13 and 52

8. The GCF of 360 and 540

Down

1. The LCM of 8, 14, and 21

3. The LCM of 16 and 12

5. The LCM of 2, 5, and 13

6. The GCF of 54 and 90

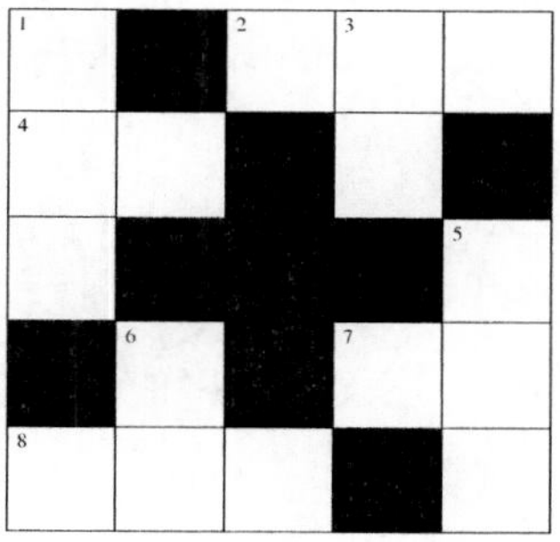

Answers

53. ______

54. ______

55. ______

Answers

1. 6 3. 12 5. 20 7. 36 9. 48

11. $12 = 2 \times 2 \times 3$; $15 = 3 \times 5$; the LCM is $2 \times 2 \times 3 \times 5 = 60$ 13. 36

15. 200 17. 30 19. 252 21. 180 23. $\frac{12}{17}, \frac{9}{10}$ 25. $\frac{3}{5}, \frac{5}{8}$

27. $\frac{1}{4}, \frac{1}{3}, \frac{3}{8}$ 29. $\frac{4}{5}, \frac{5}{6}, \frac{11}{12}$ 31. $>$ 33. $>$ 35. $<$

37. $<$ 39. 20 41. 30 43. 33 45. $\frac{3}{8}$ 47. $\frac{3}{4}$ in.

49. He added 3 to both the numerator and denominator; $\frac{1 \times 3}{4 \times 3} = \frac{3}{12}$

51. b 53. Above and Beyond 55. Above and Beyond

3.3 Adding and Subtracting Fractions with Unlike Denominators

< 3.3 Objectives >

1 > Add any two fractions

2 > Add any group of fractions

3 > Subtract any two fractions

In Section 3.1, you dealt with like fractions (fractions with a common denominator). What about a sum that deals with **unlike fractions,** such as $\frac{1}{3} + \frac{1}{4}$?

NOTE

Only *like* fractions can be added.

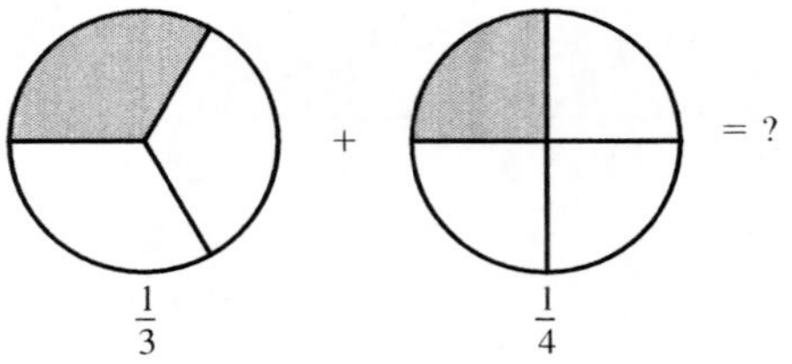

We cannot add unlike fractions because they have different denominators.

To add unlike fractions, write them as equivalent fractions with a common denominator. In this case, let's use 12 as the denominator.

NOTE

We can now add because we have like fractions.

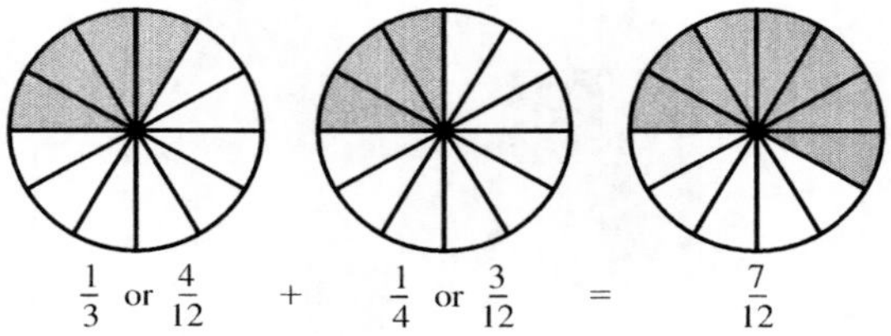

We have chosen 12 because it is a *multiple* of 3 and 4.

$\frac{1}{3}$ is equivalent to $\frac{4}{12}$.

$\frac{1}{4}$ is equivalent to $\frac{3}{12}$.

Any common multiple of the denominators will work in forming equivalent fractions. For instance, we can write $\frac{1}{3}$ as $\frac{8}{24}$ and $\frac{1}{4}$ as $\frac{6}{24}$. Our work is simplest, however, if we use the smallest possible number for the common denominator. This is called the **least common denominator (LCD).**

The LCD is the least common multiple of the denominators of the fractions. This is the *smallest* number that is a multiple of all the denominators. For example, the LCD for $\frac{1}{3}$ and $\frac{1}{4}$ is 12, *not* 24.

Step by Step

To Find the Least Common Denominator

Step 1	Write the prime factorization for each of the denominators.
Step 2	Find all the prime factors that appear in any one of the prime factorizations.
Step 3	Form the product of those prime factors, using each factor the greatest number of times it occurs in any one factorization.

We are now ready to add unlike fractions. In this case, the fractions must be renamed as equivalent fractions that have the same denominator.

Step by Step

To Add Unlike Fractions

Step 1 Find the LCD of the fractions.

Step 2 Change each unlike fraction to an equivalent fraction with the LCD as a common denominator.

Step 3 Add the resulting like fractions as before.

Example 1 shows this process.

Example 1 Adding Unlike Fractions

< Objective 1 >

NOTE

See Section 3.2 to review how we arrived at 24.

Add the fractions $\frac{1}{6}$ and $\frac{3}{8}$.

Step 1 We find that the LCD for fractions with denominators of 6 and 8 is 24.

Step 2 Convert the fractions so that they have the denominator 24.

$$\frac{1}{6} = \frac{4}{24} \quad (\times 4)$$

How many sixes are in 24? There are 4. So multiply the numerator and denominator by 4.

$$\frac{3}{8} = \frac{9}{24} \quad (\times 3)$$

How many eights are in 24? There are 3. So multiply the numerator and denominator by 3.

Step 3 We can now add the equivalent like fractions.

$$\frac{1}{6} + \frac{3}{8} = \frac{4}{24} + \frac{9}{24} = \frac{13}{24}$$

Add the numerators and place that sum over the common denominator.

Check Yourself 1

Add.

$$\frac{3}{5} + \frac{1}{3}$$

Here is a similar example. Remember that the sum should always be written in simplest form.

Example 2 Adding Unlike Fractions That Require Simplifying

Add the fractions $\frac{7}{10}$ and $\frac{2}{15}$.

Step 1 The LCD for fractions with denominators of 10 and 15 is 30.

Step 2 $\frac{7}{10} = \frac{21}{30}$

$\frac{2}{15} = \frac{4}{30}$

Do you see how the equivalent fractions are formed?

Step 3 $\frac{7}{10} + \frac{2}{15} = \frac{21}{30} + \frac{4}{30}$

$= \frac{25}{30} = \frac{5}{6}$

Add the resulting like fractions. Be sure the sum is in simplest form.

Check Yourself 2

Add.

$$\frac{1}{6} + \frac{7}{12}$$

We can use the same procedure to add more than two fractions. Example 3 illustrates this approach.

Example 3 Adding a Group of Unlike Fractions

< Objective 2 >

Add $\frac{5}{6} + \frac{2}{9} + \frac{4}{15}$.

Step 1 The LCD is 90.

Step 2 $\frac{5}{6} = \frac{75}{90}$ Multiply the numerator and denominator by 15.

$\frac{2}{9} = \frac{20}{90}$ Multiply the numerator and denominator by 10.

$\frac{4}{15} = \frac{24}{90}$ Multiply the numerator and denominator by 6.

Step 3 $\frac{75}{90} + \frac{20}{90} + \frac{24}{90} = \frac{119}{90}$ Now add.

$= 1\frac{29}{90}$ Remember, if the sum is an improper fraction, it should be changed to a mixed number.

Check Yourself 3

Add.

$$\frac{2}{5} + \frac{3}{8} + \frac{7}{20}$$

Many of the measurements you deal with in everyday life involve fractions. Following are some typical situations.

Example 4 An Application Involving the Addition of Unlike Fractions

Jack ran $\frac{1}{2}$ mi on Monday, $\frac{2}{3}$ mi on Wednesday, and $\frac{3}{4}$ mi on Friday. How far did he run during the week?

The three distances that Jack ran are the given information in the problem. We want to find a total distance, so we must add to find the solution.

$$\frac{1}{2} + \frac{2}{3} + \frac{3}{4} = \frac{6}{12} + \frac{8}{12} + \frac{9}{12}$$

$$= \frac{23}{12} = 1\frac{11}{12} \text{ mi}$$

Because we have no common denominator, we must convert to equivalent fractions before we can add.

Jack ran $1\frac{11}{12}$ mi during the week.

Check Yourself 4

Susan is designing an office complex. She needs $\frac{2}{5}$ acre for buildings, $\frac{1}{3}$ acre for driveways and parking, and $\frac{1}{6}$ acre for walks and landscaping. How much land does she need?

Example 5 An Application Involving the Addition of Unlike Fractions

Sam bought three packages of spices weighing $\frac{1}{4}$, $\frac{5}{8}$, and $\frac{1}{2}$ pound (lb). What was the total weight?

We need to find the total weight, so we must add.

NOTE

The abbreviation for pounds is "lb" from the Latin *libra,* meaning "balance" or "scales."

$$\frac{1}{4} + \frac{5}{8} + \frac{1}{2} = \frac{2}{8} + \frac{5}{8} + \frac{4}{8}$$

Write each fraction with the denominator 8.

$$= \frac{11}{8} = 1\frac{3}{8} \text{ lb}$$

The total weight was $1\frac{3}{8}$ lb.

Check Yourself 5

For three different recipes, Max needs $\frac{3}{8}$, $\frac{1}{2}$, and $\frac{3}{4}$ gallon (gal) of tomato sauce. How many gallons should he buy altogether?

To subtract unlike fractions, which are fractions that do not have the same denominator, we use the following process.

Step by Step

To Subtract Unlike Fractions

Step 1 Find the LCD of the fractions.

Step 2 Change each unlike fraction to an equivalent fraction with the LCD as a common denominator.

Step 3 Subtract the resulting like fractions as before.

Example 6 Subtracting Unlike Fractions

< Objective 3 >

Subtract $\frac{5}{8} - \frac{1}{6}$.

NOTE

You can use your calculator to check your result.

Step 1 The LCD is 24.

Step 2 Convert the fractions so that they have the common denominator 24.

$$\frac{5}{8} = \frac{15}{24}$$

$$\frac{1}{6} = \frac{4}{24}$$

The first two steps are exactly the same as if we were adding.

Step 3 Subtract the equivalent like fractions.

$$\frac{5}{8} - \frac{1}{6} = \frac{15}{24} - \frac{4}{24} = \frac{11}{24}$$

> CAUTION

Be Careful! You *cannot* subtract the numerators and subtract the denominators.

$\frac{5}{8} - \frac{1}{6}$ is *not* $\frac{4}{2}$

Check Yourself 6

Subtract.

$$\frac{7}{10} - \frac{1}{4}$$

Following is an application that involves subtracting unlike fractions.

Example 7 An Application Involving the Subtraction of Unlike Fractions

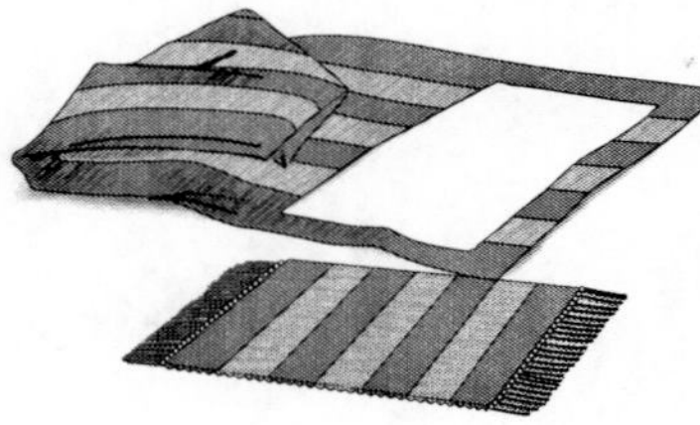

You have $\frac{7}{8}$ yards (yd) of a handwoven linen. A pattern for a placemat calls for $\frac{1}{2}$ yd. Will you have enough left for two napkins that will use $\frac{1}{3}$ yd?

First, find out how much fabric is left over after the placemat is made.

$$\frac{7}{8}\text{ yd} - \frac{1}{2}\text{ yd} = \frac{7}{8}\text{ yd} - \frac{4}{8}\text{ yd} = \frac{3}{8}\text{ yd}$$

Now compare the sizes of $\frac{1}{3}$ and $\frac{3}{8}$.

NOTE

Remember that $\frac{3}{8}$ yd is left over and that $\frac{1}{3}$ yd is needed.

$$\frac{3}{8}\text{ yd} = \frac{9}{24}\text{ yd} \quad \text{and} \quad \frac{1}{3}\text{ yd} = \frac{8}{24}\text{ yd}$$

Because $\frac{3}{8}$ yd is *more than* the $\frac{1}{3}$ yd that is needed, there is enough material for the placemat *and* two napkins.

Check Yourself 7

A concrete walk will require $\frac{3}{4}$ cubic yard (yd^3) of concrete. If you have mixed $\frac{8}{9}$ yd^3, will enough concrete remain to do a project that will use $\frac{1}{6}$ yd^3?

Our next application involves measurements. Note that on a ruler or yardstick, the marks divide each inch into $\frac{1}{2}$-in., $\frac{1}{4}$-in., and $\frac{1}{8}$-in. sections, and on some rulers, $\frac{1}{16}$-in. sections. We will use denominators of 2, 4, 8, and 16 in our measurement applications.

Example 8 An Application Involving the Subtraction of Unlike Fractions

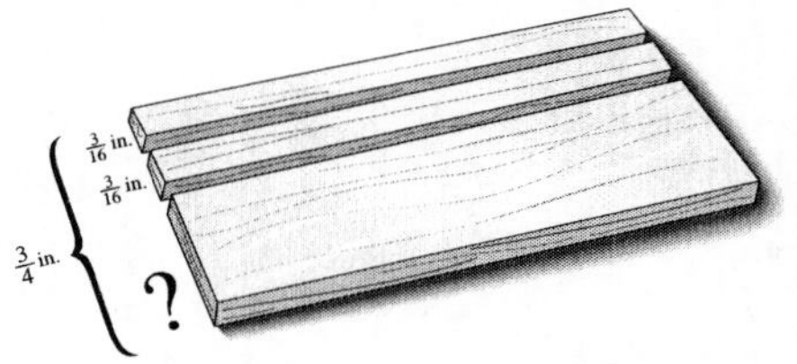

Alexei cut two $\frac{3}{16}$-in. slats from a piece of wood that is $\frac{3}{4}$ in. across. How much is left?

The two $\frac{3}{16}$-in. pieces total

$$2 \times \frac{3}{16} = \frac{6}{16} = \frac{3}{8} \text{ in.}$$

$$\frac{3}{4} = \frac{6}{8}$$

$$\frac{6}{8} - \frac{3}{8} = \frac{3}{8}$$

The remaining strip is $\frac{3}{8}$ in. wide.

Check Yourself 8

Ricardo cut three strips from a 1-in. piece of metal. Each strip has a width of $\frac{3}{16}$ in. How much metal remains after the cuts?

Check Yourself ANSWERS

1. $\frac{14}{15}$ **2.** $\frac{1}{6} + \frac{7}{12} = \frac{2}{12} + \frac{7}{12} = \frac{9}{12} = \frac{3}{4}$ **3.** $1\frac{1}{8}$ **4.** $\frac{9}{10}$ acre

5. $1\frac{5}{8}$ gal **6.** $\frac{9}{20}$

7. $\frac{5}{36}$ yd^3 remains. You do *not* have enough concrete for both projects.

8. $\frac{7}{16}$ in.

Reading Your Text

The following fill-in-the-blank exercises are designed to ensure that you understand some of the key vocabulary used in this section.

SECTION 3.3

(a) The process for finding the LCD is nearly identical to the Step by Step for finding the ____________.

(b) To add ____________ fractions, we first find the LCD of the fractions.

(c) Two fractions with the same value but different denominators are called ____________ fractions.

(d) When adding fractions with a common denominator, we add the ____________ and put that sum over the common denominator.

3.3 exercises

Boost *your* GRADE at ALEKS.com!

ALEKS

- Practice Problems
- Self-Tests
- NetTutor
- e-Professors
- Videos

Name ____________

Section ________ Date ________

Answers

1. ______ 2. ______
3. ______ 4. ______
5. ______ 6. ______
7. ______ 8. ______
9. ______ 10. ______
11. ______ 12. ______
13. ______ 14. ______
15. ______ 16. ______
17. ______ 18. ______
19. ______ 20. ______
21. ______ 22. ______
23. ______ 24. ______
25. ______ 26. ______
27. ______ 28. ______
29. ______ 30. ______
31. ______ 32. ______

Basic Skills | Challenge Yourself | Calculator/Computer | Career Applications | Above and Beyond

< Objective 1 >

Find the least common denominator (LCD) for fractions with the given denominators.

1. 3 and 4

2. 3 and 5

3. 4 and 8

4. 6 and 12

5. 9 and 27

6. 10 and 30

7. 8 and 12

8. 15 and 40

9. 14 and 21 (Videos)

10. 15 and 20

11. 48 and 80

12. 60 and 84

13. 3, 4, and 5

14. 3, 4, and 6

15. 8, 10, and 15 (Videos)

16. 6, 22, and 33

17. 5, 10, and 25

18. 8, 24, and 48

Add.

19. $\frac{2}{3} + \frac{1}{4}$

20. $\frac{3}{5} + \frac{1}{3}$

21. $\frac{1}{5} + \frac{3}{10}$

22. $\frac{1}{3} + \frac{1}{18}$

23. $\frac{3}{4} + \frac{1}{8}$

24. $\frac{4}{5} + \frac{1}{10}$

25. $\frac{1}{7} + \frac{3}{5}$ (Videos)

26. $\frac{1}{6} + \frac{2}{15}$

27. $\frac{3}{7} + \frac{3}{14}$

28. $\frac{7}{20} + \frac{9}{40}$

29. $\frac{7}{15} + \frac{2}{35}$

30. $\frac{3}{10} + \frac{3}{8}$

31. $\frac{5}{8} + \frac{1}{12}$

32. $\frac{5}{12} + \frac{3}{10}$

Basic Skills | **Challenge Yourself** | Calculator/Computer | Career Applications | Above and Beyond

Complete each statement with either **never, always,** *or* **sometimes.**

33. The sum of two like fractions is ____________ the sum of the numerators over the common denominator.

34. The LCD for two unlike proper fractions is ____________ the same as the GCF of their denominators.

35. The sum of two fractions can ____________ be simplified.

36. The difference of two proper fractions is ____________ less than either of the two fractions.

Solve each application.

37. Number Problem Paul bought $\frac{1}{2}$ pound (lb) of peanuts and $\frac{3}{8}$ lb of cashews. How many pounds of nuts did he buy?

38. Construction A countertop consists of a board $\frac{3}{4}$ inch (in.) thick and tile $\frac{3}{8}$ in. thick. What is the overall thickness? chapter 3 > Make the Connection

39. Business and Finance Amy budgets $\frac{2}{5}$ of her income for housing and $\frac{1}{6}$ of her income for food. What fraction of her income is budgeted for these two purposes? What fraction of her income remains?

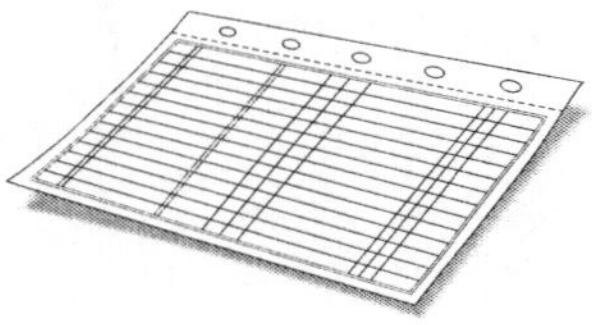

40. Social Science A person spends $\frac{3}{8}$ of a day at work and $\frac{1}{3}$ of a day sleeping. What fraction of a day do these two activities use? What fraction of the day remains?

< Objective 2 >

41. Number Problem Jose walked $\frac{3}{4}$ mile (mi) to the store, $\frac{1}{2}$ mi to a friend's house, and then $\frac{2}{3}$ mi home. How far did he walk?

42. Geometry Find the perimeter of, or the distance around, the accompanying figure.

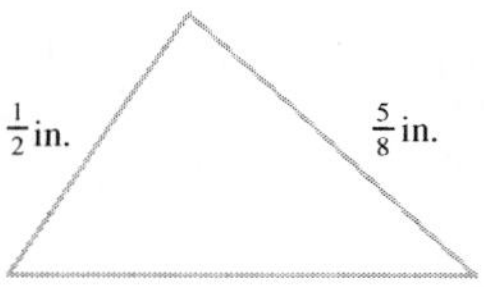

Answers

33. ____________

34. ____________

35. ____________

36. ____________

37. ____________

38. ____________

39. ____________

40. ____________

41. ____________

42. ____________

43. **Business and Finance** A budget guide states that you should spend $\frac{1}{4}$ of your salary for housing, $\frac{3}{16}$ for food, $\frac{1}{16}$ for clothing, and $\frac{1}{8}$ for transportation. What total portion of your salary do these four expenses account for?

44. **Business and Finance** Deductions from your paycheck are made roughly as follows: $\frac{1}{8}$ for federal tax, $\frac{1}{20}$ for state tax, $\frac{1}{20}$ for social security, and $\frac{1}{40}$ for a savings withholding plan. What portion of your pay is deducted?

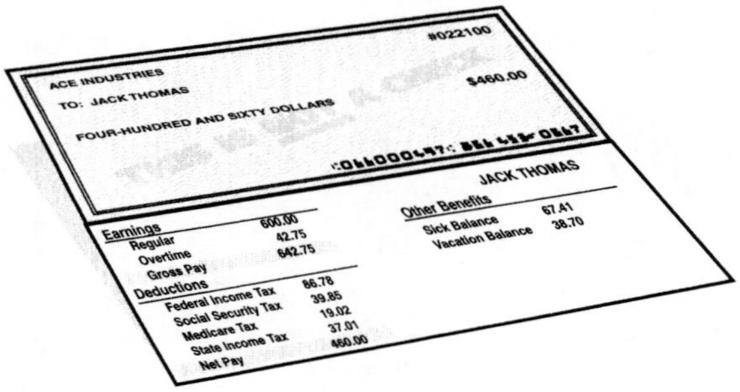

45. $\frac{1}{5} + \frac{7}{10} + \frac{4}{15}$

46. $\frac{2}{3} + \frac{1}{4} + \frac{3}{8}$

47. $\frac{1}{9} + \frac{7}{12} + \frac{5}{8}$

48. $\frac{1}{3} + \frac{5}{12} + \frac{4}{5}$

< Objective 3 >

Subtract.

49. $\frac{4}{5} - \frac{1}{3}$

50. $\frac{7}{9} - \frac{1}{6}$

51. $\frac{11}{15} - \frac{3}{5}$ Videos

52. $\frac{5}{6} - \frac{2}{7}$

53. $\frac{3}{8} - \frac{1}{4}$

54. $\frac{9}{10} - \frac{4}{5}$

55. $\frac{5}{12} - \frac{3}{8}$

56. $\frac{13}{15} - \frac{11}{20}$

Evaluate.

57. $\frac{33}{40} - \frac{7}{24} + \frac{11}{30}$ Videos

58. $\frac{13}{24} - \frac{5}{16} + \frac{3}{8}$

59. $\frac{15}{16} + \frac{5}{8} - \frac{1}{4}$

60. $\frac{9}{10} - \frac{1}{5} + \frac{1}{2}$

Answers

43. ______
44. ______
45. ______
46. ______
47. ______
48. ______
49. ______
50. ______
51. ______
52. ______
53. ______
54. ______
55. ______
56. ______
57. ______
58. ______
59. ______
60. ______

GEOMETRY *For exercises 61 and 62, find the missing dimension (?) in each figure.*

61.

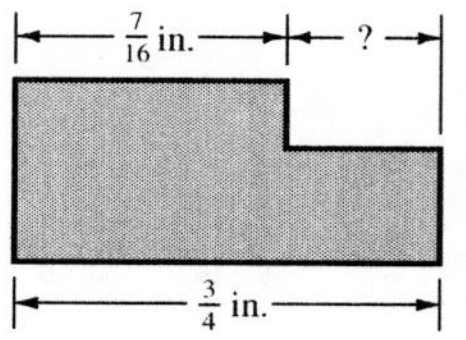

62.

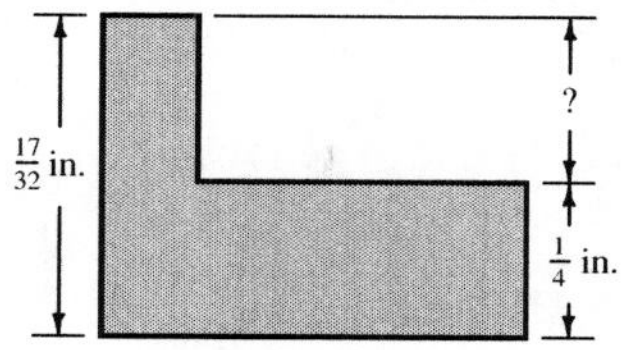

Basic Skills | Challenge Yourself | **Calculator/Computer** | Career Applications | Above and Beyond

Using Your Calculator to Add and Subtract Fractions

Adding or subtracting fractions on the calculator is very much like the multiplication and division you did in Chapter 2. The only thing that changes is the operation. Here's where the fraction calculator is a great tool for checking your work. No muss, no fuss, no searching for a common denominator. Just enter the fractions and get the right answer!

Find each sum or difference using your calculator.

63. $\dfrac{1}{10} + \dfrac{7}{12}$

64. $\dfrac{7}{15} + \dfrac{17}{24}$

65. $\dfrac{8}{9} + \dfrac{6}{7}$

66. $\dfrac{7}{15} + \dfrac{2}{5}$

67. $\dfrac{11}{18} + \dfrac{5}{12}$

68. $\dfrac{5}{8} + \dfrac{4}{9}$

69. $\dfrac{15}{17} - \dfrac{9}{11}$

70. $\dfrac{31}{43} - \dfrac{18}{53}$

71. $\dfrac{4}{9} - \dfrac{2}{5}$

72. $\dfrac{11}{13} - \dfrac{2}{3}$

Basic Skills | Challenge Yourself | Calculator/Computer | **Career Applications** | Above and Beyond

73. ALLIED HEALTH Prior to chemotherapy, a patient's malignant tumor weighed $\frac{5}{6}$ pound (lb). After a week of chemotherapy, the tumor's weight had been reduced by $\frac{1}{4}$ lb. How much did the tumor weigh at the end of the week?

74. ALLIED HEALTH Mrs. Lewis has three children who all need to take medication for the same illness. Charlie needs $\frac{3}{2}$ milliliters (mL), Sharon needs $\frac{2}{3}$ mL, and little Kevin needs $\frac{1}{4}$ mL of medication. How many milliliters of medication will Mrs. Lewis need to give each child a single dose of medicine?

Answers

61. ______

62. ______

63. ______

64. ______

65. ______

66. ______

67. ______

68. ______

69. ______

70. ______

71. ______

72. ______

73. ______

74. ______

Answers

75. ______

76. ______

77. ______

78. ______

79. ______

75. Manufacturing Technology Find the total thickness of this part.

chapter 3 > Make the Connection

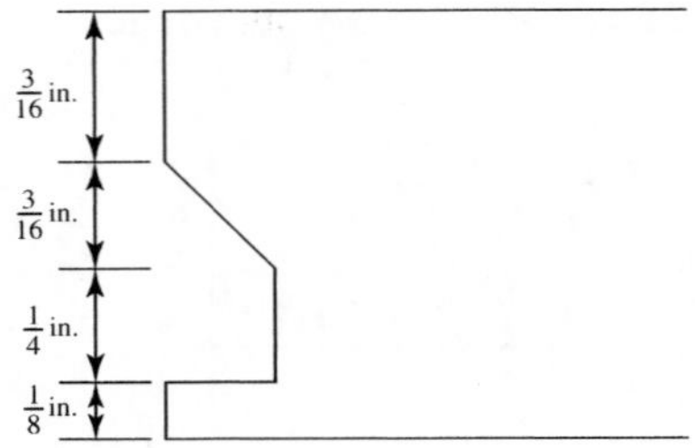

76. Manufacturing Technology Find the missing dimension (x).

chapter 3 > Make the Connection

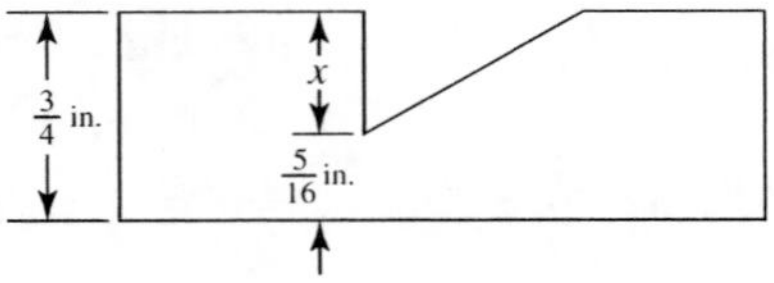

77. Electronics

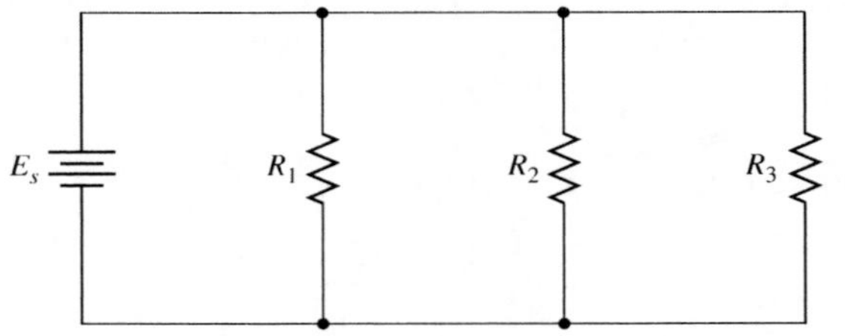

The circuit depicts three resistors (R_1, R_2, R_3) wired in parallel to a source, E_s. The circuit can be simplified by replacing the three separate resistors with a single equivalent resistor, R_{eq}, according to the following equation:

$$\frac{1}{R_{eq}} = \frac{1}{R_1} + \frac{1}{R_2} + \frac{1}{R_3}$$

If $R_1 = 10$ ohms (Ω), $R_2 = 20\ \Omega$, and $R_3 = 40\ \Omega$, what is $\frac{1}{R_{eq}}$?

What is R_{eq}?

78. Information Technology Amin wants to figure out how long it takes to transmit 1,000 bits over two networks that have transmission rates of 50,000 and 10,000 bits per second, respectively. What is the total time after the transmission? Use the fraction of the number of bits to the transmission time to figure out your answer. Represent your answer as a simplified fraction.

Basic Skills | Challenge Yourself | Calculator/Computer | Career Applications | **Above and Beyond**

79. Construction A door is $4\frac{1}{4}$ ft wide. Two hooks are to be attached to the door so that they are $1\frac{1}{2}$ in. apart and the same distance from each edge. How far from the edge of the door should each hook be located? Give your answer in feet.

chapter 3 > Make the Connection

80. Complete the following:

$\frac{1}{2} + \frac{1}{4} =$ ________.

$\frac{1}{2} + \frac{1}{4} + \frac{1}{8} =$ ________.

$\frac{1}{2} + \frac{1}{4} + \frac{1}{8} + \frac{1}{16} =$ ________.

Based on these results, predict the answer to

$\frac{1}{2} + \frac{1}{4} + \frac{1}{8} + \frac{1}{16} + \frac{1}{32} =$ ________

Now, do the addition, and check your prediction.

Answers

80. ________

Answers

1. 12 **3.** 8 **5.** 27

7. $8 = 2 \times 2 \times 2$; $12 = 2 \times 2 \times 3$; the LCD is $2 \times 2 \times 2 \times 3 = 24$ **9.** 42

11. 240 **13.** 60 **15.** 120 **17.** 50 **19.** $\frac{11}{12}$ **21.** $\frac{1}{2}$

23. $\frac{7}{8}$ **25.** $\frac{26}{35}$ **27.** $\frac{9}{14}$ **29.** $\frac{11}{21}$ **31.** $\frac{17}{24}$ **33.** always

35. sometimes **37.** $\frac{7}{8}$ lb **39.** $\frac{17}{30}, \frac{13}{30}$ **41.** $1\frac{11}{12}$ mi **43.** $\frac{5}{8}$

45. $\frac{1}{5} + \frac{7}{10} + \frac{4}{15} = \frac{6}{30} + \frac{21}{30} + \frac{8}{30} = \frac{35}{30} = 1\frac{5}{30} = 1\frac{1}{6}$ **47.** $1\frac{23}{72}$

49. $\frac{4}{5} - \frac{1}{3} = \frac{12}{15} - \frac{5}{15} = \frac{7}{15}$ **51.** $\frac{2}{15}$ **53.** $\frac{1}{8}$ **55.** $\frac{1}{24}$

57. $\frac{33}{40} - \frac{7}{24} + \frac{11}{30} = \frac{99}{120} - \frac{35}{120} + \frac{44}{120} = \frac{108}{120} = \frac{9}{10}$ **59.** $1\frac{5}{16}$

61. $\frac{5}{16}$ in. **63.** $\frac{41}{60}$ **65.** $1\frac{47}{63}$ **67.** $\frac{37}{36} = 1\frac{1}{36}$ **69.** $\frac{12}{187}$

71. $\frac{2}{45}$ **73.** $\frac{7}{12}$ lb **75.** $\frac{3}{4}$ in. **77.** $\frac{7}{40}; \frac{40}{7} = 5\frac{5}{7}$

79. 2 ft $\frac{3}{4}$ in. $= 2\frac{1}{16}$ ft

Activity 7 :: Kitchen Subflooring

Benjamin and Olivia are putting a new floor in their kitchen. To get the floor up to the desired height, they need to add $1\frac{1}{8}$ in. of subfloor. They can do this in one of two ways. They can put $\frac{1}{2}$-in. sheet on top of $\frac{5}{8}$-in. board (note that the total would be $\frac{9}{8}$ in. or $1\frac{1}{8}$ in.). They could also put $\frac{3}{8}$-in. board on top of $\frac{3}{4}$-in. sheet.

The table gives the price for each sheet of plywood from a construction materials store.

Thickness	Cost for a 4 ft × 8 ft Sheet
$\frac{1}{8}$ in.	\$9.15
$\frac{1}{4}$ in.	13.05
$\frac{3}{8}$ in.	14.99
$\frac{1}{2}$ in.	17.88
$\frac{5}{8}$ in.	19.13
$\frac{3}{4}$ in.	21.36
$\frac{7}{8}$ in.	25.23
1 in.	28.49

1. What is the combined price for a $\frac{1}{2}$-in. sheet and a $\frac{5}{8}$-in. sheet?

2. What is the combined price for a $\frac{3}{8}$-in. sheet and a $\frac{3}{4}$-in. sheet?

3. What other combination of sheets of plywood, using two sheets, yields the needed $1\frac{1}{8}$-in. thickness?

4. Of the four combinations, which is most economical?

5. The kitchen is to be 12 ft × 12 ft. Find the total cost of the plywood you have suggested in question 4.

3.4 Adding and Subtracting Mixed Numbers

< 3.4 Objectives >

1 > Add any two mixed numbers

2 > Add any group of mixed numbers

3 > Subtract any two mixed numbers

4 > Solve an application that involves addition or subtraction of mixed numbers

Once you know how to add fractions, adding mixed numbers is straightforward. Keep in mind that addition involves combining groups of the *same kind* of objects. Because mixed numbers consist of two parts—a whole number and a fraction—we can work with the whole numbers and the fractions separately.

Step by Step

To Add Mixed Numbers

Step 1	Find the LCD.
Step 2	Rewrite the fraction parts to match the LCD.
Step 3	Add the fraction parts.
Step 4	Add the whole number parts.
Step 5	Simplify if necessary.

Example 1 illustrates the use of this rule.

Example 1 Adding Mixed Numbers

< Objective 1 >

Add $3\frac{1}{5} + 4\frac{2}{5}$.

$$\begin{array}{r} 3\frac{1}{5} \\ +\ 4\frac{2}{5} \\ \hline 7\frac{3}{5} \end{array}$$

$$3\frac{1}{5} + 4\frac{2}{5} = 7\frac{3}{5}$$

Check Yourself 1

Add $2\frac{3}{10} + 3\frac{4}{10}$.

When the fractional portions of the mixed numbers have different denominators, we must rename these fractions as equivalent fractions with the least common denominator to perform the addition in step 2. Consider Example 2.

Example 2 Adding Mixed Numbers with Different Denominators

Add.

$$\begin{array}{rcl} 3\frac{1}{6} & = & 3\frac{4}{24} \\ +\ 2\frac{3}{8} & = & 2\frac{9}{24} \\ \hline & & 5\frac{13}{24} \end{array}$$

The LCD of the fractions is 24. Rename them with that denominator.

Check Yourself 2

Add $5\frac{1}{10} + 3\frac{1}{6}$.

You follow the same procedure if more than two mixed numbers are involved in the problem.

Example 3 Adding Mixed Numbers with Different Denominators

< Objective 2 >

NOTE

The LCD of the three fractions is 40. Convert to equivalent fractions.

Add.

$$\begin{array}{rcl} 2\frac{1}{5} & = & 2\frac{8}{40} \\ 3\frac{3}{4} & = & 3\frac{30}{40} \\ +\ 4\frac{1}{8} & = & 4\frac{5}{40} \\ \hline & & 9\frac{43}{40} \end{array}$$

$$9\frac{43}{40} = 9 + \frac{43}{40} = 9 + 1 + \frac{3}{40} = 10\frac{3}{40}$$

Check Yourself 3

Add $5\frac{1}{2} + 4\frac{2}{3} + 3\frac{3}{4}$.

We can use a similar technique for *subtracting* mixed numbers. The process is like adding mixed numbers.

Step by Step

To Subtract Mixed Numbers

Step 1 Find the LCD.
Step 2 Rewrite the fraction parts to match the LCD.
Step 3 Subtract the fraction parts.
Step 4 Subtract the whole number parts.
Step 5 Simplify if necessary.

Example 4 illustrates the use of this process.

Example 4 Subtracting Mixed Numbers with Like Denominators

< Objective 3 >

Subtract.

$$\begin{array}{r} 5\frac{7}{12} \\ -\ 3\frac{5}{12} \\ \hline 2\frac{2}{12} \end{array}$$

$$2\frac{2}{12} = 2\frac{1}{6}$$

Check Yourself 4

Subtract $8\frac{7}{8} - 5\frac{3}{8}$.

Again, we must rename the fractions if different denominators are involved. This approach is shown in Example 5.

Example 5 Subtracting Mixed Numbers with Different Denominators

Subtract. $8\frac{7}{10} - 3\frac{3}{8}$.

$$8\frac{7}{10} = 8\frac{28}{40}$$ Write the fractions with denominator 40.

$$-\ 3\frac{3}{8} = 3\frac{15}{40}$$

$$5\frac{13}{40}$$ Subtract as before.

Check Yourself 5

Subtract $7\frac{11}{12} - 3\frac{5}{8}$.

To subtract a mixed number from a whole number, we must use a form of regrouping, or borrowing.

Example 6 Subtracting Mixed Numbers by Borrowing

NOTE

$6 = 5 + 1$

$= 5 + \frac{4}{4}$

Subtract $6 - 2\frac{3}{4}$.

$$6 = 5\frac{4}{4}$$

$$-\ 2\frac{3}{4} = 2\frac{3}{4}$$

$$3\frac{1}{4}$$

There is no fraction from which we can subtract the $\frac{3}{4}$. We regroup so that we can borrow 1 from the 6 and write it as $\frac{4}{4}$.

Check Yourself 6

Subtract.

(a) $7 - 3\frac{2}{5}$ **(b)** $9 - 2\frac{5}{7}$

A similar technique is used whenever the fraction of the minuend is smaller than the fraction of the subtrahend.

Example 7 Subtracting Mixed Numbers by Borrowing

Subtract.

$$\begin{array}{r} 5\frac{3}{8} = 5\frac{3}{8} \\ -\ 3\frac{3}{4} = 3\frac{6}{8} \\ \hline \end{array}$$

Because you cannot subtract $\frac{6}{8}$ from $\frac{3}{8}$, borrow 1 from the 5 in the minuend.

$$\begin{array}{r} 5\frac{3}{8} = 5\frac{3}{8} = 4\frac{11}{8} \\ -\ 3\frac{3}{4} = 3\frac{6}{8} = 3\frac{6}{8} \\ \hline 1\frac{5}{8} \end{array}$$

Because $5 = 4 + 1$, rewrite the 1 as $\frac{8}{8}$ and add it to $\frac{3}{8}$ to get $\frac{11}{8}$.

Check Yourself 7

Subtract.

(a) $12\frac{5}{12} - 8\frac{2}{3}$ **(b)** $27\frac{7}{8} - 2\frac{9}{10}$

There is an alternative method that can be used when subtracting fractions. We can convert each mixed number into an improper fraction and then perform the subtraction. Although this technique requires an extra step, it eliminates the need to regroup.

Example 8 Subtracting by Converting to Improper Fractions

Subtract.

$4\frac{5}{9} - 2\frac{11}{12}$ First, convert to improper fractions.

$\frac{41}{9} - \frac{35}{12}$ The LCD is 36. Find the equivalent fractions and subtract.

$\frac{164}{36} - \frac{105}{36} = \frac{59}{36}$ Rewrite as a mixed number.

$\frac{59}{36} = 1\frac{23}{36}$

Check Yourself 8

Subtract $5\frac{1}{4} - 2\frac{5}{18}$.

Example 9 An Application of the Subtraction of Mixed Numbers

< Objective 4 >

Linda was $48\frac{1}{4}$ inches (in.) tall on her sixth birthday. By her seventh year she was $51\frac{5}{8}$ in. tall. How much did she grow during the year?

Because we want the difference in height, we must subtract $48\frac{1}{4}$ from $51\frac{5}{8}$.

$$\begin{array}{rcr} 51\frac{5}{8} & = & 51\frac{5}{8} \\ -\,48\frac{1}{4} & = & 48\frac{2}{8} \\ \hline & & 3\frac{3}{8} \end{array}$$

Linda grew $3\frac{3}{8}$ in. during the year.

Check Yourself 9

You use $4\frac{3}{4}$ yards (yd) of fabric from a 50-yd bolt. How much fabric remains on the bolt?

Often we will have to use more than one operation to find the solution to a problem. Consider Example 10.

Example 10 An Application Involving Mixed Numbers

A rectangular poster is to have a total length of $12\frac{1}{4}$ in. We want a $1\frac{3}{8}$-in. border on the top and a 2-in. border on the bottom. What is the length of the printed part of the poster?

First, we draw a sketch of the poster:

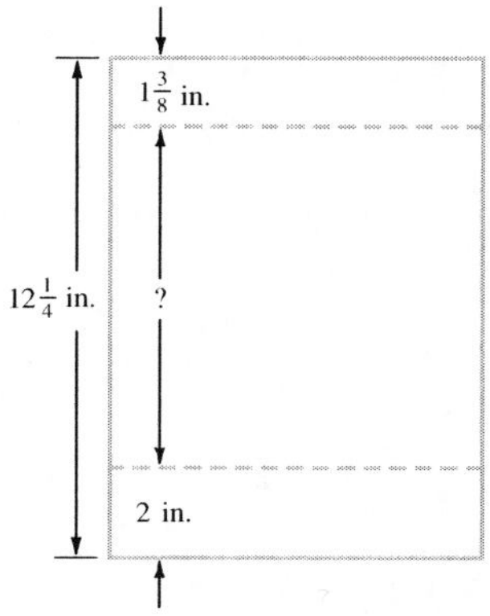

Now, we use this sketch to find the total width of the top and bottom borders.

$$\begin{array}{r} 1\frac{3}{8} \\ +\ 2 \\ \hline 3\frac{3}{8} \end{array}$$

Now *subtract* that sum (the top and bottom borders) from the total length of the poster.

$$\begin{array}{rcrcr} 12\frac{1}{4} & = & 12\frac{2}{8} & = & 11\frac{10}{8} \\ -\ 3\frac{3}{8} & = & 3\frac{3}{8} & = & 3\frac{3}{8} \\ \hline & & & & 8\frac{7}{8} \end{array}$$

The length of the printed part is $8\frac{7}{8}$ in.

Check Yourself 10

You cut one shelf $3\frac{3}{4}$ feet (ft) long and one $4\frac{1}{2}$ ft long from a 12-ft piece of lumber. Can you cut another shelf 4 ft long?

Check Yourself ANSWERS

1. $5\frac{7}{10}$ **2.** $8\frac{4}{15}$ **3.** $13\frac{11}{12}$ **4.** $3\frac{1}{2}$

5. $7\frac{11}{12} - 3\frac{5}{8} = 7\frac{22}{24} - 3\frac{15}{24} = 4\frac{7}{24}$ **6.** **(a)** $3\frac{3}{5}$; **(b)** $6\frac{2}{7}$

7. **(a)** $3\frac{3}{4}$; **(b)** $24\frac{39}{40}$ **8.** $2\frac{35}{36}$ **9.** $45\frac{1}{4}$ yd **10.** No, only $3\frac{3}{4}$ ft remains.

Reading Your Text

The following fill-in-the-blank exercises are designed to ensure that you understand some of the key vocabulary used in this section.

SECTION 3.4

(a) To add mixed numbers, we first find the ____________ of the fractions.

(b) To subtract a mixed number from a whole number, we must use a form of ____________, or borrowing.

(c) When the fractional portions of mixed numbers have different denominators, we rename the fractions as ____________ fractions.

(d) We will always need to borrow when subtracting mixed numbers if the minuend is ____________ than the subtrahend.

Basic Skills | Challenge Yourself | Calculator/Computer | Career Applications | Above and Beyond

3.4 exercises

< Objective 1 >

Perform the indicated operations.

1. $2\frac{2}{9} + 3\frac{5}{9}$

2. $5\frac{2}{9} + 6\frac{4}{9}$

3. $2\frac{1}{9} + 5\frac{5}{9}$

4. $1\frac{1}{6} + 5\frac{5}{6}$

5. $6\frac{5}{9} + 4\frac{7}{9}$ > Videos

6. $5\frac{8}{9} + 4\frac{4}{9}$

7. $1\frac{1}{3} + 2\frac{1}{5}$

8. $2\frac{1}{4} + 1\frac{1}{6}$

< Objective 2 >

9. $2\frac{1}{4} + 3\frac{5}{8} + 1\frac{1}{6}$

10. $3\frac{1}{5} + 2\frac{1}{2} + 5\frac{1}{4}$

11. $3\frac{3}{5} + 4\frac{1}{4} + 5\frac{3}{10}$ > Videos

12. $4\frac{5}{6} + 3\frac{2}{3} + 7\frac{5}{9}$

< Objective 3 >

13. $7\frac{7}{8} - 3\frac{3}{8}$

14. $3\frac{5}{6} - 1\frac{1}{6}$

15. $3\frac{2}{5} - 1\frac{4}{5}$

16. $5\frac{3}{7} - 2\frac{5}{7}$

17. $3\frac{2}{3} - 2\frac{1}{4}$ > Videos

18. $5\frac{4}{5} - 2\frac{5}{6}$

19. $7\frac{5}{12} - 3\frac{11}{18}$ > Videos

20. $9\frac{3}{7} - 2\frac{13}{21}$

21. $5 - 2\frac{1}{4}$

22. $4 - 1\frac{2}{3}$

23. $17 - 8\frac{3}{4}$

24. $23 - 11\frac{5}{8}$

25. $3\frac{3}{4} + 5\frac{1}{2} - 2\frac{3}{8}$

26. $1\frac{5}{6} + 3\frac{5}{12} - 2\frac{1}{4}$

27. $2\frac{3}{8} + 2\frac{1}{4} - 1\frac{5}{6}$

28. $1\frac{1}{15} + 3\frac{3}{10} - 2\frac{4}{5}$

Name ____________

Section ________ Date ________

Answers

1. ________ 2. ________

3. ________ 4. ________

5. ________ 6. ________

7. ________ 8. ________

9. ________ 10. ________

11. ________ 12. ________

13. ________ 14. ________

15. ________ 16. ________

17. ________ 18. ________

19. ________ 20. ________

21. ________ 22. ________

23. ________ 24. ________

25. ________ 26. ________

27. ________ 28. ________

Basic Skills | **Challenge Yourself** | Calculator/Computer | Career Applications | Above and Beyond

Answers

29. ______

30. ______

31. ______

32. ______

33. ______

34. ______

35. ______

36. ______

37. ______

38. ______

39. ______

For exercises 29 to 32, label each statement as **true** *or* **false.**

29. The LCM of 3, 6, and 12 is 24.

30. The GCF of 15, 21, and 300 is 3.

31. The LCD for $\frac{3}{4}$, $\frac{9}{10}$, and $\frac{3}{20}$ is 40.

32. The LCD for $\frac{5}{6}$, $\frac{13}{15}$, and $\frac{1}{21}$ is 3.

< Objective 4 >

Solve each application.

33. Crafts Senta is working on a project that uses three pieces of fabric with lengths of $\frac{3}{4}$, $1\frac{1}{4}$, and $\frac{5}{8}$ yd. She needs to allow for $\frac{1}{8}$ yd of waste. How much fabric should she buy?

34. Construction The framework of a wall is $3\frac{1}{2}$ in. thick. We apply $\frac{5}{8}$-in. wallboard and $\frac{1}{4}$-in. paneling to the inside. Siding that is $\frac{3}{4}$ in. thick is applied to the outside. What is the finished thickness of the wall? chapter 3 > Make the Connection

35. Business and Finance A stock was listed at $34\frac{3}{8}$ points on Monday. By closing time Friday, it was at $28\frac{3}{4}$. How much did it drop during the week?

36. Crafts A roast weighed $4\frac{1}{4}$ lb before cooking and $3\frac{3}{8}$ lb after cooking. How many pounds were lost during the cooking?

37. Crafts A roll of paper contains $30\frac{1}{4}$ yd. If $16\frac{7}{8}$ yd is cut from the roll, how much paper remains?

38. Geometry Find the missing dimension in the given figure.

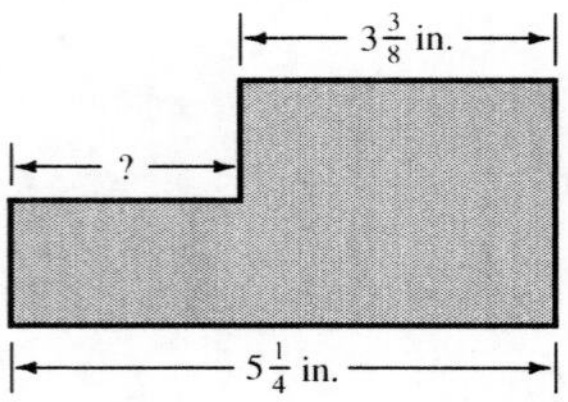

39. Crafts A $4\frac{1}{4}$-in. bolt is placed through a board that is $3\frac{1}{2}$ in. thick. How far does the bolt extend beyond the board? chapter 3 > Make the Connection

40. **Business and Finance** Ben can work 20 h per week on a part-time job. He works $5\frac{1}{2}$ h on Monday and $3\frac{3}{4}$ h on Tuesday. How many more hours can he work during the week?

41. **Geometry** Find the missing dimension in the given figure.

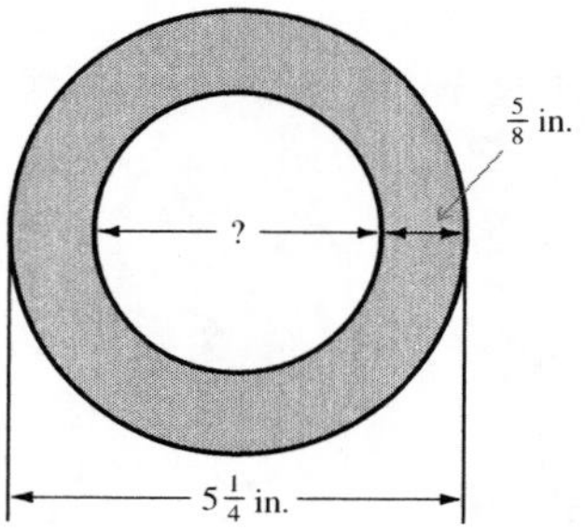

42. **Construction** The Whites used $20\frac{3}{4}$ square yards (yd^2) of carpet for their living room, $15\frac{1}{2}$ yd^2 for the dining room, and $6\frac{1}{4}$ yd^2 for a hallway. How much remains if a 50-yd^2 roll of carpet is used?

Evaluate.

43. $4\frac{1}{8} + \frac{3}{7} - 2\frac{23}{28}$

44. $5\frac{1}{3} + 1\frac{3}{7} - 5\frac{23}{42}$

45. $6\frac{1}{11} + \frac{2}{3} - 2\frac{1}{6}$

46. $3\frac{1}{5} + 1\frac{7}{8} - 5\frac{1}{20}$

47. $6\frac{1}{11} - \frac{2}{3} + 2\frac{1}{6}$

48. $3\frac{1}{5} - 1\frac{7}{8} + 5\frac{1}{20}$

Answers

40. ______

41. ______

42. ______

43. ______

44. ______

45. ______

46. ______

47. ______

48. ______

Basic Skills | Challenge Yourself | **Calculator/Computer** | Career Applications | Above and Beyond

Using Your Calculator to Add and Subtract Mixed Numbers

We have already seen how to add, subtract, multiply, and divide fractions using our calculators. Now we will use our calculators to add and subtract mixed numbers.

Scientific Calculator

To enter a mixed number on a scientific calculator, press the fraction key between both the whole number and the numerator and denominator. For example, to enter $3\frac{7}{12}$, press

3 [a b/c] 7 [a b/c] 12

Graphing Calculator

As with multiplying and dividing fractions, when using a graphing calculator, you must choose the fraction option from the math menu before pressing [Enter].

Answers

49. ______

50. ______

51. ______

52. ______

53. ______

54. ______

55. ______

56. ______

57. ______

58. ______

59. ______

For the problem $3\frac{7}{12} + 2\frac{11}{16}$, the keystroke sequence is

[( ] 3 [+] 7 [÷] 12 [ )] [+] [( ] 2 [+] 11 [÷] 16 [ )] [►Frac] [Enter]

Note that the parentheses are very important when doing subtraction. The display will read $\frac{301}{48}$. This is equivalent to $6\frac{13}{48}$.

Add or subtract.

49. $4\frac{7}{9} - 2\frac{11}{18}$

50. $7\frac{8}{11} - 4\frac{13}{22}$

51. $5\frac{11}{16} - 2\frac{5}{12}$

52. $18\frac{5}{24} - 11\frac{3}{40}$

53. $6\frac{2}{3} - 1\frac{5}{6}$

54. $131\frac{43}{45} - 99\frac{27}{60}$

55. $10\frac{2}{3} + 4\frac{1}{5} + 7\frac{2}{15}$

56. $7\frac{1}{5} + 3\frac{2}{3} + 1\frac{1}{5}$

Basic Skills | Challenge Yourself | Calculator/Computer | **Career Applications** | Above and Beyond

57. Manufacturing Technology A factory floor is made up of several layers shown in the drawing.

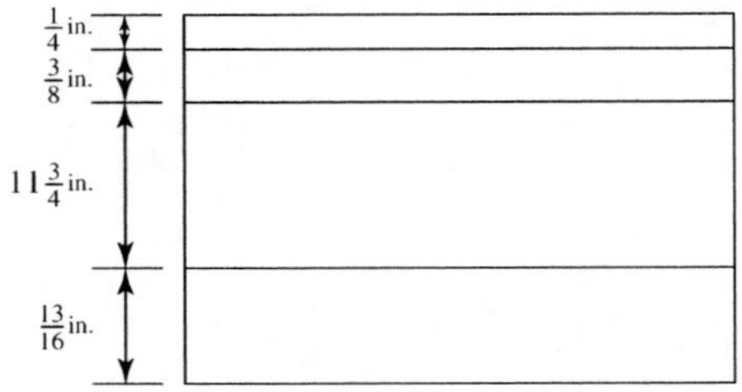

What is the total thickness of the floor?

chapter 3 > Make the Connection

58. Manufacturing Technology Pieces that are $2\frac{1}{4}$, $5\frac{1}{16}$, $4\frac{3}{4}$, and $1\frac{7}{8}$ in. long need to be cut from round stock. How long of a piece of round stock is required? (Allow $\frac{3}{32}$ in. for each saw kerf.)

chapter 3 > Make the Connection

59. Information Technology Joy is running cable in a new office building in downtown Washington, D.C. She has $60\frac{1}{4}$ ft of cable but she needs 100 ft. How much more cable is needed?

60. **INFORMATION TECHNOLOGY** Abraham has a part-time technician job while he is going to college. He works the following hours in one week: $3\frac{1}{4}$, $5\frac{3}{4}$, $4\frac{1}{2}$, 4, and $2\frac{1}{4}$. For the week, how many hours did Abraham work?

Answers

60. ______

Answers

1. $5\frac{7}{9}$ **3.** $7\frac{2}{3}$ **5.** $11\frac{1}{3}$ **7.** $3\frac{8}{15}$ **9.** $7\frac{1}{24}$ **11.** $13\frac{3}{20}$ **13.** $4\frac{1}{2}$ **15.** $1\frac{3}{5}$ **17.** $1\frac{5}{12}$ **19.** $3\frac{29}{36}$ **21.** $2\frac{3}{4}$ **23.** $8\frac{1}{4}$ **25.** $6\frac{7}{8}$ **27.** $2\frac{19}{24}$ **29.** False **31.** False **33.** $2\frac{3}{4}$ yd **35.** $5\frac{5}{8}$ points **37.** $13\frac{3}{8}$ yd **39.** $\frac{3}{4}$ in. **41.** 4 in. **43.** $1\frac{41}{56}$ **45.** $4\frac{13}{22}$ **47.** $7\frac{13}{22}$ **49.** $2\frac{1}{6}$ **51.** $3\frac{13}{48}$ **53.** $4\frac{5}{6}$ **55.** 22 **57.** $13\frac{3}{16}$ in. **59.** $39\frac{3}{4}$ ft

Activity 8 :: Sharing Costs

The Associated Student Government at CCC is sending six students to the national conference in Washington, D.C. Two of the students, Mikaila and Courtney, are in charge of making the room reservations. Looking at the hotels that are either hosting or adjacent to the conference site, they come up with the following information. Accommodations were not available for places on the table that are blank.

Hotel	Price for a Single	Price for a Double	Price for a Triple	Suite (Sleeps 6)
Wyndham	\$180	\$180	\$210	
St. Gregory	168	198	240	\$450
Hyatt	190	190	222	
Marriott	159	174		

1. If they get three double rooms at the Marriott and each pays $\frac{1}{6}$ of the bill, what is the cost per person each night?
2. If they stay at the Wyndham in a triple room, they need only two rooms. If they each pay $\frac{1}{6}$ of that total bill, what is the cost per night?
3. If they get the suite at the St. Gregory, what is the per-person cost per night?
4. The Hyatt and the St. Gregory each offer a free breakfast for each person staying there. Is it now cheaper to stay at the Hyatt in a triple room than at the Wyndham? What information would you need to make the decision?
5. What about the St. Gregory suite with a free breakfast? How do you now make the decision?

3.5 Order of Operations with Fractions

< 3.5 Objectives >

1 > Evaluate an expression with grouping symbols

2 > Solve an application that involves evaluating an expression

In Chapter 1, we introduced the order of operations. We repeat them here with a small addition to step 1.

Step by Step

Evaluating an Expression

Step 1 Do any operations within parentheses or other grouping symbols.

Step 2 Apply any exponents.

Step 3 Do all multiplication and division in order from left to right.

Step 4 Do all addition and subtraction in order from left to right.

The following examples demonstrate the use of the order of operations in evaluating expressions involving fractions. Refer to the steps as we evaluate each expression.

Example 1 Evaluating an Expression

Evaluate.

$\frac{14}{15} - \left(\frac{1}{2}\right)^2 \cdot \left(\frac{2}{3} + \frac{4}{5}\right)$ Perform operations in parentheses.

$= \frac{14}{15} - \left(\frac{1}{2}\right)^2 \cdot \left(\frac{22}{15}\right)$ The next step is to apply the exponents.

$= \frac{14}{15} - \left(\frac{1}{4}\right) \cdot \left(\frac{22}{15}\right)$ The next step is to perform the multiplication.

$= \frac{14}{15} - \frac{11}{30}$ The final step is to perform addition and subtraction.

$= \frac{17}{30}$

Check Yourself 1

Evaluate.

$\left(\frac{2}{3}\right)^3 + \left(\frac{1}{3}\right)^2 \cdot \left(\frac{1}{2} + \frac{2}{3}\right)$

Recall that, once parentheses are removed, multiplication and division are always performed left to right. Example 2 illustrates.

Example 2 Evaluating an Expression

Evaluate.

$$\left(\frac{1}{13}\right)^2 \cdot \left(\frac{1}{4} + \frac{1}{6}\right) \div \frac{5}{13}$$ Add the expression inside the parentheses.

$$= \left(\frac{1}{13}\right)^2 \cdot \left(\frac{5}{12}\right) \div \frac{5}{13}$$ Apply the exponent.

$$= \frac{1}{169} \cdot \frac{5}{12} \div \frac{5}{13}$$ Invert and multiply.

$$= \frac{1}{\cancel{169}_{13}} \cdot \frac{\cancel{5}^{1}}{12} \cdot \frac{\cancel{13}^{1}}{\cancel{5}_{1}} = \frac{1}{156}$$

Check Yourself 2

Evaluate.

$$\left(\frac{1}{5}\right)^2 \cdot \left(\frac{3}{10} + \frac{1}{2}\right) \div \frac{2}{5}$$

When mixed numbers are involved in a complex expression, it is almost always best to convert them to improper fractions before continuing.

Example 3 Evaluating an Expression with Mixed Numbers

Evaluate.

$$3\frac{3}{4} + 5 \cdot \left(2\frac{1}{2}\right)$$ Rewrite the mixed numbers as improper fractions.

$$= \frac{15}{4} + 5 \cdot \left(\frac{5}{2}\right)$$ Multiplication precedes addition in the order of operations.

$$= \frac{15}{4} + \frac{25}{2}$$ To add, use the common denominator of 4.

$$= \frac{15}{4} + \frac{50}{4} = \frac{65}{4} = 16\frac{1}{4}$$

Check Yourself 3

Evaluate.

$$4\frac{1}{3} - \frac{1}{2} \cdot \left(5\frac{1}{8}\right)$$

Example 4 illustrates an application of the material in this section.

Example 4 Solving an Application

One formula for calculating children's dosages based on the recommended adult dosage and the child's age in years is Young's rule:

$$\text{Child's dose} = \left(\frac{\text{age}}{\text{age} + 12}\right) \times \text{adult dose}$$

According to this rule, the dose prescribed to a 3-year-old child if the recommended adult dose is 24 milligrams (mg) can be found by evaluating the expression

$$\left(\frac{3}{3 + 12}\right) \times 24 \text{ mg}$$

To evaluate this expression, first we do the operations inside the parentheses.

$$\left(\frac{3}{3+12}\right) \times 24 \text{ mg}$$

$$= \left(\frac{3}{15}\right) \times 24 \text{ mg}$$

$$= \frac{1}{5} \times \frac{24}{1} \text{ mg} = \frac{24}{5} \text{ mg} = 4\frac{4}{5} \text{ mg}$$

Check Yourself 4

The approximate length of the belt pictured is given by

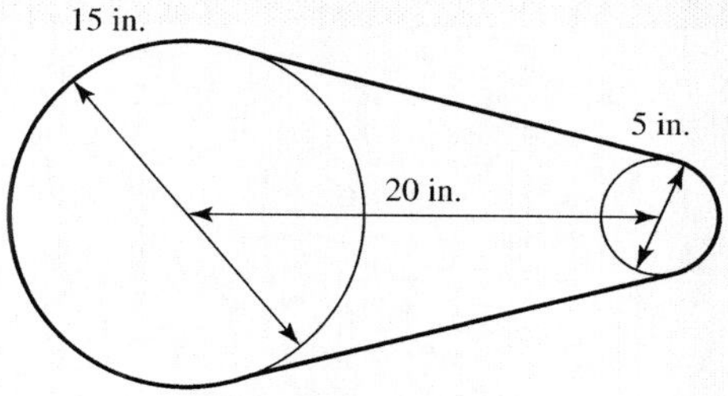

$$\frac{22}{7}\left(\frac{1}{2} \cdot 15 + \frac{1}{2} \cdot 5\right) + 2 \cdot 21$$

Find the length of the belt.

Check Yourself ANSWERS

1. $\frac{23}{54}$ **2.** $\frac{2}{25}$ **3.** $1\frac{37}{48}$ **4.** $73\frac{3}{7}$ in.

Reading Your Text

The following fill-in-the-blank exercises are designed to ensure that you understand some of the key vocabulary used in this section.

SECTION 3.5

(a) In evaluating an expression, first do operations inside parentheses or other ______________ symbols.

(b) The second step in evaluating an expression is to evaluate all ______________.

(c) When dividing by a fraction, ______________ and multiply by that fraction.

(d) When mixed numbers are involved in a complex expression, it is almost always best to convert them to __________ fractions before continuing.

3.5 exercises

Boost *your* GRADE at ALEKS.com!

ALEKS®

- Practice Problems
- Self-Tests
- NetTutor
- e-Professors
- Videos

Name ______________

Section ________ Date ________

Answers

1. ________ 2. ________
3. ________ 4. ________
5. ________ 6. ________
7. ________ 8. ________
9. ________ 10. ________
11. ________ 12. ________
13. ________ 14. ________
15. ________ 16. ________
17. ________
18. ________
19. ________
20. ________
21. ________

Basic Skills | Challenge Yourself | Calculator/Computer | Career Applications | Above and Beyond

Evaluate.

1. $\frac{1}{3} - \left(\frac{1}{2} - \frac{1}{4}\right)$ Videos

2. $\frac{2}{3} - \left(\frac{3}{4} - \frac{1}{2}\right)$

3. $\frac{3}{4} - \left(\frac{1}{2}\right)\left(\frac{1}{3}\right)$ Videos

4. $\frac{5}{6} - \left(\frac{3}{4}\right)\left(\frac{2}{3}\right)$

5. $\left(\frac{1}{2}\right)^2 - \left(\frac{1}{4} - \frac{1}{5}\right)$

6. $\left(\frac{3}{4}\right)^2 - \left(\frac{1}{2} - \frac{1}{3}\right)$

7. $\frac{1}{2} + \frac{2}{3} \cdot \frac{9}{16}$

8. $\frac{2}{3} + \frac{1}{2} \div \frac{3}{4}$

9. $\left(\frac{1}{3}\right)\left(\frac{1}{2} + \frac{1}{4}\right)$

10. $\left(\frac{3}{4}\right)\left(\frac{1}{2} - \frac{1}{3}\right)$

Basic Skills | **Challenge Yourself** | Calculator/Computer | Career Applications | Above and Beyond

11. $\left(\frac{1}{2}\right)^3 + \left(\frac{1}{3}\right) \cdot \left(\frac{1}{2} + \frac{1}{4}\right)$ Videos

12. $\left(\frac{1}{3}\right) + \left(\frac{1}{2}\right)^2 \cdot \left(\frac{1}{3} + \frac{1}{6}\right)$

13. $\left(\frac{3}{4}\right)^2 + \left(\frac{1}{2}\right)^3 \cdot \left(\frac{1}{2} + \frac{3}{4}\right)$

14. $\left(\frac{1}{10}\right) + \left(\frac{1}{2}\right)^3 \cdot \left(\frac{1}{5} + \frac{1}{15}\right)$

15. $\left(\frac{2}{3}\right)^2 \cdot \left(\frac{2}{15} + \frac{1}{2}\right) \div \frac{3}{5}$

16. $\left(\frac{1}{3}\right)^3 \cdot \left(\frac{1}{4} + \frac{1}{2}\right) \div \frac{2}{9}$

17. $2\frac{1}{5} - \frac{1}{2} \cdot \frac{1}{4}$

18. $4\frac{3}{8} - \frac{1}{2} \cdot \frac{1}{5}$

19. $11\frac{1}{10} - \frac{1}{2} \cdot \left(6\frac{2}{3}\right)$

20. $12\frac{2}{7} - \frac{1}{3} \cdot \left(3\frac{3}{7}\right)$

21. **Construction** A construction company has bids for paving roads of $1\frac{1}{2}$, $\frac{3}{4}$, and $3\frac{1}{3}$ miles (mi) for the month of July. With their present equipment, they can pave 8 mi in 1 month. How much more work can they take on in July?

22. Statistics On an 8-h trip, Jack drives $2\frac{3}{4}$ h and Pat drives $2\frac{1}{2}$ h. How many hours are left to drive?

23. Statistics A runner has told herself that she will run 20 mi each week. She runs $5\frac{1}{2}$ mi on Sunday, $4\frac{1}{4}$ mi on Tuesday, $4\frac{3}{4}$ mi on Wednesday, and $2\frac{1}{8}$ mi on Friday. How far must she run on Saturday to meet her goal?

24. Science and Medicine If paper takes up $\frac{1}{2}$ of the space in a landfill and plastic takes up $\frac{1}{10}$ of the space, how much of the landfill is used for other materials?

25. Science and Medicine If paper takes up $\frac{1}{2}$ of the space in a landfill and organic waste takes up $\frac{1}{8}$ of the space, how much of the landfill is used for other materials?

26. Business and Finance The interest rate on an auto loan in May was $12\frac{3}{8}$%. By September the rate was up to $14\frac{1}{4}$%. By how many percentage points did the interest rate increase over the period?

Basic Skills | Challenge Yourself | Calculator/Computer | **Career Applications** | Above and Beyond

27. Allied Health Simone suffers from Gaucher's disease. The recommended dosage of Cerezyme is $2\frac{1}{2}$ units per kilogram (kg) of the patient's weight. How much Cerezyme should the doctor prescribe if Simone weighs $15\frac{1}{3}$ kg?

28. Information Technology Kendra is running cable in a new office building in downtown Kansas City. She has $110\frac{1}{4}$ ft of cable, but she needs 150 ft. How much more cable is needed?

29. Manufacturing Technology A cut $3\frac{3}{8}$ in. long needs to be made in a piece of material. The cut rate is $\frac{3}{4}$ in. per minute. How many minutes does it take to make the cut?

30. Manufacturing Technology Calculate the distance from the center of hole A to the center of hole B.

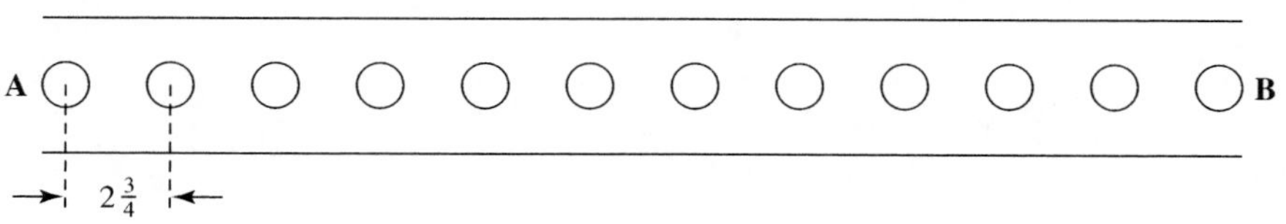

Answers

22. ______

23. ______

24. ______

25. ______

26. ______

27. ______

28. ______

29. ______

30. ______

Answers

31. ____________

32. ____________

31. **Information Technology** On average, $18\frac{1}{4}$ printed circuit boards can be completely populated with components (with all parts soldered to the board) by Amara in 1 h. Burt can complete $34\frac{2}{3}$ printed circuit boards in 2 h. If both workers continue at their respective average paces, how many total printed circuit boards can be populated in 8 h?

32. **Information Technology** If Carlos joins Amara and Burt in soldering components on circuit boards, the three workers can average 410 complete boards in 8 h. Assuming the other two workers perform at their respective averages stated in exercise 31, how many boards can Carlos average in 8 h? How many boards does Carlos average in 1 h?

Answers

1. $\frac{1}{12}$ 3. $\frac{7}{12}$ 5. $\frac{1}{5}$ 7. $\frac{7}{8}$ 9. $\frac{1}{4}$ 11. $\frac{3}{8}$ 13. $\frac{23}{32}$ 15. $\frac{38}{81}$ 17. $2\frac{3}{40}$ 19. $7\frac{23}{30}$ 21. $2\frac{5}{12}$ mi 23. $3\frac{3}{8}$ mi 25. $\frac{3}{8}$ 27. $38\frac{1}{3}$ units 29. $4\frac{1}{2}$ min 31. $284\frac{2}{3}$ or 284 completed boards

3.6 Estimation Applications

< 3.6 Objective >

1 > Use estimation to solve application problems

Units ANALYSIS

Every denominate number with a fractional unit, such as

$$25 \frac{\text{mi}}{\text{gal}}$$

has a dual denominate number, which is the reciprocal number and the reciprocal units. In this case we have

$$\frac{1}{25} \frac{\text{gal}}{\text{mi}}$$

The $25 \frac{\text{mi}}{\text{gal}}$ indicates that we can drive 25 mi on 1 gal. The $\frac{1}{25} \frac{\text{gal}}{\text{mi}}$ indicates that we use $\frac{1}{25}$ of a gallon for each mile.

EXAMPLES:

Denominate Number	Dual
$55 \frac{\text{mi}}{\text{h}}$	$\frac{1}{55} \frac{\text{h}}{\text{mi}}$
$\frac{2}{3} \frac{\text{page}}{\text{min}}$	$\frac{3}{2} \frac{\text{min}}{\text{page}}$

Of all the skills you develop in the study of arithmetic, perhaps the most useful is that of estimation. Every day, you have occasion to estimate. Here are a few estimation exercises that you may have gone through this morning.

How much flour should I put in the pancakes?

How much cash am I likely to need today?

How long will it take me to walk to the bus stop?

How long is the ride to school?

How many miles can I get on just over $\frac{1}{4}$ tank of gas?

Although you may not think of these as math problems, they are. As your estimation skills improve, so will your ability to come up with good answers to everyday problems.

Example 1 Estimating Measurements

< Objective 1 >

Based on the gauge, is the gas tank closer to $\frac{3}{4}$, $\frac{2}{3}$, $\frac{1}{3}$, or $\frac{1}{4}$ full?

At slightly more than $\frac{1}{2}$, the gauge indicates close to $\frac{2}{3}$ of a tank remains.

Check Yourself 1

Is the reading of the thermometer closer to 72°, 74°, or 76°?

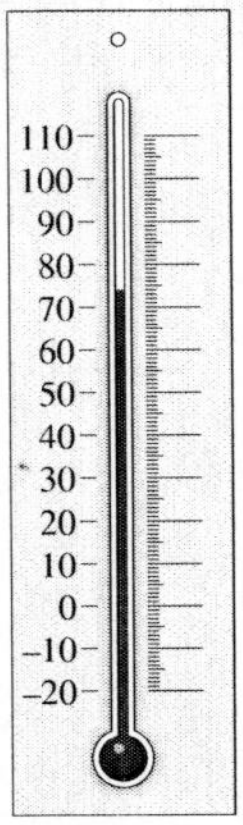

Cooking provides many opportunities for estimation. Example 2 illustrates one.

Example 2 Estimating Measurement

A recipe calls for $\frac{1}{3}$ cup of sugar. The only measuring cups you have are 1 cup, $\frac{1}{2}$ cup, and $\frac{1}{4}$ cup. What should you do?

To solve this problem you must believe that recipes are only approximations anyway. Once you accept that idea, you can estimate $\frac{1}{3}$ cup. It is between $\frac{1}{4}$ cup and $\frac{1}{2}$ cup, so fill the $\frac{1}{4}$ cup, dump it into the $\frac{1}{2}$ cup, and add a little more sugar.

Check Yourself 2

A recipe calls for $\frac{3}{4}$ cup of flour, but you have only a 1-cup, a $\frac{2}{3}$-cup, and a $\frac{1}{3}$-cup measure. How should you proceed?

Almost every shopping trip presents many estimation opportunities. Whether you are estimating the impact of car payments on your monthly budget or estimating the number of bananas you can buy for $3, you are practicing your arithmetic skills. Example 3 provides an opportunity to practice these skills.

Example 3 Estimating Total Cost

Dog food is on special at three cans for a dollar. Your puppy eats about $\frac{1}{2}$ can per day. How much should you budget for dog food over the next semester (almost 5 months)?

First, estimate the number of days in the semester. At 30 days per month, we'll use

$$30 \frac{\text{days}}{\text{month}} \times 5 \text{ months} = 150 \text{ days}$$

Next, estimate the amount of food to be consumed. We could try using $\frac{1}{2}$ can per day, which yields

$$\frac{1}{2} \frac{\text{can}}{\text{day}} \times 150 \text{ days} = 75 \text{ cans}$$

but remember that this is a puppy, so we will assume his food intake will increase over the next 5 months. To be safe, we will add 25 cans and estimate the total to be 100 cans.

Finally, we can estimate the total cost. If we buy all the food today, we can buy it at 3 cans per dollar. At $\frac{1}{3}$ dollar per can, we get

$$\frac{1}{3} \frac{\text{dollar}}{\text{can}} \times 100 \text{ cans} \approx \$33$$

The cost will be about $33.

Check Yourself 3

Cat food is also on special at seven cans for $2 $\left(\frac{7}{2} \frac{\text{cans}}{\text{dollars}}\right)$. If the cat eats about $\frac{1}{2}$ can per day, what is the approximate cost of the cat food for a 5-month semester?

Check Yourself ANSWERS

1. It is closer to 74°.
2. Fill the $\frac{2}{3}$-cup measure, dump it into the 1-cup measure, and add a little flour.
3. The cost is a little over $20.

Reading Your Text

The following fill-in-the-blank exercises are designed to ensure that you understand some of the key vocabulary used in this section.

SECTION 3.6

(a) Every denominate number with a fractional unit has a ____________ denominate number.

(b) Of all the skills you develop in the study of arithmetic, perhaps the most useful is ____________.

(c) Measurements in a recipe are ____________.

(d) Almost every shopping trip represents many ____________ opportunities.

3.6 exercises

Boost *your* GRADE at ALEKS.com!

ALEKS®

- Practice Problems
- Self-Tests
- NetTutor
- e-Professors
- Videos

Name ____________

Section ________ Date ________

< Objective 1 >

Find the dual of each denominate number.

1. $36 \frac{\text{ft}}{\text{s}}$ Videos

2. $42 \frac{\text{kilowatts}}{\text{h}}$

3. $5 \frac{\text{pages}}{\text{min}}$ Videos

4. $125 \frac{\text{joules}}{\text{s}}$

5. $18 \frac{\text{mi}}{\text{gal}}$

6. $84 \frac{\text{coulombs}}{\text{s}}$

7. $68 \frac{\text{lumens}}{\text{cm}^2}$

8. $55 \frac{\text{ergs}}{\text{min}}$

Solve each application.

9. Crafts Mark wants to make $300 by selling cupcakes at a bake sale, and his mother has offered to pay for the ingredients. He plans to sell them for $5 per dozen. A box of cake mix makes about 50 cupcakes. Approximately how many boxes should Mark buy?

10. Statistics Amy is traveling to a city 418 miles away at a speed of roughly 55 miles per hour. About how long should her trip take?

11. Social Science The map tells Manuel that it is 423 miles from Eastwick to West Goshen. He knows that, with mixed city and freeway driving, he can average about 50 miles per hour. He is currently in Eastwick and needs to be in West Goshen by noon. Make a rough estimate of the time that Manuel should leave Eastwick.

12. Business and Finance Sam works in a shipping department for a manufacturer. He is filling a customer's order for several small items. The items ordered weigh 21, 23, 18, and 7 ounces (oz). The company policy is to use a stronger box to ship products totaling more than 3 pounds (lb). Knowing 16 oz is 1 lb, estimate whether Sam should use the stronger box.

13. Construction Lauren is a contractor for a roofing job. She estimates that she will need about 4,800 roofing nails. According to a handbook, the roofing nails that are needed count out at about 189 nails per pound. Estimate how many pounds Lauren will need for the job.

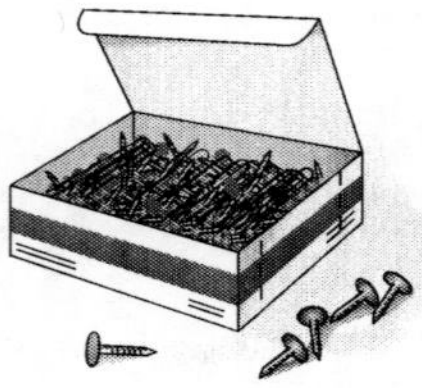

14. Business and Finance Julio works as a quality control expert in a beverage factory. The assembly line that he monitors produces about 20,000 bottles in a 24-hour period. Julio samples about 120 bottles an hour and rejects the line if he finds more than $\frac{1}{50}$ of the sample to be defective. About how many defective bottles should Julio allow before rejecting the entire line?

Answers

1. ____________
2. ____________
3. ____________
4. ____________
5. ____________
6. ____________
7. ____________
8. ____________
9. ____________
10. ____________
11. ____________
12. ____________
13. ____________
14. ____________

15. **CRAFTS** Based on the amount of liquid in the pitcher, is the pitcher closer to $\frac{1}{3}$, $\frac{2}{3}$, $\frac{1}{4}$, or $\frac{3}{4}$ full?

16. **BUSINESS AND FINANCE** Lunch meat sells for about \$3 per pound. You use about $\frac{1}{2}$ pound per day for sandwiches. How much should you budget for lunch meat over the next month (about 20 workdays)?

Basic Skills | **Challenge Yourself** | Calculator/Computer | Career Applications | Above and Beyond

Estimate each sum or difference.

17. $2\frac{1}{8} + 7\frac{9}{11} + 4\frac{6}{7} + 5\frac{1}{12}$ > Videos

18. $4\frac{5}{6} + 3\frac{1}{5} + 8\frac{1}{7} + 11\frac{8}{9}$

19. $15\frac{4}{5} - 3\frac{9}{10} - 6\frac{1}{7}$

20. $18\frac{1}{5} + 11\frac{7}{8} - 14\frac{10}{11} - 10\frac{6}{7}$

Estimate each product or quotient.

21. $2\frac{5}{6} \times 4\frac{1}{3}$

22. $3\frac{1}{7} \times 6\frac{8}{9}$

23. $9\frac{2}{9} \div 2\frac{6}{7}$

24. $17\frac{11}{12} \div 6\frac{1}{10}$

25. $15\frac{6}{7} \div 4\frac{1}{8} \times 1\frac{3}{4}$

Answers

1. $\frac{1\text{ s}}{36\text{ ft}}$ 3. $\frac{1\text{ min}}{5\text{ page}}$ 5. $\frac{1\text{ gal}}{18\text{ mi}}$ 7. $\frac{1\text{ cm}^2}{68\text{ lumen}}$ 9. 15 boxes

11. 3 A.M. 13. 24 lb 15. $\frac{3}{4}$ 17. 20 19. 6 21. 12

23. 3 25. 8

Answers

15. ________

16. ________

17. ________

18. ________

19. ________

20. ________

21. ________

22. ________

23. ________

24. ________

25. ________

Activity 9 ::
Aerobic Exercise

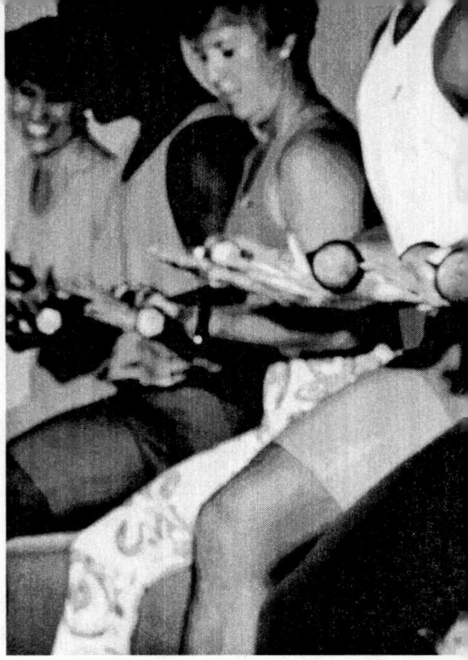

According to the website www.Fitnesszone.com, **aerobic training zone** refers to the training intensity range that will produce improvement in your level of aerobic fitness without overtaxing your cardiorespiratory system. Your aerobic training zone is based on a percentage of your maximal heart rate. As a general rule, your maximal heart rate is measured directly or estimated by subtracting your age from 220. Depending upon how physically fit you are, the lower and upper limits of your aerobic training zone are then based on a fraction of the maximal heart rate, approximately $\frac{3}{5}$ to $\frac{9}{10}$, respectively.

The chart below uses this information to determine maximal heart rate (MHR) by subtracting the age from 220. Complete the table.

Age	Maximal Heart Rate
20	200
25	
30	
35	
40	
45	
50	
55	

Using the information provided in the first paragraph, complete the following table to find the lower and upper limits for the training zone for each age. Note that when we compute the upper limit of the training zone, we round up to the next integer. For example, we will compute the upper limit for age 25.

$$195 \times \frac{9}{10} = \frac{195}{1} \times \frac{9}{10} = \frac{39}{1} \times \frac{9}{2} = \frac{351}{2} = 175\frac{1}{2}$$

Rounding up, we get an upper limit of 176.

Age	Maximal Heart Rate	Lower Limit of Zone $\left(\frac{3}{5}\text{ MHR}\right)$	Upper Limit of Zone $\left(\frac{9}{10}\text{ MHR}\right)$
20	200	120	180
25	195	117	176
30	190		
35	185		
40	180		
45	175		
50	170		
55	165		

Definition/Procedure	Example	Reference
Adding and Subtracting Fractions with Like Denominators		Section 3.1
To Add Like Fractions		
Step 1 Add the numerators. **Step 2** Place the sum over the common denominator. **Step 3** Simplify the resulting fraction if necessary.	$\frac{5}{18} + \frac{7}{18} = \frac{12}{18} = \frac{2}{3}$	*p.* 183
To Subtract Like Fractions		
Step 1 Subtract the numerators. **Step 2** Place the difference over the common denominator. **Step 3** Simplify the resulting fraction when necessary.	$\frac{17}{20} - \frac{7}{20} = \frac{10}{20} = \frac{1}{2}$	*p.* 185
Common Multiples		Section 3.2
Least Common Multiple (LCM) The LCM is the *smallest* number that is a multiple of each of a group of numbers.		*p.* 192
To Find the LCM		
Step 1 Write the prime factorization for each of the numbers in the group. **Step 2** Find all the prime factors that appear in any one of the prime factorizations. **Step 3** Form the product of those prime factors, using each factor the greatest number of times it occurs in any one factorization.	To find the LCM of 12, 15, and 18: $12 = 2 \times 2 \times 3$ $15 = 3 \times 5$ $18 = 2 \times 3 \times 3$ $2 \times 2 \times 3 \times 3 \times 5$ The LCM is $2 \times 2 \times 3 \times 3 \times 5$, or 180.	*p.* 192
Adding and Subtracting Fractions with Unlike Denominators		Section 3.3
To Find the LCD of a Group of Fractions		
Step 1 Write the prime factorization for each of the denominators. **Step 2** Find all the prime factors that appear in any one of the prime factorizations. **Step 3** Form the product of those prime factors, using each factor the greatest number of times it occurs in any one factorization.	To find the LCD of fractions with denominators 4, 6, and 15: $4 = 2 \times 2$ $6 = 2 \times 3$ $15 = 3 \times 5$ $2 \times 2 \times 3 \times 5$ The LCD $= 2 \times 2 \times 3 \times 5$, or 60.	*p.* 200

Continued

Definition/Procedure	Example	Reference
To Add Unlike Fractions **Step 1** Find the LCD of the fractions. **Step 2** Change each unlike fraction to an equivalent fraction with the LCD as a common denominator. **Step 3** Add the resulting like fractions as before.	$\frac{3}{4} + \frac{7}{10} = \frac{15}{20} + \frac{14}{20}$ $= \frac{29}{20} = 1\frac{9}{20}$	*p.* 201
To Subtract Unlike Fractions **Step 1** Find the LCD of the fractions. **Step 2** Change each unlike fraction to an equivalent fraction with the LCD as a common denominator. **Step 3** Subtract the resulting like fractions as before.	$\frac{8}{9} - \frac{5}{6} = \frac{16}{18} - \frac{15}{18} = \frac{1}{18}$	*p.* 203
Adding and Subtracting Mixed Numbers		**Section 3.4**
To Add or Subtract Mixed Numbers **Step 1** Find the LCD. **Step 2** Rewrite the fraction parts to match the LCD. **Step 3** Add or subtract the fractions. **Step 4** Add or subtract the whole number part. **Step 5** Simplify if necessary.	$2\frac{1}{4} + 3\frac{4}{5} = 2\frac{5}{20} + 3\frac{16}{20}$ $= 2 + 3 + \frac{5}{20} + \frac{16}{20} = 5 + \frac{21}{20} = 6\frac{1}{20}$	*p.* 213
Order of Operations with Fractions		**Section 3.5**
Order of Operations **Step 1** Do any operations within parentheses or other grouping symbols. **Step 2** Evaluate all powers. **Step 3** Do all multiplication and division in order from left to right. **Step 4** Do all addition and subtraction in order from left to right.	$\frac{2}{3} + \left(\frac{1}{2}\right)^2\left(\frac{1}{3} + \frac{1}{2}\right) = \frac{2}{3} + \left(\frac{1}{2}\right)^2\left(\frac{5}{6}\right)$ $= \frac{2}{3} + \left(\frac{1}{4}\right)\left(\frac{5}{6}\right)$ $= \frac{2}{3} + \frac{5}{24}$ $= \frac{16}{24} + \frac{5}{24}$ $= \frac{21}{24} = \frac{7}{8}$	*p.* 225
Estimation Applications		**Section 3.6**
Every denominate number with a fractional unit has a dual denominate number that is the reciprocal number and the reciprocal units.	Denominate Number — Dual $50 \frac{\text{mi}}{\text{h}}$ — $\frac{1}{50} \frac{\text{h}}{\text{mi}}$ $\frac{10 \text{ dollars}}{\text{ticket}}$ — $\frac{1}{10} \frac{\text{ticket}}{\text{dollars}}$	*p.* 231

This summary exercise set is provided to give you practice with each of the objectives of this chapter. Each exercise is keyed to the appropriate chapter section. When you are finished, you can check your answers to the odd-numbered exercises against those presented in the back of the text. If you have difficulty with any of these questions, go back and reread the examples from that section. The answers to the even-numbered exercises appear in the *Instructor's Solutions Manual.* Your instructor will give you guidelines on how to best use these exercises in your instructional setting.

3.1 *Add. Simplify when possible.*

1. $\frac{8}{15} + \frac{2}{15}$ **2.** $\frac{4}{7} + \frac{3}{7}$ **3.** $\frac{8}{13} + \frac{7}{13}$ **4.** $\frac{17}{18} + \frac{5}{18}$

5. $\frac{19}{24} + \frac{13}{24}$ **6.** $\frac{1}{9} + \frac{2}{9} + \frac{4}{9}$ **7.** $\frac{2}{9} + \frac{5}{9} + \frac{4}{9}$ **8.** $\frac{4}{15} + \frac{7}{15} + \frac{7}{15}$

3.2 *Find the least common multiple (LCM) for each group of numbers.*

9. 4 and 12 **10.** 8 and 16 **11.** 18 and 24 **12.** 12 and 18

13. 15 and 20 **14.** 14 and 21 **15.** 9, 12, and 24 **16.** 14, 21, and 28

Arrange the fractions in order from smallest to largest.

17. $\frac{5}{8}, \frac{7}{12}$ **18.** $\frac{5}{6}, \frac{4}{5}, \frac{7}{10}$

Complete each statement using the symbols $<$, $=$, or $>$.

19. $\frac{5}{12} \square \frac{3}{8}$ **20.** $\frac{3}{7} \square \frac{9}{21}$ **21.** $\frac{9}{16} \square \frac{7}{12}$

3.3 *Write as equivalent fractions with the LCD as a common denominator.*

22. $\frac{1}{6}, \frac{7}{8}$ **23.** $\frac{3}{10}, \frac{5}{8}, \frac{7}{12}$

Find the least common denominator (LCD) for fractions with the given denominators.

24. 6 and 24 **25.** 12 and 18 **26.** 20 and 24 **27.** 25 and 40

28. 4, 5, and 9 **29.** 3, 4, and 11 **30.** 2, 5, and 8 **31.** 3, 6, and 8

Add.

32. $\frac{3}{10} + \frac{7}{12}$ **33.** $\frac{3}{8} + \frac{5}{12}$ **34.** $\frac{5}{36} + \frac{7}{24}$ **35.** $\frac{2}{15} + \frac{9}{20}$

36. $\frac{9}{14} + \frac{10}{21}$ **37.** $\frac{7}{15} + \frac{13}{18}$ **38.** $\frac{12}{25} + \frac{19}{30}$ **39.** $\frac{1}{2} + \frac{1}{4} + \frac{1}{8}$

40. $\frac{1}{3} + \frac{1}{5} + \frac{1}{10}$ **41.** $\frac{3}{8} + \frac{5}{12} + \frac{7}{18}$ **42.** $\frac{5}{6} + \frac{8}{15} + \frac{9}{20}$

Subtract.

43. $\frac{8}{9} - \frac{3}{9}$

44. $\frac{9}{10} - \frac{6}{10}$

45. $\frac{5}{8} - \frac{1}{8}$

46. $\frac{11}{12} - \frac{7}{12}$

47. $\frac{7}{8} - \frac{2}{3}$

48. $\frac{5}{6} - \frac{3}{5}$

49. $\frac{11}{18} - \frac{2}{9}$

50. $\frac{5}{6} - \frac{1}{4}$

51. $\frac{5}{8} - \frac{1}{6}$

52. $\frac{13}{18} - \frac{5}{12}$

53. $\frac{8}{21} - \frac{1}{14}$

54. $\frac{13}{18} - \frac{7}{15}$

55. $\frac{11}{12} - \frac{1}{4} - \frac{1}{3}$

56. $\frac{13}{15} + \frac{2}{3} - \frac{3}{5}$

3.4 *Perform the indicated operations.*

57. $4\frac{5}{8} - 4\frac{3}{8}$

58. $2\frac{11}{18} - 2\frac{2}{9}$

59. $3\frac{7}{10} - 3\frac{7}{12}$

60. $9\frac{11}{27} - 9\frac{5}{18}$

61. $5\frac{4}{9} + 2\frac{5}{12} - 7\frac{3}{8}$

62. $6\frac{5}{7} + 3\frac{4}{7}$

63. $5\frac{7}{10} + 3\frac{11}{12}$

64. $2\frac{1}{2} + 3\frac{5}{6} + 3\frac{3}{8}$

65. $7\frac{7}{9} - 3\frac{4}{9}$

66. $9\frac{1}{6} - 3\frac{1}{8}$

67. $6\frac{5}{12} - 3\frac{5}{8}$

68. $2\frac{1}{3} + 5\frac{1}{6} - 2\frac{4}{5}$

Solve each application.

69. Crafts A recipe calls for $\frac{1}{3}$ cup of milk. You have $\frac{3}{4}$ cup. How much milk will be left over?

70. Construction Bradley needs two shelves, one $32\frac{3}{8}$ in. long and the other $36\frac{11}{16}$ in. long. What is the total length of shelving that is needed?

71. Geometry Find the perimeter of the triangle.

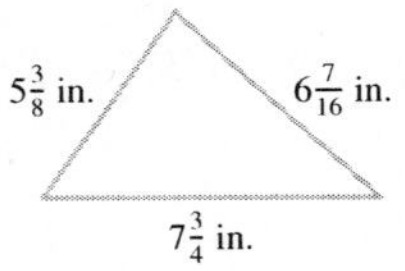

72. Statistics At the beginning of a year Miguel was $51\frac{3}{4}$ in. tall. In June, he measured $53\frac{1}{8}$ in. How much did he grow during that period?

73. Construction A bookshelf that is $42\frac{5}{16}$ in. long is cut from a board with a length of 8 ft. If $\frac{1}{8}$ in. is wasted in the cut, what length board remains?

74. Crafts Amelia buys an 8-yd roll of wallpaper on sale. After measuring, she finds that she needs the following amounts of the paper: $2\frac{1}{3}$, $1\frac{1}{2}$, and $3\frac{3}{4}$ yd. Does she have enough for the job? If so, how much will be left over?

75. **CRAFTS** Roberto used $1\frac{3}{4}$ gallon (gal) of paint in his living room, $1\frac{1}{3}$ gal in the dining room, and $\frac{1}{2}$ gal in a hallway. How much paint did he use?

76. **CONSTRUCTION** A sheet of plywood consists of two outer sections that are $\frac{3}{16}$ in. thick and a center section that is $\frac{3}{8}$ in. thick. How thick is the plywood overall?

77. **CRAFTS** A pattern calls for four pieces of fabric with lengths $\frac{1}{2}, \frac{3}{8}, \frac{1}{4},$ and $\frac{5}{8}$ yd. How much fabric must be purchased to use the pattern?

3.5 *Evaluate.*

78. $\frac{3}{4} + \left(\frac{1}{2}\right)\left(\frac{1}{3}\right)$

79. $\frac{2}{3} - \left(\frac{3}{4}\right)^2\left(\frac{1}{2}\right)$

80. $\left(4\frac{3}{8}\right)\left(1\frac{1}{2}\right) \div \left(\frac{3}{4} + \frac{1}{2}\right)$

81. $\frac{1}{3} \cdot \left(\frac{3}{4} - \frac{1}{2}\right)^2$

82. $\left(\frac{2}{3}\right)^3 - \frac{1}{2} \cdot \frac{1}{9}$

83. $2\frac{1}{3} - \left[\frac{1}{2} \cdot \left(2 - \frac{1}{3}\right)\right]$

3.6

84. **BUSINESS AND FINANCE** Jared had about \$2,800 in his checking account. He wrote five checks for equal amounts, and he knows his balance is about \$200. Estimate the amount of each check that he wrote.

85. **BUSINESS AND FINANCE** An appliance store has the following items on sale:

19″ color television for \$399

Entertainment center for \$509.95

A mini sound system for \$369.95

Estimate the cost of one entertainment center, two color televisions, and three mini sound systems.

Estimate.

86. $3\frac{5}{6} + 4\frac{1}{7} - 2\frac{6}{7}$

87. $4\frac{1}{8} \times 5\frac{11}{12}$

88. $18\frac{1}{9} \div 1\frac{8}{9} \times 4\frac{5}{6}$

self-test 3

Name ____________

Section ______ Date ______

Answers

1. ____
2. ____
3. ____
4. ____
5. ____
6. ____
7. ____
8. ____
9. ____
10. ____
11. ____
12. ____
13. ____
14. ____
15. ____

The purpose of this self-test is to help you assess your progress so that you can find concepts that you need to review before the next exam. Allow yourself about an hour to take this test. At the end of that hour, check your answers against those given in the back of this text. If you miss any, go back to the appropriate section to reread the examples until you have mastered that particular concept.

Find the least common denominator for fractions with the given denominators.

1. 12 and 15

2. 3, 4, and 18

Perform the indicated operations.

3. $7\frac{3}{8} + 2\frac{7}{8}$

4. $3\frac{5}{6} - 2\frac{2}{9}$

5. $\frac{3}{10} + \frac{6}{10}$

6. $\frac{1}{6} + \frac{3}{7}$

7. $\frac{11}{12} - \frac{3}{20}$

8. $4\frac{2}{7} + 3\frac{3}{7} + 1\frac{3}{7}$

9. $4\frac{1}{6} + 3\frac{3}{4}$

10. $\frac{5}{12} + \frac{3}{12}$

11. $3\frac{1}{2} + 4\frac{3}{4} + 5\frac{3}{10}$

12. $\frac{11}{15} + \frac{9}{20}$

Solve each application.

13. Statistics You have $\frac{5}{6}$ hour (h) to take a three-part test. You use $\frac{1}{3}$ h for the first section and $\frac{1}{4}$ h for the second. How much time do you have left to finish the last section of the test?

14. Crafts A recipe calls for $\frac{1}{2}$ cup of raisins, $\frac{1}{4}$ cup of walnuts, and $\frac{2}{3}$ cup of rolled oats. What is the total amount of these ingredients?

15. Find the least common multiple of 18, 24, and 36.

Evaluate.

16. $\frac{1}{4} + \left(\frac{1}{2}\right)^2 - \left(\frac{1}{3} + \frac{1}{12}\right)$

17. $\left(1\frac{1}{3} + 2\frac{1}{2}\right) \cdot 3\frac{1}{4}$

Perform the indicated operations.

18. $\frac{2}{5} + \frac{4}{10}$

19. $7\frac{3}{8} - 5\frac{5}{8}$

20. $7 - 5\frac{7}{15}$

21. $\frac{7}{18} - \frac{5}{18}$

22. $\frac{3}{8} + \frac{5}{12}$

23. $7\frac{1}{8} - 3\frac{1}{6}$

24. $\frac{7}{9} - \frac{4}{9}$

25. $\frac{1}{4} + \frac{5}{8} + \frac{7}{10}$

26. $5\frac{3}{10} + 2\frac{4}{10}$

27. $\frac{5}{24} + \frac{3}{8}$

28. $6\frac{3}{8} + 5\frac{7}{10}$

Solve each application.

29. STATISTICS The average person drinks about $3\frac{1}{5}$ cups of coffee per day. If a person works 5 days a week for 50 weeks every year, estimate how many cups of coffee that person will drink in a working lifetime of $51\frac{3}{4}$ years.

30. BUSINESS AND FINANCE A worker has $2\frac{1}{6}$ h of overtime on Tuesday, $1\frac{3}{4}$ h on Wednesday, and $1\frac{5}{6}$ h on Friday. What is the total overtime for the week?

Answers

16. ______

17. ______

18. ______

19. ______

20. ______

21. ______

22. ______

23. ______

24. ______

25. ______

26. ______

27. ______

28. ______

29. ______

30. ______

cumulative review chapters 1-3

Name ____________________

Section ________ Date ________

The following exercises are presented to help you review concepts from earlier chapters. This is meant as review material and not as a comprehensive exam. The answers are presented in the back of the text. Beside each answer is a section reference for the concept. If you have difficulty with any of these exercises, be certain to at least read through the summary related to that section.

Answers

1. ____________________
2. ____________________
3. ____________________
4. ____________________
5. ____________________
6. ____________________
7. ____________________
8. ____________________
9. ____________________
10. ____________________
11. ____________________
12. ____________________
13. ____________________
14. ____________________
15. ____________________
16. ____________________
17. ____________________
18. ____________________
19. ____________________

Perform the indicated operations.

1. $\begin{array}{r} 1{,}369 \\ +\ 5{,}804 \\ \hline \end{array}$

2. $\begin{array}{r} 489 \\ 562 \\ 613 \\ +\ 254 \\ \hline \end{array}$

3. $\begin{array}{r} 357 \\ 28 \\ +\ 2{,}346 \\ \hline \end{array}$

4. $\begin{array}{r} 13 \\ 2{,}543 \\ +\ 10{,}547 \\ \hline \end{array}$

5. $289 - 54$

6. $53{,}294 - 41{,}074$

7. $503 - 74$

8. $5{,}731 - 2{,}492$

9. $\begin{array}{r} 58 \\ \times\ 3 \\ \hline \end{array}$

10. Find the product of 273 and 7.

11. $\begin{array}{r} 89 \\ \times\ 56 \\ \hline \end{array}$

12. $\begin{array}{r} 538 \\ \times\ 103 \\ \hline \end{array}$

13. $281\overline{)6{,}935}$

14. $571\overline{)12{,}583}$

15. $293\overline{)61{,}382}$

Evaluate each expression.

16. $12 \div 6 + 3$

17. $4 + 12 \div 4$

18. $3^3 \div 9$

19. $28 \div 7 \times 4$

20. $26 - 2 \times 3$

21. $36 \div (3^2 + 3)$

Identify the proper fractions, improper fractions, and mixed numbers from the following group.

$\frac{5}{7}, \frac{15}{9}, 4\frac{5}{6}, \frac{8}{8}, \frac{11}{1}, \frac{2}{5}, 3\frac{5}{6}$

22. Proper: ___ Improper: ______ Mixed numbers: _____

Convert to mixed or whole numbers.

23. $\frac{16}{9}$

24. $\frac{36}{5}$

Convert to improper fractions.

25. $5\frac{3}{4}$

26. $6\frac{1}{9}$

Determine whether each pair of fractions is equivalent.

27. $\frac{8}{32}, \frac{9}{36}$

28. $\frac{6}{11}, \frac{7}{9}$

Multiply.

29. $\frac{7}{15} \times \frac{5}{21}$

30. $\frac{10}{27} \times \frac{9}{20}$

31. $4 \times \frac{3}{8}$

32. $3\frac{2}{5} \times \frac{5}{8}$

33. $5\frac{1}{3} \times 1\frac{4}{5}$

34. $1\frac{5}{12} \times 8$

35. $3\frac{1}{5} \times \frac{7}{8} \times 2\frac{6}{7}$

Answers

20. __________

21. __________

22. __________

23. __________

24. __________

25. __________

26. __________

27. __________

28. __________

29. __________

30. __________

31. __________

32. __________

33. __________

34. __________

35. __________

Answers

36. ____
37. ____
38. ____
39. ____
40. ____
41. ____
42. ____
43. ____
44. ____
45. ____
46. ____
47. ____
48. ____
49. ____
50. ____
51. ____
52. ____
53. ____

Divide.

36. $\frac{5}{12} \div \frac{5}{8}$

37. $\frac{7}{15} \div \frac{14}{25}$

38. $\frac{9}{20} \div 2\frac{2}{5}$

Add.

39. $\frac{4}{15} + \frac{8}{15}$

40. $\frac{7}{25} + \frac{8}{15}$

41. $\frac{2}{5} + \frac{3}{4} + \frac{5}{8}$

Perform the indicated operations.

42. $\frac{17}{20} - \frac{7}{20}$

43. $\frac{5}{9} - \frac{5}{12}$

44. $\frac{5}{18} + \frac{4}{9} - \frac{1}{6}$

Perform the indicated operations.

45. $3\frac{5}{7} + 2\frac{4}{7}$

46. $4\frac{7}{8} + 3\frac{1}{6}$

47. $8\frac{1}{9} - 3\frac{5}{9}$

48. $7\frac{7}{8} - 3\frac{5}{6}$

49. $9 - 5\frac{3}{8}$

50. $3\frac{1}{6} + 3\frac{1}{4} - 2\frac{7}{8}$

Solve each application.

51. Business and Finance In his part-time job, Manuel worked $3\frac{5}{6}$ hours (h) on Monday, $4\frac{3}{10}$ h on Wednesday, and $6\frac{1}{2}$ h on Friday. Find the number of hours that he worked during the week.

52. Crafts A $6\frac{1}{2}$-in. bolt is placed through a wall that is $5\frac{7}{8}$ in. thick. How far does the bolt extend beyond the wall?

53. Statistics On a 6-hour (h) trip, Carlos drove $1\frac{3}{4}$ h and then Maria drove for another $2\frac{1}{3}$ h. How many hours remained on the trip?

CHAPTER

4

Decimals

INTRODUCTION

When Barry is not at his job, he loves to be outside partaking in many outdoor activities. Some of these activities include bicycling, hiking, and tennis. Lately, Barry has been spending a lot of time on his bike. He bought a new road bike because of the long distances he was riding. Two years ago, Barry noticed a sign in his neighborhood advertising a 150-mile bike ride to raise money for muscular dystrophy. He thought it was a good cause and started training for the ride. Barry completed the ride and experienced a great feeling of accomplishment in doing so.

The MD ride inspired Barry to look for more rides that raised money for important causes. He has since ridden for cerebral palsy and cancer research. Barry likes the idea that he can raise money for a good cause while getting exercise doing something he enjoys.

Lance Armstrong is one of Barry's inspirational heroes. Armstrong is a cancer survivor who battled the disease and came back to win the Tour de France seven times. He founded the Lance Armstrong Foundation for Cancer Research and the yellow Livestrong wristbands.

You can learn more about the Tour de France by doing Activity 12 on page 303. For more information on the Tour de France or Lance Armstrong you can also go to www.letour.fr or lancewins.com.

CHAPTER 4 OUTLINE

Name ____________

Section ______ Date ______

This prerequisite test provides some exercises requiring skills that you will need to be successful in the coming chapter. The answers for these exercises can be found in the back of this text. This prerequisite test can help you identify topics that you will need to review before beginning the chapter.

Write the name of each number in words.

1. $3\frac{7}{10}$

2. $6\frac{29}{100}$

3. $17\frac{89}{1,000}$

Perform the indicated operations.

4. $183 + 5 + 69$

5. $213 - 49$

6. 426×15

7. $792 \div 10$

8. $792 \div 100$

Find the area of each figure described.

9. A rectangle has length 17 feet and width 8 feet.

10. A square has sides of length 15 inches.

Answers

1. ____________
2. ____________
3. ____________
4. ____________
5. ____________
6. ____________
7. ____________
8. ____________
9. ____________
10. ____________

4.1 Place Value and Rounding

< 4.1 Objectives >

1 > Write a number in decimal form

2 > Identify place value in a decimal fraction

3 > Write a decimal in words

4 > Write a decimal as a fraction or mixed number

5 > Compare the size of several decimals

6 > Round a decimal to the nearest tenth

7 > Round a decimal to any specified decimal place

In Chapters 2 and 3, we looked at common fractions. Now we turn to a special kind of fraction called **decimal fractions.** A decimal fraction is a fraction whose denominator is a *power of* 10. Some examples of decimal fractions are $\frac{3}{10}$, $\frac{45}{100}$, and $\frac{123}{1{,}000}$.

Earlier we talked about the idea of place value. Recall that in our decimal place-value system, each place has *one-tenth* of the value of the place to its left.

Example 1 Identifying Place Values

RECALL

The powers of 10 are 1, 10, 100, 1,000, and so on. You might want to review Section 1.7 before going on.

Label the place values for the number 538.

5	3	8
↑	↑	↑
Hundreds	Tens	Ones

The ones place value is $\frac{1}{10}$ of the tens place value; the tens place value is $\frac{1}{10}$ of the hundreds place value; and so on.

Check Yourself 1

Label the place values for the number 2,793.

NOTE

The decimal point separates the whole-number part and the fractional part of a decimal fraction.

We want to extend this idea *to the right* of the ones place. Write a period to the *right* of the ones place. This is called the **decimal point.** Each digit to the right of that decimal point will represent a fraction whose denominator is a power of 10. The first place to the right of the decimal point is the tenths place:

$$0.1 = \frac{1}{10}$$

Example 2 Writing a Number in Decimal Form

< Objective 1 >

Write the mixed number $3\frac{2}{10}$ in decimal form.

Tenths

$$3\frac{2}{10} = 3.2$$

Ones   The decimal point

Check Yourself 2

Write $5\frac{3}{10}$ in decimal form.

As you move farther to the *right,* each place value must be $\frac{1}{10}$ of the value before it. The second place value is hundredths $\left(0.01 = \frac{1}{100}\right)$. The next place is thousandths, the fourth position is the ten-thousandths place, and so on. The figure illustrates the value of each position as we move to the right of the decimal point.

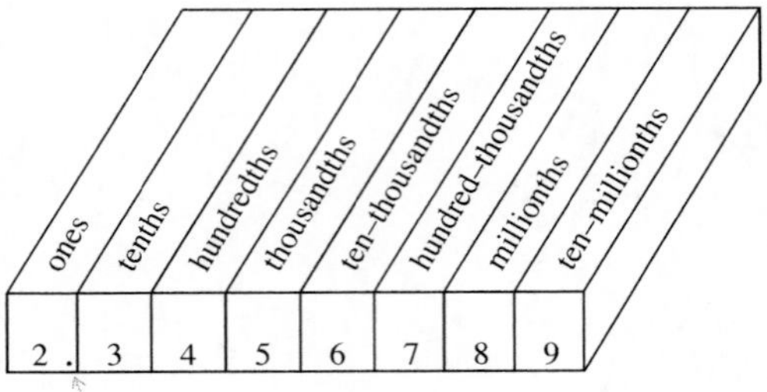

Example 3 Identifying Place Values in a Decimal Fraction

< Objective 2 >

NOTE

For convenience we shorten the term *decimal fraction* to *decimal* from this point on.

What are the place values of the 4 and 6 in the decimal 2.34567?

The place value of 4 is hundredths, and the place value of 6 is ten-thousandths.

Check Yourself 3

What is the place value of 5 in the decimal of Example 3?

Understanding place values allows you to read and write decimals. You can use the following steps.

Step by Step

Reading or Writing Decimals in Words

Step 1 Read the digits *to the left* of the decimal point as a whole number.

Step 2 Read the decimal point as the word *and*.

Step 3 Read the digits *to the right* of the decimal point as a whole number followed by the place value of the rightmost digit.

Example 4 Writing a Decimal Number in Words

< Objective 3 >

NOTE

If there are *no* nonzero digits to the left of the decimal point, start directly with step 3.

Write each decimal number in words.

5.03 is read "five and three hundredths."

Hundredths — The rightmost digit, 3, is in the hundredths position.

12.057 is read "twelve and fifty-seven thousandths."

Thousandths — The rightmost digit, 7, is in the thousandths position.

0.5321 is read "five thousand three hundred twenty-one ten–thousandths."

NOTES

An informal way of reading decimals is to simply read the digits in order and use the word *point* to indicate the decimal point. 2.58 can be read "two point five eight." 0.689 can be read "zero point six eight nine."

The number of digits to the right of the decimal point is called the number of **decimal places** in a decimal number. So, 0.35 has two decimal places.

When the decimal has no whole-number part, we have chosen to write a 0 to the left of the decimal point. This simply makes sure that you don't miss the decimal point. However, both 0.5321 and .5321 are correct.

Check Yourself 4

Write 2.58 in words.

One quick way to write a decimal as a common fraction is to remember that the number of decimal places must be the same as the number of zeros in the denominator of the common fraction.

Example 5 Writing a Decimal Number as a Mixed Number

< Objective 4 >

Write each decimal as a common fraction or mixed number.

$$0.35 = \frac{35}{100}$$

Two places ↑ Two zeros ↑

NOTE

The 0 to the right of the decimal point is a "placeholder" that is not needed in the common-fraction form.

The same method can be used with decimals that are greater than 1. Here the result will be a mixed number.

$$2.058 = 2\frac{58}{1{,}000}$$

Three places ↑ Three zeros ↑

Check Yourself 5

Write as common fractions or mixed numbers.

(a) 0.528 **(b)** 5.08

RECALL

By the Fundamental Principle of Fractions, multiplying the numerator and denominator of a fraction by the same nonzero number does not change the value of the fraction.

It is often useful to compare the sizes of two decimal fractions. One approach to comparing decimals uses the following fact.

Adding zeros to the right *does not change* the value of a decimal. The number 0.53 is the same as 0.530. Look at the fractional form:

$$\frac{53}{100} = \frac{530}{1{,}000}$$

The fractions are equivalent because we multiplied both the numerator and denominator by 10.

This allows us to compare decimals as shown in Example 6.

Example 6 Comparing the Sizes of Two Decimal Numbers

< Objective 5 >

Which is larger?

0.84 or 0.842

Write 0.84 as 0.840. Then we see that 0.842 (or 842 thousandths) is greater than 0.840 (or 840 thousandths), and we can write

$0.842 > 0.84$

Check Yourself 6

Complete the statement, using the symbols $<$ or $>$.

0.588 ______ 0.59

Whenever a decimal represents a measurement made by some instrument (a rule or a scale), the measurement is not exact. It is accurate only to a certain number of places and is called an **approximate number.** Usually, we want to make all decimals in a particular problem accurate to a specified decimal place or tolerance. This requires **rounding** the decimals. We can picture the process on a number line.

Example 7 Rounding to the Nearest Tenth

< Objective 6 >

3.74 is rounded down to the nearest tenth, 3.7, and 3.78 is rounded up to 3.8.

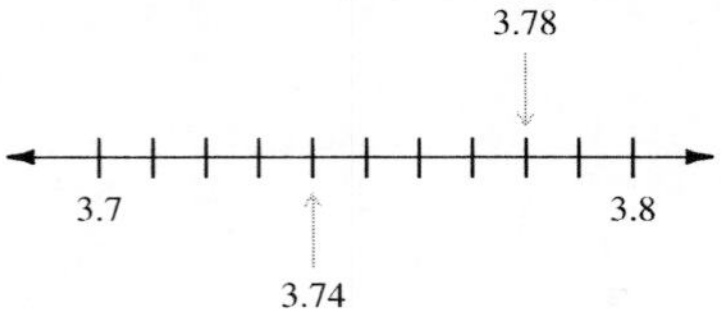

NOTE

3.74 is closer to 3.7 than it is to 3.8, while 3.78 is closer to 3.8.

Check Yourself 7

Use the number line in Example 7 to round 3.77 to the nearest tenth.

Rather than using the number line, the following rule can be applied.

Step by Step

To Round a Decimal

Step 1 Find the place to which the decimal is to be rounded.

Step 2 If the next digit to the right is 5 or more, increase the digit in the place you are rounding to by 1. Discard remaining digits to the right.

Step 3 If the next digit to the right is less than 5, just discard that digit and any remaining digits to the right.

Example 8 Rounding to the Nearest Tenth

Round 34.58 to the nearest tenth.

34.58 Locate the digit you are rounding to. The 5 is in the tenths place.

Because the next digit to the right, 8, is 5 or more, increase the tenths digit by 1. Then discard the remaining digits.

34.58 is rounded to 34.6.

NOTE

Many students find it easiest to mark the digit they are rounding to with an arrow.

Check Yourself 8

Round 48.82 to the nearest tenth.

Example 9 Rounding to the Nearest Hundredth

< Objective 7 >

Round 5.673 to the nearest hundredth.

5.673 The 7 is in the hundredths place.

The next digit to the right, 3, is less than 5. Leave the hundredths digit as it is and discard the remaining digits to the right.

5.673 is rounded to 5.67.

Check Yourself 9

Round 29.247 to the nearest hundredth.

Example 10 Rounding to a Specified Decimal Place

NOTE

The fourth place to the *right* of the decimal point is the ten-thousandths place.

Round 3.14159 to four decimal places.

3.14159 The 5 is in the ten-thousandths place.

The next digit to the right, 9, is 5 or more, so increase the digit you are rounding to by 1. Discard the remaining digits to the right.

3.14159 is rounded to 3.1416.

Check Yourself 10

Round 0.8235 to three decimal places.

Check Yourself ANSWERS

1. 2 7 9 3 (2: Thousands; 7: Hundreds; 9: Tens; 3: Ones) **2.** 5.3 **3.** Thousandths

4. Two and fifty-eight hundredths **5. (a)** $\frac{528}{1,000}$; **(b)** $5\frac{8}{100}$

6. 0.588 < 0.59 **7.** 3.8 **8.** 48.8 **9.** 29.25 **10.** 0.824

Reading Your Text

The following fill-in-the-blank exercises are designed to ensure that you understand some of the key vocabulary used in this section.

SECTION 4.1

(a) A ______________ fraction is a fraction whose denominator is a power of 10.

(b) The number of digits to the right of the decimal point is called the number of decimal ______________.

(c) Whenever a decimal represents a measure made by some instrument, the decimals are not ______________.

(d) The fourth place to the right of the decimal is called the ____________ place.

4.1 exercises

Basic Skills | Challenge Yourself | Calculator/Computer | Career Applications | Above and Beyond

Boost *your* GRADE at ALEKS.com!

ALEKS

- Practice Problems
- Self-Tests
- NetTutor
- e-Professors
- Videos

Name ______________

Section ________ Date ________

Answers

1. ______
2. ______
3. ______
4. ______
5. ______ 6. ______
7. ______ 8. ______
9. ______ 10. ______
11. ______
12. ______
13. ______
14. ______
15. ______
16. ______
17. ______ 18. ______
19. ______ 20. ______

< Objective 2 >

For the decimal 8.57932:

1. What is the place value of 7?

2. What is the place value of 5?

3. What is the place value of 3? > Videos

4. What is the place value of 2?

< Objective 1 >

Write in decimal form.

5. $\frac{23}{100}$

6. $\frac{371}{1{,}000}$

7. $\frac{209}{10{,}000}$ > Videos

8. $3\frac{5}{10}$

9. $23\frac{56}{1{,}000}$ > Videos

10. $7\frac{431}{10{,}000}$

< Objective 3 >

Write in words.

11. 0.23

12. 0.371

13. 0.071 > Videos

14. 0.0251

15. 12.07

16. 23.056

< Objective 1 >

Write in decimal form.

17. Fifty-one thousandths > Videos

18. Two hundred fifty-three ten-thousandths

19. Seven and three tenths

20. Twelve and two hundred forty-five thousandths

< Objective 4 >

Write each number as a common fraction or mixed number.

21. 0.65

22. 0.00765

23. 5.231 > Videos

24. 4.0171

< Objective 5 >

Complete each statement, using the symbols <, =, or >.

25. 0.69 ________ 0.689

26. 0.75 ________ 0.752

27. 1.23 ________ 1.230

28. 2.451 ________ 2.45

29. 10 ________ 9.9

30. 4.98 ________ 5

31. 1.459 ________ 1.46 > Videos

32. 0.235 ________ 0.2350

Arrange in order from smallest to largest.

33. 4.0339, 4.034, $4\frac{3}{10}$, $\frac{432}{100}$, 4.33

34. $\frac{38}{1{,}000}$, 0.0382, 0.04, 0.37, $\frac{39}{100}$

35. 0.71, 0.072, $\frac{7}{10}$, 0.007, 0.0069, $\frac{7}{100}$, 0.0701, 0.0619, 0.0712

36. 2.05, $\frac{25}{10}$, 2.0513, 2.059, $\frac{251}{100}$, 2.0515, 2.052, 2.051

< Objectives 6–7 >

Round to the indicated place.

37. 21.534 hundredths > Videos

38. 5.842 tenths

39. 0.342 hundredths

40. 2.3576 thousandths

41. 2.71828 thousandths

42. 1.543 tenths

43. 0.0475 tenths

44. 0.85356 ten-thousandths

Answers

21. ____________
22. ____________
23. ____________
24. ____________
25. ______ 26. ______
27. ______ 28. ______
29. ______ 30. ______
31. ______ 32. ______
33. ____________
34. ____________
35. ____________
36. ____________
37. ______ 38. ______
39. ______ 40. ______
41. ______ 42. ______
43. ______ 44. ______

Answers

45. ______

46. ______

47. ______

48. ______

49. ______

50. ______

51. ______

52. ______

53. ______

54. ______

55. ______

56. ______

57. ______

58. ______

59. ______

60. ______

61. ______

62. ______

63. ______

64. ______

45. 4.85344 ten-thousandths

46. 52.8728 thousandths

47. 6.734 two decimal places

48. 12.5467 three decimal places

49. 6.58739 four decimal places

50. 503.824 two decimal places

Round to the nearest cent or dollar, as indicated.

51. \$235.1457 cent

52. \$1,847.9895 cent

53. \$752.512 dollar

54. \$5,642.4958 dollar

Label each statement as **true** *or* **false.**

55. The only number between 8.6 and 8.8 is 8.7.

56. The smallest number that is greater than 98.6 is 98.7.

57. The place value to the right of the decimal point is tenths.

58. The number 4.586 would always be rounded as 4.6.

Basic Skills | **Challenge Yourself** | Calculator/Computer | Career Applications | Above and Beyond

59. Plot (draw a dot on the number line) the following: 3.2 and 3.7. Then estimate the location for 3.62.

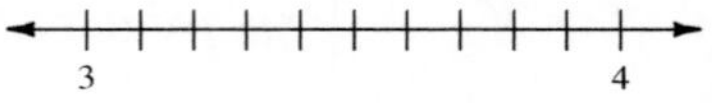

60. Plot the following on a number line: 12.51 and 12.58. Then estimate the location for 12.537.

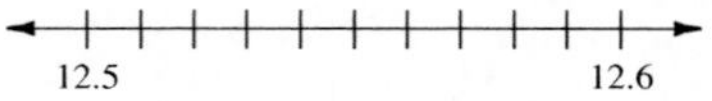

61. Plot the following on a number line: 7.124 and 7.127. Then estimate the location of 7.1253.

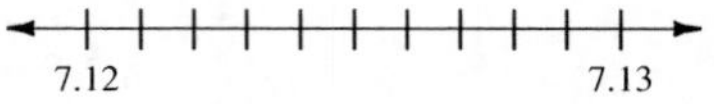

62. Plot the following on a number line: 5.73 and 5.74. Then estimate the location for 5.782.

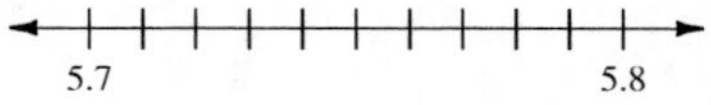

Basic Skills | Challenge Yourself | Calculator/Computer | **Career Applications** | Above and Beyond

63. **Allied Health** A nurse calculates a child's dose of Reglan to be 1.53 milligrams (mg). Round this dose to the nearest tenth of a milligram.

64. **Allied Health** A nurse calculates a young boy's dose of Dilantin to be 23.375 mg every 5 minutes. Round this dose to the nearest hundredth of a milligram.

65. Electronics Write in decimal form:

(a) Ten and thirty-five hundredths volts (V)

(b) Forty-seven hundred-thousandths of a farad (F)

(c) One hundred fifty-eight ten-thousandths of a henry (H)

66. Information Technology Josie needed to check connectivity of a PC on the network. She uses a tool called ping to see if the PC is configured properly. She receives three readings from ping: 2.1, 2.2, and 2.3 seconds. Convert the decimals to fractions and simplify if needed.

67. Manufacturing Put the following mill bits in order from smallest to largest:

0.308, 0.297, 0.31, 0.3, 0.311, 0.32

68. Manufacturing A drill size is listed as $\frac{372}{1,000}$. Express this as a decimal.

Basic Skills | Challenge Yourself | Calculator/Computer | Career Applications | **Above and Beyond**

69. (a) What is the difference in the values of the following: 0.120, 0.1200, and 0.12000?

(b) Explain in your own words why placing zeros to the right of a decimal point does not change the value of the number.

70. Lula wants to round 76.24491 to the nearest hundredth. She first rounds 76.24491 to 76.245 and then rounds 76.245 to 76.25 and claims that this is the final answer. What is wrong with this approach?

Answers

65. ____________

66. ____________

67. ____________

68. ____________

69. ____________

70. ____________

Answers

1. Hundredths **3.** Ten-thousandths **5.** 0.23 **7.** 0.0209
9. 23.056 **11.** Twenty-three hundredths **13.** Seventy-one thousandths
15. Twelve and seven hundredths **17.** 0.051 **19.** 7.3
21. $\frac{65}{100}\left(\text{or } \frac{13}{20}\right)$ **23.** $5\frac{231}{1,000}$ **25.** $0.69 > 0.689$ **27.** $1.23 = 1.230$
29. $10 > 9.9$ **31.** $1.459 < 1.46$ **33.** 4.0339, 4.034, $4\frac{3}{10}$, $\frac{432}{100}$, 4.33
35. 0.0069, 0.007, 0.0619, $\frac{7}{100}$, 0.0701, 0.0712, 0.072, $\frac{7}{10}$, 0.71 **37.** 21.53
39. 0.34 **41.** 2.718 **43.** 0.0 **45.** 4.8534 **47.** 6.73
49. 6.5874 **51.** \$235.15 **53.** \$753 **55.** False **57.** True
59. 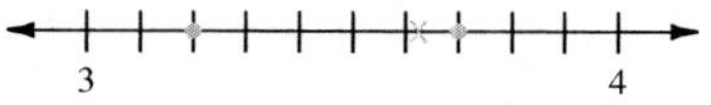

61. 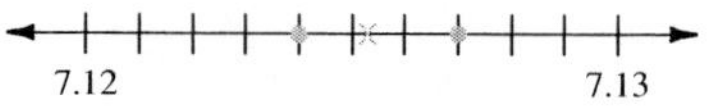

63. 1.5 mg **65. (a)** 10.35 V; **(b)** 0.00047 F; **(c)** 0.0158 H
67. 0.297, 0.3, 0.308, 0.31, 0.311, 0.32 **69.** Above and Beyond

4.2 Converting Between Fractions and Decimals

< 4.2 Objectives >

1 > Convert a common fraction to a decimal

2 > Convert a common fraction to a repeating decimal

3 > Convert a mixed number to a decimal

4 > Convert a decimal to a common fraction

Because a common fraction can be interpreted as division, you can divide the numerator of the common fraction by its denominator to convert a common fraction to a decimal. The result is called a **decimal equivalent.**

Example 1 Converting a Fraction to a Decimal Equivalent

< Objective 1 >

RECALL

5 can be written as 5.0, 5.00, 5.000, and so on.

Write $\frac{5}{8}$ as a decimal.

To begin, write a decimal point to the right of 5. The decimal point in the quotient is placed directly above this decimal point. We continue the division process by adding zeros to the right of the decimal point in the dividend until a zero remainder is reached.

$$\begin{array}{r} 0.625 \\ 8\overline{)5.000} \\ \underline{4\,8} \\ 20 \\ \underline{16} \\ 40 \\ \underline{40} \\ 0 \end{array}$$

Because $\frac{5}{8}$ means $5 \div 8$, divide 8 into 5.

We see that $\frac{5}{8} = 0.625$; 0.625 is the decimal equivalent of $\frac{5}{8}$.

Check Yourself 1

Find the decimal equivalent of $\frac{7}{8}$.

Some fractions are used so often that we have listed their decimal equivalents here as a reference.

NOTE

The division used to find these decimal equivalents stops when a zero remainder is reached. The equivalents are called **terminating decimals.**

Some Common Decimal Equivalents

$\frac{1}{2} = 0.5$	$\frac{1}{4} = 0.25$	$\frac{1}{5} = 0.2$	$\frac{1}{8} = 0.125$
	$\frac{3}{4} = 0.75$	$\frac{2}{5} = 0.4$	$\frac{3}{8} = 0.375$
		$\frac{3}{5} = 0.6$	$\frac{5}{8} = 0.625$
		$\frac{4}{5} = 0.8$	$\frac{7}{8} = 0.875$

If a decimal equivalent does not terminate, you can round the result to approximate the fraction to some specified number of decimal places. Consider Example 2.

Example 2 Converting a Fraction to a Decimal Equivalent

Write $\frac{3}{7}$ as a decimal. Round the answer to the nearest thousandth.

$$\begin{array}{r} 0.4285 \\ 7\overline{)3.0000} \\ \underline{2\ 8} \\ 20 \\ \underline{14} \\ 60 \\ \underline{56} \\ 40 \\ \underline{35} \\ 5 \end{array}$$

In this example, we are choosing to round to three decimal places, so we must add enough zeros to carry the division to four decimal places.

So $\frac{3}{7} = 0.429$ (to the nearest thousandth)

Check Yourself 2

Find the decimal equivalent of $\frac{5}{11}$ to the nearest thousandth.

If the decimal equivalent of a fraction does *not* terminate, it will *repeat* a sequence of digits. These decimals are called **repeating decimals.**

Example 3 Converting a Fraction to a Repeating Decimal

< Objective 2 >

(a) Write $\frac{1}{3}$ as a decimal.

$$\begin{array}{r} 0.333 \\ 3\overline{)1.000} \\ \underline{9} \\ 10 \\ \underline{9} \\ 10 \\ \underline{9} \end{array}$$

The digit 3 will just repeat indefinitely because each new remainder will be 1.

Adding more zeros and going on will simply lead to more 3s in the quotient.

We can say $\frac{1}{3} = 0.333\ldots$

The three dots mean "and so on" and tell us that 3 will repeat itself indefinitely.

(b) Write $\frac{5}{12}$ as a decimal.

$$\begin{array}{r} 0.4166\ldots \\ 12\overline{)5.0000} \\ \underline{4\ 8} \\ 20 \\ \underline{12} \\ 80 \\ \underline{72} \\ 80 \\ \underline{72} \\ 8 \end{array}$$

In this example, the digit 6 will just repeat itself because the remainder, 8, will keep occurring if we add more zeros and continue the division.

so $\frac{5}{12} = 0.4166\ldots$

Check Yourself 3

Find the decimal equivalent of each fraction.

(a) $\frac{2}{3}$ **(b)** $\frac{7}{12}$

Some important decimal equivalents (rounded to the nearest thousandth) are shown here as a reference.

$\frac{1}{3} = 0.333$ $\frac{1}{6} = 0.167$ $\frac{2}{3} = 0.667$ $\frac{5}{6} = 0.833$

Another way to write a repeating decimal is with a bar placed over the digit or digits that repeat. For example, we can write

0.37373737 . . .

as

$0.\overline{37}$

The bar placed over the digits indicates that 37 repeats indefinitely.

Example 4 Converting a Fraction to a Repeating Decimal

Write $\frac{5}{11}$ as a decimal.

```
        0.4545
  11 )5.0000
       4 4
       ---
         60
         55
         --
  5 ──→   50
          44
          --
           60
           55
           --
            5
```

As soon as a remainder repeats itself, as 5 does here, the pattern of digits will repeat in the quotient.

$\frac{5}{11} = 0.\overline{45}$

$= 0.4545 \ldots$

Check Yourself 4

Use the bar notation to write the decimal equivalent of $\frac{5}{7}$. (Be patient. You'll have to divide for a while to find the repeating pattern.)

You can find the decimal equivalents for mixed numbers in a similar way. Find the decimal equivalent of the fractional part of the mixed number and then combine that with the whole-number part. Example 5 illustrates this approach.

Example 5 Converting a Mixed Number to a Decimal Equivalent

< Objective 3 >

Find the decimal equivalent of $3\frac{5}{16}$.

$\frac{5}{16} = 0.3125$ First find the equivalent of $\frac{5}{16}$ by division.

$3\frac{5}{16} = 3.3125$ Add 3 to the result.

Check Yourself 5

Find the decimal equivalent of $2\frac{5}{8}$.

We have learned something important in this section. To find the decimal equivalent of a fraction, we use long division. Because the remainder must be less than the divisor, the remainder must *either repeat or become zero.* Thus, *every common fraction* has a *repeating* or a *terminating* decimal as its decimal equivalent.

Next, using what we learned about place values, you can write decimals as common fractions. The following rule is used.

Step by Step

To Convert a Terminating Decimal Less Than 1 to a Common Fraction

Step 1 Write the digits of the decimal without the decimal point. This will be the numerator of the common fraction.

Step 2 The denominator of the fraction is a 1 followed by as many zeros as there are places in the decimal.

Example 6 Converting a Decimal to a Common Fraction

< Objective 4 >

$$0.7 = \frac{7}{10} \qquad 0.09 = \frac{9}{100} \qquad 0.257 = \frac{257}{1{,}000}$$

One place — One zero; Two places — Two zeros; Three places — Three zeros

Check Yourself 6

Write as common fractions.

(a) 0.3 **(b)** 0.311

When a decimal is converted to a common fraction, that resulting common fraction should be written in lowest terms.

Example 7 Converting a Decimal to a Common Fraction

NOTE

Divide the numerator and denominator by 5.

Convert 0.395 to a fraction and write the result in lowest terms.

$$0.395 = \frac{395}{1{,}000} = \frac{79}{200}$$

Check Yourself 7

Write 0.275 as a common fraction.

If the decimal has a whole-number portion, write the digits to the right of the decimal point as a proper fraction and then form a mixed number for your result.

Example 8 Converting a Decimal to a Mixed Number

Write 12.277 as a mixed number.

$$0.277 = \frac{277}{1{,}000}$$

so

$$12.277 = 12\frac{277}{1{,}000}$$

NOTE

Repeating decimals can also be written as common fractions, although the process is more complicated. We will limit ourselves to the conversion of terminating decimals in this textbook.

Check Yourself 8

Write 32.433 as a mixed number.

Comparing the sizes of common fractions and decimals requires finding the decimal equivalent of the common fraction and then comparing the resulting decimals.

Example 9 Comparing the Sizes of Common Fractions and Decimals

Which is larger, $\frac{3}{8}$ or 0.38?

Write the decimal equivalent of $\frac{3}{8}$. That decimal is 0.375. Now comparing 0.375 and 0.38, we see that 0.38 is the larger of the numbers:

$$0.38 > \frac{3}{8}$$

RECALL

0.38 can be written as 0.380. Comparing this to 0.375, we see that 0.380 > 0.375.

Check Yourself 9

Which is larger, $\frac{3}{4}$ or 0.8?

Check Yourself ANSWERS

1. 0.875 **2.** $\frac{5}{11} = 0.455$ (to the nearest thousandth)
3. **(a)** 0.666 . . . ; **(b)** 0.583 . . . The digit 3 will continue indefinitely.
4. $\frac{5}{7} = 0.\overline{714285}$ **5.** 2.625 **6.** **(a)** $\frac{3}{10}$; **(b)** $\frac{311}{1{,}000}$ **7.** $\frac{11}{40}$
8. $32\frac{433}{1{,}000}$ **9.** $0.8 > \frac{3}{4}$

Reading Your Text

The following fill-in-the-blank exercises are designed to ensure that you understand some of the key vocabulary used in this section.

SECTION 4.2

(a) You can ______________ the numerator of a fraction by its denominator to convert a common fraction to a decimal.

(b) We can write a repeating decimal with a ______________ placed over the digit or digits that repeat.

(c) Every common fraction has a repeating or a ______________ decimal as its equivalent.

(d) The denominator of a fraction that is equivalent to a given decimal is a 1 followed by as many zeros as there are ______________ in the decimal.

4.2 exercises

Name ____________

Section ________ Date ________

< Objective 1 >

Find the decimal equivalent for each fraction.

1. $\frac{3}{4}$ **2.** $\frac{4}{5}$

3. $\frac{9}{20}$ **4.** $\frac{3}{10}$

5. $\frac{1}{5}$ **6.** $\frac{1}{8}$

7. $\frac{5}{16}$ **8.** $\frac{11}{20}$

9. $\frac{7}{10}$ > Videos **10.** $\frac{7}{16}$

11. $\frac{27}{40}$ **12.** $\frac{17}{32}$

Find the decimal equivalents rounded to the indicated place.

13. $\frac{5}{6}$ thousandths > Videos **14.** $\frac{7}{12}$ hundredths

15. $\frac{4}{15}$ thousandths

< Objective 2 >

Write the decimal equivalents, using the bar notation.

16. $\frac{1}{18}$ **17.** $\frac{4}{9}$ **18.** $\frac{3}{11}$

< Objective 3 >

Find the decimal equivalent for each mixed number.

19. $5\frac{3}{5}$ > Videos **20.** $4\frac{7}{16}$

< Objective 4 >

Write each number as a common fraction or mixed number, in simplest terms.

21. 0.9 **22.** 0.3

23. 0.8 **24.** 0.6

25. 0.37 **26.** 0.97

27. 0.587 **28.** 0.379

29. 0.48 > Videos **30.** 0.75

Answers

1. ________ 2. ________
3. ________ 4. ________
5. ________ 6. ________
7. ________ 8. ________
9. ________ 10. ________
11. ________ 12. ________
13. ________ 14. ________
15. ________ 16. ________
17. ________ 18. ________
19. ________ 20. ________
21. ________ 22. ________
23. ________ 24. ________
25. ________ 26. ________
27. ________ 28. ________
29. ________ 30. ________

31. 0.58 **32.** 0.65

33. 0.425 **34.** 0.116

35. 0.375 **36.** 0.225

37. 0.136 **38.** 0.575

39. 0.059 Videos **40.** 0.067

Basic Skills | **Challenge Yourself** | Calculator/Computer | Career Applications | Above and Beyond

41. STATISTICS In a weekend baseball tournament, Joel had 4 hits in 13 times at bat. That is, he hit safely $\frac{4}{13}$ of the time. Write the decimal equivalent for Joel's hitting, rounding to three decimal places. (That number is Joel's batting average.)

42. STATISTICS The following table gives the wins and losses of some teams in the National League East as of mid-September in a recent season. The winning percentage of each team is calculated by writing the number of wins over the total games played and converting this fraction to a decimal. Convert this fraction to a decimal for every team, rounding to three decimal places.

Team	Wins	Losses
Atlanta	92	56
New York	90	58
Philadelphia	70	77
Florida	57	89

43. STATISTICS The following table gives the wins and losses of all the teams in the Western Division of the National Football Conference for a recent season. Determine the fraction of wins over total games played for every team, rounding to three decimal places for each of the teams.

Team	Wins	Losses
San Francisco	10	6
St. Louis	7	9
Seattle	7	9
Arizona	5	11

44. STATISTICS The following table gives the free throws attempted (FTA) and the free throws made (FTM) for the top five players in the NBA for a recent season. Calculate the free throw percentage for each player by writing the FTM over the FTA and converting this fraction to a decimal. Round to three decimal places.

Answers

31. ____

32. ____

33. ____

34. ____

35. ____

36. ____

37. ____

38. ____

39. ____

40. ____

41. ____

42. ____

43. ____

44. ____

Player	FTM	FTA
Allan Houston	363	395
Ray Allen	316	345
Steve Nash	308	339
Troy Hudson	208	231
Reggie Miller	207	230

Find the decimal equivalent for each fraction. Use the bar notation.

45. $\frac{1}{11}$ **46.** $\frac{1}{111}$ **47.** $\frac{1}{1,111}$

48. From the pattern of exercises 45 to 47, can you guess the decimal representation for $\frac{1}{11,111}$?

Insert > or < to form a true statement.

49. $\frac{31}{34}$ ☐ 0.9118 **50.** $\frac{21}{37}$ ☐ 0.5664 **51.** $\frac{13}{17}$ ☐ 0.7657

52. $\frac{7}{8}$ ☐ 0.87 Videos **53.** $\frac{5}{16}$ ☐ 0.313 **54.** $\frac{9}{25}$ ☐ 0.4

Basic Skills | Challenge Yourself | **Calculator/Computer** | Career Applications | Above and Beyond

A calculator is very useful in converting common fractions to decimals. Just divide the numerator by the denominator, and the decimal equivalent will be in the display. Often, you will have to round the result in the display. For example, to find the decimal equivalent of $\frac{5}{24}$ to the nearest hundredth, enter

5 [÷] 24 [=]

The display may show 0.2083333, and rounding, we have $\frac{5}{24} = 0.21$.

When you are converting a mixed number to a decimal, addition must also be used. To change $7\frac{5}{8}$ to a decimal, for example, enter

7 [+] 5 [÷] 8 [=]

The result is 7.625.

Use your calculator to find the decimal equivalents.

55. $\frac{7}{8}$ **56.** $\frac{9}{16}$

57. $\frac{5}{32}$ to the thousandth **58.** $\frac{11}{75}$ to the thousandth

59. $\frac{3}{11}$ using bar notation **60.** $\frac{16}{33}$ using bar notation

61. $3\frac{7}{8}$ **62.** $8\frac{3}{16}$

Answers

45. ______
46. ______
47. ______
48. ______
49. ______
50. ______
51. ______
52. ______
53. ______
54. ______
55. ______
56. ______
57. ______
58. ______
59. ______
60. ______
61. ______
62. ______

Answers

63. ______

64. ______

65. ______

66. ______

67. ______

Basic Skills | Challenge Yourself | Calculator/Computer | **Career Applications** | Above and Beyond

63. **Allied Health** The internal diameter, in millimeters (mm), of an endotracheal tube for a child is calculated using the formula $\frac{\text{Height}}{20}$, which is based on the child's height in centimeters (cm). Determine the size of endotracheal tube needed for a girl who is 110 cm tall.

64. **Allied Health** The stroke volume, which measures the average cardiac output per heartbeat (liters/beat), is based on a patient's cardiac output (CO), in liters per minute (L/min), and heart rate (HR), in beats per minute (beats/min). It is calculated using the fraction $\frac{\text{CO}}{\text{HR}}$. Determine the stroke volume for a patient whose cardiac output is 4 L/min and whose heart rate is 80 beats/min. Write your answer as a decimal.

65. **Information Technology** The propagation delay for a satellite connection is 0.350 seconds (s). Convert to a fraction and simplify.

66. **Information Technology** From your computer, it takes 0.0021 s to transmit a ping packet to another computer. Convert to a fraction and simplify.

Basic Skills | Challenge Yourself | Calculator/Computer | Career Applications | **Above and Beyond**

67. Write the decimal equivalent of each fraction, using bar notation.

$\frac{1}{7}, \frac{2}{7}, \frac{3}{7}, \frac{4}{7}, \frac{5}{7}$

Describe any patterns that you see. Predict the decimal equivalent of $\frac{6}{7}$.

Answers

1. 0.75 3. 0.45 5. 0.2 7. 0.3125 9. 0.7 11. 0.675 13. $0.8\overline{3}$ 15. $0.2\overline{6}$ 17. $0.\overline{4}$ 19. 5.6 21. $\frac{9}{10}$ 23. $\frac{4}{5}$ 25. $\frac{37}{100}$ 27. $\frac{587}{1,000}$ 29. $\frac{12}{25}$ 31. $\frac{29}{50}$ 33. $\frac{17}{40}$ 35. $\frac{3}{8}$ 37. $\frac{17}{125}$ 39. $\frac{59}{1,000}$ 41. 0.308 43. 0.625, 0.438, 0.438, 0.313 45. 0.09 47. 0.0009 49. < 51. < 53. < 55. 0.875 57. 0.156 59. $0.\overline{27}$ 61. 3.875 63. 5.5 mm 65. $\frac{7}{20}$ 67. Above and Beyond

Activity 10 ::
Terminate or Repeat?

Every fraction has a decimal equivalent that either terminates (for example, $\frac{1}{4} = 0.25$) or repeats (for example, $\frac{2}{9} = 0.\overline{2}$). Work with a group to discover which fractions have terminating decimals and which have repeating decimals. You may assume that the numerator of each fraction you consider is one and focus your attention on the denominator. As you complete the following table, you will find that the key to this question lies with the prime factorization of the denominator.

Fraction	Decimal Form	Terminate?	Prime Factorization of the Denominator
$\frac{1}{2}$			
$\frac{1}{3}$			
$\frac{1}{4}$			
$\frac{1}{5}$			
$\frac{1}{6}$			
$\frac{1}{7}$			
$\frac{1}{8}$			
$\frac{1}{9}$			
$\frac{1}{10}$			
$\frac{1}{11}$			
$\frac{1}{12}$			

State a general rule describing which fractions have decimal forms that terminate and which have decimal forms that repeat.

Now test your rule on at least three new fractions. That is, be able to predict whether a fraction such as $\frac{1}{25}$ or $\frac{1}{30}$ has a terminating decimal or a repeating decimal. Then confirm your prediction.

4.3

Adding and Subtracting Decimals

< 4.3 Objectives >

1 > Add two or more decimals

2 > Use addition of decimals to solve application problems

3 > Subtract one decimal from another

4 > Use subtraction of decimals to solve application problems

Working with decimals rather than common fractions makes the basic operations much easier. First we will look at addition. One method for adding decimals is to write the decimals as common fractions, add, and then change the sum back to a decimal.

$$0.34 + 0.52 = \frac{34}{100} + \frac{52}{100} = \frac{86}{100} = 0.86$$

It is much more efficient to leave the numbers in decimal form and perform the addition in the same way as we did with whole numbers. You can use the following rule.

Step by Step

To Add Decimals

Step 1 Write the numbers being added in column form *with their decimal points in a vertical line.*

Step 2 Add just as you would with whole numbers.

Step 3 Place the decimal point of the sum in line with the decimal points of the addends.

Example 1 illustrates the use of this rule.

Example 1 Adding Decimals

< Objective 1 >

NOTE

Placing the decimal points in a vertical line ensures that we are adding digits of the same place value.

Add 0.13, 0.42, and 0.31.

$$\begin{array}{r} 0.13 \\ 0.42 \\ +\ 0.31 \\ \hline 0.86 \end{array}$$

Check Yourself 1

Add 0.23, 0.15, and 0.41.

When adding decimals, you can use the *carrying process* just as you did when adding whole numbers. Consider the following.

Example 2 Adding Decimals by Carrying

Add 0.35, 1.58, and 0.67.

$$\begin{array}{r} {\scriptstyle 1\ 2} \\ 0.35 \\ 1.58 \\ +\ 0.67 \\ \hline 2.60 \end{array}$$

← Carries

In the hundredths column:
5 + 8 + 7 = 20
Write 0 and carry 2 to the tenths column.
In the tenths column:
2 + 3 + 5 + 6 = 16
Write 6 and carry 1 to the ones column.

Note: The carrying process works with decimals, just as it did with whole numbers, because each place value is again $\frac{1}{10}$ the value of the place to its left.

Check Yourself 2

Add 23.546, 0.489, 2.312, and 6.135.

When adding decimals, the numbers may not have the same number of decimal places. Just fill in as many zeros as needed so that all the numbers added have the same number of decimal places.

Recall that adding zeros to the right *does not change* the value of a decimal. The number 0.53 is the same as 0.530. We see this in Example 3.

Example 3 Adding Decimals

NOTE

Be sure that the decimal points are in a vertical line.

Add 0.53, 4, 2.7, and 3.234.

$$\begin{array}{r} 0.53 \\ 4. \\ 2.7 \\ +\ 3.234 \\ \hline \end{array}$$

Note that for a whole number, the decimal is understood to be to its right. So 4 = 4.

Now fill in the missing zeros and add as before.

$$\begin{array}{r} 0.530 \\ 4.000 \\ 2.700 \\ +\ 3.234 \\ \hline 10.464 \end{array}$$

Now all the numbers being added have *three* decimal places.

Check Yourself 3

Add 6, 2.583, 4.7, and 2.54.

Many applied problems require working with decimals. For instance, filling up at a gas station means reading decimal amounts.

Example 4 An Application of the Addition of Decimals

< Objective 2 >

NOTE

Because we want a total amount, we use addition to find the solution.

On a trip the Chang family kept track of the gas purchases. If they bought 12.3, 14.2, 10.7, and 13.8 gallons (gal), how much gas did they use on the trip?

$$\begin{array}{r} 12.3 \\ 14.2 \\ 10.7 \\ +\ 13.8 \\ \hline 51.0 \text{ gal} \end{array}$$

Check Yourself 4

The Higueras kept track of the gasoline they purchased on a recent trip. If they bought 12.4, 13.6, 9.7, 11.8, and 8.3 gal, how much gas did they buy on the trip?

Every day you deal with amounts of money. Because our system of money is a decimal system, most problems involving money also involve operations with decimals.

Example 5 An Application of the Addition of Decimals

Andre makes deposits of \$3.24, \$15.73, \$50, \$28.79, and \$124.38 during May. What is the total of his deposits for the month?

$$\begin{array}{r} \$\ \ 3.24 \\ 15.73 \\ 50.00 \\ 28.79 \\ +\ 124.38 \\ \hline \$222.14 \end{array}$$

Simply add the amounts of money deposited as decimals. Note that we write \$50 as \$50.00.

← The total of deposits for May

Check Yourself 5

Your textbooks for the fall term cost \$63.50, \$78.95, \$43.15, \$82, and \$85.85. What was the total cost of textbooks for the term?

In Chapter 1, we defined *perimeter* as the distance around the outside of a straight-edged shape. Finding the perimeter often requires that we add decimal numbers.

Example 6 An Application Involving the Addition of Decimals

Rachel is going to put a fence around the perimeter of her farm. The figure represents the land, measured in kilometers (km). How much fence does she need to buy?

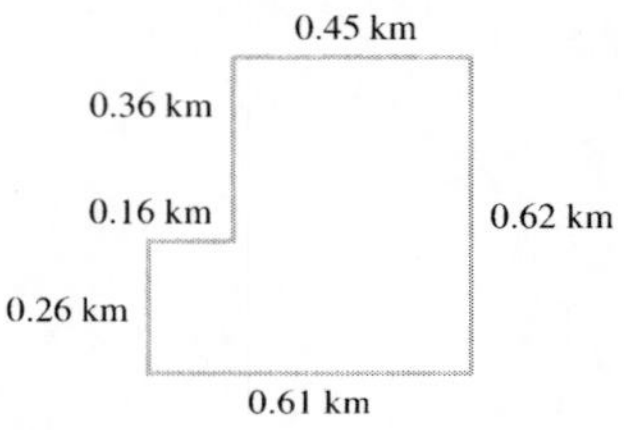

The perimeter is the sum of the lengths of the sides, so we add those lengths to find the total fencing needed.

$0.26 + 0.16 + 0.36 + 0.45 + 0.62 + 0.61 = 2.46$

Rachel needs 2.46 km of fence for the perimeter of her farm.

Check Yourself 6

Manuel intends to build a walkway around the perimeter of his garden. What will the total length of the walkway be?

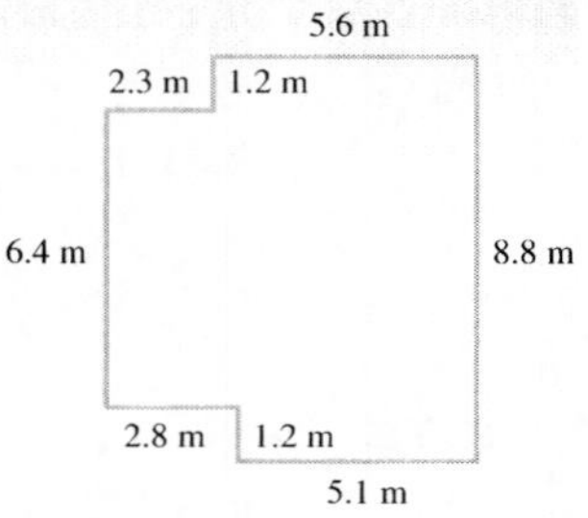

Much of what we have said about adding decimals is also true of subtraction. To subtract decimals, we use the following rule:

Step by Step

To Subtract Decimals

Step 1 Write the numbers being subtracted in column form *with their decimal points in a vertical line.*

Step 2 Subtract just as you would with whole numbers.

Step 3 Place the decimal point of the difference in line with the decimal points of the numbers being subtracted.

Example 7 illustrates the use of this rule.

Example 7 Subtracting a Decimal

< Objective 3 >

Subtract 1.23 from 3.58.

$$\begin{array}{r} 3.58 \\ -\ 1.23 \\ \hline 2.35 \end{array}$$

Subtract in the hundredths, the tenths, and then the ones columns.

RECALL

The number that follows the word *from*, here 3.58, is written first. The number we are subtracting, here 1.23, is then written beneath 3.58.

Check Yourself 7

Subtract 9.87 − 5.45.

Because each place value is $\frac{1}{10}$ the value of the place to its left, borrowing, when you are subtracting decimals, works just as it did in subtracting whole numbers.

Example 8 Decimal Subtraction That Involves Borrowing

Subtract 1.86 from 6.54.

$$\begin{array}{r} {}^{5}\,{}^{1}{}^{4}{}_{1} \\ \not{6}.\not{5}4 \\ -\ 1.86 \\ \hline 4.68 \end{array}$$

Here, borrow from the tenths and ones places to do the subtraction.

Check Yourself 8

Subtract 35.35 − 13.89.

In subtracting decimals, as in adding, we can add zeros to the right of the decimal point so that both decimals have the same number of decimal places.

Example 9 Subtracting a Decimal

(a) Subtract 2.36 from 7.5.

$$\begin{array}{r} {}^{4\,1} \\ 7.\not{5}\,0 \\ -\ 2.36 \\ \hline 5.14 \end{array}$$

We have added a 0 to 7.5. Next, borrow 1 tenth from the 5 tenths in the minuend.

NOTES

When you are subtracting, align the decimal points, and then add zeros to the right to align the digits.

9 has been rewritten as 9.000.

(b) Subtract 3.657 from 9.

$$\begin{array}{r} {}^{8\ 9\,9} \\ \not{9}.\not{0}\not{0}0 \\ -\ 3.657 \\ \hline 5.343 \end{array}$$

In this case, move left to the ones place to begin the borrowing process.

Check Yourself 9

Subtract 5 − 2.345.

We can apply the subtraction methods of the previous examples in solving applications.

Example 10 An Application of the Subtraction of a Decimal Number

< Objective 4 >

Jonathan was 98.3 centimeters (cm) tall on his sixth birthday. On his seventh birthday he was 104.2 cm. How much did he grow during the year?

NOTE

We want to find the difference between the two measurements, so we subtract.

$$\begin{array}{r} 104.2 \text{ cm} \\ -\ \ 98.3 \text{ cm} \\ \hline 5.9 \text{ cm} \end{array}$$

Jonathan grew 5.9 cm during the year.

Check Yourself 10

A car's highway mileage before a tune-up was 28.8 miles per gallon (mi/gal). After the tune-up, it measured 30.1 mi/gal. What was the increase in mileage?

The same methods can be used in working with money.

Example 11 An Application of the Subtraction of a Decimal Number

At the grocery store, Sally buys a roast that is marked $12.37. She pays for her purchase with a $20 bill. How much change does she receive?

NOTE

Sally's change is the *difference* between the price of the roast and the $20 paid. We must use subtraction for the solution.

$$\begin{array}{r} \$20.00 \\ -\ 12.37 \\ \hline \$\ \ 7.63 \end{array}$$

Add zeros to write $20 as $20.00. Then subtract as before.

Sally receives $7.63 in change after her purchase.

Check Yourself 11

A stereo system that normally sells for $549.50 is discounted (or marked down) to $499.95 for a sale. What is the savings?

Balancing a checkbook requires addition and subtraction of decimal numbers.

Example 12 An Application Involving the Addition and Subtraction of Decimals

For the following check register, find the running balance.

Beginning balance	$234.15
Check # 301	23.88
Balance	______
Check # 302	38.98
Balance	______
Check # 303	114.66
Balance	______
Deposit	175.75
Balance	______
Check # 304	212.55
Ending balance	______

To keep a running balance, we add the deposits and subtract the checks.

Beginning balance	$234.15
Check # 301	23.88
Balance	210.27
Check # 302	38.98
Balance	171.29
Check # 303	114.66
Balance	56.63
Deposit	175.75
Balance	232.38
Check # 304	212.55
Ending balance	19.83

Check Yourself 12

For the following check register, add the deposits and subtract the checks to find the balance.

	Beginning balance	$398.00
	Check # 401	19.75
(a)	Balance	______
	Check # 402	56.88
(b)	Balance	______
	Check # 403	117.59
(c)	Balance	______
	Deposit	224.67
(d)	Balance	______
	Check # 404	411.48
(e)	Ending balance	______

Check Yourself ANSWERS

1. 0.79 **2.** 32.482 **3.**

$$\begin{array}{r} 6.000 \\ 2.583 \\ 4.700 \\ +\ 2.540 \\ \hline 15.823 \end{array}$$

4. 55.8 gal **5.** \$353.45 **6.** 33.4 m **7.** 4.42 **8.** 21.46 **9.** 2.655 **10.** 1.3 mi/gal **11.** \$49.55
12. **(a)** \$378.25; **(b)** \$321.37; **(c)** \$203.78; **(d)** \$428.45; **(e)** \$16.97

Reading Your Text

The following fill-in-the-blank exercises are designed to ensure that you understand some of the key vocabulary used in this section.

SECTION 4.3

(a) To add decimals, write the numbers being added in column form with their ______________ ______________ in a vertical line.

(b) Adding zeros to the right does not change the ______________ of a decimal.

(c) ______________ is the distance around the outside of a straight-edged shape.

(d) When subtracting one number from another, the number ____________ the word *from* is written first.

Basic Skills | Challenge Yourself | Calculator/Computer | Career Applications | Above and Beyond

4.3 exercises

Name ____________

Section ________ Date ________

< Objective 1 >

Add.

1. $\begin{array}{r} 0.28 \\ +\ 0.79 \\ \hline \end{array}$ > Videos

2. $\begin{array}{r} 2.59 \\ +\ 0.63 \\ \hline \end{array}$

3. $\begin{array}{r} 13.58 \\ 7.239 \\ +\ \ 1.5 \\ \hline \end{array}$

4. $\begin{array}{r} 8.625 \\ 2.45 \\ +\ 12.6 \\ \hline \end{array}$

5. $\begin{array}{r} 25.3582 \\ 6.5 \\ 1.898 \\ +\ \ 0.69 \\ \hline \end{array}$

6. $\begin{array}{r} 1.336 \\ 15.6857 \\ 7.9 \\ +\ 0.85 \\ \hline \end{array}$

7. $0.43 + 0.8 + 0.561$ > Videos

8. $1.25 + 0.7 + 0.259$

9. $42.731 + 1.058 + 103.24$

10. $27.4 + 213.321 + 39.38$

< Objective 3 >

Subtract.

11. $\begin{array}{r} 0.85 \\ -\ 0.59 \\ \hline \end{array}$

12. $\begin{array}{r} 5.68 \\ -\ 2.65 \\ \hline \end{array}$

13. $\begin{array}{r} 3.82 \\ -\ 1.565 \\ \hline \end{array}$

14. $\begin{array}{r} 8.59 \\ -\ 5.6 \\ \hline \end{array}$

15. $\begin{array}{r} 7.02 \\ -\ 4.7 \\ \hline \end{array}$

16. $\begin{array}{r} 45.6 \\ -\ \ 8.75 \\ \hline \end{array}$

17. $\begin{array}{r} 12 \\ -\ \ 5.35 \\ \hline \end{array}$ > Videos

18. $\begin{array}{r} 15 \\ -\ \ 8.85 \\ \hline \end{array}$

19. Subtract 2.87 from 6.84. > Videos

20. Subtract 3.69 from 10.57.

21. Subtract 7.75 from 9.4.

22. Subtract 5.82 from 12.

23. Subtract 0.24 from 5.

24. Subtract 8.7 from 16.32.

Basic Skills | Challenge Yourself | Calculator/Computer | Career Applications | Above and Beyond

< Objectives 2, 4 >

Solve each application.

25. **Business and Finance** On a 3-day trip, Dien bought 12.7, 15.9, and 13.8 gallons (gal) of gas. How many gallons of gas did he buy? > Videos

Answers

1. ________ 2. ________
3. ________ 4. ________
5. ________ 6. ________
7. ________ 8. ________
9. ________ 10. ________
11. ________ 12. ________
13. ________ 14. ________
15. ________ 16. ________
17. ________ 18. ________
19. ________ 20. ________
21. ________ 22. ________
23. ________ 24. ________
25. ________

Answers

26. ______

27. ______

28. ______

29. ______

30. ______

31. ______

32. ______

33. ______

26. Science and Medicine Felix ran 2.7 miles (mi) on Monday, 1.9 mi on Wednesday, and 3.6 mi on Friday. How far did he run during the week?

27. Social Science Rainfall was recorded in centimeters (cm) during the winter months, as indicated on the bar graph.

(a) How much rain fell during those months?

(b) How much more rain fell in December than in February?

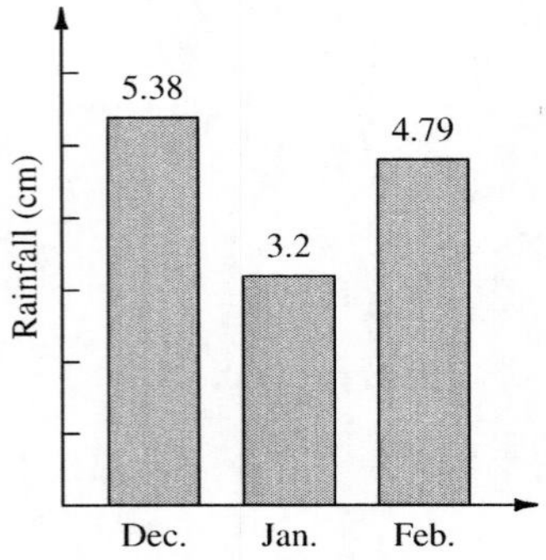

28. Construction A metal fitting has three sections, with lengths 2.5, 1.775, and 1.45 inches (in.). What is the total length of the fitting?

29. Business and Finance Nicole had the following expenses on a business trip: gas, \$45.69; food, \$123; lodging, \$95.60; and parking and tolls, \$8.65. What were her total expenses during the trip?

30. Business and Finance The deposit slip shown indicates the amounts that made up a deposit Peter Rabbit made. What was the total amount of his deposit?

DEPOSIT TICKET

Peter Rabbit
123 East Derbunny St.

DATE ______
DEPOSITS MAY NOT BE AVAILABLE FOR IMMEDIATE WITHDRAWAL

______
SIGN HERE FOR CASH RECEIVED (IF REQUIRED) *

Briarpatch National Bank

√ CASH ▶	75.35
3-50/310	
▶	58.00
▶	7.89
▶	100.00
(OR TOTAL FROM OTHER SIDE) SUB TOTAL ▶	.
* LESS CASH RECEIVED ▶	.
\$	.

31. Construction Lupe is putting a fence around her yard. Her yard is rectangular and measures 8.16 yards (yd) long and 12.68 yd wide. How much fence should Lupe purchase?

32. Geometry Find the perimeter of the given figure.

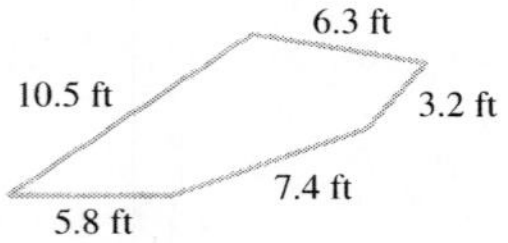

33. Construction The figure gives the distance in miles (mi) of the boundary sections around a ranch. How much fencing is needed for the property?

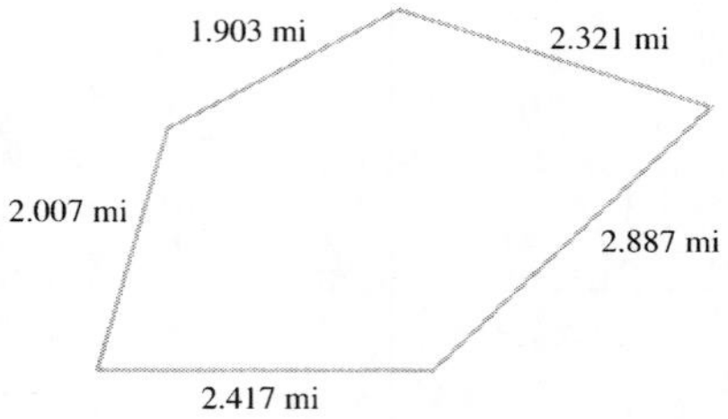

34. **Business and Finance** A television set selling for $399.50 is discounted (or marked down) to $365.75. What is the savings?

35. **Crafts** The outer radius of a piece of tubing is 2.8325 inches (in.). The inner radius is 2.775 in. What is the thickness of the wall of the tubing?

36. **Geometry** Given the following figure, find dimension a.

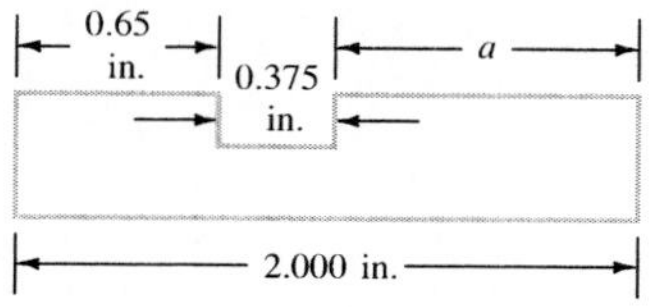

37. **Business and Finance** You make charges of $37.25, $8.78, and $53.45 on a credit card. If you make a payment of $73.50, how much do you still owe?

38. **Business and Finance** For the following check register, find the running balance.

Beginning balance	$896.74
Check # 501	$425.69
Balance	______
Check # 502	$ 56.34
Balance	______
Check # 503	$ 41.89
Balance	______
Deposit	$123.91
Balance	______
Check # 504	$356.98
Ending balance	______

39. **Business and Finance** For the following check register, find the running balance.

Beginning balance	$456.00
Check # 601	$199.29
Balance	______
Service charge	$ 18.00
Balance	______
Check # 602	$ 85.78
Balance	______
Deposit	$250.45
Balance	______
Check # 603	$201.24
Ending balance	______

Answers

34. ______

35. ______

36. ______

37. ______

38. ______

39. ______

Answers

40. ________

41. ________

42. ________

40. BUSINESS AND FINANCE For the following check register, find the running balance.

Beginning balance	\$589.21
Check # 678	\$175.63
Balance	______
Check # 679	\$ 56.92
Balance	______
Deposit	\$121.12
Balance	______
Check # 680	\$345.99
Ending balance	______

41. BUSINESS AND FINANCE For the following check register, find the running balance.

Beginning balance	\$1,345.23
Check # 821	\$ 234.99
Balance	______
Check # 822	\$ 555.77
Balance	______
Deposit	\$ 126.77
Balance	______
Check # 823	\$ 53.89
Ending balance	______

Estimation can be a useful tool when working with decimal fractions. To estimate a sum, one approach is to round the addends to the nearest whole number and add for your estimate. For instance, to estimate the following sum:

	Round		
19.8	→	20	
3.5		4	
24.2		24	
+ 10.4		+ 10	Add to get
		58	the estimate

Use estimation to solve this application.

42. BUSINESS AND FINANCE Alem's restaurant bill is pictured here. Estimate his total by rounding to the nearest dollar.

Maggie's Kitchen	
calf's liver	\$18.25
caesar salad	\$8.75
2 martinis	\$6.80
2 chocolate cakes	\$7.40
coffee	\$1.70
Tip	
Total	

Basic Skills | Challenge Yourself | **Calculator/Computer** | Career Applications | Above and Beyond

Entering decimals in your calculator is similar to entering whole numbers. There is just one difference: The decimal point key [•] is used to place the decimal point as you enter the number.

Often both addition and subtraction are involved in a calculation. In this case, just enter the decimals and the operation signs, + or −, as they appear in the problem. To find 23.7 − 5.2 + 3.87 − 2.341, enter

23.7 [−] 5.2 [+] 3.87 [−] 2.341 [=]

The display should show 20.029.

Solve each exercise, using your calculator.

43. 10,345.2 + 2,308.35 + 153.58

44. 8.7675 + 2.8 − 3.375 − 6

Solve each application, using your calculator.

45. Business and Finance Your checking account has a balance of $532.89. You write checks of $50, $27.54, and $134.75 and make a deposit of $50. What is your ending balance?

46. Business and Finance Your checking account has a balance of $278.45. You make deposits of $200 and $135.46. You write checks for $389.34, $249, and $53.21. What is your ending balance? Be careful with this exercise. A negative balance means that your account is overdrawn.

47. Business and Finance A small store makes a profit of $934.20 in the first week of a given month, $1,238.34 in the second week, and $853 in the third week. If the goal is a profit of $4,000 for the month, what profit must the store make during the remainder of the month?

Basic Skills | Challenge Yourself | Calculator/Computer | **Career Applications** | Above and Beyond

48. Allied Health Respiratory therapists calculate the humidity deficit, in milligrams per liter (mg/L), for a patient by subtracting the actual humidity content of inspired air from 43.9 mg/L, which is the maximum humidity content at body temperature. Determine the humidity deficit if the inspired air has a humidity content of 32.7 mg/L.

49. Allied Health A patient is given three capsules of Tc99m sodium pertechnetate containing 79.4, 15.88, and 3.97 millicuries (mCi), respectively. What was the total activity, in millicuries, administered to the patient?

50. Manufacturing A dimension on a computer-aided design (CAD) drawing is given as 3.084 in. ± 0.125 in. What is the minimum and maximum length the feature may be?

51. Electronics Sandy purchased a lot of 12-volt (V) batteries from an online auction. There were 10 batteries in the lot. If the batteries were connected in series, the total open-voltage would be the sum of the battery voltages; therefore, she expected an open-voltage of 120 V. Unfortunately, her voltmeter (used to measure voltage) doesn't read above 100 V. So she measured each battery's voltage and recorded it in the table on the next page. Calculate the actual open-voltage of the batteries if they are connected in series.

Answers

43. ________

44. ________

45. ________

46. ________

47. ________

48. ________

49. ________

50. ________

51. ________

Answers

52. ______

53. ______

54. ______

55. ______

56. ______

57. ______

Battery	Measured Voltage (in volts)	Battery	Measured Voltage (in volts)
1	12.20	6	12.82
2	13.84	7	11.93
3	11.42	8	11.01
4	13.00	9	12.77
5	12.45	10	12.03

Basic Skills | Challenge Yourself | Calculator/Computer | Career Applications | **Above and Beyond**

52. **Business and Finance** Following are charges on a credit card account: \$8.97, \$32.75, \$15.95, \$67.32, \$215.78, \$74.95, \$83.90, and \$257.28

 (a) Estimate the total bill for the charges by rounding each number to the nearest dollar and adding the results.

 (b) Estimate the total bill by adding the charges and then rounding to the nearest dollar.

 (c) What are the advantages and disadvantages of the methods in (a) and (b)?

53. **Number Problem** Find the next number in the following sequence: 3.125, 3.375, 3.625, . . .

Recall that a magic square is one in which the sum of every row, column, and diagonal is the same. Complete each magic square.

54.

2.4		7.2
10.8		
4.8		

55.

1.6		1.2
	1	
0.8		

56. **(a)** Determine the average amount of rainfall (to the nearest hundredth of an inch) in your town or city for each of the past 24 months.

 (b) Determine the difference in rainfall amounts per month for each month from one year to the next.

57. Find the next two numbers in each of the following sequences:

 (a) 0.75 0.62 0.5 0.39 **(b)** 1.0 1.5 0.9 3.5 0.8

Answers

1. 1.07 **3.** 22.319 **5.** 34.4462 **7.** 1.791 **9.** 147.029
11. 0.26 **13.** 2.255 **15.** 2.32 **17.** 6.65 **19.** 3.97
21. 1.65 **23.** 4.76 **25.** 42.4 gal **27.** **(a)** 13.37 cm; **(b)** 0.59 cm
29. \$272.94 **31.** 41.68 yd **33.** 11.535 mi **35.** 0.0575 in.
37. \$25.98 **39.** \$256.71; \$238.71; \$152.93; \$403.38; \$202.14
41. \$1,110.24; \$554.47; \$681.24; \$627.35 **43.** 12,807.13
45. \$370.60 **47.** \$974.46 **49.** 99.25 mCi **51.** 123.47 V
53. 3.875 **55.**

1.6	0.2	1.2
0.6	1	1.4
0.8	1.8	0.4

57. **(a)** 0.29, 0.20; **(b)** 5.5, 0.7

4.4 Multiplying Decimals

< 4.4 Objectives >

1 > Multiply two or more decimals

2 > Use multiplication of decimals to solve application problems

3 > Multiply a decimal by a power of 10

4 > Use multiplication by a power of 10 to solve an application problem

To start our discussion of the multiplication of decimals, write the decimals in common-fraction form and then multiply.

Example 1 Multiplying Two Decimals

< Objective 1 >

$$0.32 \times 0.2 = \frac{32}{100} \times \frac{2}{10} = \frac{64}{1{,}000} = 0.064$$

Here 0.32 has *two* decimal places, and 0.2 has *one* decimal place. The product 0.064 has *three* decimal places.

Note: $2 + 1 = 3$ (Places in 0.32; Place in 0.2; Places in the product 0.064)

Check Yourself 1

Find the product and the number of decimal places.

0.14 × 0.054

You do not need to write decimals as common fractions to multiply. Our work suggests the following rule.

Step by Step

To Multiply Decimals

Step 1 Multiply the decimals as though they were whole numbers. Temporarily ignore the decimal points.

Step 2 Count the number of decimal places in the numbers being multiplied.

Step 3 Place the decimal point in the product so that the number of decimal places in the product is the sum of the number of decimal places in the factors.

Example 2 illustrates this rule.

Example 2 Multiplying Two Decimals

Multiply 0.23 by 0.7.

```
  0.23  ← Two places
×  0.7  ← One place
 0.161  ← Three places
```

Check Yourself 2

Multiply 0.36 × 1.52.

You may have to affix zeros to the left in the product to place the decimal point. Consider Example 3.

Example 3 Multiplying Two Decimals

Multiply.

$$\begin{array}{r} 0.136 \\ \times\ 0.28 \\ \hline 1088 \\ 272 \\ \hline 0.03808 \end{array}$$

0.136 ← Three places
× 0.28 ← Two places
3 + 2 = 5
0.03808 ← Five places
Insert 0

Insert a 0 to mark off five decimal places.

Check Yourself 3

Multiply 0.234 × 0.24.

Estimation is also helpful in multiplying decimals.

Example 4 Estimating the Product of Two Decimals

Estimate the product 24.3 × 5.8.

$$\begin{array}{r} 24.3 \\ \times\ 5.8 \\ \hline \end{array} \xrightarrow{\text{Round}} \begin{array}{r} 24 \\ \times\ 6 \\ \hline 144 \end{array}$$

Multiply to get the estimate.

Check Yourself 4

Estimate the product.

17.95 × 8.17

Many applications require decimal multiplication.

Example 5 An Application Involving the Multiplication of Two Decimals

< Objective 2 >

A sheet of paper has dimensions 27.5 by 21.5 centimeters (cm). What is its area?

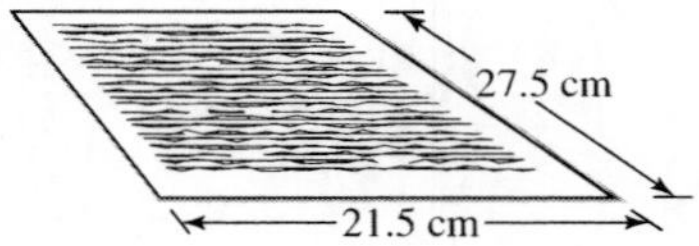

We multiply to find the required area.

$$\begin{array}{r} 27.5 \text{ cm} \\ \times\ 21.5 \text{ cm} \\ \hline 137\ 5\phantom{\text{ cm}} \\ 275\phantom{0\text{ cm}} \\ 550\phantom{00\text{ cm}} \\ \hline 591.25 \text{ cm}^2 \end{array}$$

The area of the paper is 591.25 cm^2.

RECALL

The area of a rectangle is length times width, so multiplication is the necessary operation.

Check Yourself 5

If 1 kilogram (kg) is 2.2 pounds (lb), how many pounds equal 5.3 kg?

Example 6 An Application Involving the Multiplication of Two Decimals

NOTE

Usually in problems dealing with money we round the result to the nearest cent (hundredth of a dollar).

Jack buys 8.7 gallons (gal) of propane at 98.9 cents per gallon. Find the cost of the propane.

We multiply the cost per gallon by the number of gallons. Then we round the result to the nearest cent. Note that the units of the answer will be cents.

$$\begin{array}{r} 98.9 \\ \times \;\; 8.7 \\ \hline 69\,23 \\ 791\,2 \\ \hline 860.43 \end{array}$$

The product 860.43 (cents) is rounded to 860 (cents), or \$8.60.

The cost of Jack's propane is \$8.60.

Check Yourself 6

One liter (L) is approximately 0.265 gal. On a trip to Europe, the Bernards purchased 88.4 L of gas for their rental car. How many gallons of gas did they purchase, to the nearest tenth of a gallon?

Sometimes we will have to use more than one operation for a solution, as Example 7 shows.

Example 7 An Application Involving Two Operations

Steve purchased a television set for \$299.50. He agreed to pay for the set by making payments of \$27.70 for 12 months. How much extra does he pay on the installment plan?

First we multiply to find the amount actually paid.

$$\begin{array}{r} \$\;27.70 \\ \times \quad\;\; 12 \\ \hline 55\,40 \\ 277\,0 \\ \hline \$332.40 \end{array}$$

← Amount paid

Now subtract the listed price. The difference will give the extra amount Steve paid.

$$\begin{array}{r} \$332.40 \\ -\;\; 299.50 \\ \hline \$\;\;32.90 \end{array}$$

← Extra amount

Steve will pay an additional \$32.90 on the installment plan.

Check Yourself 7

Sandy's new car had a list price of \$10,985. She paid \$1,500 down and will pay \$305.35 per month for 36 months on the balance. How much extra will she pay with this loan arrangement?

There are enough applications involving multiplication by the powers of 10 to make it worthwhile to develop a special rule so you can do such operations quickly and easily. Look at the patterns in some of these special multiplications.

$$\begin{array}{r} 0.679 \\ \times \quad 10 \\ \hline 6.790, \text{ or } 6.79 \end{array} \qquad \begin{array}{r} 23.58 \\ \times \quad 10 \\ \hline 235.80, \text{ or } 235.8 \end{array}$$

NOTE

The digits remain the same. Only the *position* of the decimal point is changed.

Do you see that multiplying by 10 has moved the decimal point *one place to the right?* What happens when we multiply by 100?

$$\begin{array}{r} 0.892 \\ \times \quad 100 \\ \hline 89.200 \end{array} \text{, or } 89.2 \qquad \begin{array}{r} 5.74 \\ \times \ 100 \\ \hline 574.00 \end{array} \text{, or } 574$$

Multiplying by 100 shifts the decimal point *two places to the right.* The pattern of these examples gives us the following rule:

Property

To Multiply by a Power of 10

Move the decimal point to the right the same number of places as there are zeros in the power of 10.

Example 8 Multiplying by Powers of 10

< Objective 3 >

NOTE

Multiplying by 10, 100, or any other larger power of 10 makes the number *larger*. Move the decimal point to *the right*.

$2.356 \times 10 = 23.56$

One zero — The decimal point has moved one place to the right.

$34.788 \times 100 = 3,478.8$

Two zeros — The decimal point has moved two places to the right.

$3.67 \times 1,000 = 3,670.$

Three zeros — The decimal point has moved three places to the right. Note that we added a 0 to place the decimal point correctly.

RECALL

10^5 is just a 1 followed by five zeros.

$0.005672 \times 10^5 = 567.2$

Five zeros — The decimal point has moved five places to the right.

Check Yourself 8

Multiply.

(a) 43.875×100 **(b)** 0.0083×10^3

Example 9 is just one of many applications that require multiplying by a power of 10.

Example 9 An Application Involving Multiplication by a Power of 10

< Objective 4 >

NOTES

There are 1,000 meters in 1 kilometer.

If the result is a whole number, there is no need to write the decimal point.

To convert from kilometers to meters, multiply by 1,000. Find the number of meters (m) in 2.45 kilometers (km).

$2.45 \text{ km} = 2,450. \text{ m}$ Just move the decimal point three places right to make the conversion. Note that we added a zero to place the decimal point correctly.

Check Yourself 9

To convert from kilograms to grams, multiply by 1,000. Find the number of grams (g) in 5.23 kilograms (kg).

Check Yourself ANSWERS

1. 0.00756, five decimal places **2.** 0.5472 **3.** 0.05616 **4.** 144 **5.** 11.66 lb **6.** 23.4 gal **7.** $1,507.60 **8.** **(a)** 4,387.5; **(b)** 8.3 **9.** 5,230 g

Reading Your Text

The following fill-in-the-blank exercises are designed to ensure that you understand some of the key vocabulary used in this section.

SECTION 4.4

(a) When multiplying decimals, ______________ the number of decimal places in the numbers being multiplied.

(b) The decimal point in the ______________ is placed so that the number of places is the sum of the number of decimal places in the factors.

(c) It is sometimes necessary to affix ______________ to the left of the product of two decimals to accurately place the decimal point.

(d) Multiplying by 100 shifts the decimal point two places to the ______________.

4.4 exercises

Basic Skills | Challenge Yourself | Calculator/Computer | Career Applications | Above and Beyond

Boost *your* GRADE at ALEKS.com!

ALEKS®

- Practice Problems
- Self-Tests
- NetTutor
- e-Professors
- Videos

Name ____________

Section ________ Date ________

Answers

1. ________ 2. ________
3. ________ 4. ________
5. ________ 6. ________
7. ________ 8. ________
9. ________ 10. ________
11. ________ 12. ________
13. ________ 14. ________
15. ________ 16. ________
17. ________ 18. ________
19. ________ 20. ________
21. ________ 22. ________
23. ________ 24. ________
25. ________

< Objective 1 >

Multiply.

1. 2.3×3.4

2. 6.5×4.3

3. 8.4×5.2 > Videos

4. 9.2×4.6

5. 2.56×72

6. 56.7×35

7. 0.78×2.3

8. 9.5×0.45

9. 15.7×2.35

10. 28.3×0.59

11. 0.354×0.8

12. 0.624×0.85

13. 3.28×5.07

14. 0.582×6.3

15. 5.238×0.48

16. 0.372×58

17. 1.053×0.552

18. 2.375×0.28

19. 0.0056×0.082

20. 1.008×0.046

21. 0.8×2.376

22. 3.52×58

23. 0.3085×4.5 > Videos

24. 0.028×0.685

Basic Skills | Challenge Yourself | Calculator/Computer | Career Applications | Above and Beyond

< Objective 2 >

Solve each application.

25. **Business and Finance** Kurt bought four shirts on sale as pictured. What was the total cost of the purchase?

26. **Business and Finance** Juan makes monthly payments of \$123.65 on his car. What will he pay in 1 year?

27. **Science and Medicine** If 1 gallon (gal) of water weighs 8.34 pounds (lb), how much does 2.5 gal weigh?

28. **Business and Finance** Malik worked 37.4 hours (h) in 1 week. If his hourly rate of pay is \$8.75, what was his pay for the week?

29. **Business and Finance** To find the amount of simple interest on a loan at $9\frac{1}{2}$%, we have to multiply the amount of the loan by 0.095. Find the simple interest on a \$1,500 loan for 1 year.

30. **Business and Finance** A beef roast weighing 5.8 lb costs \$3.25 per pound. What is the cost of the roast?

31. **Business and Finance** Tom's state income tax is found by multiplying his income by 0.054. If Tom's income is \$23,450, find the amount of his tax.

> Videos

32. **Business and Finance** Claudia earns \$9.40 per hour (h). For overtime (each hour over 40 h) she earns \$14.10. If she works 48.5 h in a week, what pay should she receive?

33. **Geometry** A sheet of typing paper has dimensions as shown. What is its area?

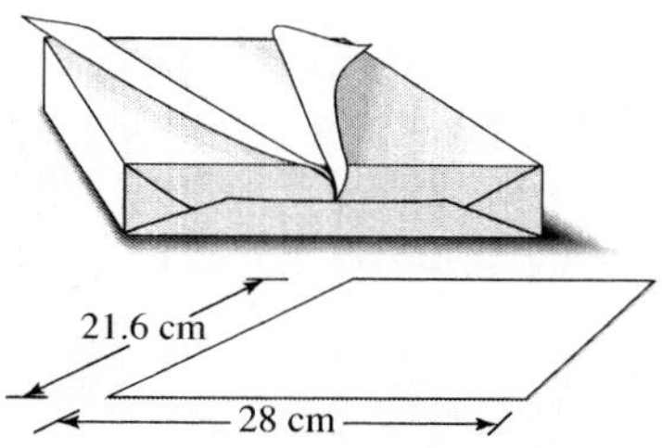

34. **Business and Finance** A rental car costs \$24 per day plus 18 cents per mile (mi). If you rent a car for 5 days and drive 785 mi, what will the total car rental bill be?

Label each statement as **true** *or* **false.**

35. The decimal points must be aligned when finding the sum of two decimals.

36. The decimal points must be aligned when finding the difference of two decimals.

37. The decimal points must be aligned when finding the product of two decimals.

38. The decimal points must be aligned when finding the better looking of two decimals.

39. The number of decimal places in the product of two factors will be the product of the number of places in the two factors.

40. When multiplying a decimal by a power of 10, the decimal point is moved to the left the number of places as there are zeros in the power of 10.

Answers

26. ______
27. ______
28. ______
29. ______
30. ______
31. ______
32. ______
33. ______
34. ______
35. ______
36. ______
37. ______
38. ______
39. ______
40. ______

Answers

41. ______ 42. ______

43. ______ 44. ______

45. ______ 46. ______

47. ______ 48. ______

49. ______ 50. ______

51. ______ 52. ______

53. ______ 54. ______

55. ______ 56. ______

57. ______ 58. ______

59. ______ 60. ______

61. ______ 62. ______

63. ______ 64. ______

< Objective 3 >

Multiply.

41. 5.89×10 > Videos

42. 0.895×100

43. 23.79×100

44. 2.41×10

45. 0.045×10

46. 5.8×100

47. 0.431×100

48. 0.025×10

49. 0.471×100

50. $0.95 \times 10{,}000$

51. $0.7125 \times 1{,}000$

52. $23.42 \times 1{,}000$

53. 4.25×10^2 > Videos

54. 0.36×10^3

55. 3.45×10^4

56. 0.058×10^5

< Objective 4 >

Solve each application.

57. Business and Finance A store purchases 100 items at a cost of \$1.38 each. Find the total cost of the order.

58. Science and Medicine To convert from meters (m) to centimeters (cm), multiply by 100. How many centimeters are there in 5.3 m?

59. Science and Medicine How many grams (g) are there in 2.2 kilograms (kg)? Multiply by 1,000 to make the conversion.

60. Business and Finance An office purchases 1,000 pens at a cost of 17.8 cents each. What is the cost of the purchase in dollars?

Meyer's Office Supply
371 Maple Dr., Treynor IA 50001

Item	Quantity	Item Price	Total
Pens	1000	\$0.178	

Basic Skills | Challenge Yourself | **Calculator/Computer** | Career Applications | Above and Beyond

The steps for finding the product of decimals on a calculator are similar to the ones we used for multiplying whole numbers. To multiply $2.8 \times 3.45 \times 3.725$, enter

2.8 [×] 3.45 [×] 3.725 [=]

The display should read 35.9835.

You can also easily find powers of decimals with your calculator by using a similar procedure. To find $(2.35)^3$, you can enter

2.35 [×] 2.35 [×] 2.35 [=]

The display should read 12.977875.

Some calculators have keys that will find powers more quickly. Look for keys marked [x^2] or [y^x]. Other calculators have a power key marked [∧]. To find $(2.35)^3$, enter 2.35 [∧] 3 [=] or 2.35 [y^x] 3 [=].

Again, the result is 12.977875.

Use your calculator for each exercise.

61. $127.85 \times 0.055 \times 15.84$

62. $18.28 \times 143.45 \times 0.075$

63. $(3.95)^3$

64. $(0.521)^2$

65. **GEOMETRY** Find the area of a rectangle with length 3.75 in. and width 2.35 in.

66. **BUSINESS AND FINANCE** Mark works 38.4 h in a given week. If his hourly rate of pay is \$7.85, what will he be paid for the week?

67. **BUSINESS AND FINANCE** If fuel oil costs \$1.879 per gallon, what will 150.4 gal cost?

68. **BUSINESS AND FINANCE** To find the simple interest on a loan for 1 year at 12.5%, multiply the amount of the loan by 0.125. What simple interest will you pay on a loan of \$1,458 at 12.5% for 1 year?

69. **BUSINESS AND FINANCE** You are the office manager for Dr. Rogers. The increasing cost of making photocopies is a concern to Dr. Rogers. She wants to examine alternatives to the current financing plan. The office currently leases a copy machine for \$110 per month and pays \$0.025 per copy. A 3-year payment plan is available that costs \$125 per month and \$0.015 per copy.

(a) If the office expects to run 100,000 copies per year, which is the better plan?

(b) How much money will the better plan save over the other plan?

70. **BUSINESS AND FINANCE** In a bottling company, a machine can fill a 2-liter (L) bottle in 0.5 second (s) and move the next bottle into place in 0.1 s. How many 2-L bottles can be filled by the machine in 2 h?

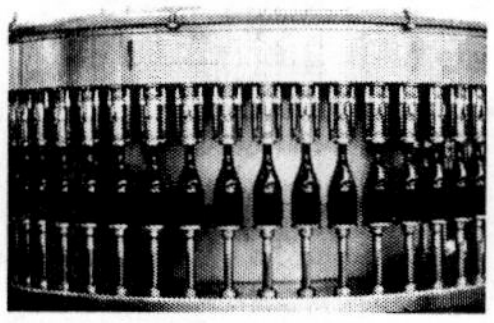

What happens when your calculator wants to display an answer that is too big to fit in the display? Suppose you want to evaluate 10^{10}. If you enter 10 [^] 10 [=], your calculator will probably display 1 E 10 or perhaps 1^{10}, both of which mean 1×10^{10}. Answers that are displayed in this way are said to be in **scientific notation.** This is a topic that you will study later. For now, we can use the calculator to see the relationship between numbers written in scientific notation and in decimal notation. For example, 3.485×10^4 is written in scientific notation. To write it in decimal notation, use your calculator to enter

3.485 [×] 10 [y^x] 4 [=]   or   3.485 [×] 10 [^] 4 [=]

The result should be 34,850. Note that the decimal point has moved four places (the power of 10) to the right.

Write each number in decimal notation.

71. 3.365×10^3 **72.** 4.128×10^3 **73.** 4.316×10^5

74. 8.163×10^6 **75.** 7.236×10^8 **76.** 5.234×10^7

Answers

1. 7.82 **3.** 43.68 **5.** 184.32 **7.** 1.794 **9.** 36.895 **11.** 0.2832 **13.** 16.6296 **15.** 2.51424 **17.** 0.581256 **19.** 0.0004592 **21.** 1.9008 **23.** 1.38825 **25.** \$39.92 **27.** 20.85 lb **29.** \$142.50 **31.** \$1,266.30 **33.** 604.8 cm^2 **35.** True **37.** False **39.** False **41.** 58.9 **43.** 2,379 **45.** 0.45 **47.** 43.1 **49.** 47.1 **51.** 712.5 **53.** 425 **55.** 34,500 **57.** \$138 **59.** 2,200 g **61.** 111.38292 **63.** 61.629875 **65.** 8.8125 $in.^2$ **67.** \$282.60 **69. (a)** 3-year plan; current plan: \$11,460; 3-year lease: \$9,000; **(b)** \$2,460 **71.** 3,365 **73.** 431,600 **75.** 723,600,000

Answers

65. ______

66. ______

67. ______

68. ______

69. ______

70. ______

71. ______

72. ______

73. ______

74. ______

75. ______

76. ______

Activity 11 :: Safe Dosages?

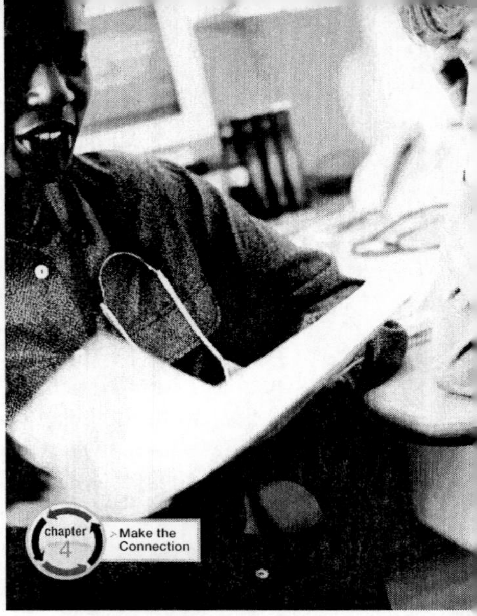

Chemotherapy drug dosages are generally calculated based on a patient's body surface area (BSA) in square meters (m^2). A patient's BSA is calculated using a nomogram and is based on the patient's height and weight. Print out the adult nomogram from the Science Museum of Minnesota's website www.smm.org/heart/lessons/nomogram_adult.htm. Draw a line connecting the patient's height with his or her weight. The point where this line crosses the middle column denotes the patient's BSA.

Dosages are then calculated using the formula

$$\text{Dose} = \text{recommended dose} \times \text{BSA}$$

In each case, determine if the prescribed dose falls within the recommended dose range for the given patient.

1. The doctor has prescribed Blenoxane to treat an adult male patient with testicular cancer. The patient is 70 inches (in.) tall and weighs 260 pounds (lb). According to the RxList website (www.rxlist.com), the recommended dose of Blenoxane in the treatment of testicular cancer should be between 10 to 20 units per square meter (units/m^2). The ordered dose is 50 units once per week.

2. The doctor has prescribed BiCNU to treat an adult patient with a brain tumor. The patient is 65 in. tall and weighs 150 lb. According to the RxList website, the recommended dose of BiCNU should be between 150 to 200 milligrams per square meter (mg/m^2). The ordered dose is 300 mg once every 6 weeks.

3. The doctor has prescribed Cisplatin to treat an adult patient with advanced bladder cancer. The patient is 73 in. tall and weighs 275 lb. According to the RxList website, the recommended dose of Cisplatin should be between 50 to 70 mg/m^2. The ordered dose is 150 mg once every 3 to 4 weeks.

4.5

Dividing Decimals

< 4.5 Objectives >

1 > Divide a decimal by a whole number

2 > Use division of decimals to solve application problems

3 > Divide a decimal by a decimal

4 > Divide a decimal by a power of 10

Division of decimals is very similar to our earlier work dividing whole numbers. The only difference is in learning to place the decimal point in the quotient. Let's start with the case of dividing a decimal by a whole number. Here, placing the decimal point is easy. You can apply the following rule.

Step by Step

To Divide a Decimal by a Whole Number

Step 1 Place the decimal point in the quotient *directly above* the decimal point of the dividend.

Step 2 Divide as you would with whole numbers.

Example 1 Dividing a Decimal by a Whole Number

< Objective 1 >

NOTE

Do the division just as if you were dealing with whole numbers. Just remember to place the decimal point in the quotient *directly above* the one in the dividend.

Divide 29.21 by 23.

```
     1.27
23)29.21
   23
    6 2
    4 6
    1 61
    1 61
       0
```

The quotient is 1.27.

Check Yourself 1

Divide 80.24 by 34.

Here is another example of dividing a decimal by a whole number.

Example 2 Dividing a Decimal by a Whole Number

NOTE

Again place the decimal point of the quotient above that of the dividend.

Divide 122.2 by 52.

```
      2.3
52)122.2
   104
    18 2
    15 6
     2 6
```

RECALL

Affixing a zero at the end of a decimal does not change the value of the dividend. It simply allows us to complete the division process in this case.

We normally do not use a remainder when dealing with decimals. Add a 0 to the dividend and continue.

$$
\begin{array}{r}
2.35 \\
52\overline{)122.20} \\
\underline{104} \\
18\;2 \\
\underline{15\;6} \\
2\;60 \\
\underline{2\;60} \\
0
\end{array}
\quad \leftarrow \text{Add a zero.}
$$

So $122.2 \div 52 = 2.35$. The quotient is 2.35.

Check Yourself 2

Divide 234.6 by 68.

Often you will be asked to give a quotient to a certain place value. In this case, continue the division process to *one digit past* the indicated place value. Then round the result back to the desired accuracy.

When working with money, for instance, we normally give the quotient to the nearest hundredth of a dollar (the nearest cent). This means carrying the division out to the thousandths place and then rounding.

Example 3 Dividing a Decimal by a Whole Number and Rounding the Result

NOTE

Find the quotient to *one place past* the desired place and then round the result.

Find the quotient of $25.75 \div 15$ to the nearest hundredth.

$$
\begin{array}{r}
1.716 \\
15\overline{)25.750} \\
\underline{15} \\
10\;7 \\
\underline{10\;5} \\
25 \\
\underline{15} \\
100 \\
\underline{90} \\
10
\end{array}
$$

Add a zero to carry the division to the thousandths place.

So $25.75 \div 15 = 1.72$ (to the nearest hundredth).

Check Yourself 3

Find $99.26 \div 35$ to the nearest hundredth.

As we mentioned, problems similar to the one in Example 3 often occur when we are working with money. Example 4 is one of the many applications of this type of division.

Example 4 An Application Involving the Division of a Decimal

< Objective 2 >

A carton of 144 items costs \$56.10. What is the price per item to the nearest cent?

To find the price per item, divide the total price by 144.

NOTE

You might want to review the rules for rounding decimals in Section 4.1.

$$
\begin{array}{r}
0.389 \\
144\overline{)56.100} \\
\underline{43\ 2} \\
12\ 90 \\
\underline{11\ 52} \\
1\ 380 \\
\underline{1\ 296} \\
84
\end{array}
$$

Carry the division to the thousandths place and then round.

The cost per item is rounded to \$0.39, or 39¢.

Check Yourself 4

An office paid \$26.55 for 72 pens. What was the cost per pen, to the nearest cent?

We now want to look at division *by* decimals. Here is an example using a fractional form.

Example 5 Rewriting a Problem That Requires Dividing by a Decimal

< Objective 3 >

NOTE

It is always easy to rewrite a division problem so that you are dividing by a whole number. Dividing by a whole number makes it easy to place the decimal point in the quotient.

Divide.

$2.57 \div 3.4 = \dfrac{2.57}{3.4}$ Write the division as a fraction.

$= \dfrac{2.57 \times 10}{3.4 \times 10}$ We multiply the numerator and denominator by 10 so the divisor is a whole number. This *does not change* the value of the fraction.

$= \dfrac{25.7}{34}$ Multiplying by 10, shift the decimal point in the numerator and denominator *one place to the right*.

$= 25.7 \div 34$ Our division problem is rewritten so that the divisor is a whole number.

So

$2.57 \div 3.4 = 25.7 \div 34$ After we multiply the numerator and denominator by 10, we see that $2.57 \div 3.4$ is the same as $25.7 \div 34$.

RECALL

Multiplying by any whole-number power of 10 greater than 1 is just a matter of shifting the decimal point to the right.

Check Yourself 5

Rewrite the division problem so that the divisor is a whole number.

$3.42 \div 2.5$

Do you see the rule suggested by example 5? We multiplied the numerator and the denominator (the dividend and the divisor) by 10. We made the divisor a whole number without altering the actual digits involved. All we did was shift the decimal point in the divisor and dividend the same number of places. This leads us to the following rule.

Step by Step

To Divide by a Decimal

Step 1 Move the decimal point in the divisor to the *right,* making the divisor a whole number.

Step 2 Move the decimal point in the dividend to the right *the same number of places.* Add zeros if necessary.

Step 3 Place the decimal point in the quotient directly above the decimal point of the dividend.

Step 4 Divide as you would with whole numbers.

Now look at an example of the use of our division rule.

Example 6 Rounding the Result of Dividing by a Decimal

Divide 1.573 by 0.48 and give the quotient to the nearest tenth.

Write

$$0.48\overline{)1.573}$$

Shift the decimal points two places to the right to make the divisor a whole number.

NOTE

Once the division statement is rewritten, place the decimal point in the quotient above that in the dividend.

Now divide:

```
     3.27
48)157.30
   144
    13 3
     9 6
     3 70
     3 36
       34
```

Note that we add a zero to carry the division to the hundredths place. In this case, we want to find the quotient to the nearest tenth.

Round 3.27 to 3.3. So

$1.573 \div 0.48 = 3.3$ (to the nearest tenth)

Check Yourself 6

Divide, rounding the quotient to the nearest tenth.

3.4 ÷ 1.24

Many applications involve decimal division.

Example 7 Solving an Application Involving the Division of Decimals

Andrea worked 41.5 hours in a week and earned $488.87. What was her hourly rate of pay?

To find the hourly rate of pay we use division. We divide the number of hours worked into the total pay.

```
          1 1.78
41.5 )488.8 70
      415
       73 8
       41 5
       32 3 7
       29 0 5
        3 3 20
        3 3 20
             0
```

NOTE

We add a zero to the dividend to complete the division process.

Andrea's hourly rate of pay was $11.78.

Check Yourself 7

A developer wants to subdivide a 12.6-acre piece of land into 0.45-acre lots. How many lots are possible?

Example 8 Solving an Application Involving the Division of Decimals

At the start of a trip the odometer read 34,563. At the end of the trip, it read 36,235. If 86.7 gallons (gal) of gas were used, find the number of miles per gallon (to the nearest tenth).

First, find the number of miles traveled by subtracting the initial reading from the final reading.

```
  36,235   Final reading
− 34,563   Initial reading
   1,672   Miles traveled
```

Next, divide the miles traveled by the number of gallons used. This will give us the miles per gallon.

```
            1 9. 28
86.7 )1,672.0 00
       867
       805 0
       780 3
        24 7 0
        17 3 4
         7 3 60
         6 9 36
           4 24
```

Round 19.28 to 19.3 mi/gal.

Check Yourself 8

John starts his trip with an odometer reading of 15,436 and ends with a reading of 16,238. If he used 45.9 gallons (gal) of gas, find the number of miles per gallon (mi/gal) (to the nearest tenth).

Recall that you can multiply decimals by powers of 10 by simply shifting the decimal point to the right. A similar approach works for division by powers of 10.

Example 9 Dividing a Decimal by a Power of 10

< Objective 4 >

(a) Divide.

```
     3.53
10)35.30
   30
    5 3
    5 0
      30
      30
       0
```

The dividend is 35.3. The quotient is 3.53. The decimal point has been shifted *one place to the left*. Note also that the divisor, 10, has *one* zero.

(b) Divide.

```
      3.785
100)378.500
    300
     78 5
     70 0
      8 50
      8 00
        500
        500
          0
```

Here the dividend is 378.5, whereas the quotient is 3.785. The decimal point is now shifted *two places to the left*. In this case the divisor, 100, has *two* zeros.

Check Yourself 9

Perform each division.

(a) 52.6 ÷ 10 **(b)** 267.9 ÷ 100

Example 9 suggests the following rule.

Property

To Divide a Decimal by a Power of 10

Move the decimal point *to the left* the same number of places as there are zeros in the power of 10.

Example 10 Dividing a Decimal by a Power of 10

NOTE

We may add zeros to correctly place the decimal point.

RECALL

10^4 is a 1 followed by *four zeros.*

Divide.

(a) 27.3 ÷ 10 = 2 7.3 Shift one place to the left.
= 2.73

(b) 57.53 ÷ 100 = 0 57.53 Shift two places to the left.
= 0.5753

(c) 39.75 ÷ 1,000 = 0 039.75 Shift three places to the left.
= 0.03975

(d) 85 ÷ 1,000 = 0 085. The decimal after the 85 is implied.
= 0.085

(e) 235.72 ÷ 10^4 = 0 0235.72 Shift four places to the left.
= 0.023572

Check Yourself 10

Divide.

(a) 3.84 ÷ 10 **(b)** 27.3 ÷ 1,000

Now, look at an application of our work in dividing by powers of 10.

Example 11 Solving an Application Involving a Power of 10

To convert from millimeters (mm) to meters (m), we divide by 1,000. How many meters does 3,450 mm equal?

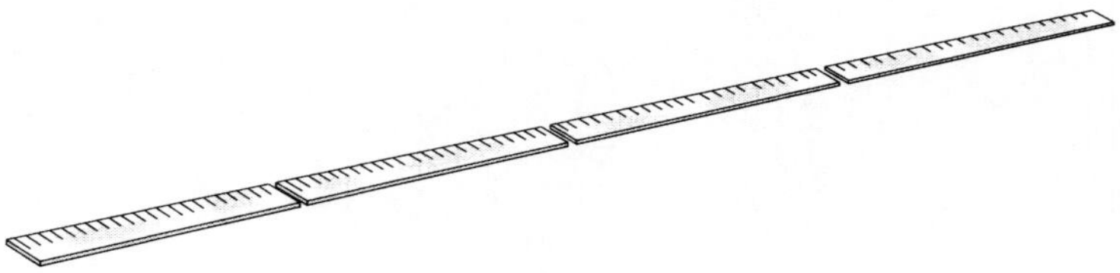

3,450 mm = 3 450. m Shift three places to the left to divide by 1,000.
= 3.450 m

Check Yourself 11

A shipment of 1,000 notebooks cost a stationery store \$658. What was the cost per notebook to the nearest cent?

Recall that the order of operations is always used to simplify a mathematical expression with several operations. You should recall the following order of operations.

Property

The Order of Operations

1. Perform any operations enclosed in **parentheses.**
2. Evaluate any **exponents.**
3. Do any **multiplication** and **division,** in order from left to right.
4. Do any **addition** and **subtraction,** in order from left to right.

Example 12 Applying the Order of Operations

Simplify each expression.

(a) $4.6 + (0.5 \times 4.4)^2 - 3.93$ — Parentheses
$= 4.6 + (2.2)^2 - 3.93$ — Exponent
$= 4.6 + 4.84 - 3.93$ — Add (left of the subtraction)
$= 9.44 - 3.93$ — Subtract
$= 5.51$

(b) $16.5 - (2.8 + 0.2)^2 + 4.1 \times 2$ — Parentheses
$= 16.5 - (3)^2 + 4.1 \times 2$ — Exponent
$= 16.5 - 9 + 4.1 \times 2$ — Multiply
$= 16.5 - 9 + 8.2$ — Subtraction (left of the addition)
$= 7.5 + 8.2$ — Add
$= 15.7$

Check Yourself 12

Simplify each expression.

(a) $6.35 + (0.2 \times 8.5)^2 - 3.7$ **(b)** $2.5^2 - (3.57 - 2.14) + 3.2 \times 1.5$

Check Yourself ANSWERS

1. 2.36 **2.** 3.45 **3.** 2.84 **4.** \$0.37, or 37¢ **5.** $34.2 \div 25$ **6.** 2.7 **7.** 28 lots **8.** 17.5 mi/gal **9.** **(a)** 5.26; **(b)** 2.679 **10.** **(a)** 0.384; **(b)** 0.0273 **11.** 66¢ **12.** **(a)** 5.54; **(b)** 9.62

Reading Your Text

The following fill-in-the-blank exercises are designed to ensure that you understand some of the key vocabulary used in this section.

SECTION 4.5

(a) When dividing decimals, place the decimal point in the quotient directly ______________ the decimal point of the dividend.

(b) When asked to give a quotient to a certain place value, continue the division process to one digit ______________ the indicated place value.

(c) When dividing by a decimal, first move the decimal point in the divisor to the right, making the divisor a ______________ ______________.

(d) To divide a decimal by a power of 10, move the decimal point to the ______________ the same number of places as there are zeros in the power of 10.

Basic Skills | Challenge Yourself | Calculator/Computer | Career Applications | Above and Beyond

4.5 exercises

Boost *your* GRADE at ALEKS.com!

ALEKS

- Practice Problems
- Self-Tests
- NetTutor
- e-Professors
- Videos

Name ______________

Section ________ Date ________

< Objectives 1–3 >

Divide.

1. $16.68 \div 6$ > Videos
2. $43.92 \div 8$
3. $1.92 \div 4$
4. $5.52 \div 6$
5. $5.48 \div 8$
6. $2.76 \div 8$
7. $\dfrac{13.89}{6}$ > Videos
8. $\dfrac{21.92}{5}$
9. $\dfrac{185.6}{32}$
10. $\dfrac{165.6}{36}$
11. $79.9 \div 34$
12. $179.3 \div 55$
13. $52\overline{)13.78}$
14. $76\overline{)26.22}$
15. $0.6\overline{)11.07}$
16. $0.8\overline{)10.84}$
17. $\dfrac{7.22}{3.8}$
18. $\dfrac{13.34}{2.9}$
19. $\dfrac{11.622}{5.2}$
20. $\dfrac{3.616}{6.4}$
21. $0.27\overline{)1.8495}$ > Videos
22. $0.038\overline{)0.8132}$
23. $0.046\overline{)1.587}$
24. $0.52\overline{)3.2318}$
25. $0.658 \div 2.8$
26. $0.882 \div 0.36$

< Objective 4 >

Divide by moving the decimal point.

27. $5.8 \div 10$
28. $5.1 \div 10$
29. $4.568 \div 100$
30. $3.817 \div 100$
31. $24.39 \div 1{,}000$ > Videos
32. $8.41 \div 100$
33. $6.9 \div 1{,}000$
34. $7.2 \div 1{,}000$

Answers

1. ________	2. ________
3. ________	4. ________
5. ________	6. ________
7. ________	8. ________
9. ________	10. ________
11. ________	12. ________
13. ________	14. ________
15. ________	16. ________
17. ________	18. ________
19. ________	20. ________
21. ________	22. ________
23. ________	24. ________
25. ________	26. ________
27. ________	28. ________
29. ________	30. ________
31. ________	32. ________
33. ________	34. ________

Answers

35. ______ 36. ______

37. ______ 38. ______

39. ______ 40. ______

41. ______ 42. ______

43. ______ 44. ______

45. ______ 46. ______

47. ______ 48. ______

49. ______ 50. ______

51. ______ 52. ______

53. ______

54. ______

55. ______

56. ______

57. ______

58. ______

35. $7.8 \div 10^2$

36. $3.6 \div 10^3$

37. $45.2 \div 10^5$

38. $57.3 \div 10^4$

Divide and round the quotient to the indicated decimal place.

39. $23.8 \div 9$ tenths

40. $5.27 \div 8$ hundredths

41. $38.48 \div 46$ hundredths

Videos

42. $3.36 \div 36$ thousandths

43. $125.4 \div 52$ tenths

44. $2.563 \div 54$ thousandths

45. $0.7\overline{)1.642}$ hundredths

46. $0.6\overline{)7.695}$ tenths

47. $4.5\overline{)8.415}$ tenths

48. $5.8\overline{)16}$ hundredths

49. $3.12\overline{)4.75}$ hundredths

50. $64.2\overline{)16.3}$ thousandths

Basic Skills | **Challenge Yourself** | Calculator/Computer | Career Applications | Above and Beyond

< Objective 2 >

Solve each application.

51. **Business and Finance** Marv paid $40.41 for three CDs on sale. What was the cost per CD?

52. **Business and Finance** Seven employees of an office donated a total of $172.06 during a charity drive. What was the average donation?

53. **Business and Finance** A shipment of 72 paperback books cost a store $190.25. What was the average cost per book to the nearest cent?

54. **Business and Finance** A restaurant bought 50 glasses at a cost of $39.90. What was the cost per glass to the nearest cent?

55. **Business and Finance** The cost of a box of 48 pens is $28.20. What is the cost of an individual pen to the nearest cent?

56. **Business and Finance** An office bought 18 handheld calculators for $284. What was the cost per calculator to the nearest cent?

57. **Business and Finance** Al purchased a new refrigerator that cost $736.12 with interest included. He paid $100 as a down payment and agreed to pay the remainder in 18 monthly payments. What amount will he be paying per month?

58. **Business and Finance** The cost of a television set with interest is $490.64. If you make a down payment of $50 and agree to pay the balance in 12 monthly payments, what will be the amount of each monthly payment?

Simplify each expression.

59. $79 - 28.2 + 13.7$

60. $63.1 - 4.8 + 5.2$

61. $29.64 - (4.2 + 12.39)$

62. $53.6 - (14 + 6.21)$

63. $8.2 \div 0.25 \times 3.6$

64. $7.14 \div 0.3 \times 5.1$

65. $\frac{7.8 + 4.2}{9.1 - 6.6}$

66. $\frac{6.08 + 3.58}{7.65 - 3.45}$

67. $6.4 + 1.3^2$

68. $(6.4 + 1.3)^2$

69. $15.9 - 4.2 \times 3.5$

70. $23.7 - 8.6 \times 0.8$

71. $6.1 + 2.3 \times (8.08 - 5.9)$

72. $2.09 + 4.5 \times (12.37 - 7.27)$

73. $5.2 - 3.1 \times 1.5 + (3.1 + 0.4)^2$

74. $150 + 4.1 \times 1.5 - (2.5 \times 1.6)^3 \times 2.4$

75. $17.9 \times 1.1 - (2.3 \times 1.1)^2 + (13.4 - 2.1 \times 4.6)$

76. $6.89^2 - 3.14 \times 2.5 + (3.2 \times 1.6 - 4.1)^2$

Basic Skills | Challenge Yourself | **Calculator/Computer** | Career Applications | Above and Beyond

Using your calculator to divide decimals is a good way to check your work and is also a reasonable way to solve applications. However, when using it for applications, we generally round off our answers to an appropriate place value.

Using your calculator, divide and round to the indicated place.

77. $2.546 \div 1.38$ hundredths

78. $45.8 \div 9.4$ tenths

79. $0.5782 \div 1.236$ thousandths

80. $1.25 \div 0.785$ hundredths

81. $1.34 \div 2.63$ two decimal places

82. $12.364 \div 4.361$ three decimal places

Basic Skills | Challenge Yourself | Calculator/Computer | **Career Applications** | Above and Beyond

83. **Allied Health** Since people vary in body size, the cardiac index is used to normalize cardiac output measurements. The cardiac index, in liters per minute per square meters L/(min · m^2), is calculated by dividing a patient's cardiac output, in liters per minute (L/min), by his or her body surface area, in m^2. Calculate the cardiac index for a male patient whose cardiac output is 4.8 L/min if his body surface area is 2.03 m^2. Round your answer to the nearest hundredth.

84. **Allied Health** The specific concentration of a radioactive drug, or radiopharmaceutical, is defined as the activity, in millicuries (mCi), divided by the volume, in milliliters (mL). Determine the specific concentration of a vial containing 7.3 mCi of I131 sodium iodide in 0.25 mL. Round your answer to the nearest tenth.

Answers

59. ______ 60. ______
61. ______ 62. ______
63. ______ 64. ______
65. ______ 66. ______
67. ______ 68. ______
69. ______ 70. ______
71. ______ 72. ______
73. ______ 74. ______
75. ______ 76. ______
77. ______ 78. ______
79. ______ 80. ______
81. ______ 82. ______
83. ______
84. ______

Answers

85. ______

86. ______

87. ______

88. ______

89. ______

90. ______

85. **Information Technology** A Web developer is responsible for designing a Web application for a customer. She uses a program called FTP to transmit pages from her local machine to a Web server. She needs to transmit 2.5 megabytes (Mbytes) of data. She notices it takes 10.2 seconds (s) to transmit the data. How fast is her connection to the Web server in Mbits/s? Round your answer to the nearest hundredth.

86. **Information Technology** After creating a presentation for a big customer, Joe sees that the size of the file is 1.6 Mbytes. Joe has a special application that allows him to save files across multiple disks. How many floppy disks will he need to store the file (a floppy disk can handle 1.4 Mbytes of data)?

Basic Skills | Challenge Yourself | Calculator/Computer | Career Applications | **Above and Beyond**

87. The blood alcohol content (BAC) of a person who has been drinking is determined by the Widmark formula. Find that formula using a search engine and use it to solve the following.

A 125-lb person is driving and is stopped by a policewoman on suspicion of driving under the influence (DUI). The driver claims that in the past 2 h he only consumed six 12-oz bottles of 3.9% beer. If he undergoes a breathalyzer test, what will his BAC be? Will this amount be under the legal limit for your state?

88. Four brands of soap are available in a local store.

Brand	Ounces	Total Price	Unit Price
Squeaky Clean	5.5	$0.36	
Smell Fresh	7.5	0.41	
Feel Nice	4.5	0.31	
Look Bright	6.5	0.44	

Compute the unit price and decide which brand is the best buy.

89. Sophie is a quality control expert. She inspects boxes of number 2 pencils. Each pencil weighs 4.4 grams (g). The contents of a box of pencils weigh 66.6 g. If a box is labeled CONTENTS: 16 PENCILS, should Sophie approve the box as meeting specifications? Explain your answer.

90. Write a plan to determine the number of miles per gallon (mi/gal) your car (or your family car) gets. Use this plan to determine your car's actual mileage.

Answers

1. 2.78 **3.** 0.48 **5.** 0.685 **7.** 2.315 **9.** 5.8 **11.** 2.35 **13.** 0.265 **15.** 18.45 **17.** 1.9 **19.** 2.235 **21.** 6.85 **23.** 34.5 **25.** 0.235 **27.** 0.58 **29.** 0.04568 **31.** 0.02439 **33.** 0.0069 **35.** 0.078 **37.** 0.000452 **39.** 2.6 **41.** 0.84 **43.** 2.4 **45.** 2.35 **47.** 1.9 **49.** 1.52 **51.** $13.47 **53.** $2.64 **55.** $0.59, or 59¢ **57.** $35.34 **59.** 64.5 **61.** 13.05 **63.** 118.08 **65.** 4.8 **67.** 8.09 **69.** 1.2 **71.** 11.114 **73.** 12.8 **75.** 17.0291 **77.** 1.84 **79.** 0.468 **81.** 0.51 **83.** 2.36 L/(min · m²) **85.** 0.25 Mbits/s **87.** Above and Beyond **89.** Above and Beyond

Activity 12 :: The Tour de France

The Tour de France is perhaps the most grueling of all sporting events. It is a bicycle race that spans 22 days (including 2 rest days), and involves 20 stages of riding in a huge circuit around the country of France. This includes several stages that take the riders through two mountainous regions, the Alps and the Pyrenees. The following table presents the winners of each stage in the 2005 race, along with the winning time in hours and the length of the stage expressed in miles. For each stage, compute the winner's average speed by dividing the miles traveled by the winning time. Round your answers to the nearest tenth of a mile per hour.

Stage	Winner	Length (mi)	Time (h)	Speed (mi/h)
Prologue	Zabriskie	11.8	0.35	
1	Boonen	112.8	3.86	
2	Boonen	132	4.60	
3	Discovery Channel	41.9	1.18	
4	McEwen	113.7	3.77	
5	Bernucci	123.7	4.21	
6	McEwen	142	5.06	
7	Weening	143.8	5.07	
8	Rasmussen	106.3	4.14	
9	Valverde	110.9	4.84	
10	Vinokourov	107.5	4.79	
11	Moncoutie	116.2	4.34	
12	McEwen	107.8	3.72	
13	Totsehnig	137	5.73	
14	Hincapie	127.7	6.11	
15	Pereiro	112.2	4.64	
16	Savoldelli	148.8	5.69	
17	Serrano	117.4	4.63	
18	Guerini	95.4	3.55	
19	Armstrong	34.5	1.20	
20	Vinokourov	89.8	3.68	

Find the total number of miles traveled.

By examining the speeds of the stages, can you identify which stages occurred in the mountains?

The overall tour winner was Lance Armstrong with a total winning time of 86.25 hours. Compute his average speed for the entire race, again rounding to the nearest tenth of a mile per hour.

Definition/Procedure	Example	Reference
Place Value and Rounding		**Section 4.1**
Decimal Fraction A fraction whose denominator is a power of 10. We call decimal fractions *decimals*.	$\frac{7}{10}$ and $\frac{47}{100}$ are decimal fractions.	p. 249
Decimal Place Each position for a digit to the right of the decimal point. Each decimal place has a place value that is $\frac{1}{10}$ the value of the place to its left.	2.3456 Ten-thousandths Thousandths Hundredths Tenths	p. 249
Reading and Writing Decimals in Words		
Step 1 Read the digits *to the left* of the decimal point as a whole number. **Step 2** Read the decimal point as the word *and*. **Step 3** Read the digits *to the right* of the decimal point as a whole number followed by the place value of the rightmost digit.	Hundredths 8.15 is read "eight and fifteen hundredths."	p. 250
Rounding Decimals		
Step 1 Find the place to which the decimal is to be rounded. **Step 2** If the next digit to the right is 5 or more, increase the digit in the place you are rounding to by 1. Discard any remaining digits to the right. **Step 3** If the next digit to the right is less than 5, just discard that digit and any remaining digits to the right.	To round 5.87 to the nearest tenth: 5.87 is rounded to 5.9 To round 12.3454 to the nearest thousandth: 12.3454 is rounded to 12.345.	p. 252
Converting Between Fractions and Decimals		**Section 4.2**
To Convert a Common Fraction to a Decimal		
Step 1 Divide the numerator of the common fraction by its denominator. **Step 2** The quotient is the decimal equivalent of the common fraction.	To convert $\frac{1}{2}$ to a decimal: $2\overline{)1.0}$ = 0.5 $\underline{1\ 0}$ 0	p. 258
To Convert a Terminating Decimal Less Than 1 to a Common Fraction		
Step 1 Write the digits of the decimal without the decimal point. This will be the numerator of the common fraction. **Step 2** The denominator of the fraction is a 1 followed by as many zeros as there are places in the decimal.	To convert 0.275 to a common fraction: $0.275 = \frac{275}{1{,}000} = \frac{11}{40}$	p. 261

Definition/Procedure	Example	Reference
Adding and Subtracting Decimals		**Section 4.3**
To Add Decimals		
Step 1 Write the numbers being added in column form with their decimal points in a vertical line. **Step 2** Add just as you would with whole numbers. **Step 3** Place the decimal point of the sum in line with the decimal points of the addends.	To add 2.7, 3.15, and 0.48: $\begin{array}{r} 2.7 \\ 3.15 \\ +\ 0.48 \\ \hline 6.33 \end{array}$	*p.* 268
To Subtract Decimals		
Step 1 Write the numbers being subtracted in column form with their decimal points in a vertical line. You may have to place zeros to the right of the existing digits. **Step 2** Subtract just as you would with whole numbers. **Step 3** Place the decimal point of the difference in line with the decimal points of the numbers being subtracted.	To subtract 5.875 from 8.5: $\begin{array}{r} 8.500 \\ -\ 5.875 \\ \hline 2.625 \end{array}$	*p.* 270
Multiplying Decimals		**Section 4.4**
To Multiply Decimals		
Step 1 Multiply the decimals as though they were whole numbers. **Step 2** Count the number of decimal places in the factors. **Step 3** Place the decimal point in the product so that the number of decimal places in the product is the sum of the number of decimal places in the factors.	To multiply 2.85×0.045: $\begin{array}{r} 2.85 \\ \times\ 0.045 \\ \hline 1425 \\ 1140 \\ \hline 0.12825 \end{array}$ 2.85 ← Two places × 0.045 ← Three places 0.12825 ← Five places	*p.* 281
Multiplying by Powers of 10		
Move the decimal point to the right the same number of places as there are zeros in the power of 10.	$2.37 \times 10 = 23.7$ $0.567 \times 1{,}000 = 567$	*p.* 284
Dividing Decimals		**Section 4.5**
To Divide by a Decimal		
Step 1 Move the decimal point in the divisor to the right, making the divisor a whole number. **Step 2** Move the decimal point in the dividend to the right the same number of places. Add zeros if necessary. **Step 3** Place the decimal point in the quotient directly above the decimal point of the dividend. **Step 4** Divide as you would with whole numbers.	To divide 16.5 by 5.5, move the decimal points: $\begin{array}{r} 3 \\ 5.5_{\wedge}\overline{)\,16.5_{\wedge}} \\ 16\ 5 \\ \hline 0 \end{array}$	*p.* 293
To Divide by a Power of 10		
Move the decimal point to the left the same number of places as there are zeros in the power of 10.	$25.8 \div 10 = 2_{\wedge}5.8 = 2.58$	*p.* 296

summary exercises :: chapter 4

This summary exercise set is provided to give you practice with each of the objectives of this chapter. Each exercise is keyed to the appropriate chapter section. When you are finished, you can check your answers to the odd-numbered exercises against those presented in the back of the text. If you have difficulty with any of these questions, go back and reread the examples from that section. The answers to the even-numbered exercises appear in the *Instructor's Solutions Manual.* Your instructor will give you guidelines on how to best use these exercises in your instructional setting.

4.1 *Find the indicated place values.*

1. 7 in 3.5742

2. 3 in 0.5273

Write the fractions in decimal form.

3. $\frac{37}{100}$

4. $\frac{307}{10{,}000}$

Write the decimals in words.

5. 0.071

6. 12.39

Write the fractions in decimal form.

7. Four and five tenths

8. Four hundred and thirty-seven thousandths

Complete each statement, using the symbol $<$, $=$, or $>$.

9. 0.79 ______ 0.785

10. 1.25 ______ 1.250

11. 12.8 ______ 13

12. 0.832 ______ 0.83

Round to the indicated place.

13. 5.837 hundredths

14. 9.5723 thousandths

15. 4.87625 three decimal places

Write each number as a common fraction or a mixed number.

16. 0.0067

17. 21.857

4.2 *Find the decimal equivalents.*

18. $\frac{7}{16}$

19. $\frac{3}{7}$ (round to the thousandth)

20. $\frac{4}{15}$ (use bar notation)

21. $3\frac{3}{4}$

Write as common fractions or mixed numbers. Simplify your answers.

22. 0.21

23. 0.084

24. 5.28

4.3 *Add.*

25. $\begin{array}{r} 2.58 \\ +\ 0.89 \\ \hline \end{array}$

26. $\begin{array}{r} 3.14 \\ 0.8 \\ 2.912 \\ +\ 12 \\ \hline \end{array}$

27. 1.3, 25, 5.27, and 6.158

28. Add eight, forty-three thousandths, five and nineteen hundredths, and seven and three tenths.

Subtract.

29. $\begin{array}{r} 29.21 \\ -\ 5.89 \\ \hline \end{array}$

30. $\begin{array}{r} 6.73 \\ -\ 2.485 \\ \hline \end{array}$

31. 1.735 from 2.81

32. 12.38 from 19

Solve each application.

33. GEOMETRY Find the perimeter (to the nearest hundredth of a centimeter) of a rectangle that has dimensions 5.37 cm by 8.64 cm.

34. SCIENCE AND MEDICINE Janice ran 4.8 miles (mi) on Sunday, 5.3 mi on Tuesday, 3.9 mi on Thursday, and 8.2 mi on Saturday. How far did she run during the week?

35. GEOMETRY Find dimension *a* in the figure.

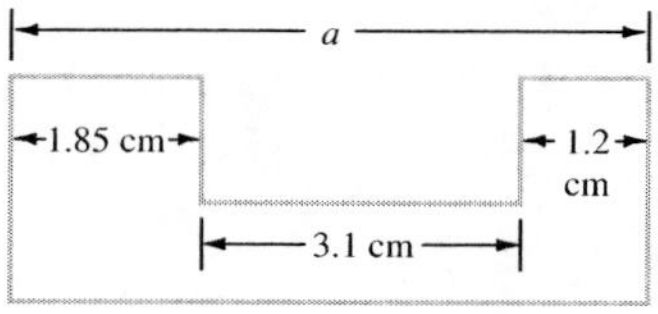

36. BUSINESS AND FINANCE A stereo system that normally sells for \$499.50 is discounted (or marked down) to \$437.75 for a sale. Find the savings.

37. BUSINESS AND FINANCE If you cash a \$50 check and make purchases of \$8.71, \$12.53, and \$9.83, how much money do you have left?

4.4 *Multiply.*

38. $\begin{array}{r} 22.8 \\ \times\ 0.72 \\ \hline \end{array}$

39. $\begin{array}{r} 0.0045 \\ \times\ 0.058 \\ \hline \end{array}$

40. 1.24×56

41. 0.0025×0.491

42. $0.052 \times 1{,}000$

43. 0.045×10^4

Solve each application.

44. **Business and Finance** Neal worked for 37.4 hours (h) during a week. If his hourly rate of pay was \$7.25, how much did he earn?

45. **Business and Finance** To find the simple interest on a loan at $11\frac{1}{2}\%$ for 1 year, we must multiply the amount of the loan by 0.115. Find the simple interest on a \$2,500 loan at $11\frac{1}{2}\%$ for 1 year.

46. **Business and Finance** A television set has an advertised price of \$499.50. You buy the set and agree to make payments of \$27.15 per month for 2 years. How much extra are you paying by buying with this installment plan?

47. **Business and Finance** A stereo dealer buys 100 portable radios for a promotion sale. If she pays \$57.42 per radio, what is her total cost?

4.5 *Divide. Round answers to the nearest hundredth.*

48. $8\overline{)3.08}$

49. $58\overline{)269.7}$

50. $55\overline{)17.69}$

Divide. Round answers to the nearest thousandth.

51. $0.7\overline{)1.865}$

52. $3.042 \div 0.37$

53. $5.3\overline{)6.748}$

54. $0.2549 \div 2.87$

Divide.

55. $7.6 \div 10$

56. $80.7 \div 1{,}000$

57. $457 \div 10^4$

Solve each application.

58. **Business and Finance** During a charity fund-raising drive 37 employees of a company donated a total of \$867.65. What was the donation per employee?

59. **Business and Finance** Faith always fills her gas tank as soon as the gauge hits the $\frac{1}{4}$ full mark. In six readings, Faith's gas mileage was 38.9, 35.3, 39.0, 41.2, 40.5, and 40.8 miles per gallon (mi/gal). What was the average mileage to the nearest tenth of a mile per gallon? (*Hint:* First find the sum of the mileages. Then divide the sum by 6, because there are 6 mileage readings.)

60. **Construction** A developer is planning to subdivide an 18.5-acre piece of land. She estimates that 5 acres will be used for roads and wants individual lots of 0.25 acre. How many lots are possible?

61. **Business and Finance** Paul drives 949 mi, using 31.8 gal of gas. What is his mileage for the trip (to the nearest tenth of a mile per gallon)?

62. **Business and Finance** A shipment of 1,000 videotapes cost a dealer \$7,090. What was the cost per tape to the dealer?

self-test 4

Name ____________

Section ______ Date ______

The purpose of this self-test is to help you assess your progress so that you can find concepts that you need to review before the next exam. Allow yourself about an hour to take this test. At the end of that hour, check your answers against those given in the back of this text. If you miss any, go back to the appropriate section to reread the examples until you have mastered that particular concept.

Complete each statement, using the symbols < or >.

1. 0.889 ______ 0.89

2. 0.531 ______ 0.53

Find the decimal equivalents of the common fractions. When indicated, round to the given place value.

3. $\frac{7}{16}$

4. $\frac{3}{7}$ thousandths

5. $\frac{7}{11}$ use bar notation

Divide.

6. $4.983 \div 1{,}000$

7. $523 \div 10^5$

Write the decimals as common fractions or mixed numbers. Simplify your answer.

8. 0.072

9. 4.44

10. Find the place value of 8 in 0.5248.

11. Write 2.53 in words.

Round to the indicated place.

12. 0.5977 thousandths

13. 23.5724 two decimal places

14. 36,139.0023 thousands

15. Write $\frac{49}{1{,}000}$ in decimal form.

16. Write twelve and seventeen thousandths in decimal form.

Perform the indicated operations.

17. $\begin{array}{r} 3.45 \\ 0.6 \\ +\ 12.59 \\ \hline \end{array}$

18. $\begin{array}{r} 18.32 \\ -\ 7.78 \\ \hline \end{array}$

19. $4.1\overline{)10.455}$

20. 2.75×0.53

21. $27\overline{)63.45}$

22. Add: 2.4, 35, 4.73, and 5.123

23. $\begin{array}{r} 32.9 \\ \times\ 0.53 \\ \hline \end{array}$

24. $\begin{array}{r} 40 \\ -\ 15.625 \\ \hline \end{array}$

Answers

1. ______
2. ______
3. ______
4. ______
5. ______
6. ______
7. ______
8. ______
9. ______
10. ______
11. ______
12. ______
13. ______
14. ______
15. ______
16. ______
17. ______
18. ______
19. ______
20. ______
21. ______
22. ______
23. ______
24. ______

Answers

25. ______
26. ______
27. ______
28. ______
29. ______
30. ______
31. ______
32. ______
33. ______
34. ______
35. ______
36. ______
37. ______
38. ______
39. ______
40. ______
41. ______
42. ______

25. **Business and Finance** A college bookstore purchases 1,000 pens at a cost of 54.3 cents per pen. Find the total cost of the order in dollars.

26. **Business and Finance** On a business trip, Martin bought the following amounts of gasoline: 14.4, 12, 13.8, and 10 gallons (gal). How much gasoline did he purchase on the trip?

27. **Construction** A 14-acre piece of land is being developed into home lots. If 2.8 acres of land will be used for roads and each home site is to be 0.35 acre, how many lots can be formed?

28. Insert $<$ or $>$ to form a true statement.

$0.168 \underline{\qquad} \frac{3}{25}$

29. Add: seven, seventy-nine hundredths, and five and thirteen thousandths

30. Find the area of a rectangle with length 3.5 inches (in.) and width 2.15 in.

Multiply.

31. $0.735 \times 1,000$

32. 1.257×10^4

33. **Construction** A street improvement project will cost $57,340, and that cost is to be divided among the 100 families in the area. What will be the cost to each individual family?

34. **Business and Finance** You pay for purchases of $13.99, $18.75, $9.20, and $5 with a $50 bill. How much cash will you have left?

Perform the indicated operation.

35. Subtract: 1.742 from 5.63

36. $8\overline{)3.72}$

37. $\begin{array}{r} 0.049 \\ \times\ 0.57 \\ \hline \end{array}$

38. $0.6\overline{)1.431}$

39. A baseball team has a winning percentage of 0.458. Write this as a fraction in simplest form.

Divide. When indicated, round to the given place value.

40. $3.969 \div 0.54$

41. $2.72 \div 53$ thousandths

42. $0.263 \div 3.91$ three decimal places

Name ______________________

Section ________ Date ________

The following exercises are presented to help you review concepts from earlier chapters. This is meant as review material and not as a comprehensive exam. The answers are presented in the back of the text. Before each answer is a section reference for the concept. If you have difficulty with any of these exercises, be certain to at least read through the summary related to that section.

1. Write 286,543 in words.

2. What is the place value of 5 in the number 343,563?

In exercises 3 to 8, perform the indicated operations.

3.
$$\begin{array}{r} 2{,}340 \\ 685 \\ +\ 31{,}569 \\ \hline \end{array}$$

4.
$$\begin{array}{r} 75{,}363 \\ -\ 26{,}475 \\ \hline \end{array}$$

5. 83×61

6. 231×305

7. $21\overline{)357}$

8. $463\overline{)16{,}216}$

9. Evaluate the expression $18 \div 2 + 4 \times 2^3 - (18 - 6)$.

10. Round each number to the nearest hundred and find an estimated sum.

$294 + 725 + 2{,}321 + 689$

11. Find the perimeter and area of the given figure.

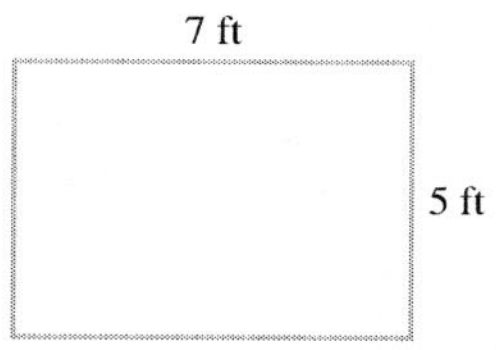

12. Write the fraction $\frac{15}{51}$ in simplest form.

Answers

1. ______________________
2. ______________________
3. ______________________
4. ______________________
5. ______________________
6. ______________________
7. ______________________
8. ______________________
9. ______________________
10. ______________________
11. ______________________
12. ______________________

Answers

13. ____________
14. ____________
15. ____________
16. ____________
17. ____________
18. ____________
19. ____________
20. ____________
21. ____________
22. ____________
23. ____________
24. ____________
25. ____________
26. ____________
27. ____________
28. ____________
29. ____________
30. ____________
31. ____________

Perform the indicated operations.

13. $\frac{2}{3} \times \frac{9}{8}$

14. $1\frac{2}{3} \times 1\frac{5}{7}$

15. $\frac{3}{4} \div \frac{17}{12}$

16. $\frac{6}{7} - \frac{3}{7} + \frac{2}{7}$

17. $\frac{4}{5} - \frac{7}{10} + \frac{4}{30}$

18. $6\frac{3}{5} - 2\frac{7}{10}$

19. $35.218 - 22.75$

20. $2.262 \div 0.58$

21. $523.8 \div 10^5$

22. 2.53×0.45

23. 1.53×10^4

24. Write 0.43 as a fraction.

25. Write the decimal equivalent of each number. Round to the given place value when indicated.

(a) $\frac{5}{8}$

(b) $\frac{9}{23}$ hundredths

26. Sam has had 15 hits in his last 35 at bats. That is, he has had a hit in $\frac{15}{35}$ of his times at bat. Write this as a decimal, rounding to the nearest thousandth.

Evaluate each expression.

27. $18.4 - 3.16 \times 2.5 + 6.71$

28. $17.6 \div 2.3 \times 3.4 + 13.812$ (Round to the nearest thousandth.)

Solve each application.

29. **Geometry** If the perimeter of a square is 19.2 cm, how long is each side?

30. **Business and Finance** In 1 week, Tom earned $356.60 by working 36.25 hours (h). What was his hourly rate of pay to the nearest cent?

31. **Construction** An 80.5-acre piece of land is being subdivided into 0.35-acre lots. How many lots are possible in the subdivision?

CHAPTER

5

Ratios and Proportions

INTRODUCTION

Sandra is a community college math instructor who loves teaching math and helping her students learn difficult concepts. When she is not teaching her classes, she spends a lot of time working out in the gym.

One day, during a particularly grueling yoga class, one of the participants asked Sandra to show him the right way to do the mountain pose. While Sandra was demonstrating this pose, she realized that she could become a personal trainer.

Sandra did some research and learned that she needed some coursework and that by passing an exam she could obtain a certificate through the American Fitness Professionals & Associates (AFPA). Some of the classes that personal trainers can teach include senior fitness, nutrition, group fitness, strength training, weight loss, and rehabilitative training.

Sandra learned some interesting facts about burning calories and weight loss such as the fact that a person has to burn off a lot more calories than he or she takes in just to lose one pound. In Activity 15 on page 355, we use ratios to determine the number of calories burned by various activities.

CHAPTER 5 OUTLINE

5 prerequisite test

Name ____________

Section ______ Date ______

This prerequisite test provides some exercises requiring skills that you will need to be successful in the coming chapter. The answers for these exercises can be found in the back of this text. This prerequisite test can help you identify topics that you will need to review before beginning the chapter.

Answers

1. ____________
2. ____________
3. ____________
4. ____________
5. ____________
6. ____________
7. ____________
8. ____________
9. ____________
10. ____________
11. ____________

Simplify each fraction.

1. $\frac{24}{32}$

2. $\frac{280}{525}$

3. $\frac{\frac{45}{2}}{30}$

Rewrite the mixed number as an improper fraction.

4. $5\frac{3}{5}$

Perform the indicated operations.

5. $\frac{45}{2} \times \frac{1}{30}$

6. 5.25×100

7. Find the GCF of 280 and 525.

Write each fraction as a decimal. Round to the nearest hundredth.

8. $\frac{50}{9}$

9. $\frac{260}{36}$

Determine whether the two given fractions are equivalent.

10. $\frac{6}{17}$ and $\frac{4}{11}$

11. $\frac{7}{15}$ and $\frac{84}{180}$

5.1 Ratios

< 5.1 Objectives >

1 > Write the ratio of two quantities

2 > Write the ratio of two quantities in simplest form

In Chapter 2, you learned two meanings for a fraction:

1. A fraction can name a certain number of parts of a whole. The fraction $\frac{3}{5}$ names 3 parts of a whole that has been divided into 5 equal parts.
2. A fraction can indicate division. The fraction $\frac{3}{5}$ is the quotient $3 \div 5$.

We now want to turn to a third meaning for a fraction—a fraction can be a **ratio.**

Definition

Ratio — A **ratio** is a comparison of two numbers or like quantities.

> **NOTE**
> In this text, we write ratios as simplified fractions.

The ratio a to b can also be written as $a : b$ and $\frac{a}{b}$. Ratios are always written in simplest form.

Example 1 Writing a Ratio as a Fraction

< Objective 1 >

> **NOTE**
> Alternatively, the ratio of 3 to 5 can be written as 3:5.

Write the ratio 3 to 5 as a fraction.

To compare 3 to 5, we write the ratio of 3 to 5 as $\frac{3}{5}$.

So, $\frac{3}{5}$ also means "the ratio of 3 to 5."

Check Yourself 1

Write the ratio of 7 to 12 as a fraction.

> **RECALL**
> Numbers with units attached are called *denominate numbers*.

Ratios are often used to compare *like quantities* such as quarts to quarts, centimeters to centimeters, and apples to apples. In this case, we can simplify the fraction by "canceling" the units. In its simplest form, a ratio is always written without units.

Example 2 Ratios of Denominate Numbers

A rectangle measures 7 cm wide and 19 cm long.

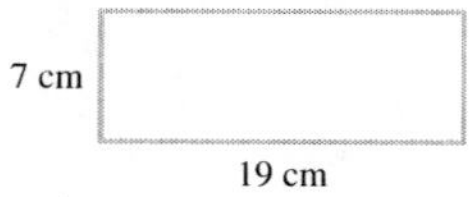

(a) Write the ratio of its width to its length, as a fraction.

$$\frac{7 \text{ cm}}{19 \text{ cm}} = \frac{7 \cancel{\text{cm}}}{19 \cancel{\text{cm}}} = \frac{7}{19}$$

We are comparing centimeters to centimeters, so we can simplify the fraction.

NOTE

Ratios are *never* written as mixed numbers. Ratios are always written as improper fractions, in simplest terms, when necessary.

(b) Write the ratio of its length to its width, as a fraction.

We need to write the ratio in the order requested by the example, rather than in the order given in the preceding description.

$$\frac{19\text{ cm}}{7\text{ cm}} = \frac{19\ \cancel{\text{cm}}}{7\ \cancel{\text{cm}}} = \frac{19}{7}$$

Check Yourself 2

A basketball team wins 17 of its 29 games in a season.

(a) Write the ratio of wins to games played.
(b) Write the ratio of wins to losses.

Because a ratio is a fraction, we can simplify it, as in Example 3.

Example 3 Simplifying a Ratio

< Objective 2 >

RECALL

This ratio may also be written as 2:3.

Write the ratio of 20 to 30 in simplest terms.

Begin by writing the fraction that represents the ratio: $\frac{20}{30}$. Now, simplify this fraction.

$$\frac{20}{30} = \frac{2}{3}$$

Simplify the fraction by dividing both the numerator and denominator by 10.

Check Yourself 3

Write the ratio of 24 to 32 in simplest terms.

Because ratios are used to compare like quantities, a simplified ratio has no units. In Example 4, we need to simplify both the numbers and the units.

Example 4 Simplifying the Ratio of Denominate Numbers

NOTE

On DVDs, widescreen movies are often in 16:9 format.

A common size for a movie screen is 32 ft by 18 ft. Write this ratio in simplest form.

$$\frac{32\text{ ft}}{18\text{ ft}} = \frac{32\ \cancel{\text{ft}}}{18\ \cancel{\text{ft}}} = \frac{32}{18} = \frac{16}{9}$$

The GCF of 32 and 18 is 2.

Check Yourself 4

A common computer display mode is 640 pixels (picture elements) by 480 pixels. Write this as a ratio in simplest terms.

Often, the quantities in a ratio are given as fractions or decimals. In either of these cases, the ratio should be rewritten as an equivalent ratio comparing whole numbers.

Example 5 Simplifying Ratios

(a) Loren sank a $22\frac{1}{2}$-ft putt and Carrie sank a 30-ft putt. Express the ratio of the two distances as a ratio of whole numbers.

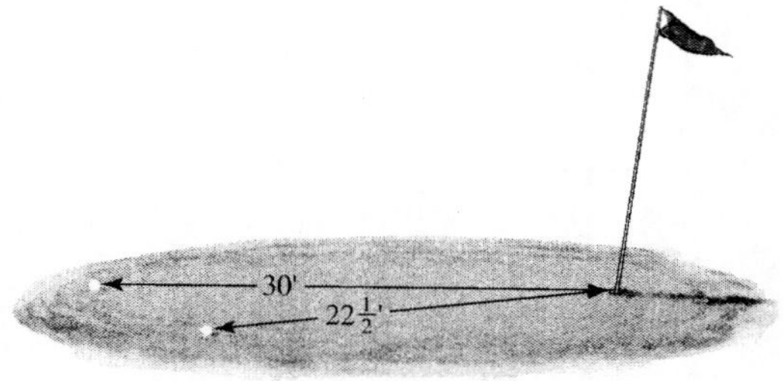

RECALL

In Section 2.3, you learned to rewrite $22\frac{1}{2}$ as $\frac{45}{2}$.

We begin by writing the ratio of the two distances: $\dfrac{22\frac{1}{2}\text{ ft}}{30\text{ ft}}$. Then, we cancel the units and rewrite the mixed number as an improper fraction.

$$\frac{22\frac{1}{2}\text{ ft}}{30\text{ ft}} = \frac{\frac{45}{2}}{30}$$

RECALL

In Section 2.6, you learned to simplify complex fractions.

In order to simplify this complex fraction, we rewrite it as a division problem.

$$\frac{\frac{45}{2}}{30} = \frac{45}{2} \div 30$$

$$= \frac{45}{2} \times \frac{1}{30} \quad \text{Invert, and multiply.}$$

$$= \frac{\overset{3}{\cancel{45}} \times 1}{2 \times \underset{2}{\cancel{30}}} \quad \text{The GCF of 45 and 30 is 15.}$$

$$= \frac{3}{4}$$

The ratio 3 to 4 is equivalent to the ratio $22\frac{1}{2}$ ft to 30 ft.

(b) The diameter of a 20-oz bottle is 2.8 in. The diameter of a 2-L bottle is 5.25 in. Express the ratio of the two diameters as a ratio of whole numbers.

$$\frac{2.8\text{ in.}}{5.25\text{ in.}} = \frac{2.8}{5.25}$$

In order to simplify this fraction, we need to rewrite it as an equivalent fraction of whole numbers, that is, without the decimals.

If we multiply the numerator by 10, it would be a whole number. However, we need to multiply the denominator by 100 in order to make it a whole number. Because we want to write an equivalent fraction, we multiply it by $1 = \frac{100}{100}$.

RECALL

In Section 4.4, you learned to multiply a decimal by a power of 10 by moving the decimal point.

$$\frac{2.8}{5.25} \cdot \frac{100}{100} = \frac{280}{525}$$

$$= \frac{8}{15}$$

Divide numerator and denominator by 5, and then again by 7. Or, we can determine that the GCF of 280 and 525 is 35, and simplify with one division.

The ratio of the bottle diameters is 8 to 15.

Check Yourself 5

(a) One morning Rita jogged $3\frac{1}{2}$ mi, while Yi jogged $4\frac{1}{4}$ mi. Express the ratio of the two distances as a ratio of whole numbers.
(b) A standard newspaper column is 2.625 in. wide and 19.5 in. long. Express the ratio of the two measurements as a ratio of whole numbers.

NOTE

We will learn to convert measurements in more depth in Chapter 7.

Sometimes, we use a ratio to compare the same type of measurement using different units. In Example 6, both quantities are measures of time. In order to construct and simplify the ratio, we must express both quantities in the same units.

Example 6 Rewriting Denominate Numbers to Find a Ratio

Joe took 2 hours (h) to complete his final exam. Jamie finished hers in 75 minutes (min). Write the ratio of the two times in simplest terms.

To find the ratio, both quantities must have the same units. Therefore, we rewrite 2 h as 120 min. This way, both quantities use minutes as the unit.

$$\frac{2\text{ h}}{75\text{ min}} = \frac{120\text{ min}}{75\text{ min}} \qquad 2\text{ h} = 120\text{ min.}$$

$$= \frac{120}{75} = \frac{8}{5} \qquad \text{The GCF of 120 and 75 is 15.}$$

Check Yourself 6

Find the ratio of whole numbers that is equivalent to the ratio of 15 ft to 9 yd.

Check Yourself ANSWERS

1. $\frac{7}{12}$ 2. (a) $\frac{17}{29}$; (b) $\frac{17}{12}$ 3. $\frac{3}{4}$ 4. $\frac{4}{3}$ 5. (a) $\frac{14}{17}$; (b) $\frac{7}{52}$ 6. $\frac{5}{9}$

Reading Your Text

The following fill-in-the-blank exercises are designed to ensure that you understand some of the key vocabulary used in this section.

SECTION 5.1

(a) A ______________ can indicate division.

(b) A ratio is a means of comparing two ______________ quantities.

(c) Because a ratio is a fraction, we can write it in ______________ terms.

(d) Ratios are never written as ______________ numbers.

< Objectives 1–2 >

Write each ratio in simplest form.

1. The ratio of 9 to 13

2. The ratio of 5 to 4

3. The ratio of 9 to 4

4. The ratio of 5 to 12

5. The ratio of 10 to 15 > Videos

6. The ratio of 16 to 12

7. The ratio of $3\frac{1}{2}$ to 14

8. The ratio of $5\frac{3}{5}$ to $2\frac{1}{10}$

9. The ratio of 10.5 to 2.7 > Videos

10. The ratio of 2.2 to 0.6

11. The ratio of 12 miles (mi) to 18 mi

12. The ratio of 100 centimeters (cm) to 90 cm

13. The ratio of 40 ft to 65 ft

14. The ratio of 12 oz to 18 oz

15. The ratio of \$48 to \$42

16. The ratio of 20 ft to 24 ft

Solve each application.

17. Social Science An algebra class has 7 men and 13 women. Write the ratio of men to women. Write the ratio of women to men.

18. Statistics A football team wins 9 of its 16 games with no ties. Write the ratio of wins to games played. Write the ratio of wins to losses.

19. Social Science In a school election 4,500 yes votes were cast, and 3,000 no votes were cast. Write the ratio of yes to no votes. > Videos

20. Business and Finance One car has an $11\frac{1}{2}$-gal tank and another has a $17\frac{3}{4}$-gal tank. Express the ratio of the capacities as a ratio of whole numbers.

21. Business and Finance One refrigerator holds $2\frac{2}{3}$ cubic feet (ft^3) of food, and another holds $5\frac{3}{4}$ ft^3 of food. Express the ratio of the capacities as a ratio of whole numbers. > Videos

22. Science and Medicine The price of an antibiotic in one drugstore is \$12.50 although the price of the same antibiotic in another drugstore is \$8.75. Write the ratio of the prices as a ratio of whole numbers.

23. Social Science A company employs 24 women and 18 men. Write the ratio of men to women employed by the company.

24. Geometry If a room is 30 ft long by 6 yd wide, write the ratio of the length to the width of the room.

Name ______________

Section ________ Date ________

Answers

1. ________ 2. ________

3. ________ 4. ________

5. ________ 6. ________

7. ________ 8. ________

9. ________ 10. ________

11. ________ 12. ________

13. ________ 14. ________

15. ________ 16. ________

17. ________ 18. ________

19. ________ 20. ________

21. ________ 22. ________

23. ________ 24. ________

Answers

25. ______
26. ______
27. ______
28. ______
29. ______
30. ______
31. ______
32. ______
33. ______
34. ______
35. ______
36. ______
37. ______
38. ______
39. ______
40. ______

Determine whether each statement is **true** *or* **false.**

25. We use ratios to compare like quantities.

26. We use ratios to compare different types of measurements.

Fill in each blank with **always, sometimes,** *or* **never.**

27. A ratio should __________ be written in simplest form.

28. A ratio is __________ written as a mixed number.

Basic Skills | **Challenge Yourself** | Calculator/Computer | Career Applications | Above and Beyond

Write each ratio in simplest form.

29. The ratio of 75 seconds (s) to 3 minutes (min)

30. The ratio of 7 oz to 3 lb

31. The ratio of 4 nickels to 5 dimes

32. The ratio of 8 in. to 3 ft

33. The ratio of 2 days to 10 h (Videos)

34. The ratio of 4 ft to 4 yd

35. The ratio of 5 gallons (gal) to 12 quarts (qt)

36. The ratio of 7 dimes to 3 quarters

Basic Skills | Challenge Yourself | Calculator/Computer | **Career Applications** | Above and Beyond

37. **Information Technology** Millicent can fix 5 cell phones per hour. Tyler can fix 4 cell phones per hour. Express the ratio of the number of cell phones that Millicent can fix to the number that Tyler can fix as a fraction.

38. **Allied Health** In preparing specimens for testing, it is often necessary to dilute the original solution. The dilution ratio is the ratio of the volume of original solution to the total volume. Each of these volumes is usually measured in milliliters (mL).

Determine the dilution ratio when 2.8 mL of blood serum is diluted with 47.2 mL of water.

39. **Mechanical Engineering** A gear ratio is the ratio of the number of teeth on the driven gear to the number of teeth on the driving gear. In general, the driving gear is attached to the power source or motor. Write the gear ratio for the system shown.

40. **Manufacturing Operations Technology** Of the 384 parts manufactured during a shift, 26 were defective.

(a) Write the ratio of defective parts to total parts.

(b) Write the ratio of defective parts to good parts.

41. Agricultural Technology A soil test indicates that a field requires a fertilizer containing 400 lb of nitrogen and 500 lb of phosphorus. Write the ratio of nitrogen to phosphorus needed.

42. Information Technology Shakira connects to the Internet from home using a phone line. Her modem generally connects at a speed of 56,000 bits per second (bits/s). Her brother, Carl, connects with an older computer at 28,800 bits/s. Write the ratio of Shakira's connection speed to Carl's speed.

Basic Skills | Challenge Yourself | Calculator/Computer | Career Applications | **Above and Beyond**

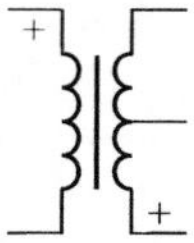

The accompanying image is a common symbol on a schematic (electrical diagram) for a transformer. A transformer uses electromagnetism to change voltage levels. Commonly, two coils of wire (or some conductor) are located in close proximity but kept from directly touching or conducting. Some sort of ferromagnetic core (such as iron) is typically used. When alternating current (AC) is applied to one conductor or coil, referred to as the primary winding, current is induced on the second or secondary winding.

There is a relationship between the voltage supplied to the primary winding and the open-voltage induced in the secondary winding, based on the number of turns in each winding. This relationship is called the turns ratio (a):

$$a = \frac{N_p}{N_s}$$

in which N_p represents the number of turns in the primary winding and N_s represents the number of turns in the secondary winding.

Theoretically, the turns ratio is also equal to the voltage ratio:

$$a = \frac{V_p}{V_s}$$

in which V_p represents the voltage supplied to the primary winding and V_s represents the voltage induced in the secondary winding.

After setting the two ratios equal to one another and performing a multiplication manipulation to isolate V_p, this relationship can be expressed as

$$V_p = \frac{N_p}{N_s}V_s$$

43. Give three combinations of turns of the primary and secondary windings that achieve a turns ratio for a transformer of 3.2.

44. Using a turns ratio of 3.2 and a secondary voltage of 35 volts (V) AC, calculate the voltage supplied to the primary winding.

45. If the turns ratio is 4.5 and the primary voltage is 28 V AC, what is the induced open-voltage on the secondary winding?

46. If the turns ratio from exercise 45 is doubled, how will that affect the voltage on the secondary winding?

Answers

41. ______

42. ______

43. ______

44. ______

45. ______

46. ______

Answers

47. ______________________

48. ______________________

47. **(a)** Buy a 1.69-oz (medium-size) bag of M&M's. For each color, determine the ratio of M&M's that are that color to the total number of M&M's in the bag.

(b) Compare your ratios from part **(a)** to those of a classmate.

(c) Use the information from parts **(a)** and **(b)** to estimate the correct ratios for all the different color M&M's in a bag.

(d) Go to the M&M's manufacturer's website (Mars, Inc.) and see how your ratios compare to their claimed color distribution.

48. Sarah is a field service technician for ABC Networks, Inc. She has been asked to design a wireless home-network for a customer. This customer wants to have the fastest throughput for the wireless network in his home.

From your experience, you know that wireless networks come in different varieties: 802.11a, b, and g. The standard for most coffeehouses and restaurants is 802.11b.

If it takes 1 second to transmit a packet on 802.11b, how long does it take to transmit a packet on 802.11a and g?

Which technology will you recommend and why?

Answers

1. $\frac{9}{13}$ **3.** $\frac{9}{4}$ **5.** $\frac{2}{3}$ **7.** $\frac{1}{4}$ **9.** $\frac{35}{9}$ **11.** $\frac{2}{3}$ **13.** $\frac{8}{13}$ **15.** $\frac{8}{7}$

17. $\frac{7}{13}; \frac{13}{7}$ **19.** $\frac{3}{2}$ **21.** $\frac{32}{69}$ **23.** $\frac{3}{4}$ **25.** True **27.** always

29. $\frac{5}{12}$ **31.** $\frac{2}{5}$ **33.** $\frac{24}{5}$ **35.** $\frac{5}{3}$ **37.** $\frac{5}{4}$ **39.** $\frac{5}{8}$ **41.** $\frac{4}{5}$

43. Answers will vary **45.** $6\frac{2}{9}$ V AC **47.** Above and Beyond

Activity 13 ::
Working with Ratios Visually

To solve the following problems, we think that you and your group members will find one of these three approaches useful: (1) You may wish to use actual black and white markers; (2) you may wish to make sketches of such markers; or (3) you may wish to simply imagine the necessary markers. Each line in the following table is a new (and different) problem, and you are to fill in the missing parts in a given line. Be sure to express a ratio by using the smallest possible whole numbers.

	Ratio of Black to White Markers	Number of Black Markers	Number of White Markers	Total Number of Markers
1.	to		15	20
2.	to	12		30
3.	to		9	21
4.	to	15		33
5.	2 to 5	6		
6.	5 to 3		24	
7.	4 to 1	28		
8.	3 to 7		21	
9.	1 to 3			36
10.	3 to 5			40
11.	7 to 2			360
12.	4 to 7			550
13.				
14.				

For problems 13 and 14, create (and solve!) your own problems of the same sort. You might challenge another group with these.

5.2 Rates and Unit Pricing

< 5.2 Objectives >

1 > Write a rate as a unit rate

2 > Interpret and compare unit rates

3 > Find a unit price

4 > Use unit prices to compare the cost of two items

In Section 5.1, we used ratios to compare two like quantities. For instance, the ratio of 9 seconds to 12 seconds is $\frac{3}{4}$.

$$\frac{9\ \cancel{\text{sec}}}{12\ \cancel{\text{sec}}} = \frac{\overset{3}{\cancel{9}}}{\underset{4}{\cancel{12}}} = \frac{3}{4}$$

RECALL

When simplified, a ratio has no units.

Because the units in the numerator and denominator are the same, we can "cancel" them and simplify the fraction.

We also learned that as long as the two quantities represented the same type of measurement, we could compare them using ratios. For example, if both quantities are measurements of length, then we can convert one of the measurements so that they are like quantities.

In Chapter 7, you will study measurement conversions in more depth. For now, we can do straightforward conversions. For example, we can use a ratio to compare 4 in. and 3 ft by converting 3 ft to 36 in.

$$\frac{4\text{ in.}}{3\text{ ft}} = \frac{4\text{ in.}}{36\text{ in.}} \quad 3\text{ ft} = 36\text{ in.}$$

$$= \frac{4}{36}$$

$$= \frac{1}{9}$$

RECALL

Denominate numbers have units "attached."

Often, we want to compare denominate numbers with different types of units. For example, we might be interested in the gas mileage that a car gets. In such a case, we are comparing the miles driven (distance) and the gas used (volume). We make this comparison in part **(b)** of Example 1.

When we compare denominate numbers with different types of units, we get a *rate.*

Definition

Rate

A **rate** is a comparison of two denominate numbers with different types of units.

For example, if an animal moves 3 feet in 4 seconds, we can express the rate as:

$$\frac{3\text{ ft}}{4\text{ s}}$$

We read this rate as "3 feet per 4 seconds." In general, rates are presented in simplified form as *unit rates.*

Definition

Unit Rate

A **unit rate** is a *rate* that is simplified so that it compares a denominate number with a *single unit* of a different denominate number.

A **unit rate** is written so that the numerical value is given followed by the units, written as a fraction. For example, to express the rate $\frac{3\text{ ft}}{4\text{ s}}$ as a unit rate, we write it as $\frac{3}{4}\frac{\text{ft}}{\text{s}}$. We read this as "$\frac{3}{4}$ feet per second."

Example 1 Finding a Unit Rate

< Objective 1 >

NOTE

We read the rate $20\frac{\text{mi}}{\text{gal}}$ as "twenty miles *per* gallon."

Express each rate as a unit rate.

(a) $\frac{12\text{ feet}}{16\text{ seconds}} = \frac{12}{16}\frac{\text{ft}}{\text{s}} = \frac{3}{4}\frac{\text{ft}}{\text{s}}$

(b) $\frac{200\text{ miles}}{10\text{ gallons}} = \frac{200}{10}\frac{\text{mi}}{\text{gal}} = 20\frac{\text{mi}}{\text{gal}}$

(c) $\frac{10\text{ gallons}}{200\text{ miles}} = \frac{10}{200}\frac{\text{gal}}{\text{mi}} = \frac{1}{20}\frac{\text{gal}}{\text{mi}}$

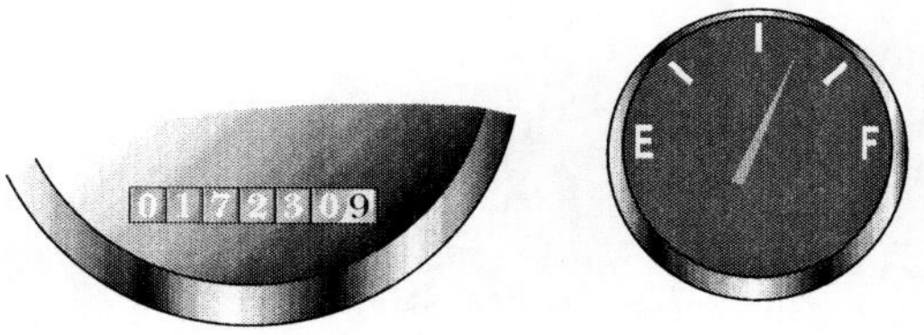

Check Yourself 1

Express each rate as a unit rate.

(a) $\frac{\text{250 miles}}{\text{10 hours}}$ **(b)** $\frac{\$60{,}000}{\text{2 years}}$ **(c)** $\frac{\text{2 years}}{\$60{,}000}$

Consider part (a) in Example 1. We begin with 12 ft (length) compared to 16 seconds (time). We simplify the rate so that we know the number of feet, $\frac{3}{4}$, per 1 second. In general, we simplify a rate so that we are comparing the quantity of the numerator's units per one of the denominator's units.

In Example 2, we consider parts (b) and (c) of Example 1.

Example 2 Comparing Unit Rates

< Objective 2 >

NOTE

We could also write this rate as a decimal,

$\frac{1}{20}\frac{\text{gal}}{\text{mi}} = 0.05\frac{\text{gal}}{\text{mi}}$

(a) Write the rate $20\frac{\text{mi}}{\text{gal}}$ in words.

We write this rate as "twenty miles per gallon."

(b) Write the rate $\frac{1}{20}\frac{\text{gal}}{\text{mi}}$ in words.

We write this rate as "one-twentieth of a gallon per mile."

(c) Describe the difference between the rates in parts (a) and (b).

The rate $20\frac{\text{mi}}{\text{gal}}$ states that 20 miles can be traveled on a single gallon of fuel. The rate $\frac{1}{20}\frac{\text{gal}}{\text{mi}}$ states that $\frac{1}{20}$ of a gallon of fuel is used when traveling 1 mile.

We can also interpret these as 20 miles are traveled for each gallon of fuel used and $\frac{1}{20}$ of a gallon of fuel is used for each mile traveled, respectively.

Check Yourself 2

(a) Write the rate $30{,}000 \dfrac{\text{dollars}}{\text{yr}}$ in words.

(b) Write the rate $\dfrac{1}{30{,}000} \dfrac{\text{yr}}{\text{dollar}}$ in words.

(c) Describe the difference between the rates in parts **(a)** and **(b)**.

Sometimes, we need to find the appropriate rate within a written statement, as in Example 3.

Example 3 Finding a Unit Rate

RECALL

In Section 5.1 we stated that mixed numbers were inappropriate for ratios. When we write unit rates, mixed numbers and decimals are not only appropriate, they are preferred.

Randy Johnson had 320 strikeouts in 280 innings. What was his strikeout per inning rate?

$$\frac{320 \text{ strikeouts}}{280 \text{ innings}} = \frac{320}{280} \frac{\text{strikeouts}}{\text{inning}}$$

$$= 1\frac{1}{7} \frac{\text{strikeouts}}{\text{inning}}$$

Check Yourself 3

Chamique Holdsclaw scored 450 points in 15 games. What was her points per game rate?

One purpose for computing a rate is for comparison. As we see in Example 4, it is often convenient to write a rate in decimal form.

Example 4 Comparing Rates

Player A scores 50 points in 9 games and player B scores 260 points in 36 games. Which player scored at a higher rate?

Player A's rate was $\dfrac{50 \text{ points}}{9 \text{ games}} = \dfrac{50}{9} \dfrac{\text{points}}{\text{game}}$

$$\approx 5.56 \frac{\text{points}}{\text{game}}$$

$\frac{50}{9} = 50 \div 9 \approx 5.56$

Player B's rate was $\dfrac{260 \text{ points}}{36 \text{ games}} = \dfrac{260}{36} \dfrac{\text{points}}{\text{game}}$

$$= \frac{65}{9} \frac{\text{points}}{\text{game}}$$

$$\approx 7.22 \frac{\text{points}}{\text{game}}$$

$65 \div 9 \approx 7.22$

Player B scored at a higher rate.

Check Yourself 4

Hassan scored 25 goals in 8 games and Lee scored 52 goals in 18 games. Which player scored at a higher rate?

Unit pricing represents one of the most common uses of rates. Posted on nearly every item in a supermarket or grocery store is the price of the item as well as its *unit price*.

Definition

Unit Price — The **unit price** relates a price to some common unit.

A unit price is a price *per unit.* The unit used may be ounces, pints, pounds, or some other unit.

Example 5 Finding a Unit Price

< Objective 3 >

Find the unit price for each item.

(a) 8 ounces (oz) of cream cost \$1.53.

$$\frac{\$1.53}{8\text{ oz}} = \frac{153\text{ cents}}{8\text{ oz}} = \frac{153}{8}\,\frac{\text{cents}}{\text{oz}}$$

$$\approx 19\,\frac{\text{cents}}{\text{oz}}$$

(b) 20 pounds (lb) of potatoes cost \$3.98.

$$\frac{\$3.98}{20\text{ lb}} = \frac{398\text{ cents}}{20\text{ lb}}$$

$$= \frac{398}{20}\,\frac{\text{cents}}{\text{lb}}$$

$$\approx 20\,\frac{\text{cents}}{\text{lb}}$$

Check Yourself 5

Find the unit price for each item.

(a) 12 soda cans cost \$2.98.
(b) 25 pounds (lb) of dog food cost \$9.99.

As with ratios, rates are most often used for comparisons. For instance, unit pricing allows people to compare the cost of different size items.

In Example 6, we use unit prices to determine whether a glass of milk is less expensive when poured from a 128-oz container (gallon) or a 32-oz container (quart).

Example 6 Using Unit Prices to Compare Cost

< Objective 4 >

A store sells a 1-gallon carton (128 oz) of organic whole milk for \$4.89. They sell a 1-quart carton (32 oz) for \$1.29. Which is the better buy?

We begin by determining the unit price of each item. To do this, we compute the cost per ounce for each carton of milk. We choose to use cents instead of dollars to make the decimal easier to work with.

NOTE

Usually, we round money to the nearest cent. When comparing unit prices, however, we may round to four decimal places (or more, if necessary).

Gallon

$$\frac{\$4.89}{128\text{ oz}} = \frac{489\text{ cents}}{128\text{ oz}} = \frac{489}{128}\,\frac{\text{cents}}{\text{oz}} \approx 3.8203\,\frac{\text{cents}}{\text{oz}}$$

Quart

$$\frac{\$1.29}{32\text{ oz}} = \frac{129\text{ cents}}{32\text{ oz}} = \frac{129}{32}\,\frac{\text{cents}}{\text{oz}} \approx 4.0313\,\frac{\text{cents}}{\text{oz}}$$

At these prices, the gallon of milk is the better buy.

Check Yourself 6

A store sells a 5-lb bag of Valencia oranges for $2.29. A 12-lb case sells for $5.69. Which is the better buy?

If we compare the two unit prices in Example 6, we see that both items round to 4¢ per ounce. However, milk sold by the gallon is about 0.211¢ cheaper per ounce than milk sold by the quart. We need to consider this small fraction of a cent because we are not buying 1 ounce of milk. Rather, we are buying cartons of milk, and for a whole quart of milk, the fraction adds up to nearly 7¢ (it adds up to 27¢ for a whole gallon).

Check Yourself ANSWERS

1. **(a)** $25 \frac{\text{mi}}{\text{h}}$; **(b)** $30{,}000 \frac{\text{dollars}}{\text{yr}}$; **(c)** $\frac{1}{30{,}000} \frac{\text{yr}}{\text{dollar}}$
2. **(a)** Thirty-thousand dollars per year. **(b)** One thirty-thousandth of a year per dollar. **(c)** The rate in part **(a)** describes the amount of money for each year. The rate in part **(b)** describes the amount of time per dollar.
3. $30 \frac{\text{points}}{\text{game}}$
4. Hassan had a higher rate.
5. **(a)** $\approx 25 \frac{\text{cents}}{\text{can}}$; **(b)** $\approx 40 \frac{\text{cents}}{\text{pound}}$
6. The 5-lb bag is the better buy at 45.8¢ per pound compared to approximately 47.4¢ per pound for the case.

Reading Your Text

The following fill-in-the-blank exercises are designed to ensure that you understand some of the key vocabulary used in this section.

SECTION 5.2

(a) Ratios are used to compare ______________ quantities.

(b) When we compare measurements with different types of units, we get a ______________.

(c) ______________ numbers are preferable to improper fractions, when simplifying a rate.

(d) ______________ prices are used to compare the cost of items in different size packages.

5.2 exercises

Boost *your* GRADE at ALEKS.com!

ALEKS

- Practice Problems
- Self-Tests
- NetTutor
- e-Professors
- Videos

Name ____________

Section ________ Date ________

< Objective 1 >

Write each rate as a unit rate.

1. $\frac{300 \text{ mi}}{4 \text{ h}}$ > Videos

2. $\frac{95 \text{ cents}}{5 \text{ pencils}}$

3. $\frac{\$10{,}000}{5 \text{ yr}}$

4. $\frac{680 \text{ ft}}{17 \text{ s}}$

5. $\frac{7{,}200 \text{ revolutions}}{16 \text{ mi}}$

6. $\frac{57 \text{ oz}}{3 \text{ cans}}$

7. $\frac{\$2{,}000{,}000}{4 \text{ yr}}$ > Videos

8. $\frac{150 \text{ cal}}{3 \text{ oz}}$

9. $\frac{240 \text{ lb of fertilizer}}{6 \text{ lawns}}$

10. $\frac{192 \text{ diapers}}{32 \text{ babies}}$

< Objective 2 >

Write each rate in words.

11. $120{,}000 \frac{\text{dollars}}{\text{yr}}$

12. $32 \frac{\text{ft}}{\text{s}}$

13. $\frac{1}{120{,}000} \frac{\text{yr}}{\text{dollar}}$

14. $\frac{1}{32} \frac{\text{s}}{\text{ft}}$

< Objective 3 >

Find the unit price of each item.

15. \$57.50 for 5 shirts > Videos

16. \$104.93 for 7 CDs

17. \$5.16 for a dozen oranges

18. \$10.44 for 18 bottles of water

Answers

1. ________ 2. ________

3. ________ 4. ________

5. ________ 6. ________

7. ________

8. ________ 9. ________

10. ________

11. ________

12. ________

13. ________

14. ________

15. ________

16. ________

17. ________

18. ________

Answers

19. ______

20. ______

21. ______

22. ______

23. ______

24. ______

< Objective 4 >

Find the best buy in each exercise.

19. Dishwashing liquid:

(a) 12 fl oz for $1.58
(b) 22 fl oz for $2.58

20. Canned corn:

(a) 10 oz for 42¢
(b) 17 oz for 78¢

21. Syrup:

(a) 12 oz for $1.98
(b) 24 oz for $3.18
(c) 36 oz for $4.38

22. Shampoo:

(a) 4 oz for $2.32
(b) 7 oz for $3.04
(c) 15 oz for $6.78

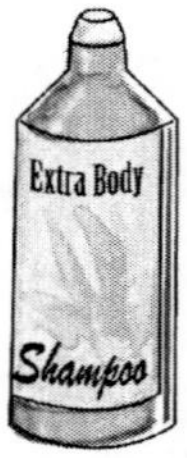

23. Salad oil (1 qt is 32 oz):

(a) 18 oz for $1.78
(b) 1 qt for $2.78
(c) 1 qt 16 oz for $4.38

24. Tomato juice (1 pt is 16 oz):

(a) 8 oz for 74¢
(b) 1 pt 10 oz for $2.38
(c) 1 qt 14 oz for $3.98

25. Peanut butter (1 lb is 16 oz):

(a) 12 oz for $2.50
(b) 18 oz for $3.44
(c) 1 lb 12 oz for $5.08
(d) 2 lb 8 oz for $7.52

26. Laundry detergent:

(a) 1 lb 2 oz for $3.98
(b) 1 lb 12 oz for $5.78
(c) 2 lb 8 oz for $8.38
(d) 5 lb for $15.98

Solve each application.

27. Trac uses 8 gallons of gasoline on a 256-mile drive. How many miles per gallon does his car get?

28. Seven pounds of fertilizer covers 1,400 square feet. How many square feet are covered by 1 pound of fertilizer?

29. A local college has 6,000 registered vehicles for 2,400 campus parking spaces. How many vehicles are there for each parking space? Videos

30. A water pump can produce 280 gallons in 24 hours. How many gallons per hour is this?

31. The sum of $5,992 was spent for 214 shares of stock. What was the cost per share?

32. A printer produces 4 pages of print in 6 seconds. How many pages are produced per second?

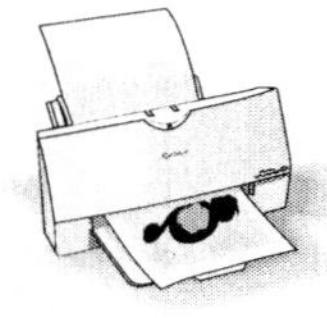

33. A 12-ounce can of tuna costs $4.80. What is the cost of tuna per ounce?

34. The fabric for a dress costs $76.45 for 9 yards. What is the cost per yard?

35. Gerry laid 634 bricks in 35 minutes and his friend Matt laid 515 bricks in 27 minutes. Who is the faster bricklayer?

36. Mike drove 135 miles (mi) in 2.5 hours (h). Sam drove 91 mi in 1.75 h. Who drove faster?

37. Luis Gonzalez had 137 hits in 387 at bats. Larry Walker had 119 hits in 324 at bats. Who had the higher batting average?

38. Which is the better buy: 5 lb of sugar for $4.75 or 20 lb of sugar for $19.92?

Answers

25. ____________
26. ____________
27. ____________
28. ____________
29. ____________
30. ____________
31. ____________
32. ____________
33. ____________
34. ____________
35. ____________
36. ____________
37. ____________
38. ____________

Answers

39. ______

40. ______

41. ______

42. ______

43. ______

44. ______

45. ______

46. ______

47. ______

48. ______

49. ______

50. ______

51. ______

52. ______

Basic Skills | **Challenge Yourself** | Calculator/Computer | Career Applications | Above and Beyond

Determine whether each statement is **true** *or* **false.**

39. We use rates to compare like quantities.

40. We use rates to compare different types of measurements.

Fill in each blank with **always, sometimes,** *or* **never.**

41. The units __________ cancel in a rate.

42. The units __________ cancel in a ratio.

Find each rate.

43. $\frac{69 \text{ ft}}{3 \text{ s}}$

44. $\frac{3 \text{ s}}{69 \text{ ft}}$

45. $\frac{5 \text{ yr}}{\$10{,}000}$

46. $\frac{480 \text{ mi}}{15 \text{ gal}}$

47. $\frac{15 \text{ gal}}{480 \text{ mi}}$

48. $\frac{657{,}200 \text{ library books}}{5{,}200 \text{ students}}$

Basic Skills | Challenge Yourself | Calculator/Computer | **Career Applications** | Above and Beyond

49. **MECHANICAL ENGINEERING** The pitch of a gear is given by the quotient of the number of teeth on the gear and the diameter of the gear (distance from end to end, through the center). Calculate the pitch of the gear shown.

50. **ALLIED HEALTH** A patient's tidal volume, in milliliters (mL) per breath, is the quotient of his or her minute volume (mL/min) and his or her respiratory rate (breaths/min).

Report the tidal volume for an adult, female patient whose minute volume is 7,500 mL/min if her respiratory rate is 12 breaths/min.

chapter 5 > Make the Connection

51. **BUSINESS AND FINANCE** Determine the unit price of a 1,000-ft cable that costs $99.99.

52. **ELECTRICAL ENGINEERING** A 20-volt (V) DC pulse is sent down a 4,000-meter (m) length of conductor (see the figure). Because of resistance, when the pulse reaches the other end, the voltmeter measures the voltage as 4 V. What is the rate of voltage drop per meter of conductor?

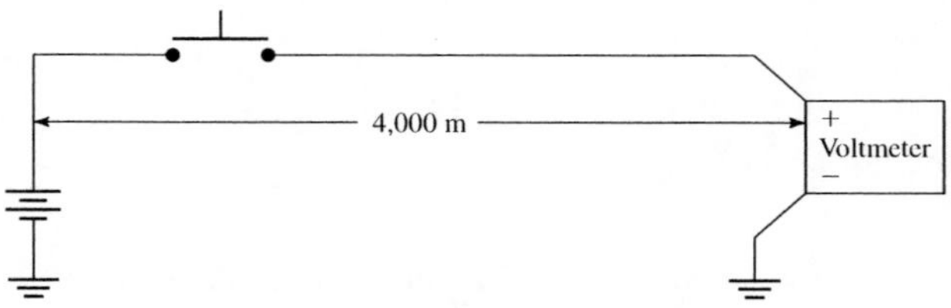

53. **Business and Finance** A 200-bushel load of soybeans sells for \$1,780. What is the price per bushel?

54. **Mechanical Engineering** Stress is calculated as the rate of force applied compared to the cross-sectional area of a post. What is the stress on a post that supports 13,475 lb and has a cross-sectional area of 12.25 square inches?

Basic Skills | Challenge Yourself | Calculator/Computer | Career Applications | **Above and Beyond**

55. Describe the difference between the rates $\frac{\$120{,}000}{\text{yr}}$ and $\frac{1}{120{,}000}\frac{\text{yr}}{\text{dollar}}$.

56. Describe the difference between the rates $32\,\frac{\text{ft}}{\text{s}}$ and $\frac{1}{32}\frac{\text{s}}{\text{ft}}$.

57. In your own words, explain the difference between a ratio and a rate.

58. Find several real-world examples of ratios and of rates.

59. Explain why unit pricing is useful.

60. Go to a supermarket or grocery store. Choose five items that have price and unit price listed. Check to see if the unit price given for each item is accurate.

Answers

53. ______
54. ______
55. ______
56. ______
57. ______
58. ______
59. ______
60. ______

Answers

1. $75\,\frac{\text{mi}}{\text{h}}$ **3.** $2{,}000\,\frac{\text{dollars}}{\text{yr}}$ **5.** $450\,\frac{\text{rev}}{\text{mi}}$ **7.** $500{,}000\,\frac{\text{dollars}}{\text{yr}}$
9. $40\,\frac{\text{lb}}{\text{lawn}}$ **11.** One hundred twenty thousand dollars per year
13. One one-hundred twenty thousandth of a year per dollar **15.** $11.50\,\frac{\text{dollars}}{\text{shirt}}$
17. $0.43\,\frac{\text{dollars}}{\text{orange}}$ **19.** (b) **21.** (c) **23.** (b) **25.** (c)
27. $32\,\frac{\text{mi}}{\text{gal}}$ **29.** $2.5\,\frac{\text{vehicles}}{\text{space}}$ **31.** $28\,\frac{\text{dollars}}{\text{share}}$ **33.** $40\,\frac{\text{cents}}{\text{oz}}$
35. Matt **37.** Larry Walker **39.** False **41.** never **43.** $23\,\frac{\text{ft}}{\text{s}}$
45. $0.0005\,\frac{\text{yr}}{\text{dollar}}$ **47.** $\frac{1}{32}\frac{\text{gal}}{\text{mi}}$ **49.** $8\,\frac{\text{teeth}}{\text{in.}}$ **51.** $\approx 0.10\,\frac{\text{dollars}}{\text{ft}}$
53. $8.90\,\frac{\text{dollars}}{\text{bushel}}$ **55.** Above and Beyond **57.** Above and Beyond
59. Above and Beyond

Activity 14 :: Baseball Statistics

There are many statistics in the sport of baseball that are expressed in decimal form. Two of these are batting average and earned run average. Both are actually examples of rates.

A batting average is a rate for which the units are "hits per at bat." To compute the batting average for a hitter, divide the number of hits (H) by the number of times at bat (AB). The result will be a decimal less than 1 (unless the batter always gets a hit!), and it is always expressed to the nearest thousandth. For example, if a hitter has 2 hits in 7 at bats, we divide 2 by 7, getting 0.285714. . . . The batting average is then rounded to 0.286.

Compute the batting average for each of the following major league players.

	Player	Hits	At Bats	Average
1	Pujols	139	373	
2	Helton	134	384	
3	Guillen	99	290	
4	Suzuki	142	419	
5	Mora	99	293	

The earned run average (ERA) for a pitcher is also a rate; its units are "earned runs per 9 innings." It represents the number of earned runs the pitcher gives up in 9 innings. To compute the ERA for a pitcher, multiply the number of earned runs allowed by the pitcher by 9, and then divide by the number of innings pitched. The result is always rounded to the nearest hundredth.

Compute the earned run average for each of the following major league players.

	Player	Earned Runs	Innings	ERA
6	Loaiza	33	$137\frac{1}{3}$	
7	Martinez	27	110	
8	Brown	31	$123\frac{1}{3}$	

Challenge: Suppose a hitter has 54 hits in 200 times at bat. How many hits in a row must the hitter get in order to raise his average to at least 0.300?

5.3 Proportions

< 5.3 Objectives >

1 > Write a proportion

2 > Determine whether two fractions are proportional

3 > Determine whether two rates are proportional

Definition

Proportion — A statement that two fractions or rates are equal is called a **proportion.**

NOTES

This is the same as saying the fractions are equivalent. They name the same number.

We call a letter representing an unknown value a *variable*. Here *a*, *b*, *c*, and *d* are variables. We could have chosen any other letter.

Because the ratio of 1 to 3 is equal to the ratio of 2 to 6, we can write the proportion

$$\frac{1}{3} = \frac{2}{6}$$

The proportion $\frac{a}{b} = \frac{c}{d}$ is read "*a* is to *b* as *c* is to *d*." We read the proportion $\frac{1}{3} = \frac{2}{6}$ as "one is to three as two is to six."

Example 1 Writing a Proportion

< Objective 1 >

Write the proportion 3 is to 7 as 9 is to 21.

$$\frac{3}{7} = \frac{9}{21}$$

Check Yourself 1

Write the proportion 4 is to 12 as 6 is to 18.

When you write a proportion for two rates, placement of similar units is important.

Example 2 Writing a Proportion with Two Rates

Write a proportion that is equivalent to the statement: If it takes 3 hours to mow 4 acres of grass, it will take 6 hours to mow 8 acres.

$$\frac{3 \text{ hours}}{4 \text{ acres}} = \frac{6 \text{ hours}}{8 \text{ acres}}$$

Note that, in both fractions, the hours units are in the numerator and the acres units are in the denominator.

Check Yourself 2

Write a proportion that is equivalent to the statement: If it takes 5 rolls of wallpaper to cover 400 square feet, it will take 7 rolls to cover 560 square feet.

If two fractions form a true proportion, we say that they are **proportional.**

Property

The Proportion Rule

If $\frac{a}{b} = \frac{c}{d}$, then $a \cdot d = b \cdot c$.

We say that the fractions $\frac{a}{b}$ and $\frac{c}{d}$ are proportional.

Example 3 Determining Whether Two Fractions Are Proportional

< Objective 2 >

NOTE

Use the centered dot (·) for multiplication rather than the cross (×), so that the cross won't be confused with the letter *x*.

RECALL

We saw this same test in Section 2.4 called "Testing for Equivalence."

Determine whether each pair of fractions is proportional.

(a) $\frac{5}{6} \stackrel{?}{=} \frac{10}{12}$

Multiply:

$5 \cdot 12 = 60$
$6 \cdot 10 = 60$ Equal

Because $a \cdot d = b \cdot c$, $\frac{5}{6}$ and $\frac{10}{12}$ are proportional.

(b) $\frac{3}{7} \stackrel{?}{=} \frac{4}{9}$

Multiply:

$3 \cdot 9 = 27$
$7 \cdot 4 = 28$ Not equal

The products are not equal, so $\frac{3}{7}$ and $\frac{4}{9}$ are not proportional.

Check Yourself 3

Determine whether each pair of fractions is proportional.

(a) $\frac{5}{8} \stackrel{?}{=} \frac{20}{32}$ (b) $\frac{7}{9} \stackrel{?}{=} \frac{3}{4}$

The proportion rule can also be used when fractions or decimals are involved.

Example 4 Verifying a Proportion

Determine whether each pair of fractions is proportional.

(a) $\frac{3}{\frac{1}{2}} \stackrel{?}{=} \frac{30}{5}$

$3 \cdot 5 = 15$

$\frac{1}{2} \cdot 30 = 15$

Because the products are equal, the fractions are proportional.

(b) $\frac{0.4}{20} \stackrel{?}{=} \frac{3}{100}$

$0.4 \cdot 100 = 40$

$20 \cdot 3 = 60$

Because the products are *not* equal, the fractions are not proportional.

Check Yourself 4

Determine whether each pair of fractions is proportional.

(a) $\frac{0.5}{8} \stackrel{?}{=} \frac{3}{48}$ (b) $\frac{\frac{1}{4}}{6} \stackrel{?}{=} \frac{3}{80}$

The proportion rule can also be used to verify that rates are proportional.

Example 5 Determining Whether Two Rates are Proportional

< Objective 3 >

NOTE

Colones are the monetary unit of Costa Rica.

Is the rate $\frac{5 \text{ U.S. dollars}}{15{,}000 \text{ colones}}$ proportional to the rate $\frac{27 \text{ U.S. dollars}}{81{,}000 \text{ colones}}$?

US Dollars	Colones
$1.00	3000
$0.00033	1.0

We want to know if the following is true.

$$\frac{5}{15{,}000} \stackrel{?}{=} \frac{27}{81{,}000}$$

$$5 \cdot 81{,}000 = 405{,}000$$

$$27 \cdot 15{,}000 = 405{,}000$$

The rates are proportional.

Check Yourself 5

Is the rate $\frac{50 \text{ pages}}{45 \text{ minutes}}$ proportional to the rate $\frac{30 \text{ pages}}{25 \text{ minutes}}$?

In Section 5.4, we will use proportions to solve many applications. For instance, if a 12-ft piece of steel stock weighs 27.6 lb, how much would a 25-ft piece weigh? Here, we check the accuracy of such a proportion.

Example 6 An Application of Proportions

A 12-ft piece of steel stock weighs 27.6 lb. If 57.5 lb is the weight of a 25-ft piece, do the two pieces have the same density?

We check that the two rates are proportional.

RECALL

Be sure to align the units, regardless of the order in which the information appears in the problem.

$$\frac{12 \text{ ft}}{27.6 \text{ lb}} \stackrel{?}{=} \frac{25 \text{ ft}}{57.5 \text{ lb}}$$

$$12 \cdot 57.5 = 690$$

$$27.6 \cdot 25 = 690$$

Because the two products are equal, we have a true proportion, so the two pieces have the same density.

Check Yourself 6

One supplier sells a 200-lb lot of steel for $522.36. A second supplier charges $789.09 for a 300-lb lot of steel. Determine whether the suppliers are offering steel for the same price per pound.

Check Yourself ANSWERS

1. $\frac{4}{12} = \frac{6}{18}$ **2.** $\frac{5 \text{ rolls}}{400 \text{ square feet}} = \frac{7 \text{ rolls}}{560 \text{ square feet}}$ **3.** **(a)** Yes; **(b)** no

4. **(a)** Yes; **(b)** no **5.** No **6.** No

Reading Your Text

The following fill-in-the-blank exercises are designed to ensure that you understand some of the key vocabulary used in this section.

SECTION 5.3

(a) A statement that two rates are ______________ is called a proportion.

(b) A letter used to represent an unknown value is called a ______________.

(c) If two fractions form a true ______________, we say that they are proportional.

(d) When writing a proportion for two ______________, corresponding units must be similarly placed.

Basic Skills | Challenge Yourself | Calculator/Computer | Career Applications | Above and Beyond

5.3 exercises

Boost *your* GRADE at ALEKS.com!

ALEKS

- Practice Problems
- Self-Tests
- NetTutor
- e-Professors
- Videos

Name ______________

Section ________ Date ________

< Objective 1 >

Write each statement as a proportion.

1. 4 is to 9 as 8 is to 18.

2. 6 is to 11 as 18 is to 33.

3. 2 is to 9 as 8 is to 36.

4. 10 is to 15 as 20 is to 30.

5. 3 is to 5 as 15 is to 25.

6. 8 is to 11 as 16 is to 22.

7. 9 is to 13 as 27 is to 39.

8. 15 is to 21 as 60 is to 84.

< Objective 2 >

Determine whether each pair of fractions is proportional.

9. $\frac{3}{4} \stackrel{?}{=} \frac{9}{12}$ > Videos

10. $\frac{6}{7} \stackrel{?}{=} \frac{18}{21}$

11. $\frac{3}{4} \stackrel{?}{=} \frac{15}{20}$

12. $\frac{3}{5} \stackrel{?}{=} \frac{6}{10}$

13. $\frac{11}{15} \stackrel{?}{=} \frac{9}{13}$ > Videos

14. $\frac{9}{10} \stackrel{?}{=} \frac{2}{7}$

15. $\frac{8}{3} \stackrel{?}{=} \frac{24}{9}$

16. $\frac{5}{8} \stackrel{?}{=} \frac{15}{24}$

17. $\frac{6}{17} \stackrel{?}{=} \frac{9}{11}$

18. $\frac{5}{12} \stackrel{?}{=} \frac{8}{20}$

19. $\frac{7}{16} \stackrel{?}{=} \frac{21}{48}$

20. $\frac{2}{5} \stackrel{?}{=} \frac{7}{9}$

21. $\frac{10}{3} \stackrel{?}{=} \frac{150}{50}$

22. $\frac{5}{8} \stackrel{?}{=} \frac{75}{120}$

23. $\frac{3}{7} \stackrel{?}{=} \frac{18}{42}$

24. $\frac{12}{7} \stackrel{?}{=} \frac{96}{50}$

25. $\frac{7}{15} \stackrel{?}{=} \frac{84}{180}$

26. $\frac{76}{24} \stackrel{?}{=} \frac{19}{6}$

< Objective 3 >

Determine if the given rates are proportional.

27. $\frac{\text{7 cups of flour}}{\text{4 loaves of bread}} \stackrel{?}{=} \frac{\text{4 cups of flour}}{\text{3 loaves of bread}}$ > Videos

28. $\frac{\text{6 U.S. dollars}}{\text{50 Krone}} \stackrel{?}{=} \frac{\text{15 U.S. dollars}}{\text{125 Krone}}$

Answers

1. ______ 2. ______
3. ______ 4. ______
5. ______ 6. ______
7. ______ 8. ______
9. ______ 10. ______
11. ______ 12. ______
13. ______ 14. ______
15. ______ 16. ______
17. ______ 18. ______
19. ______ 20. ______
21. ______ 22. ______
23. ______ 24. ______
25. ______ 26. ______
27. ______ 28. ______

Answers

29. ______

30. ______

31. ______

32. ______

33. ______

34. ______

35. ______

36. ______

37. ______

38. ______

39. ______ 40. ______

41. ______ 42. ______

43. ______ 44. ______

45. ______ 46. ______

29. $\dfrac{22 \text{ miles}}{15 \text{ gallons}} \stackrel{?}{=} \dfrac{55 \text{ miles}}{35 \text{ gallons}}$

30. $\dfrac{46 \text{ pages}}{30 \text{ minutes}} \stackrel{?}{=} \dfrac{18 \text{ pages}}{8 \text{ minutes}}$

31. $\dfrac{9 \text{ inches}}{57 \text{ miles}} \stackrel{?}{=} \dfrac{6 \text{ inches}}{38 \text{ miles}}$

32. $\dfrac{12 \text{ yen}}{5 \text{ pesos}} \stackrel{?}{=} \dfrac{108 \text{ yen}}{45 \text{ pesos}}$

Write the proportion that is equivalent to the given statement.

33. If 15 pounds (lb) of string beans cost \$4, then 45 lb will cost \$12.

Videos

34. If Maria hit 8 home runs in 15 softball games, then she should hit 24 home runs in 45 games.

35. If 3 credits at Bucks County Community College cost \$216, then 12 credits cost \$864.

36. If 16 pounds (lb) of fertilizer cover 1,520 square feet (ft^2), then 21 lb should cover 1,995 ft^2.

37. If Audrey travels 180 miles (mi) on interstate I-95 in 3 hours (h), then she should travel 300 mi in 5 h.

38. If 2 vans can transport 18 people, then 5 vans can transport 45 people.

Basic Skills | **Challenge Yourself** | Calculator/Computer | Career Applications | Above and Beyond

Determine whether each statement is **true** *or* **false.**

39. Two ratios must be equal in order for the ratios to be proportional.

40. If $\dfrac{a}{b} = \dfrac{c}{d}$, then $a \cdot c = b \cdot d$.

Fill in each blank with **always, sometimes,** *or* **never.**

41. Proportions are ______________ used to compare two rates.

42. When writing a proportion for two rates, the placement of units is ______________ important.

Determine whether each pair of fractions or rates is proportional.

43. $\dfrac{60}{36} \stackrel{?}{=} \dfrac{25}{15}$

44. $\dfrac{\frac{1}{2}}{4} \stackrel{?}{=} \dfrac{5}{40}$

45. $\dfrac{3}{\frac{1}{5}} \stackrel{?}{=} \dfrac{30}{6}$

46. $\dfrac{\frac{2}{3}}{6} \stackrel{?}{=} \dfrac{1}{12}$

47. $\dfrac{\frac{3}{4}}{12} \stackrel{?}{=} \dfrac{1}{16}$ > Videos

48. $\dfrac{0.3}{4} \stackrel{?}{=} \dfrac{1}{20}$

49. $\dfrac{3}{60} \stackrel{?}{=} \dfrac{0.3}{6}$

50. $\dfrac{0.6}{0.12} \stackrel{?}{=} \dfrac{2}{0.4}$

51. $\dfrac{0.6}{15} \stackrel{?}{=} \dfrac{2}{75}$

52. $\dfrac{\text{12 gallons of paint}}{8{,}329\ \text{ft}^2} \stackrel{?}{=} \dfrac{\text{9 gallons of paint}}{1{,}240\ \text{ft}^2}$

53. $\dfrac{\text{12 inches of snow}}{\text{1.4 inches of rain}} \stackrel{?}{=} \dfrac{\text{36 inches of snow}}{\text{7 inches of rain}}$

54. $\dfrac{\text{9 people}}{\text{2 cars}} \stackrel{?}{=} \dfrac{\text{11 people}}{\text{3 cars}}$

Basic Skills | Challenge Yourself | Calculator/Computer | **Career Applications** | Above and Beyond

55. **Allied Health** Quinidine is an antiarrhythmic heart medication. It is available for injection as an 80 milligrams per milliliter (mg/mL) solution. A patient receives a prescription for 300 mg of quinidine dissolved in 3.75 mL of solution. Are these rates proportional?

56. **Information Technology** A computer transmits 5 Web pages in 2 seconds (s) to a Web server. A second computer transmits 20 pages in 10 s to the server. Are these two computers transmitting at the same speed?

57. **Mechanical Engineering** A gear has a pitch diameter of 5 in. and 20 teeth. A second gear has a pitch diameter of 18 in. and 68 teeth. In order to mesh, the teeth to diameter rates must be proportional. Will these two gears mesh?

58. **Agricultural Technology** A 13-acre field requires 7,020 lb of fertilizer. Will 11,340 lb of fertilizer cover a 21-acre field?

Answers

1. $\dfrac{4}{9} = \dfrac{8}{18}$ 3. $\dfrac{2}{9} = \dfrac{8}{36}$ 5. $\dfrac{3}{5} = \dfrac{15}{25}$ 7. $\dfrac{9}{13} = \dfrac{27}{39}$

9. Yes 11. Yes 13. No 15. Yes 17. No 19. Yes

21. No 23. Yes 25. Yes 27. No 29. No 31. Yes

33. $\dfrac{15\text{ lb}}{\$4} = \dfrac{45\text{ lb}}{\$12}$ 35. $\dfrac{3\text{ credits}}{\$216} = \dfrac{12\text{ credits}}{\$864}$ 37. $\dfrac{180\text{ mi}}{3\text{ h}} = \dfrac{300\text{ mi}}{5\text{ h}}$

39. True 41. sometimes 43. Yes 45. No 47. Yes

49. Yes 51. No 53. No 55. Yes 57. No

Answers

47. ________ 48. ________

49. ________ 50. ________

51. ________ 52. ________

53. ________ 54. ________

55. ________ 56. ________

57. ________ 58. ________

5.4 Solving Proportions

< 5.4 Objectives >

1 > Solve a proportion for an unknown value

2 > Solve an application involving a proportion

NOTE

$\frac{?}{3} = \frac{10}{15}$ is a proportion in which the first value is unknown. Our work in this section involves learning how to find that unknown value.

A proportion consists of four values. If three of the four values of a proportion are known, you can always find the missing or unknown value.

In the proportion $\frac{a}{3} = \frac{10}{15}$, the first value is unknown. We have chosen to represent the unknown value with the letter a. Using the proportion rule, we can proceed as follows.

$$\frac{a}{3} = \frac{10}{15}$$

$$15 \cdot a = 3 \cdot 10 \qquad \text{or} \qquad 15 \cdot a = 30$$

The equal sign tells us that $15 \cdot a$ and 30 are just different names for the same number. This type of statement is called an **equation.**

Definition

Equation

An **equation** is a statement that two expressions are equal.

One important property of an equation is that we can divide both sides by the same nonzero number. Here we divide by 15.

NOTE

We always divide by the number multiplying the variable. This is called the *coefficient* of the variable.

$$15 \cdot a = 30$$

$$\frac{15 \cdot a}{15} = \frac{30}{15}$$

$$\frac{\overset{1}{\cancel{15}} \cdot a}{\underset{1}{\cancel{15}}} = \frac{\overset{2}{\cancel{30}}}{\underset{1}{\cancel{15}}}$$

Divide by the coefficient of the variable. Do you see why we divided by 15? It leaves our unknown a by itself in the left term.

$$a = 2$$

You should always check your result. It is easy in this case. We found a value of 2 for a. Replace the unknown a with that value. Then verify that the fractions are proportional. We started with $\frac{a}{3} = \frac{10}{15}$ and found a value of 2 for a. So we write

NOTE

Replace a with 2 and multiply.

$$\frac{2}{3} \stackrel{?}{=} \frac{10}{15}$$

$$2 \cdot 15 \stackrel{?}{=} 3 \cdot 10$$

$$30 = 30$$

The value of 2 for a is correct.

The procedure for solving a proportion is summarized as follows.

Step by Step

To Solve a Proportion

Step 1 Use the proportion rule to write the equivalent equation $a \cdot d = b \cdot c$.

Step 2 Divide both terms of the equation by the coefficient of the variable.

Step 3 Use the value found to replace the unknown in the original proportion. Check that the ratios or the rates are proportional.

Example 1 Solving Proportions for Unknown Values

< Objective 1 >

NOTE

You are really using algebra to solve these proportions. In algebra, we write the product $6 \cdot x$ as $6x$, omitting the dot. Multiplication of the number and the variable is understood.

Find the unknown value.

(a) $\frac{8}{x} = \frac{6}{9}$

Step 1 Using the proportion rule, we have the following:

$$6 \cdot x = 8 \cdot 9$$

or $6x = 72$

Step 2 Locate the coefficient of the variable, 6, and divide both sides of the equation by that coefficient.

$$\frac{\overset{1}{\cancel{6}}x}{\underset{1}{\cancel{6}}} = \frac{\overset{12}{\cancel{72}}}{\underset{1}{\cancel{6}}}$$

$$x = 12$$

NOTE

This gives us the unknown value. Now check the result.

Step 3 To check, replace x with 12 in the original proportion.

$$\frac{8}{12} \stackrel{?}{=} \frac{6}{9}$$

Multiply:

$$12 \cdot 6 \stackrel{?}{=} 8 \cdot 9$$

$$72 = 72$$ The value of 12 checks for x.

(b) $\frac{3}{4} = \frac{c}{25}$

Step 1 Use the proportion rule.

$$4 \cdot c = 3 \cdot 25$$

or $4c = 75$

Step 2 Locate the coefficient of the variable, 4, and divide both sides of the equation by that coefficient.

$$\frac{\overset{1}{\cancel{4}}c}{\underset{1}{\cancel{4}}} = \frac{75}{4}$$

$$c = \frac{75}{4}$$

Step 3 To check, replace c with $\frac{75}{4}$ in the original proportion.

$$\frac{3}{4} \stackrel{?}{=} \frac{\left(\frac{75}{4}\right)}{25}$$

Multiply:

$$3 \cdot 25 = 75$$

$$4 \cdot \frac{75}{4} = 75$$ The products are the same, so the value of $\frac{75}{4}$ checks for c.

RECALL

In the proportion equation $\frac{a}{b} = \frac{c}{d}$, we check to see if $ad = bc$.

Check Yourself 1

Solve the proportions for n. Check your result.

(a) $\frac{4}{5} = \frac{n}{25}$ **(b)** $\frac{5}{9} = \frac{12}{n}$

In solving for a missing term in a proportion, we may find an equation involving fractions or decimals. Example 2 involves finding the unknown value in such cases.

Example 2 Solving Proportions for Unknown Values

(a) Solve the proportion for x.

$$\frac{\frac{1}{4}}{3} = \frac{4}{x}$$

$$\frac{1}{4}x = 12$$

$$\frac{\frac{1}{4}x}{\frac{1}{4}} = \frac{12}{\frac{1}{4}}$$ We divide by the coefficient of x. In this case it is $\frac{1}{4}$.

$$x = \frac{12}{\frac{1}{4}}$$ Remember: $\frac{12}{\frac{1}{4}}$ is $12 \div \frac{1}{4}$. Invert the divisor and multiply.

$$x = 48$$

RECALL

The coefficient is the number multiplying the variable, in this case $\frac{1}{4}$.

To check, replace x with 48 in the original proportion.

$$\frac{\frac{1}{4}}{3} \stackrel{?}{=} \frac{4}{48}$$

$$\frac{1}{4} \cdot 48 \stackrel{?}{=} 3 \cdot 4$$

$$12 = 12$$

(b) Solve the proportion for d.

$$\frac{0.5}{2} = \frac{3}{d}$$

$$0.5d = 6$$

$$\frac{0.5d}{0.5} = \frac{6}{0.5}$$ Divide by the coefficient, 0.5.

$$d = 12$$

NOTE

Here we must divide 6 by 0.5 to find the unknown value. The steps of that division are shown here for review.

```
      1 2.
0.5 )6.0
     5
     1 0
     1 0
       0
```

We leave it to you to confirm that $0.5 \cdot 12 = 2 \cdot 3$.

Check Yourself 2

(a) **Solve for d.** **(b)** **Solve for x.**

$$\frac{\frac{1}{2}}{5} = \frac{3}{d} \qquad \frac{0.4}{x} = \frac{2}{30}$$

Now that we have learned how to find an unknown value in a proportion, we can solve many applications.

Step by Step

Solving Applications of Proportions

Step 1 Read the problem carefully to determine the given information.

Step 2 Write the proportion necessary to solve the problem. Use a letter to represent the unknown quantity. Be sure to include the units in writing the proportion.

Step 3 Solve, answer the question of the original problem, and check the proportion.

Example 3 Solve an Application Involving a Proportion

< Objective 2 >

(a) In a shipment of 400 parts, 14 are found to be defective. How many defective parts should be expected in a shipment of 1,000?

Assume that the ratio of defective parts to the total number remains the same.

$$\frac{14 \text{ defective}}{400 \text{ total}} = \frac{x \text{ defective}}{1{,}000 \text{ total}}$$

We decided to let x be the unknown number of defective parts.

Multiply:

$$400x = 14{,}000$$

Divide by the coefficient, 400.

$$x = 35$$

So 35 defective parts should be expected in the shipment.

Checking the original proportion, we get

$$14 \cdot 1{,}000 \stackrel{?}{=} 400 \cdot 35$$

$$14{,}000 = 14{,}000$$

(b) Jill works 4.2 h and receives \$21. How much will she get if she works 10 h?

The rate comparing hours worked and the amount of pay remains the same.

$$\frac{4.2 \text{ h}}{\$21} = \frac{10 \text{ h}}{\$a}$$

Let a be the unknown amount of pay.

$$4.2a = 210$$

$$\frac{4.2a}{4.2} = \frac{210}{4.2}$$

Divide both sides by 4.2.

$$a = \$50$$

Check Yourself 3

(a) An investment of \$3,000 earned \$330 for 1 year. How much will an investment of \$10,000 earn at the same rate for 1 year?

(b) A piece of cable 8.5 centimeters (cm) long weighs 68 grams (g). What does a 10-cm length of the same cable weigh?

Example 4 Using Proportions to Solve a Map-Scale Application

The scale on a map is given as $\frac{1}{4}$ inch (in.) = 3 miles (mi). The distance between two towns is 4 in. on the map. How far apart are the towns in miles?

NOTE

We could divide both sides by $\frac{1}{4}$:

$$\frac{\frac{1}{4}\cdot x}{\frac{1}{4}} = \frac{3\cdot 4}{\frac{1}{4}}$$

$$x = \frac{3\cdot 4}{\frac{1}{4}}$$

$$x = \frac{12}{\frac{1}{4}}$$

then invert and multiply.

$$x = \frac{12}{1}\cdot\frac{4}{1}$$
$$= 48$$

For this solution we use the fact that the ratio of inches (on the map) to miles remains the same. We also use another important property of an equation: We can multiply both sides of the equation by the same non-zero number.

$$\frac{\frac{1}{4}\text{ in.}}{3\text{ mi}} = \frac{4\text{ in.}}{x\text{ mi}}$$

$$\frac{1}{4}\cdot x = 3\cdot 4$$

$$4\cdot\frac{1}{4}\cdot x = 4\cdot 3\cdot 4$$ We multiply both sides of the equation by 4, since $4\cdot\frac{1}{4} = 1$.

$$1\cdot x = 4\cdot 3\cdot 4$$

$$x = 48\text{ (mi)}$$

Check Yourself 4

Jack drives 125 mi in $2\frac{1}{2}$ hours (h). At the same rate, how far will he be able to travel in 4 h? (Hint: Write $2\frac{1}{2}$ as an improper fraction.)

In Example 5 we must convert the units stated in the problem.

Example 5 Using Proportions to Solve an Application

A machine can produce 15 tin cans in 2 minutes (min). At this rate how many cans can it make in an 8-h period?

In writing a proportion for this problem, we must write the times involved in terms of the same units.

NOTE

Always check that your units are properly placed.

$$\frac{15\text{ cans}}{2\text{ min}} = \frac{x\text{ cans}}{480\text{ min}}$$ Because 1 h is 60 min, convert 8 h to 480 min.

$$15\cdot 480 = 2x$$

or $$7{,}200 = 2x$$

$$x = 3{,}600\text{ cans}$$

Check Yourself 5

Instructions on a can of film developer call for 2 ounces (oz) of concentrate to 1 quart (qt) of water. How much of the concentrate is needed to mix with 1 gallon (gal) of water? (4 qt = 1 gal.)

Proportions are important when working with *similar* geometric figures. These are figures that have the same shape and whose corresponding sides are proportional. For instance, in the similar triangles shown here, a proportion involving corresponding sides is

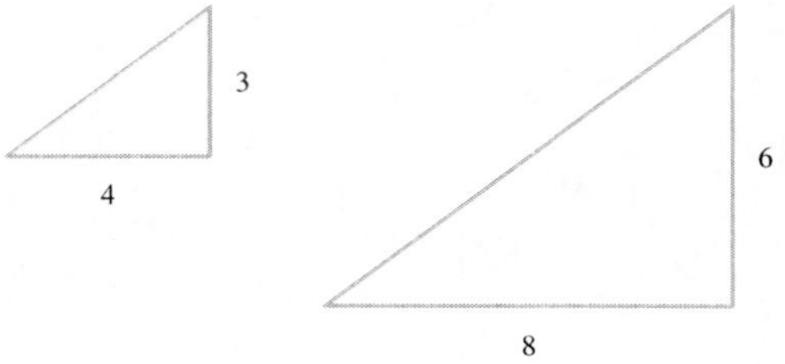

$$\frac{3}{4} = \frac{6}{8}$$

Example 6 Solving an Application Using Similar Triangles

NOTE

Connect the top of the tree to the end of the shadow to create a triangle. Connecting the top of the man to the end of his shadow creates a similar triangle.

If a 6-foot-tall man casts a shadow that is 10 feet (ft) long, how tall is a tree that casts a shadow that is 140 ft long?

Look at a picture of the two triangles involved.

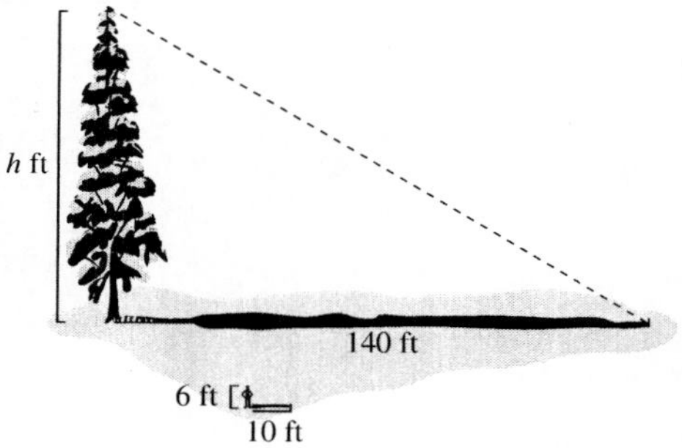

From the similar triangles, we have the proportion

$$\frac{6}{10} = \frac{h}{140}$$

Using the proportion rule, we have $6 \cdot 140 = 10 \cdot h$, so

$$10 \cdot h = 840$$

$$\frac{10 \cdot h}{10} = \frac{840}{10}$$

$$h = 84$$

The tree is 84 ft tall.

Check Yourself 6

If a woman who is $5\frac{1}{2}$ ft tall casts a shadow that is 3 ft long, how tall is a building that casts a shadow that is 90 ft long?

Proportions are used in solving a variety of problems such as the allied health application in Example 7.

Example 7 An Application of Proportions

> CAUTION

Solving for x does not give us an answer directly. x represents the total volume, which includes both water and serum. We still need to subtract 8.5 from x to get a final answer.

In preparing specimens for testing, it is often necessary to dilute the original solution. The dilution ratio is the ratio of the volume, in milliliters (mL), of original solution to the total volume, also in mL, of the diluted solution. How much water is required to make a $\frac{1}{20}$ dilution from 8.5 mL of serum?

We set up a proportion equation. The original solution is the 8.5 mL of serum, so that should be in the numerator. We name the denominator x.

$$\frac{1}{20} = \frac{8.5}{x}$$

$$1 \cdot x = 20 \cdot 8.5$$

$$x = 170$$

Therefore, the total volume should be 170 mL. Because 8.5 mL of the total solution is serum, we need to add $170 - 8.5 = 161.5$ mL of water.

Check Yourself 7

How much water is required to make a $\frac{3}{50}$ dilution from 11.25 mL of serum?

Check Yourself ANSWERS

1. **(a)** $n = 20$; **(b)** $n = \frac{108}{5}$ **2.** **(a)** $d = 30$; **(b)** $x = 6$ **3.** **(a)** \$1,100; **(b)** 80 g **4.** 200 mi **5.** 8 oz **6.** 165 ft **7.** 176.25 mL

Reading Your Text

The following fill-in-the-blank exercises are designed to ensure that you understand some of the key vocabulary used in this section.

SECTION 5.4

(a) An ______________ is a statement that two expressions are equal.

(b) When a number and a variable are multiplied, the number is called a ______________.

(c) The first step to solving application problems is to ______________ the problem carefully.

(d) Two triangles are similar if corresponding sides are ______________.

5.4 exercises

Name ____________

Section ________ Date ________

< Objective 1 >

Solve for the unknown in each proportion.

1. $\frac{x}{3} = \frac{6}{9}$ > Videos

2. $\frac{x}{6} = \frac{3}{9}$

3. $\frac{10}{n} = \frac{15}{6}$

4. $\frac{4}{3} = \frac{8}{n}$

5. $\frac{4}{7} = \frac{y}{14}$

6. $\frac{5}{8} = \frac{a}{16}$

7. $\frac{5}{7} = \frac{x}{35}$

8. $\frac{4}{15} = \frac{8}{n}$

9. $\frac{11}{a} = \frac{2}{44}$

10. $\frac{35}{40} = \frac{7}{n}$

11. $\frac{x}{8} = \frac{15}{24}$

12. $\frac{7}{12} = \frac{m}{24}$

13. $\frac{18}{12} = \frac{12}{p}$ > Videos

14. $\frac{20}{15} = \frac{100}{a}$

15. $\frac{5}{35} = \frac{a}{28}$

16. $\frac{20}{24} = \frac{p}{18}$

17. $\frac{12}{100} = \frac{3}{x}$

18. $\frac{b}{7} = \frac{21}{49}$

19. $\frac{p}{24} = \frac{25}{120}$

20. $\frac{5}{x} = \frac{20}{88}$

< Objective 2 >

Solve each application.

21. **Business and Finance** If 12 books are purchased for \$80, how much will you pay for 18 books at the same rate? > Videos

22. **Construction** If an 8-foot (ft) two-by-four costs \$1.92, what should a 12-ft two-by-four cost?

23. **Business and Finance** A box of 18 tea bags is marked \$2.70. At that price, what should a box of 48 tea bags cost?

24. **Business and Finance** A worker can complete the assembly of 15 MP3 players in 6 hours (h). At this rate, how many can the worker complete in a 40-h workweek?

25. **Social Science** The ratio of yes to no votes in an election was 3 to 2. How many no votes were cast if there were 2,880 yes votes?

Answers

1. ________ 2. ________
3. ________ 4. ________
5. ________ 6. ________
7. ________ 8. ________
9. ________ 10. ________
11. ________ 12. ________
13. ________ 14. ________
15. ________ 16. ________
17. ________ 18. ________
19. ________ 20. ________
21. ________ 22. ________
23. ________
24. ________
25. ________

Answers

26. ______

27. ______

28. ______

29. ______

30. ______

31. ______

32. ______

33. ______

34. ______

35. ______

36. ______

26. **Social Science** The ratio of men to women at a college is 7 to 5. How many women students are there if there are 3,500 men?

27. **Crafts** A photograph 5 inches (in.) wide by 6 in. high is to be enlarged so that the new width is 15 in. What will the height of the enlargement be?

28. **Business and Finance** Christy can travel 110 miles (mi) in her new car on 5 gallons (gal) of gas. How far can she travel on a full (12 gal) tank?

29. **Business and Finance** The Changs purchased a $120,000 home, and the property taxes were $2,100. If they make improvements and the house is now valued at $150,000, what will the new property tax be?

30. **Business and Finance** A car travels 165 mi in 3 h. How far will it travel in 8 h if it continues at the same speed?

Using the given map, find the distances between the cities named in exercises 31 to 34. Measure distances to the nearest sixteenth of an inch.

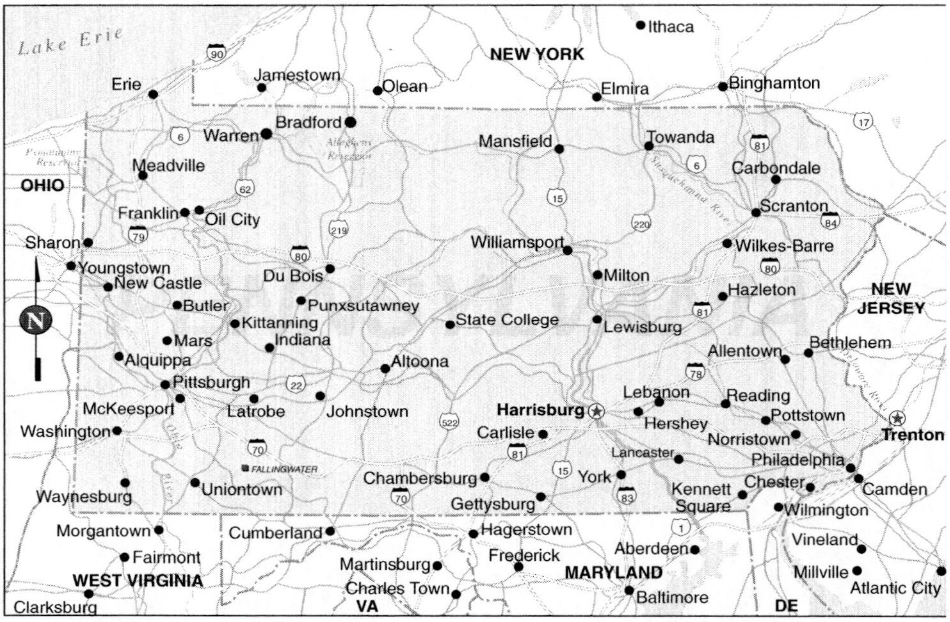

© MAGELLAN Geographix℠Santa Barbara, CA (800) 929-4MAP

31. Find the distance from Harrisburg to Philadelphia.

32. Find the distance from Punxsutawney (home of the groundhog) to State College (home of the Nittany Lions).

33. Find the distance from Gettysburg to Meadville.

34. Find the distance from Scranton to Waynesburg.

35. **Business and Finance** An inspection reveals 30 defective parts in a shipment of 500. How many defective parts should be expected in a shipment of 1,200?

36. **Business and Finance** You invest $4,000 in a stock that pays a $180 dividend in 1 year. At the same rate, how much will you need to invest to earn $270?

37. **Construction** A 6-ft fence post casts a 9-ft shadow. How tall is a nearby pole that casts a 15-ft shadow?

38. **Construction** A 9-ft light pole casts a 15-ft shadow. Find the height of a nearby tree that is casting a 40-ft shadow.

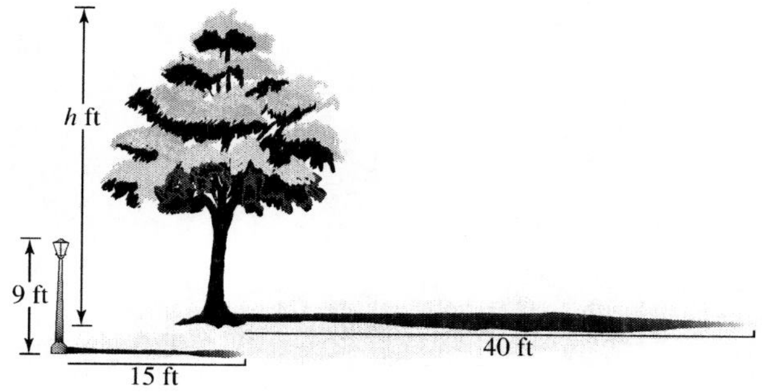

39. **Construction** On the blueprint of the Wilsons' new home, the scale is 5 in. equals 7 ft. What will the actual length of a bedroom be if it measures 10 in. long on the blueprint?

> Videos

40. **Social Science** The scale on a map is $\frac{1}{2}$ in. = 50 mi. If the distance between two towns on the map is 6 in., how far apart are they in miles?

41. **Science and Medicine** A metal bar expands $\frac{1}{4}$ in. for each 12°F rise in temperature. How much will it expand if the temperature rises 48°F?

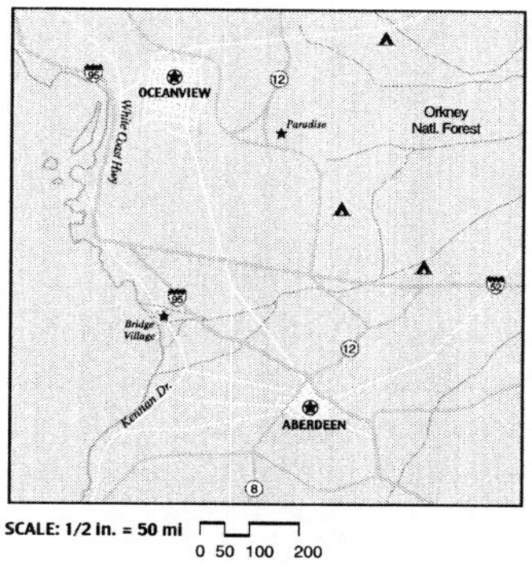

42. **Business and Finance** Your car burns $2\frac{1}{2}$ quarts (qt) of oil on a trip of 5,000 mi. How many quarts should you expect to use when driving 7,200 mi?

43. **Social Science** Approximately 7 out of every 10 people in the U.S. workforce drive to work alone. During morning rush hour there are 115,000 cars on the streets of a medium-sized city. How many of these cars have one person in them?

44. **Social Science** Approximately 15 out of every 100 people in the U.S. workforce carpool to work. There are an estimated 320,000 people in the workforce of a given city. How many of these people are in car pools?

Use a proportion to find the unknown side labeled x, in each pair of similar figures.

45.

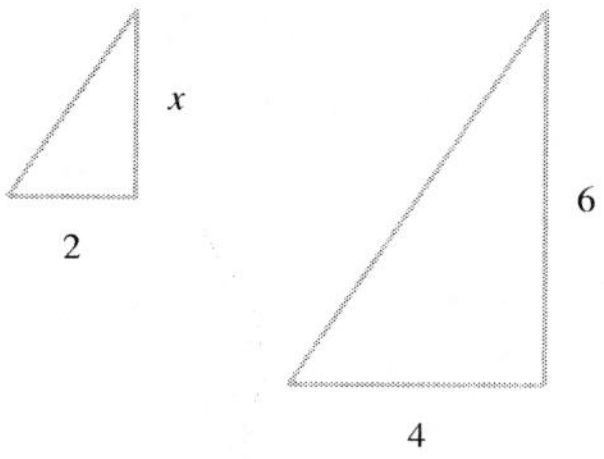

> Videos

46.

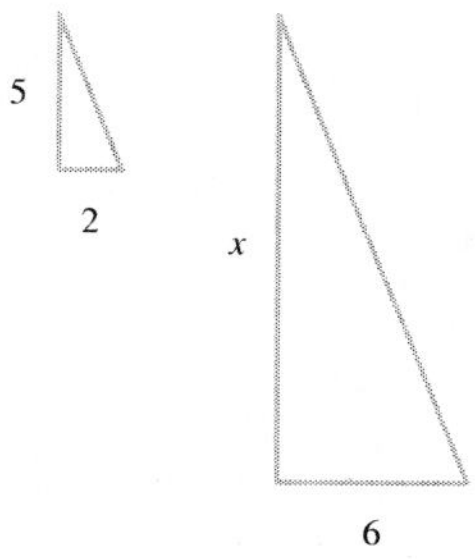

Answers

37. ______

38. ______

39. ______

40. ______

41. ______

42. ______

43. ______

44. ______

45. ______

46. ______

Answers

47. ______ 48. ______

49. ______ 50. ______

51. ______ 52. ______

53. ______ 54. ______

55. ______ 56. ______

57. ______ 58. ______

59. ______ 60. ______

61. ______ 62. ______

63. ______ 64. ______

65. ______ 66. ______

67. ______ 68. ______

69. ______ 70. ______

71. ______ 72. ______

47.

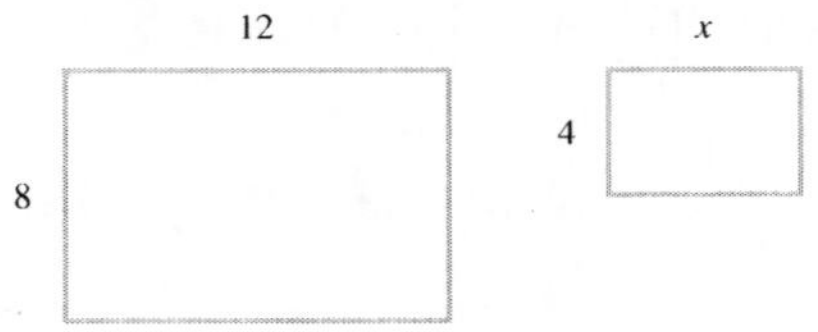

48.

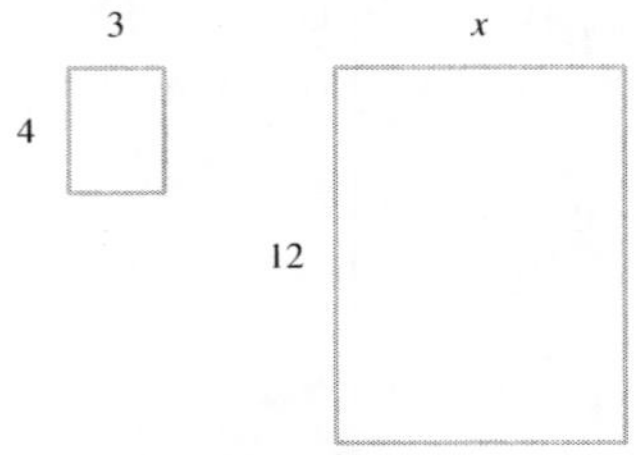

Basic Skills | **Challenge Yourself** | Calculator/Computer | Career Applications | Above and Beyond

Determine whether each statement is **true** *or* **false.**

49. Given the product of a number and a variable, the variable is called a coefficient.

50. Given the product of a number and a variable, the number is called a coefficient.

Fill in each blank with **always, sometimes,** *or* **never.**

51. In solving a proportion, we can __________ divide by the coefficient of the variable.

52. Two similar triangles ________ have corresponding sides that are proportional.

Solve for the unknown in each proportion.

53. $\dfrac{\frac{1}{2}}{2} = \dfrac{3}{a}$

54. $\dfrac{x}{5} = \dfrac{2}{\frac{1}{3}}$

55. $\dfrac{\frac{1}{4}}{12} = \dfrac{m}{40}$

56. $\dfrac{12}{\frac{1}{3}} = \dfrac{80}{y}$

57. $\dfrac{1}{6} = \dfrac{\frac{2}{x}}{18}$

58. $\dfrac{3}{4} = \dfrac{4}{\frac{x}{10}}$

59. $\dfrac{\frac{2}{5}}{8} = \dfrac{1.2}{n}$

60. $\dfrac{4}{a} = \dfrac{\frac{1}{4}}{0.8}$

61. $\dfrac{0.2}{2} = \dfrac{1.2}{a}$

62. $\dfrac{0.5}{x} = \dfrac{1.25}{5}$

63. $\dfrac{x}{3.3} = \dfrac{1.1}{6.6}$

64. $\dfrac{2.4}{5.7} = \dfrac{m}{1.1}$

65. $\dfrac{3}{2} = \dfrac{1}{x}$

66. $\dfrac{4}{2} = \dfrac{2}{x}$

67. $\dfrac{2}{t} = \dfrac{12}{5}$

68. $\dfrac{4}{x} = \dfrac{14}{15}$

69. $\dfrac{n}{5} = \dfrac{1}{20}$

70. $\dfrac{m}{2} = \dfrac{5}{24}$

71. $\dfrac{3}{4} = \dfrac{x}{6}$

72. $\dfrac{1}{14} = \dfrac{c}{7}$

Basic Skills | Challenge Yourself | **Calculator/Computer** | Career Applications | Above and Beyond

When dealing with practical applications, the numbers involved in a proportion may be large or contain inconvenient decimals. A calculator is likely to be the tool of choice for solving such proportions. Typically, we set up the solution without doing any calculating, and then we put the calculator to work, usually rounding the result to an appropriate place value. For example, suppose you drive 278 miles (mi) on 13.6 gallons (gal) of gas. If the gas tank holds 21 gal, and you want to know how far you can travel on a full tank of gas, you write

$$\frac{278 \text{ mi}}{13.6 \text{ gal}} = \frac{x \text{ mi}}{21 \text{ gal}}$$

Solving for x, you obtain

$$x = \frac{(278)(21)}{13.6}$$

With your calculator, you enter

278 [×] 21 [÷] 13.6 [=]

The display shows 429.26471. Rounding to the nearest mile, you can travel 429 mi.

Use your calculator to solve each proportion.

73. $\frac{630}{1,365} = \frac{15}{a}$

74. $\frac{770}{1,988} = \frac{n}{71}$

75. $\frac{x}{4.7} = \frac{11.8}{16.9}$ (to nearest tenth)

76. $\frac{13.9}{8.4} = \frac{n}{9.2}$ (to nearest hundredth)

77. $\frac{2.7}{3.8} = \frac{5.9}{n}$ (to nearest tenth)

78. $\frac{12.2}{0.042} = \frac{x}{0.08}$ (to nearest hundredth)

Solve each application.

79. BUSINESS AND FINANCE Bill earns $248.40 for working 34.5 hours (h). How much will he receive if he works at the same pay rate for 31.75 h?

80. CONSTRUCTION Construction-grade lumber costs $384.50 per 1,000 board-feet. What will be the cost of 686 board-feet? Round your answer to the nearest cent.

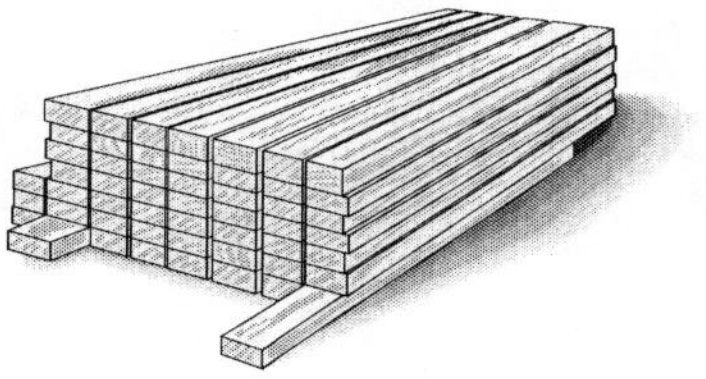

81. SCIENCE AND MEDICINE A speed of 88 feet per second (ft/s) is equal to a speed of 60 miles per hour (mi/h). If the speed of sound is 750 mi/h, what is the speed of sound in feet per second?

82. BUSINESS AND FINANCE A shipment of 75 parts is inspected, and 6 are found to be faulty. At the same rate, how many defective parts should be found in a shipment of 139? Round your result to the nearest whole number.

Answers

73. ______

74. ______

75. ______

76. ______

77. ______

78. ______

79. ______

80. ______

81. ______

82. ______

Answers

83. ________

84. ________

85. ________

86. ________

87. ________

Basic Skills | Challenge Yourself | Calculator/Computer | **Career Applications** | Above and Beyond

83. **Information Technology** A computer transmits 5 Web pages in 2 seconds to a Web server. How many pages can the computer transmit in 1 min?

84. **Automotive Technology** A tire shows $\frac{1}{8}$ in. of tread wear after 32,000 mi. Assuming that the rate of wear remains constant, how much tread wear would you expect the tire to show after 48,000 mi?

85. **Manufacturing Technology** Cutting 7 holes removes 0.322 pounds of material from a frame. How much weight would 43 holes remove?

86. **Electrical Engineering** The voltage output V_{out} of a transformer is given by the proportion

$$\frac{N_{out}}{N_{in}} = \frac{V_{out}}{V_{in}}$$

in which N gives the number of turns in the coil (see the figure).

In the system shown, what voltage input is required in order for the output voltage to reach 630 volts?

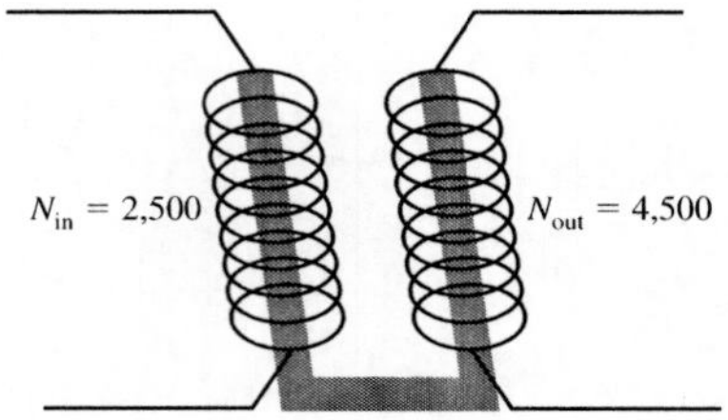

Basic Skills | Challenge Yourself | Calculator/Computer | Career Applications | **Above and Beyond**

87. A recipe for 12 servings lists the following ingredients:

12 cups ziti	7 cups spaghetti sauce	4 cups ricotta cheese
$\frac{1}{2}$ cup parsley	1 teaspoon garlic powder	$\frac{1}{2}$ teaspoon pepper
4 cups mozzarella cheese	2 tablespoons parmesan cheese	

Determine the amount of ingredients necessary to serve 5 people.

Answers

1. $x = 2$ 3. $n = 4$ 5. $y = 8$ 7. $x = 25$ 9. $a = 242$ 11. $x = 5$ 13. $p = 8$ 15. $a = 4$ 17. $x = 25$ 19. $p = 5$ 21. \$120 23. \$7.20 25. 1,920 no votes 27. 18 in. 29. \$2,625 31. 110 mi 33. 215 mi 35. 72 defective parts 37. 10 ft 39. 14 ft 41. 1 in. 43. 80,500 cars with one person 45. 3 47. 6 49. False 51. always 53. $a = 12$ 55. $m = \frac{5}{6}$ 57. $x = \frac{2}{3}$ 59. $n = 24$ 61. $a = 12$ 63. $x = 0.55$ 65. $x = \frac{2}{3}$ 67. $t = \frac{5}{6}$ 69. $n = \frac{1}{4}$ 71. $x = \frac{9}{2}$ 73. $a = 32.5$ 75. $x \approx 3.3$ 77. $n \approx 8.3$ 79. \$228.60 81. 1,100 ft/s 83. 150 Web pages 85. 1.978 lb 87. Above and Beyond

Activity 15 ::
Burning Calories

Many people are interested in losing weight through exercise. An important fact to consider is that a person needs to burn off 3,500 calories more than he or she takes in to lose 1 pound, according to the American Dietetic Association.

The table shows the number of calories burned per hour (cal/h) for a variety of activities, where the figures are based on a 150-pound person.

Activity	Cal/h	Activity	Cal/h
Bicycling 6 mi/h	240	Running 10 mi/h	1,280
Bicycling 12 mi/h	410	Swimming 25 yd/min	275
Cross-country skiing	700	Swimming 50 yd/min	500
Jogging $5\frac{1}{2}$ mi/h	740	Tennis (singles)	400
Jogging 7 mi/h	920	Walking 2 mi/h	240
Jumping rope	750	Walking 3 mi/h	320
Running in place	650	Walking $4\frac{1}{2}$ mi/h	440

Work with your group members to solve the following problems. You may find that setting up proportions is helpful.

For problems 1 through 4, assume a 150-pound person.

1. If a person jogs at a rate of $5\frac{1}{2}$ mi/h for $3\frac{1}{2}$ h in a week, how many calories will the person burn?

2. If a person runs in place for 15 minutes, how many calories will the person burn?

3. If a person cross-country skis for 35 minutes, how many calories will the person burn?

4. How many hours would a person have to jump rope in order to lose 1 pound? (Assume calorie consumption is just enough to maintain weight, with no activity.)

Heavier people burn more calories (for the same activity), and lighter people burn fewer. In fact, you can calculate similar figures for burning calories by setting up the appropriate proportion.

5. Assuming that the calories burned are proportional, at what rate would a 120-pound person burn calories while bicycling at 12 mi/h?

6. Assuming that the calories burned are proportional, at what rate would a 180-pound person burn calories while bicycling at 12 mi/h?

7. Assuming that the calories burned are proportional, how many hours of jogging at $5\frac{1}{2}$ mi/h would be needed for a 200-pound person to lose 5 pounds? (Again, assume calorie consumption is just enough to maintain weight, with no activity.)

Definition/Procedure	Example	Reference
Ratios		Section 5.1
Ratio A means of comparing two numbers or like quantities. A ratio can be written as a fraction.	$\frac{4}{7}$ can be thought of as "the ratio of 4 to 7."	p. 315
Rates and Unit Pricing		Section 5.2
Rate A fraction involving two unlike denominate numbers. **Unit Rate** A rate that has been simplified and read so that the denominator is one unit.	$\frac{50 \text{ home runs}}{150 \text{ games}} = \frac{1}{3} \frac{\text{home run}}{\text{game}}$	pp. 324–325
Unit Price The cost per unit.	$\frac{\$2}{5 \text{ rolls}} = \$0.40 \text{ per roll}$ $= 40 \frac{\text{cents}}{\text{roll}}$	p. 327
Proportions		Section 5.3
Proportion A statement that two fractions or rates are equal.	$\frac{3}{5} = \frac{6}{10}$ is a proportion read "three is to five as six is to ten."	p. 335
The Proportion Rule If $\frac{a}{b} = \frac{c}{d}$, then $a \cdot d = b \cdot c$.	If $\frac{3}{5} = \frac{6}{10}$, then $3 \cdot 10 = 5 \cdot 6$	p. 336
Solving Proportions		Section 5.4
To Solve a Proportion **Step 1** Use the proportion rule to write the equivalent equation $a \cdot d = b \cdot c$. **Step 2** Divide both terms of the equation by the coefficient of the variable. **Step 3** Use the value found to replace the unknown in the original proportion. Check that the ratios or rates are proportional.	To solve: $\frac{x}{5} = \frac{16}{20}$ $20x = 5 \cdot 16$ $20x = 80$ $\frac{\cancel{20}^{1}x}{\cancel{20}_{1}} = \frac{80}{20}$ $x = 4$ Check: $\frac{4}{5} \stackrel{?}{=} \frac{16}{20}$ $4 \times 20 \stackrel{?}{=} 5 \times 16$ $80 = 80$	p. 342

Definition/Procedure	Example	Reference
To Solve a Problem by Using Proportions		
Step 1 Read the problem carefully to determine the given information. **Step 2** Write the proportion necessary to solve the problem, using a letter to represent the unknown quantity. Be sure to include the units in writing the proportion. **Step 3** Solve, answer the question of the original problem, and check the proportion as before.	A machine can produce 250 units in 5 min. At this rate, how many can it produce in a 12 h period? $\frac{250 \text{ units}}{5 \text{ min}} = \frac{x \text{ units}}{12 \text{ h}}$ $\frac{250 \text{ units}}{5 \text{ min}} = \frac{x \text{ units}}{720 \text{ min}}$ $250 \cdot 720 = 5x$ or $5x = 180{,}000$ $x = 36{,}000$ The machine can produce 36,000 units in 12 h.	p. 345

summary exercises :: chapter 5

This summary exercise set is provided to give you practice with each of the objectives of this chapter. Each exercise is keyed to the appropriate chapter section. When you are finished, you can check your answers to the odd-numbered exercises against those presented in the back of the text. If you have difficulty with any of these questions, go back and reread the examples from that section. The answers to the even-numbered exercises appear in the *Instructor's Solutions Manual.* Your instructor will give you guidelines on how to best use these exercises in your instructional setting.

5.1 *Write each ratio in simplest form.*

1. The ratio of 4 to 17

2. The ratio of 28 to 42

3. For a football team that has won 10 of its 16 games, the ratio of wins to games played

4. For a rectangle of length 30 inches and width 18 inches, the ratio of its length to its width

5. The ratio of $2\frac{1}{3}$ to $5\frac{1}{4}$

6. The ratio of 7.5 to 3.25

7. The ratio of 7 in. to 3 ft

8. The ratio of 72 h to 4 days

5.2 *Express each rate as a unit rate.*

9. $\frac{600 \text{ miles}}{6 \text{ hours}}$

10. $\frac{270 \text{ miles}}{9 \text{ gallons}}$

11. $\frac{350 \text{ calories}}{7 \text{ ounces}}$

12. $\frac{36{,}000 \text{ dollars}}{9 \text{ years}}$

13. $\frac{5{,}000 \text{ feet}}{25 \text{ seconds}}$

14. $\frac{10{,}500 \text{ revolutions}}{3 \text{ minutes}}$

15. A baseball team has had 117 hits in 18 games. Find the team's hits per game rate.

16. A basketball team has scored 216 points in 8 quarters. Find the team's points per quarter rate.

17. Taniko scored 246 points in 20 games. Marisa scored 216 points in 16 games. Which player has the highest points per game rate?

18. One shop will charge \$306 for a job that takes $4\frac{1}{2}$ hours. A second shop can do the same job in 4 hours and will charge \$290. Which shop has the higher cost per hour rate?

5.2 *Find the unit price for each item.*

19. A 32-oz bottle of dishwashing liquid costs \$2.88.

20. A 35-oz box of breakfast cereal costs \$5.60.

21. A 24-oz loaf of bread costs \$2.28.

22. Five large jars of fruit cost \$67.30.

23. Three CDs cost \$44.85.

24. Six tickets cost \$267.60.

5.3 *Write each proportion.*

25. 4 is to 9 as 20 is to 45.

26. 7 is to 5 as 56 is to 40.

27. If Jorge can travel 110 miles (mi) in 2 hours (h), he can travel 385 mi in 7 h.

28. If it takes 4 gallons (gal) of paint to cover 1,000 square feet (ft^2), it takes 10 gal of paint to cover 2,500 ft^2.

Determine whether the given fractions are proportional.

29. $\frac{4}{13} \stackrel{?}{=} \frac{7}{22}$

30. $\frac{8}{11} \stackrel{?}{=} \frac{24}{33}$

31. $\frac{9}{24} \stackrel{?}{=} \frac{12}{32}$

32. $\frac{7}{18} \stackrel{?}{=} \frac{35}{80}$

33. $\frac{5}{\frac{1}{6}} \stackrel{?}{=} \frac{120}{4}$

34. $\frac{0.8}{4} \stackrel{?}{=} \frac{12}{50}$

35. Is $\frac{35 \text{ Euros}}{40 \text{ dollars}}$ proportional to $\frac{75.25 \text{ Euros}}{86 \text{ dollars}}$?

36. Is $\frac{188 \text{ words}}{8 \text{ minutes}}$ proportional to $\frac{121 \text{ words}}{5 \text{ minutes}}$?

5.4 *Solve for the unknown in each proportion.*

37. $\frac{16}{24} = \frac{m}{3}$

38. $\frac{6}{a} = \frac{27}{18}$

39. $\frac{14}{35} = \frac{t}{10}$

40. $\frac{55}{88} = \frac{10}{p}$

41. $\frac{\frac{1}{2}}{18} = \frac{5}{w}$

42. $\frac{\frac{3}{2}}{9} = \frac{5}{a}$

43. $\frac{5}{x} = \frac{0.6}{12}$

44. $\frac{s}{2.5} = \frac{1.5}{7.5}$

Solve each application.

45. Business and Finance If 4 tickets to a civic theater performance cost \$90, what is the price for 6 tickets?

46. Social Science The ratio of first-year to second-year students at a school is 8 to 7. If there are 224 second-year students, how many first-year students are there?

47. Crafts A photograph that is 5 inches (in.) wide by 7 in. tall is to be enlarged so that the new height will be 21 in. What will be the width of the enlargement?

48. Business and Finance Marcia assembles disk drives for a computer manufacturer. If she can assemble 11 drives in 2 hours (h), how many can she assemble in a workweek (40 h)?

49. Business and Finance A firm finds 14 defective parts in a shipment of 400. How many defective parts can be expected in a shipment of 800 parts?

50. Social Science The scale on a map is $\frac{1}{4}$ in. = 10 miles (mi). How many miles apart are two towns that are 3 in. apart on the map?

51. Business and Finance A piece of tubing that is 16.5 centimeters (cm) long weighs 55 grams (g). What is the weight of a piece of the same tubing that is 42 cm long?

52. Crafts If 1 quart (qt) of paint covers 120 square feet (ft^2), how many square feet does 2 gallons (gal) cover? (1 gal = 4 qt.)

self-test 5

Name ________________

Section ________ Date ________

The purpose of this self-test is to help you assess your progress so that you can find concepts that you need to review before the next exam. Allow yourself about an hour to take this test. At the end of that hour, check your answers against those given in the back of this text. If you miss any, go back to the appropriate section to reread the examples until you have mastered that particular concept.

Express each rate as a unit rate.

1. $\dfrac{840 \text{ miles}}{175 \text{ gallons}}$

2. $\dfrac{132 \text{ dollars}}{16 \text{ hours}}$

Solve for the unknown in each proportion.

3. $\dfrac{45}{75} = \dfrac{12}{x}$

4. $\dfrac{a}{26} = \dfrac{45}{65}$

5. Find the unit price, if 11 gallons of milk cost $28.16.

6. A basketball team wins 26 of its 33 games during a season. What is the ratio of wins to games played? What is the ratio of wins to losses?

Solve for the unknown in each proportion.

7. $\dfrac{\frac{1}{2}}{p} = \dfrac{5}{30}$

8. $\dfrac{3}{m} = \dfrac{0.9}{4.8}$

Write each ratio in simplest form.

9. The ratio of 7 to 19

10. The ratio of 75 to 45

11. The ratio of 8 ft to 4 yd

12. The ratio of 6 h to 3 days

Solve each application using a proportion.

13. **Business and Finance** If ballpoint pens are marked 5 for 95¢, how much does a dozen cost?

14. **Business and Finance** Your new compact car travels 324 miles on 9 gallons of gas. If the tank holds 16 usable gallons, how far can you drive on a tank of gas?

15. **Business and Finance** An assembly line can install 5 car mufflers in 4 minutes. At this rate, how many mufflers can be installed in an 8-hour shift?

16. **Crafts** Instructions on a package of concentrated plant food call for 2 teaspoons (tsp) to 1 qt of water. We wish to use 3 gal of water. How much of the plant food concentrate should be added to the 3 gal of water?

Answers

1. ________
2. ________
3. ________
4. ________
5. ________
6. ________
7. ________
8. ________
9. ________
10. ________
11. ________
12. ________
13. ________
14. ________
15. ________
16. ________

Answers

17. ______

18. ______

19. ______

20. ______

Determine whether the given fractions are proportional.

17. $\frac{3}{9} \stackrel{?}{=} \frac{27}{81}$

18. $\frac{6}{7} \stackrel{?}{=} \frac{9}{11}$

19. $\frac{9}{10} \stackrel{?}{=} \frac{27}{30}$

20. $\frac{\frac{1}{2}}{5} \stackrel{?}{=} \frac{2}{18}$

The following exercises are presented to help you review concepts from earlier chapters. This is meant as review material and not as a comprehensive exam. The answers are presented in the back of the text. Beside each answer is a section reference for the concept. If you have difficulty with any of these exercises, be certain to at least read through the summary related to that section.

1. Write 45,789 in words.

2. What is the place value of 2 in the number 621,487?

Perform the indicated operations.

3. $\begin{array}{r} 2{,}790 \\ 831 \\ +\ 22{,}683 \\ \hline \end{array}$

4. $\begin{array}{r} 84{,}793 \\ -\ 36{,}987 \\ \hline \end{array}$

5. 76×58

6. $72\overline{)5{,}683}$

7. Luis owes $815 on a credit card after a trip. He makes payments of $125, $80, and $90. Interest amounting to $48 is charged. How much does he still owe on the account?

8. Evaluate the expression: $48 \div 8 \times 2 - 3^2$.

9. Find the perimeter and area of the given figure.

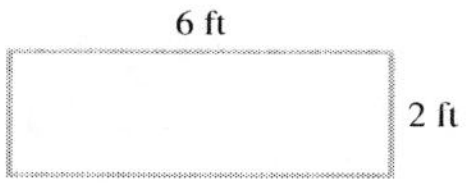

10. A room that measures 6 yd by 8 yd is to be carpeted. The carpet costs $23 per square yard. What will be the cost of the carpet?

11. Write the prime factorization of 924.

12. Find the greatest common factor (GCF) of 42 and 56.

13. Write the fraction $\frac{42}{168}$ in simplest form.

Perform the indicated operations.

14. $\frac{3}{4} \times \frac{24}{15}$

15. $2\frac{2}{3} \times 3\frac{3}{4}$

16. $\frac{6}{7} \div \frac{4}{21}$

17. $5\frac{1}{2} \div 3\frac{1}{4}$

18. $\frac{9}{11} - \frac{3}{4} + \frac{1}{2}$

19. $4\frac{5}{6} + 2\frac{3}{4}$

20. $8\frac{2}{7} - 3\frac{11}{14}$

Name ____________________

Section ________ Date ________

Answers

1. ____________________
2. ____________________
3. ____________________
4. ____________________
5. ____________________
6. ____________________
7. ____________________
8. ____________________
9. ____________________
10. ____________________
11. ____________________
12. ____________________

13. ________ 14. ________

15. ________ 16. ________

17. ________ 18. ________

19. ________ 20. ________

Answers

21. ______
22. ______
23. ______
24. ______
25. ______
26. ______
27. ______
28. ______
29. ______
30. ______
31. ______
32. ______
33. ______
34. ______
35. ______
36. ______
37. ______
38. ______
39. ______
40. ______

21. Find the least common multiple (LCM) of 36 and 60.

22. Maria drove at an average speed of 55 mi/h for $3\frac{1}{5}$ h. How many miles did she travel?

23. Stefan drove 132 miles in $2\frac{3}{4}$ h. What was his average speed?

Perform the indicated operations.

24. $36.169 - 28.341$

25. $3.1488 \div 2.56$

26. 4.89×1.35

27. Write 0.36 as a fraction and simplify.

28. Write the decimal equivalent of $\frac{7}{22}$ (to the nearest hundredth).

29. Find the perimeter of a rectangle that has dimensions 4.23 m by 2.8 m.

30. Find the area of a rectangle with dimensions 8 cm by 6.28 cm.

Write each ratio in simplest form.

31. 12 to 26

32. 60 to 18

33. 6 dimes to 3 quarters

Determine whether the given fractions are proportional.

34. $\frac{5}{6} \stackrel{?}{=} \frac{20}{24}$

35. $\frac{3}{7} \stackrel{?}{=} \frac{9}{22}$

Solve for the unknown.

36. $\frac{x}{3} = \frac{8}{12}$

37. $\frac{5}{x} = \frac{4}{12}$

38. Give the unit price for an item that weighs 20 oz and costs $4.88.

39. On a map, 3 cm represents 250 km. How far apart are two cities if the distance between them on the map is 7.2 cm?

40. A company finds 15 defective items in a shipment of 600 items. How many defective items can be expected in a shipment of 2,000 items?

CHAPTER

6

Percents

INTRODUCTION

When she retired, Roberta decided that she wanted to study the stock market and investments. She learned to watch small companies and to purchase stocks whose value is greater than listed.

Roberta enrolled in continuing education courses covering business and finance at her local community college. She learned how to track data and where to find financial advice articles on the Internet.

Now, after purchasing stock in a company, Roberta continues to monitor the company through quarterly financial statements and tries to gauge the best time to sell her stocks. Her goal is to sell her stocks when she thinks their value has peaked.

A less risky way to invest is to put money in a savings account or some other vehicle with a fixed interest rate. In these accounts, money grows continually as the interest is added at regular intervals.

In Activity 17 on page 399, you will have the opportunity to conduct a more in-depth study of interest calculations and the growth of investments.

CHAPTER 6 OUTLINE

Name ________________

Section ________ Date ________

This prerequisite test provides some exercises requiring skills that you will need to be successful in the coming chapter. The answers for these exercises can be found in the back of this text. This prerequisite test can help you identify topics that you will need to review before beginning the chapter.

Answers

1. ________
2. ________
3. ________
4. ________
5. ________
6. ________
7. ________
8. ________
9. ________
10. ________

Simplify the fraction.

1. $\frac{44}{100}$

Write the fraction as a decimal.

2. $\frac{5}{16}$

Evaluate.

3. $0.04 \times 1{,}040$

4. $\frac{2{,}300}{115}$

5. $\frac{1{,}800}{15}$

6. $\frac{5{,}250}{100}$

Solve each proportion.

7. $\frac{4}{5} = \frac{x}{60}$

8. $\frac{7}{12} = \frac{x}{100}$

9. $\frac{28}{x} = \frac{40}{100}$

10. $\frac{280}{x} = \frac{3.5}{100}$

6.1 Writing Percents as Fractions and Decimals

< 6.1 Objectives >

1 > Use percent notation

2 > Write a percent as a fraction or mixed number

3 > Write a percent as a decimal

When we considered parts of a whole in earlier chapters, we used fractions and decimals. *Percents* are another useful way of naming parts of a whole. We can think of percents as ratios whose denominators are 100. In fact, the word **percent** means "for each hundred." Consider the following figure:

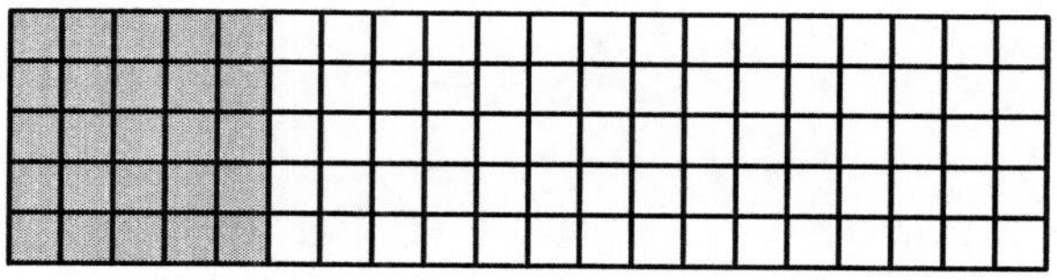

RECALL

Multiplying by $\frac{1}{100}$ is the same as dividing by 100.

The symbol for percent, %, represents multiplication by the number $\frac{1}{100}$. In the figure, 25 of 100 squares are shaded. As a fraction, we write this as $\frac{25}{100}$.

$$\frac{25}{100} = 25\left(\frac{1}{100}\right) = 25\%$$

25 percent of the squares are shaded.

Example 1 Using Percent Notation

< Objective 1 >

RECALL

You learned to solve proportions in Section 5.4.

(a) Four out of five geography students passed their midterm exams. Write this statement, using percent notation.

The ratio of passing students to all students is $\frac{4}{5}$, which we need to write as an equivalent fraction with a denominator of 100.

$$\frac{4}{5} = \frac{x}{100}$$

Using the proportion rule, we have

$$5 \cdot x = 4 \cdot 100$$

or $\quad 5x = 400$

The coefficient of the variable is 5, so we divide both sides of the equation by 5.

$$\frac{5x}{5} = \frac{400}{5}$$

$$x = 80 \qquad 400 \div 5 = 80$$

Therefore, we write

$$\frac{4}{5} = \frac{80}{100} = 80\left(\frac{1}{100}\right) = 80\%$$

and we say that 80% of the geography students passed their midterm exams.

NOTE

The ratio of compact cars to all cars is $\frac{35}{50}$.

(b) Of 50 automobiles sold by a dealer in 1 month, 35 were compact cars. Write this statement, using percent notation.

$$\frac{35}{50} = \frac{70}{100} = 70\left(\frac{1}{100}\right) = 70\%$$

We can say that 70% of the cars sold were compact cars.

Check Yourself 1

Rewrite the following statement using percent notation: 4 of the 50 parts in a shipment were defective.

Because there are different ways of naming the parts of a whole, you need to know how to change from one of these ways to another. First, we look at writing a percent as a fraction. Because a percent is a fraction or a ratio with denominator of 100, we can use the following rule.

Property

Writing a Percent as a Fraction

To change a percent to a fraction, replace the percent symbol with $\frac{1}{100}$ and multiply.

The use of this rule is shown in Example 2.

Example 2 Writing a Percent as a Fraction

< Objective 2 >

NOTE

You should write $\frac{25}{100}$ in simplest form.

Write each percent as a fraction.

(a) $7\% = 7\left(\frac{1}{100}\right) = \frac{7}{100}$

(b) $25\% = 25\left(\frac{1}{100}\right) = \frac{25}{100} = \frac{1}{4}$

Check Yourself 2

Write 12% as a fraction.

If a percent is *greater than 100,* the resulting fraction will be *greater than 1,* as shown in Example 3.

Example 3 Writing a Percent as a Mixed Number

Write 150% as a mixed number.

$$150\% = 150\left(\frac{1}{100}\right) = \frac{150}{100} = 1\frac{50}{100} = 1\frac{1}{2}$$

Check Yourself 3

Write 125% as a mixed number.

In Examples 2 and 3, we wrote percents as fractions by replacing the percent sign with $\frac{1}{100}$ and multiplying. How do we convert percents to decimal form? Since multiplying by $\frac{1}{100}$ is the same as dividing by 100, we just move the decimal point two places to the left. A shortened version of this process is given below.

Property

Writing a Percent as a Decimal

To write a percent as a decimal, remove the percent symbol and move the decimal point two places to the left.

Example 4 Writing a Percent as a Decimal

< Objective 3 >

Change each percent to its decimal equivalent.

(a) 25% = 0.25 The decimal point in 25% is understood to be after the 5.

(b) 8% = 0.08 We must add a zero to place the decimal point.

(c) 130% = 1.30

NOTE

A percent greater than 100 gives a decimal greater than 1.

Check Yourself 4

Write as decimals.

(a) 5% **(b)** 32% **(c)** 115%

Example 5 involves fractions of a percent, in this case, decimal fractions.

Example 5 Writing a Percent as a Decimal

Write as decimals.

(a) 4.5% = 0.045

(b) 0.5% = 0.005

Check Yourself 5

Write as decimals.

(a) 8.5% **(b)** 0.3%

There are many situations in which common fractions are involved in a percent. Example 6 illustrates this situation.

Example 6 Writing a Percent as a Decimal

NOTE

Write the common fraction as a decimal. Then remove the percent symbol by our earlier rule.

Write as decimals.

(a) $9\frac{1}{2}\% = 9.5\% = 0.095$

(b) $\frac{3}{4}\% = 0.75\% = 0.0075$

Check Yourself 6

Write as decimals.

(a) $7\frac{1}{2}\%$ **(b)** $\frac{1}{2}\%$

Writing a percent in fraction or decimal form is required in many applications. One such application is presented in Example 7.

Example 7 A Technology Application

A motor has an 86% efficiency rating. Express its efficiency rating as a fraction and as a decimal.

To express 86% as a fraction, we replace the % symbol with $\frac{1}{100}$ and simplify.

$$86\% = \frac{86}{100} = \frac{43}{50}$$

To express 86% as a decimal, we remove the % symbol and move the decimal point two places to the left.

$$86\% = 0.86$$

Check Yourself 7

An inspection of Carina's hard drive reveals that it is 60% full. Write the amount of hard drive capacity that is full as a fraction and as a decimal.

Check Yourself ANSWERS

1. 8% were defective **2.** $12\% = \frac{12}{100} = \frac{3}{25}$ **3.** $1\frac{1}{4}$

4. **(a)** 0.05; **(b)** 0.32; **(c)** 1.15 **5.** **(a)** 0.085; **(b)** 0.003

6. **(a)** 0.075; **(b)** 0.005 **7.** $\frac{3}{5}$; 0.6

Reading Your Text

The following fill-in-the-blank exercises are designed to ensure that you understand some of the key vocabulary used in this section.

SECTION 6.1

(a) The word *percent* means, "for each ______________."

(b) To rewrite a percent as a ______________, divide the number before the percent symbol by 100 and simplify.

(c) To write a percent in decimal form, remove the % symbol and move the decimal two places to the ______________.

(d) A percent that is larger than 100% is equivalent to a number ______________ than 1.

6.1 exercises

Name ______________

Section ________ Date ________

< Objective 1 >

Use percents to name the shaded portion of each drawing.

1. 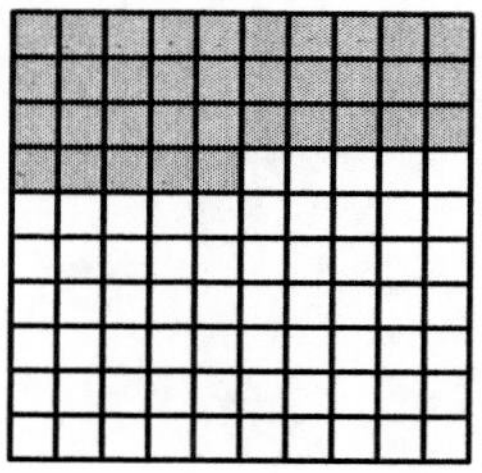

2. 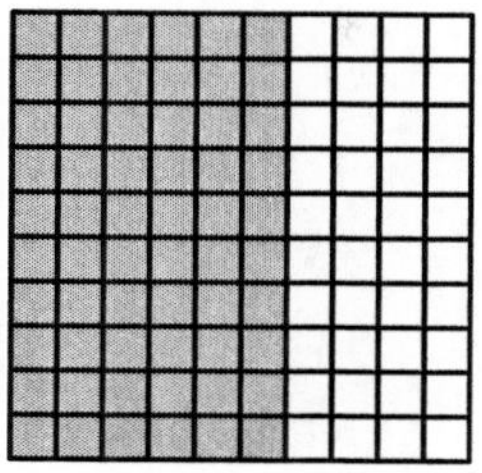

3. 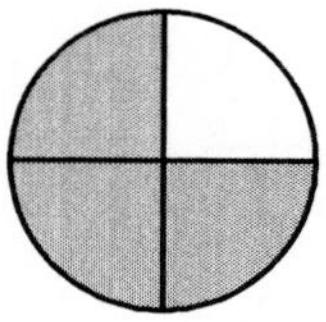 > Videos

4. 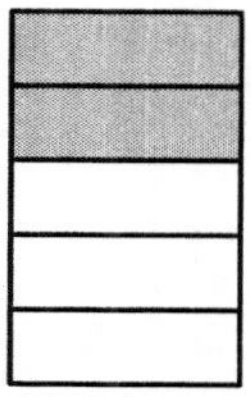

Rewrite each statement, using percent notation.

5. Out of every 100 eligible people, 53 voted in a recent election. > Videos

6. You receive \$5 in interest for every \$100 saved for 1 year.

7. Out of every 100 entering students, 74 register for English composition.

8. Of 100 people surveyed, 29 watched a particular sports event on television.

9. Out of 10 voters in a state, 3 are registered as independents.

10. A dealer sold 9 of the 20 cars available during a 1-day sale.

11. Of 50 houses in a development, 27 are sold.

12. Of the 25 employees of a company, 9 are part-time.

13. Out of 50 people surveyed, 23 prefer decaffeinated coffee.

14. 17 out of 20 college students work at part-time jobs.

15. Of the 20 students in an algebra class, 5 receive a grade of A. > Videos

16. Of the 50 families in a neighborhood, 31 have children in public schools.

Answers

1. ______________
2. ______________
3. ______________
4. ______________
5. ______________
6. ______________
7. ______________
8. ______________
9. ______________
10. ______________
11. ______________
12. ______________
13. ______________
14. ______________
15. ______________
16. ______________

Answers

17. ______
18. ______
19. ______
20. ______
21. ______
22. ______
23. ______
24. ______
25. ______
26. ______
27. ______
28. ______
29. ______ 30. ______
31. ______ 32. ______
33. ______ 34. ______
35. ______ 36. ______
37. ______ 38. ______
39. ______ 40. ______
41. ______ 42. ______
43. ______

< Objective 2 >

Write as fractions.

17. 6% Videos

18. 17%

19. 75%

20. 20%

21. 65%

22. 48%

23. 50%

24. 52%

25. 46%

26. 35%

27. 66%

28. 4%

< Objective 3 >

Write as decimals.

29. 20%

30. 70%

31. 35%

32. 75%

33. 39%

34. 27%

35. 5% Videos

36. 7%

37. 135%

38. 250%

39. 240%

40. 160%

41. **Social Science** Automobiles account for 85% of the travel between cities in the United States. What fraction does this percent represent?

42. **Social Science** Automobiles and small trucks account for 84% of the travel to and from work in the United States. What fraction does this percent represent?

43. Convert the discount shown to a decimal and to a simplified fraction.

44. Convert the discount shown to a decimal and to a simplified fraction.

45. The daily reference values (DRVs) for certain foods are given. They are based on a 2,000 calorie per day diet. Find decimal and fractional notation for the percent notation in each sentence.

(a) 1 ounce of Tostitos provides 9% of the DRV of fat.

(b) $\frac{1}{2}$ cup of B & M baked beans contains 15% of the DRV of sodium.

(c) $\frac{1}{2}$ cup of Campbells' New England clam chowder provides 6% of the DRV of iron.

(d) 2 ounces of Star Kist tuna provide 27% of the DRV of protein.

(e) Four 4-in. Aunt Jemima pancakes provide 33% of the DRV of sodium.

(f) 36 grams of Pop-Secret butter popcorn provide 2% of the DRV of sodium.

Answers

44. ______

45. (a) ______

(b) ______

(c) ______

(d) ______

(e) ______

(f) ______

Basic Skills | **Challenge Yourself** | Calculator/Computer | Career Applications | Above and Beyond

Answers

46. ______

47. ______

48. ______

49. ______

50. ______

51. ______

52. ______

53. ______

54. ______

46. Complete the chart for the percentages given in the bar graph.

Nations Most Reliant on Nuclear Energy, 1997
(Nuclear electricity generation as % of total)

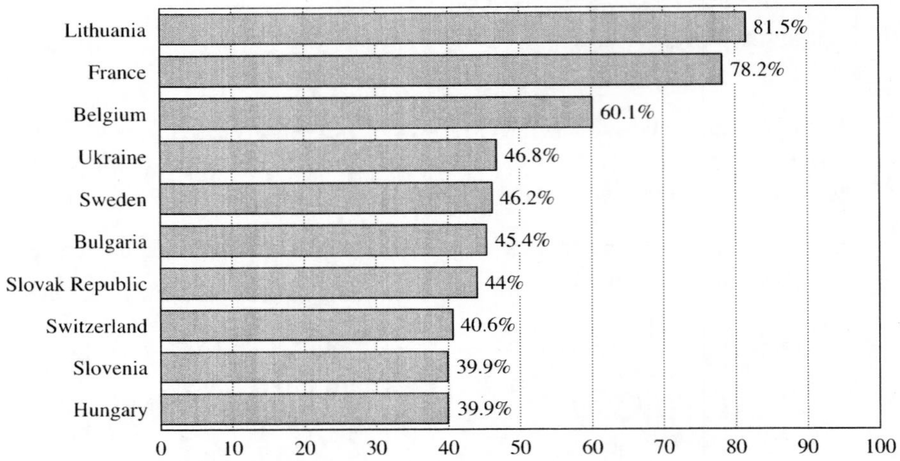

Source: International Atomic Energy Agency, May 1998

Country	Decimal Equivalent	Fraction Equivalent
Lithuania		
France		
Belgium		
Ukraine		
Sweden		
Bulgaria		
Slovak Republic		
Switzerland		
Slovenia		
Hungary		

Rewrite each percent as a mixed number.

47. 150% **48.** 140% **49.** 225% **50.** 450%

51. $166\frac{2}{3}\%$ **52.** $233\frac{1}{3}\%$ **53.** $212\frac{1}{2}\%$ **54.** $116\frac{2}{3}\%$

Rewrite each percent in decimal form.

55. 23.6% **56.** 10.5% **57.** 6.4% **58.** 3.5%

59. 0.2% **60.** 0.5% **61.** 1.05% **62.** 0.023%

63. $7\frac{1}{2}\%$ **64.** $8\frac{1}{4}\%$ **65.** $87\frac{1}{2}\%$ **66.** $16\frac{2}{5}\%$

67. $128\frac{3}{4}\%$ **68.** $220\frac{3}{20}\%$ **69.** $\frac{1}{2}\%$ **70.** $\frac{3}{4}\%$

Basic Skills | Challenge Yourself | Calculator/Computer | **Career Applications** | Above and Beyond

71. Information Technology An information technology project manager has a yearly budget of $49,000. She spent 10.2% of her budget in March. What fraction of her annual budget did she spend?

72. Manufacturing Technology A packaging company advertises that 87.5% of the machines that it produced in the last 20 years are still in operation. Express the proportion of machines still in service as a fraction.

73. Manufacturing Technology On an assembly line, 12% of all products are produced in the color red. Express this as a decimal and as a simplified fraction.

74. Construction Technology A board that starts with a width of 5.5 in. shrinks to 95% of its original width as it dries. What fraction is the dry width of the original width?

75. Mechanical Engineering As a piece of metal cools, it shrinks 3.125%. What fraction of its original size is lost due to shrinkage?

76. Agricultural Technology 12.5% of a growing season's 52 in. of rain fell in August. Write the percent of rain that fell in August as a decimal and as a simplified fraction.

Basic Skills | Challenge Yourself | Calculator/Computer | Career Applications | **Above and Beyond**

77. Match each percent in column A with the equivalent fraction in column B.

Column A	Column B
(a) $37\frac{1}{2}\%$	(1) $\frac{3}{5}$
(b) 5%	(2) $\frac{5}{8}$
(c) $33\frac{1}{3}\%$	(3) $\frac{1}{20}$
(d) $83\frac{1}{3}\%$	(4) $\frac{3}{8}$
(e) 60%	(5) $\frac{5}{6}$
(f) $62\frac{1}{2}\%$	(6) $\frac{1}{3}$

Answers

55. ______ 56. ______
57. ______ 58. ______
59. ______ 60. ______
61. ______ 62. ______
63. ______ 64. ______
65. ______ 66. ______
67. ______ 68. ______
69. ______ 70. ______
71. ______
72. ______
73. ______
74. ______
75. ______
76. ______
77. ______

Answers

78. ______________________

78. Explain the difference between $\frac{1}{4}$ of a quantity and $\frac{1}{4}$% of a quantity.

Answers

1. 35% 3. 75% 5. 53% 7. 74% 9. 30% 11. 54% 13. 46% 15. 25% 17. $\frac{3}{50}$ 19. $\frac{3}{4}$ 21. $\frac{13}{20}$ 23. $\frac{1}{2}$ 25. $\frac{23}{50}$ 27. $\frac{33}{50}$ 29. 0.2 31. 0.35 33. 0.39 35. 0.05 37. 1.35 39. 2.4 41. $\frac{17}{20}$ 43. 0.15; $\frac{3}{20}$ 45. (a) 0.09; $\frac{9}{100}$; (b) 0.15; $\frac{3}{20}$; (c) 0.06; $\frac{3}{50}$; (d) 0.27; $\frac{27}{100}$; (e) 0.33; $\frac{33}{100}$; (f) 0.02; $\frac{1}{50}$ 47. $1\frac{1}{2}$ 49. $2\frac{1}{4}$ 51. $1\frac{2}{3}$ 53. $2\frac{1}{8}$ 55. 0.236 57. 0.064 59. 0.002 61. 0.0105 63. 0.075 65. 0.875 67. 1.2875 69. 0.005 71. $\frac{51}{500}$ 73. 0.12; $\frac{3}{25}$ 75. $\frac{1}{32}$ 77. (a)-(4); (b)-(3); (c)-(6); (d)-(5); (e)-(1); (f)-(2)

6.2 Writing Decimals and Fractions as Percents

< 6.2 Objectives >

1 > Write a decimal as a percent

2 > Write a fraction or mixed number as a percent

Writing a decimal as a percent is the opposite of writing a percent in decimal form. We simply reverse the process given in Section 6.1.

Property

Writing a Decimal as a Percent

To write a decimal as a percent, move the decimal point *two* places to the *right* and attach the percent symbol.

Example 1 Writing a Decimal as a Percent

< Objective 1 >

(a) Write 0.18 as a percent.

0.18 = 18%

(b) Write 0.03 as a percent.

0.03 = 3%

NOTE

$$0.18 = \frac{18}{100} = 18\left(\frac{1}{100}\right) = 18\%$$

$$0.03 = \frac{3}{100} = 3\left(\frac{1}{100}\right) = 3\%$$

Check Yourself 1

Write each decimal in percent form.

(a) 0.27 **(b)** 0.05

There are many instances in which we use percents greater than 100%. For example, if a retailer marks goods up 25%, then the retail price is 125% of the wholesale price.

Example 2 Writing a Decimal as a Percent

Write 1.25 as a percent.

1.25 = 125%

NOTE

$$1.25 = \frac{125}{100} = 125\left(\frac{1}{100}\right)$$

$$= 125\%$$

Check Yourself 2

Write 1.3 as a percent.

If a percent includes numbers to the right of the decimal point after the decimal is moved two places to the right, the fractional portion can be written as a decimal or as a fraction.

Example 3 Writing a Decimal as a Percent

< Objective 1 >

Write as a percent.

(a) $0.045 = 4.5\%$ or $4\frac{1}{2}\%$

(b) $0.003 = 0.3\%$ or $\frac{3}{10}\%$

Check Yourself 3

Write 0.075 as a percent.

The following rule allows us to change fractions to percents.

Property

Writing a Fraction as a Percent

To write a fraction as a percent, write the decimal equivalent of the fraction. Then use the previous rule to change the decimal to a percent.

Example 4 Writing a Fraction as a Percent

< Objective 2 >

RECALL

We learned to write fractions as decimals in Section 4.2.

Write $\frac{3}{5}$ as a percent.

First write the decimal equivalent.

$\frac{3}{5} = 0.6$ To find the decimal equivalent, just divide the denominator into the numerator.

Now write the percent.

$\frac{3}{5} = 0.60 = 60\%$ Affix zeros to the right of the decimal if necessary.

Check Yourself 4

Write $\frac{3}{4}$ as a percent.

Again, you will find both decimals and fractions used in writing percents. Consider Example 5.

Example 5 Writing a Fraction as a Percent

Write $\frac{1}{8}$ as a percent.

$\frac{1}{8} = 0.125 = 12.5\%$ or $12\frac{1}{2}\%$

Check Yourself 5

Write $\frac{3}{8}$ as a percent.

Units ANALYSIS

We rarely express the units when computing percentages. When we say "percent" we are essentially saying, "numerator units per 100 denominator units."

EXAMPLES:

Of 800 students, 200 were boys. What percent of the students were boys?

$$\frac{200\text{ boys}}{800\text{ students}} = 0.25 = 25\%$$

But what happened to our units? At the decimal, the units boys/student (0.25 boy per student) wouldn't make much sense, but we can read the % as

25 "boys per 100 students"

and have a reasonable unit phrase.

Of 500 computers sold, 180 were equipped with a scanner. What percent were equipped with a scanner?

$$\frac{180}{500} = 0.36 = 36\%$$

36 were equipped with a scanner for each 100 computers sold.

To write a mixed number as a percent, we use exactly the same steps.

Example 6 Writing a Mixed Number as a Percent

NOTE

The resulting percent must be greater than 100% because the original mixed number is greater than 1.

Write $1\frac{1}{4}$ as a percent.

$$1\frac{1}{4} = 1.25 = 125\%$$

Check Yourself 6

Write $1\frac{2}{5}$ as a percent.

Some fractions have repeating-decimal equivalents. In writing these as percents, we either round to some indicated place or we write the percent as an exact fraction.

Example 7 Writing a Fraction as a Percent

(a) Write $\frac{1}{3}$ as a percent, using an exact fraction.

Dividing 1 by 3 gives:

$$\frac{1}{3} = 0.333333\cdots$$

Note that the 3's continue forever. Moving the decimal point two places to the right and attaching a percent symbol gives us:

$$\frac{1}{3} = 33.3333\cdots\%$$

Now we recognize that $0.3333\cdots$ is the decimal form for $\frac{1}{3}$, so we have:

$$\frac{1}{3} = 33\frac{1}{3}\%$$

(b) Write $\frac{5}{7}$ as a percent, rounding to the nearest tenth of a percent.

When we divide 5 by 7, we find:

$$\frac{5}{7} = 0.7142857\cdots$$

Then

$$\frac{5}{7} = 71.42857\cdots\%$$

Rounding to the nearest tenth of a percent, we have $\frac{5}{7} = 71.4\%$.

When rounding to a tenth of a percent, we need only divide far enough to round the decimal form to four places: 0.7142. We can then move the decimal point, round properly, and attach the percent symbol.

Check Yourself 7

(a) Write $\frac{2}{3}$ as a percent, using an exact fraction.

(b) Write $\frac{2}{9}$ as a percent, rounding to the nearest tenth of a percent.

Some students prefer to use the proportion method when writing a fraction as a percent. The proportion method gives an easier way of writing a fraction as an *exact value* percent instead of as an approximation. We demonstrate this method in Example 8.

Example 8 Using the Proportion Method

RECALL

You learned to solve proportions in Section 5.4.

(a) Write $\frac{7}{12}$ as a percent, using an exact fraction.

To use the proportion method, we write $\frac{7}{12}$ as an equivalent fraction whose denominator is 100.

$$\frac{7}{12} = \frac{x}{100}$$

Using the proportion rule, we have

$$12 \cdot x = 7 \cdot 100$$

$$12x = 700$$

Divide both sides by the coefficient of the variable, 12.

$$\frac{12x}{12} = \frac{700}{12} \qquad 700 \div 12 = 58\frac{4}{12} = 58\frac{1}{3}$$

$$x = 58\frac{1}{3}$$

Therefore,

$$\frac{7}{12} = \frac{58\frac{1}{3}}{100} = 58\frac{1}{3}\%$$

RECALL

$\frac{58\frac{1}{3}}{100}$ may be read as "$58\frac{1}{3}$ per 100."

(b) Write $\frac{1}{7}$ as a percent, using an exact fraction.

Again, we look for an equivalent fraction with a denominator of 100.

$$\frac{1}{7} = \frac{x}{100}$$

$$7x = 100$$

$$x = \frac{100}{7} = 14\frac{2}{7}$$

Therefore, $\frac{1}{7} = 14\frac{2}{7}\%$.

Check Yourself 8

Write each fraction as a percent, using an exact fraction.

(a) $\frac{5}{6}$ **(b)** $\frac{10}{9}$ **(c)** $\frac{3}{7}$

Applications often require that we write fractions and decimals in percent form, as in Example 9.

Example 9 An Application of Percents

The hard drive in Emma's computer has a 74.5-gigabyte (GB) capacity. Currently, she is using 10.8 GB. What percent of her hard drive's capacity is Emma using?

We begin by constructing a fraction based on the given information.

$$\frac{\text{Used}}{\text{Capacity}} = \frac{10.8 \text{ GB}}{74.5 \text{ GB}}$$

$$= \frac{10.8 \not{\text{GB}}}{74.5 \not{\text{GB}}} \qquad \text{As with proportions, we can simply "cancel" the units.}$$

$$= \frac{108}{745} \qquad \text{Multiply the top and bottom by 10 to remove the decimal.}$$

$$\approx 0.145 \qquad \text{Divide and round the result to the nearest thousandth.}$$

$$= 14.5\%$$

Emma is using 14.5% of her hard drive's capacity.

Check Yourself 9

Three cylinders are not firing properly in an 8-cylinder engine. What percent of the cylinders are firing properly?

Certain percents appear frequently enough that you should memorize their fraction and decimal equivalents.

$100\% = 1$

$200\% = 2$

$25\% = 0.25 = \frac{1}{4}$

$50\% = 0.5 = \frac{1}{2}$

$75\% = 0.75 = \frac{3}{4}$

$5\% = 0.05 = \frac{1}{20}$

$10\% = 0.1 = \frac{1}{10}$

$20\% = 0.2 = \frac{1}{5}$

$30\% = 0.3 = \frac{3}{10}$

$40\% = 0.4 = \frac{2}{5}$

$60\% = 0.6 = \frac{3}{5}$

$70\% = 0.7 = \frac{7}{10}$

$80\% = 0.8 = \frac{4}{5}$

$90\% = 0.9 = \frac{9}{10}$

$12\frac{1}{2}\% = 0.125 = \frac{1}{8}$

$37\frac{1}{2}\% = 0.375 = \frac{3}{8}$

$62\frac{1}{2}\% = 0.625 = \frac{5}{8}$

$87\frac{1}{2}\% = 0.875 = \frac{7}{8}$

$33\frac{1}{3}\% = 0.\overline{3} = \frac{1}{3}$

$66\frac{2}{3}\% = 0.\overline{6} = \frac{2}{3}$

Check Yourself ANSWERS

1. **(a)** 27%; **(b)** 5% **2.** 130% **3.** 7.5% or $7\frac{1}{2}\%$ **4.** 75%

5. 37.5% or $37\frac{1}{2}\%$ **6.** 140% **7.** **(a)** $66\frac{2}{3}\%$; **(b)** 22.2%

8. **(a)** $83\frac{1}{3}\%$; **(b)** $111\frac{1}{9}\%$; **(c)** $42\frac{6}{7}\%$ **9.** 62.5%

Reading Your Text

The following fill-in-the-blank exercises are designed to ensure that you understand some of the key vocabulary used in this section.

SECTION 6.2

(a) To write a decimal in percent form, move the decimal two places to the ______________ and add the % symbol.

(b) To write a fraction as a percent, first convert the fraction to a __________.

(c) When writing a repeating decimal as a ______________, we round to some indicated place or we write the percent using an exact fraction.

(d) When writing a decimal as a percent, we may need to add ____________ to the right as placeholders.

Basic Skills | Challenge Yourself | Calculator/Computer | Career Applications | Above and Beyond

6.2 exercises

< Objective 1 >

Write each number as a percent.

1. 0.08 > Videos

2. 0.09

3. 0.05

4. 0.13

5. 0.18

6. 0.63

7. 0.86

8. 0.45

9. 0.4

10. 0.3

11. 0.7

12. 0.6

13. 1.10 > Videos

14. 2.50

15. 4.40

16. 5

17. 0.065 > Videos

18. 0.095

19. 0.025

20. 0.085

< Objective 2 >

21. $\frac{1}{4}$

22. $\frac{4}{5}$

23. $\frac{2}{5}$

24. $\frac{1}{2}$

25. $\frac{1}{5}$ > Videos

26. $\frac{3}{4}$

Name ____________

Section ________ Date ________

Answers

1. ________ 2. ________

3. ________ 4. ________

5. ________ 6. ________

7. ________ 8. ________

9. ________ 10. ________

11. ________ 12. ________

13. ________ 14. ________

15. ________ 16. ________

17. ________

18. ________

19. ________

20. ________

21. ________ 22. ________

23. ________ 24. ________

25. ________ 26. ________

Answers

27. ______

28. ______

29. ______

30. ______

31. ______

32. ______

33. ______

34. ______

35. ______

36. ______

37. ______

38. ______

39. ______

40. ______

27. $\frac{5}{8}$

28. $\frac{7}{8}$

29. $\frac{5}{16}$

30. $1\frac{1}{5}$

31. $3\frac{1}{2}$ > Videos

32. $\frac{2}{3}$

Express each partially shaded region as a decimal, a fraction, and a percent.

33.

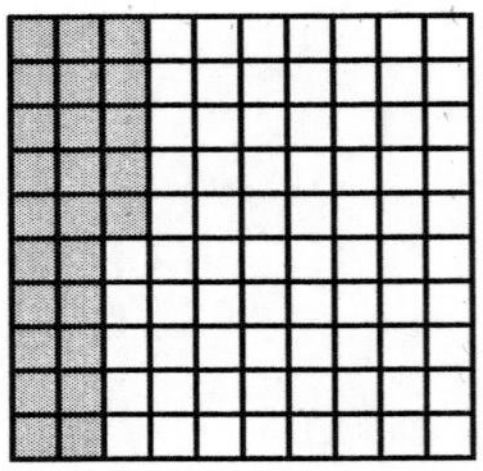

34.

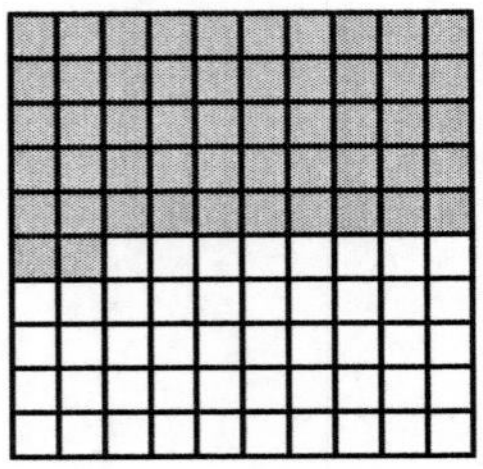

35.

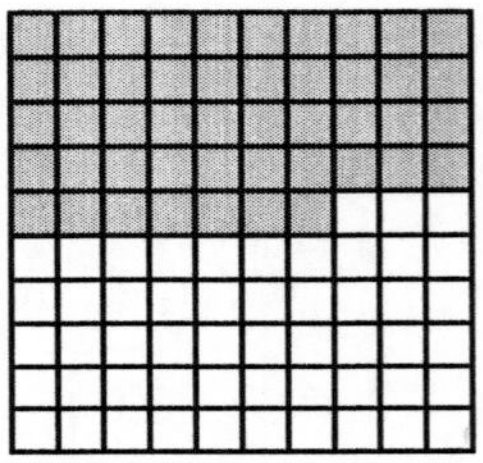

36.

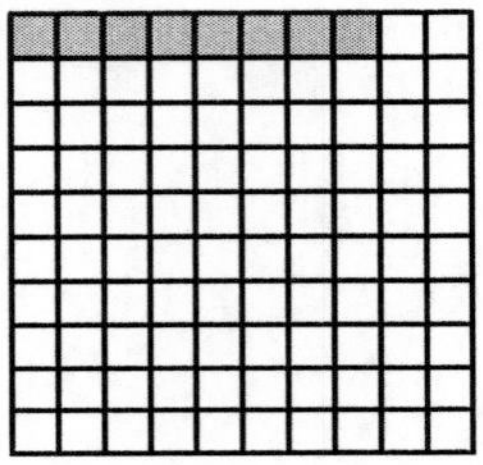

37.

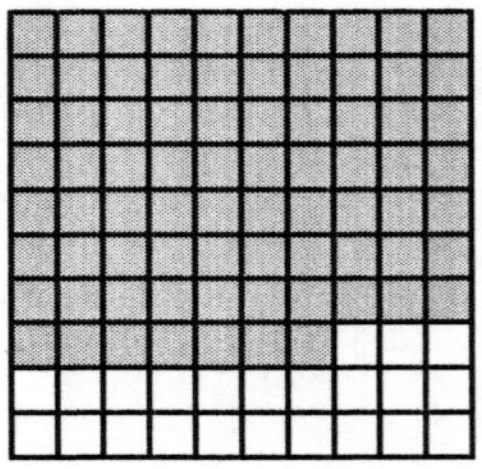

38.

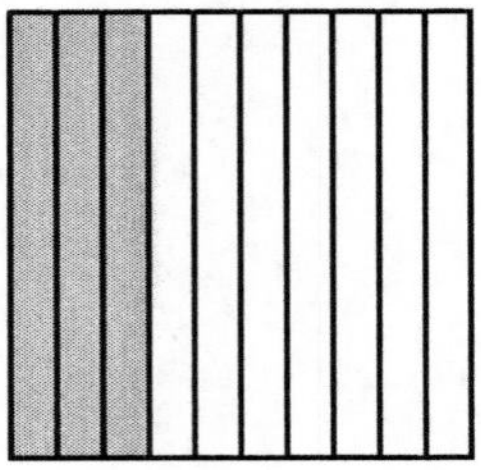

39.

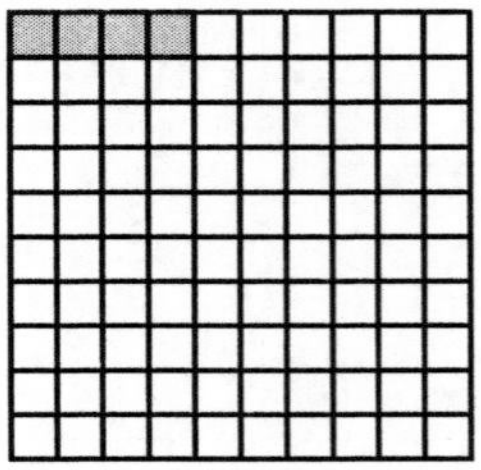

40.

Between 1980 and 2001, the average fuel efficiency of new U.S. cars increased from 24.3 to 28.6 miles per gallon (mi/gal). During this same time, the average fuel efficiency for the entire fleet of U.S. cars rose from 16.0 to 22.1 mi/gal. For exercises 41 and 42, solve the applications involving fuel efficiency.

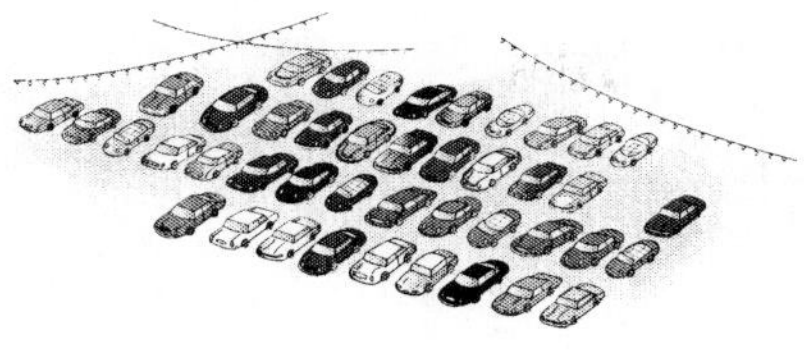

41. **BUSINESS AND FINANCE** The increase in fuel efficiency for new cars is given by the fraction $\frac{28.6 - 24.3}{24.3}$. Change this fraction to a percent. Round your answer to the nearest tenth of a percent.

42. **BUSINESS AND FINANCE** The increase in fuel efficiency for the fleet of U.S. cars is given by the fraction $\frac{22.1 - 16.0}{16.0}$. Change this fraction to a percent. Round your answer to the nearest tenth of a percent.

Business travelers were asked how much they spent on different items during a business trip. The circle graph shows the results for every $1,000 spent. Use this information to answer exercises 43 to 46.

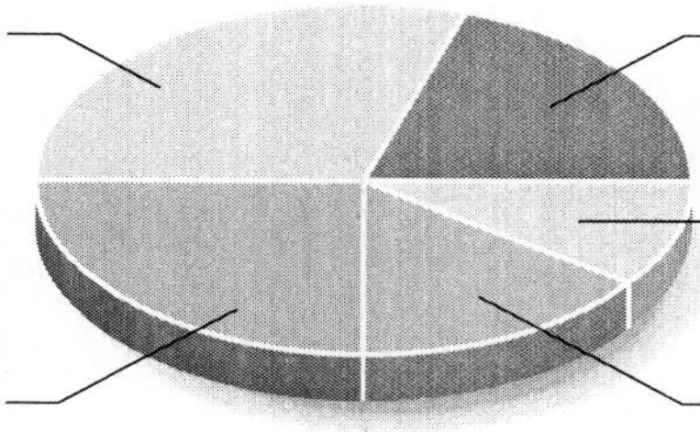

43. What percent was spent on car expenses?

44. What percent was spent on food?

45. Where was the least amount of money spent? What percent was this?

46. What percent was spent on food and lodging together?

Basic Skills | **Challenge Yourself** | Calculator/Computer | Career Applications | Above and Beyond

Determine whether each statement is **true** *or* **false.**

47. To write a decimal as a percent, move the decimal two places to the right and add the % symbol.

48. To write a decimal as a percent, move the decimal two places to the left and add the % symbol.

Fill in each blank with **always, sometimes,** *or* **never.**

49. A decimal greater than 1 is ________ equivalent to a percent greater than 100%.

50. A percent less than 100% can ________ be written as a mixed number.

Answers

41. ________

42. ________

43. ________

44. ________

45. ________

46. ________

47. ________

48. ________

49. ________

50. ________

Answers

51. ____

52. ____

53. ____

54. ____

55. ____

56. ____

57. ____

58. ____

59. ____

60. ____

61. ____

62. ____

63. ____

64. ____

65. ____

66. ____

67. ____

Write each number as a percent.

51. 0.002

52. 0.008

53. 0.004

54. 0.001

55. $\frac{1}{6}$ (exact value)

56. $\frac{3}{16}$

57. $\frac{7}{9}$ (to nearest tenth of a percent)

58. $\frac{5}{11}$ (to nearest tenth of a percent)

59. $\frac{7}{9}$ (exact value)

60. $\frac{5}{11}$ (exact value)

61. $5\frac{1}{4}$

62. $1\frac{3}{4}$

63. $4\frac{1}{3}$ (exact value)

64. $2\frac{11}{12}$ (exact value)

Basic Skills | Challenge Yourself | Calculator/Computer | **Career Applications** | Above and Beyond

65. Automotive Technology When an automobile engine is cold, its fuel efficiency is only $\frac{13}{16}$ of its maximum efficiency. Express this as a percent.

66. Welding Technology It was found that 165 of a total of 172 welds exceeded the required tensile strength. What percent of the welds exceeded the required tensile strength? Round your answer to the nearest whole percent.

67. Electrical Engineering The efficiency of an electric motor is defined as the output power divided by the input power. It is usually written as a percent. For a particular motor, the output power is measured to be 400 watts (W) given an input power level of 435 W. What is the efficiency of this motor? Round your answer to the nearest whole percent.

68. **Manufacturing Technology** A manufacturer determines that 2 out of every 27 products will be returned due to defects. What percent of the products will be returned? Round to the nearest tenth of a percent.

69. **Agricultural Technology** There were 52 in. of rainfall in one growing season. If 6.5 in. fell in August, what percent of the season's rainfall fell in August?

Basic Skills | Challenge Yourself | Calculator/Computer | Career Applications | **Above and Beyond**

70. Complete the following table of equivalents. Round decimals to the nearest ten-thousandth. Round percents to the nearest hundredth of a percent.

Fraction	Decimal	Percent
$\frac{7}{12}$		
	0.08	
		35%
	0.265	
		$4\frac{3}{8}\%$
$\frac{11}{18}$		

71. When writing a fraction as a percent, explain when you should convert the fraction to a decimal and then write it as a percent, rather than using the proportion method.

72. When writing a fraction as a percent, explain when you should use the proportion method rather than converting the fraction to a decimal and then writing it as a percent.

Answers

68. ______
69. ______
70. ______
71. ______
72. ______

Answers

1. 8% 3. 5% 5. 18% 7. 86% 9. 40% 11. 70%
13. 110% 15. 440% 17. 6.5% 19. 2.5% 21. 25%
23. 40% 25. 20% 27. 62.5% 29. 31.25% 31. 350%
33. 0.25; $\frac{1}{4}$; 25% 35. 0.47; $\frac{47}{100}$; 47% 37. 0.77; $\frac{77}{100}$; 77%
39. 0.04; $\frac{1}{25}$; 4% 41. 17.7% 43. 20% 45. Miscellaneous; 10%
47. True 49. always 51. 0.2% 53. 0.4% 55. $16\frac{2}{3}\%$
57. 77.8% 59. $77\frac{7}{9}\%$ 61. 525% 63. $433\frac{1}{3}\%$ 65. 81.25%
67. 92% 69. 12.5% 71. Above and Beyond

Activity 16 ::
M&M's

According to M&M's/MARS, M&M's are produced and packaged with approximately the following percentages.

Brown:	30%
Yellow:	20%
Red:	20%
Orange:	10%
Green:	10%
Blue:	10%

A typical pack was opened, yielding the following counts:

Brown	Yellow	Red	Orange	Green	Blue
14	8	15	6	6	10

Calculate the percent for each color M&M in this pack. Round to the nearest percent.

Brown	Yellow	Red	Orange	Green	Blue

Do any of these seem to differ markedly from the percents named by the M&M's/MARS company? If so, give reasons why this may have occurred.

Obtain your own package of M&M's and determine the percents for each color. Comment on how closely your percents agree with the percents named by the company.

6.3 The Three Types of Percent Problems

< 6.3 Objectives >

1 > Identify the rate in a percent problem
2 > Identify the base in a percent problem
3 > Identify the amount in a percent problem
4 > Solve the three types of percent problems

There are many practical applications of our work with percents. All of these problems have three basic parts that need to be identified. Here are some definitions that will help with that process.

Definition

Base, Amount, and Rate

The **base**, denoted B, is the whole in a problem. It is the standard used for comparison.

The **amount**, denoted A, is the part of the whole being compared to the base.

The **rate**, denoted R, is the ratio of the amount to the base. It is written as a percent.

The following examples provide some practice in determining the parts of a percent problem.

Example 1 Identifying Rates

< Objective 1 >

NOTE

The *rate R* is the easiest of the terms to identify. The rate is written with the percent symbol (%) or the word *percent.*

Identify each rate.

(a) What is 15% of 200? (R = 15%)

Here 15% is the rate because it has the percent symbol attached.

(b) 25% of what number is 50? (R = 25%)

25% is the rate.

(c) 20 is what percent of 40? (R = what percent)

Here the rate is unknown.

Check Yourself 1

Identify the rate.

(a) 15% of what number is 75?
(b) What is 8.5% of 200?
(c) 200 is what percent of 500?

Instructor's note: In this section, we use proportions to solve percent problems. After introducing students to algebra, we take an equations approach in Section 11.5.

The *base B* is the whole, or 100%, in the problem. The base often follows the word *of,* as shown in Example 2.

Example 2 Identifying Bases

< Objective 2 >

Identify each base.

(a) What is 15% of 200? — 200 is B.

200 is the base. It follows the word *of*.

(b) 25% of what number is 50? — "what number" is B.

Here the base is the unknown.

(c) 20 is what percent of 40? — 40 is B.

40 is the base.

Check Yourself 2

Identify the base.

(a) 70 is what percent of 350? **(b)** What is 25% of 300?
(c) 14% of what number is 280?

The *amount A* is the part of the problem remaining once the rate and the base have been identified.

In many applications, the amount is found with the word *is.*

Example 3 Identifying Amounts

< Objective 3 >

Identify the amount.

(a) What is 15% of 200? — "What" is A.

Here the amount is the unknown part of the problem. Note that the word *is* follows.

(b) 25% of what number is 50? — 50 is A.

Here the amount, 50, follows the word *is*.

(c) 20 is what percent of 40? — 20 is A.

Again the amount, here 20, can be found with the word *is*.

Check Yourself 3

Identify the amount.

(a) 30 is what percent of 600? **(b)** What is 12% of 5,000?
(c) 24% of what number is 96?

In Example 4, we identify all three parts in a percent problem.

Example 4 Identifying the Rate, Base, and Amount

Determine the rate, base, and amount in this problem:

12% of 800 is what number?

Finding the *rate* is not difficult. Just look for the percent symbol or the word *percent*. In this exercise, 12% is the rate.

The *base* is the whole. Here it follows the word *of*. 800 is the whole or the base.

The *amount* remains when the rate and the base have been found. Here the amount is the unknown. It follows the word *is*. "What number" asks for the unknown amount.

Check Yourself 4

Find the rate, base, and amount in the following statements or questions.

(a) 75 is 25% of 300. **(b) 20% of what number is 50?**

We use percents to solve a variety of applied problems. In all these situations, you have to identify the three parts of the problem. Example 5 is intended to help you build that skill.

Example 5 Identifying the Rate, Base, and Amount

(a) Determine the rate, base, and amount in the following application.

In an algebra class of 35 students, 7 received a grade of A. What percent of the class received an A?

The *base* is the whole in the problem, or the number of students in the class. 35 is the base.

The *amount* is the portion of the base, here the number of students that receive the A grade. 7 is the amount.

The *rate* is the unknown in this example. "What percent" asks for the unknown rate.

(b) Determine the rate, base, and amount in the following application:

Doyle borrows $2,000 for 1 year. If the interest rate is 12%, how much interest will he pay?

The *base* is again the whole, the size of the loan in this example. $2,000 is the base.

The *rate* is, of course, the interest rate. 12% is the rate.

The *amount* is the quantity left once the base and rate have been identified. Here the amount is the amount of interest that Doyle must pay. The amount is the unknown in this example.

Check Yourself 5

(a) Determine the rate, base, and amount in the following application: In a shipment of 150 parts, 9 of the parts were defective. What percent were defective?

(b) Determine the rate, base, and amount in the following application: Robert earned $120 interest from a savings account paying 8% interest. What amount did he have invested?

So far, you have learned that statements and problems about percents consist of three parts: the rate, base, and amount. In fact, every problem involving percents consists of these three parts.

In nearly every percent problem, one of these three parts is missing. Solving a percent problem is a matter of identifying and computing the missing part. To do this, we use the **percent proportion.**

Property

The Percent Proportion

$$\frac{A}{B} = \frac{r}{100}$$

where A is the amount, B is the base, and $\frac{r}{100}$ is the rate.

Previously, we said that the rate, R, is written as a percent. Note that R and r represent different things. For example, if $R = 54\%$ then $r = 54$. This means that r is the number before the percent symbol. The use of these symbols (A, B, r, and R) will become clear through the following examples.

Example 6 Finding an Unknown Amount

< Objective 4 >

What is 18% of 300?

We know that the rate, R, is 18%. This means that $r = 18$. We also know the base, B, equals 300. The amount, A, is unknown. Use the percent relationship to write the following proportion:

$$\frac{A}{300} = \frac{18}{100}$$

Applying the proportion rule that we learned in Section 5.3 gives

$$100 \cdot A = 18 \cdot 300$$

or

$$100A = 5{,}400$$

We identify the coefficient of the variable as 100 and divide by this number.

$$\frac{100A}{100} = \frac{5{,}400}{100}$$

$$A = 54$$

So, 54 is 18% of 300.

Check Yourself 6

Find 65% of 200.

The second type of percent problem requires us to find an unknown rate. We solve such a problem in the same way as before—we write the percent proportion and solve it.

Example 7 Finding an Unknown Rate

30 is what percent of 150?

We know that 30 is the amount, A, and 150 is the base, B. The rate, R, is the unknown.

$$\frac{30}{150} = \frac{r}{100} \qquad \frac{A}{B} = \frac{r}{100}$$

$$150 \cdot r = 30 \cdot 100 = 3{,}000$$

Rewrite the equation using the proportion rule. The coefficient of the variable is 150.

$$\frac{150r}{150} = \frac{3{,}000}{150}$$

Divide both sides by the coefficient of the variable.

$$r = 20 \qquad 3{,}000 \div 150 = 20$$

Since $r = 20$, the rate R is 20%.

Therefore, 30 is 20% of 150.

Check Yourself 7

75 is what percent of 300?

The final type of percent problem is one with a missing base.

Example 8 Finding an Unknown Base

RECALL

$\frac{A}{B} = \frac{r}{100}$

28 is 40% of what number?

The amount, A, is 28 and the rate, R, is 40%. This means that $r = 40$. We use these to set up the percent proportion with a missing base.

$$\frac{28}{B} = \frac{40}{100}$$

As before, we use the proportion rule to solve this.

$$40B = 2{,}800 \qquad 28 \cdot 100 = 2{,}800$$

$$\frac{40B}{40} = \frac{2{,}800}{40} \qquad \text{40 is the coefficient of the variable.}$$

$$B = 70 \qquad 2{,}800 \div 40 = 70$$

Therefore, 28 is 40% of 70.

Check Yourself 8

70 is 35% of what number?

Remember that a percent (the rate) can be greater than 100.

Example 9 Finding an Unknown Rate

NOTE

The rate is 125%. The base is 300.

What is 125% of 300?

In the percent proportion, we have

$$\frac{A}{300} = \frac{125}{100} \qquad \text{Since } R = 125\%,\ r = 125.$$

So $100A = 300 \cdot 125$.

Dividing by 100 yields

$$\frac{100A}{100} = \frac{300 \cdot 125}{100} = \frac{37{,}500}{100} = 375$$

NOTE

When the rate is greater than 100%, the amount will be *greater than* the base.

So $A = 375$. Therefore, 375 is 125% of 300.

Check Yourself 9

Find 150% of 500.

We next look at an example of a percent problem involving a fraction of a percent.

Example 10 Finding an Unknown Base

NOTE

The amount is 34 and the rate is 8.5%. We want to find the base.

34 is 8.5% of what number?

Using the percent proportion yields

$$\frac{34}{B} = \frac{8.5}{100} \qquad \text{Since } R = 8.5\%,\ r = 8.5.$$

Solving the proportion we have

$8.5B = 34 \cdot 100$

NOTE

Divide by 8.5.

$$\frac{8.5B}{8.5} = \frac{34 \cdot 100}{8.5} = \frac{3{,}400}{8.5} = 400$$

So $B = 400$, and we have

34 is 8.5% of 400.

Check Yourself 10

12.5% of what number is 75?

Check Yourself ANSWERS

1. **(a)** 15%; **(b)** 8.5%; **(c)** "what percent" (the unknown) **2.** **(a)** 350; **(b)** 300; **(c)** "what number" (the unknown) **3.** **(a)** 30; **(b)** "What" (the unknown); **(c)** 96 **4.** **(a)** $R = 25\%$, $B = 300$, $A = 75$; **(b)** $R = 20\%$, $B =$ "What number," $A = 50$ **5.** **(a)** $R =$ "What percent" (the unknown), $B = 150$, $A = 9$; **(b)** $R = 8\%$, $B =$ "What amount," $A = \$120$ **6.** 130 **7.** 25% **8.** 200 **9.** 750 **10.** 600

Reading Your Text

The following fill-in-the-blank exercises are designed to ensure that you understand some of the key vocabulary used in this section.

SECTION 6.3

(a) In percent problems, the ______________ is the standard used for comparison.

(b) In percent problems, the ______________ is the ratio of the amount to the base.

(c) In percent problems, the ______________ is often written as a percent.

(d) In percent problems, the ______________ is the part of the whole being compared to the base.

Basic Skills | Challenge Yourself | Calculator/Computer | Career Applications | Above and Beyond

6.3 exercises

Boost *your* GRADE at ALEKS.com!

ALEKS®

- Practice Problems
- Self-Tests
- NetTutor
- e-Professors
- Videos

Name ____________

Section ________ Date ________

< Objectives 1–3 >

Identify the rate, base, and amount in each statement or question. Do not solve *the exercise at this point.*

1. 23% of 400 is 92. > Videos

2. 150 is 20% of 750.

3. 40% of 600 is 240.

4. 200 is 40% of 500.

5. What is 7% of 325?

6. 80 is what percent of 400?

7. 16% of what number is 56? > Videos

8. What percent of 150 is 30?

9. 480 is 60% of what number?

10. What is 60% of 250?

11. What percent of 120 is 40? > Videos

12. 150 is 75% of what number?

Identify the rate, base, and amount in each application. Do not solve *the application at this point.*

13. Business and Finance Jan has a 5% commission rate on all her sales. If she sells $40,000 worth of merchandise in 1 month, what commission will she earn? > Videos

14. Business and Finance 22% of Shirley's monthly salary is deducted for withholding. If those deductions total $209, what is her salary?

15. Science and Medicine In a chemistry class of 30 students, 5 received a grade of A. What percent of the students received A's?

16. Business and Finance A can of mixed nuts contains 80% peanuts. If the can holds 16 ounces, how many ounces of peanuts does it contain?

Answers

1. ____
2. ____
3. ____
4. ____
5. ____
6. ____
7. ____
8. ____
9. ____
10. ____
11. ____
12. ____
13. ____
14. ____
15. ____
16. ____

Answers

17. ______
18. ______
19. ______
20. ______
21. ______
22. ______
23. ______ 24. ______
25. ______ 26. ______
27. ______ 28. ______
29. ______ 30. ______
31. ______ 32. ______
33. ______ 34. ______
35. ______ 36. ______
37. ______ 38. ______
39. ______ 40. ______
41. ______ 42. ______

17. Business and Finance The sales tax rate in a state is 5.5%. If you pay a tax of $3.30 on an item that you purchase, what is its selling price? > Videos

18. Business and Finance In a shipment of 750 parts, 75 were found to be defective. What percent of the parts were faulty?

19. Social Science A college had 9,000 students at the start of a school year. If there is an enrollment increase of 6% by the beginning of the next year, how many additional students are there?

20. Business and Finance Paul invested $5,000 in a time deposit. What interest will he earn for 1 year if the interest rate is 3.5%? chapter 6 > Make the Connection

Determine whether each statement is **true** *or* **false.**

21. The rate, in a percent problem, is never greater than 100%.

22. The base, in a percent problem, often follows the word *of.*

< Objective 4 >

Solve each percent problem.

23. What is 35% of 600? > Videos

24. 20% of 400 is what number?

25. 45% of 200 is what number?

26. What is 40% of 1,200?

27. Find 40% of 2,500.

28. What is 75% of 120?

29. What percent of 50 is 4? > Videos

30. 51 is what percent of 850?

31. What percent of 500 is 45?

32. 14 is what percent of 200?

33. What percent of 200 is 340?

34. 392 is what percent of 2,800?

35. 46 is 8% of what number? > Videos

36. 7% of what number is 42?

37. Find the base if 11% of the base is 55.

38. 16% of what number is 192?

39. 58.5 is 13% of what number?

40. 21% of what number is 73.5?

41. Find 110% of 800.

42. What is 115% of 600?

43. What is 108% of 4,000?

44. Find 160% of 2,000.

45. 210 is what percent of 120?

46. What percent of 40 is 52?

47. 360 is what percent of 90?

48. What percent of 15,000 is 18,000?

49. 625 is 125% of what number?

50. 140% of what number is 350?

51. Find the base if 110% of the base is 935.

52. 130% of what number is 1,170?

Basic Skills | **Challenge Yourself** | Calculator/Computer | Career Applications | Above and Beyond

53. Find 8.5% of 300.

54. $8\frac{1}{4}$% of 800 is what number?

55. Find $11\frac{3}{4}$% of 6,000.

56. What is 3.5% of 500?

57. What is 5.25% of 3,000?

58. What is 7.25% of 7,600?

59. 60 is what percent of 800?

60. 500 is what percent of 1,500?

61. What percent of 180 is 120?

62. What percent of 800 is 78?

63. What percent of 1,200 is 750?

64. 68 is what percent of 800?

65. 10.5% of what number is 420?

66. Find the base if $11\frac{1}{2}$% of the base is 46.

67. 58.5 is 13% of what number?

68. 6.5% of what number is 325?

69. 195 is 7.5% of what number?

70. 21% of what number is 73.5?

Basic Skills | Challenge Yourself | Calculator/Computer | **Career Applications** | Above and Beyond

Identify the rate, base, and amount in each statement or question. Do not solve *the problems at this point.*

71. **Allied Health** How much 25% alcohol solution can be prepared using 225 milliliters (mL) of ethyl alcohol?

72. **Information Technology** An Ethernet network transmits a maximum packet size of 1,500 bytes. 1.7% of each packet is "overhead." How much information (in bytes) in a maximum-size packet is overhead?

73. **Agricultural Technology** Milk that is labeled "3.5%" is made up of 3.5% butterfat. How many grams of butterfat are in 1 liter (938 g) of 3.5% milk?

74. **Environmental Technology** In some communities, "green" laws require that 40% of a lot remains green (covered in grass or other vegetation). How much green space is required in a 12,680-square-foot lot?

Answers

43. ______ 44. ______
45. ______ 46. ______
47. ______ 48. ______
49. ______ 50. ______
51. ______ 52. ______
53. ______ 54. ______
55. ______ 56. ______
57. ______ 58. ______
59. ______ 60. ______
61. ______ 62. ______
63. ______ 64. ______
65. ______ 66. ______
67. ______ 68. ______
69. ______ 70. ______
71. ______
72. ______
73. ______
74. ______

Answers

1. 23% of 400 is 92
   ↑ ↑ ↑
   R B A

3. 40% of 600 is 240
   ↑ ↑ ↑
   R B A

5. What is 7% of 325
   ↑ ↑ ↑
   A R B

7. 16% of what number is 56
   ↑ ↑ ↑
   R B A

9. 480 is 60% of what number
   ↑ ↑ ↑
   A R B

11. What percent of 120 is 40
    ↑ ↑ ↑
    R B A

13. \$40,000 is the base. 5% is the rate. Her commission, the unknown, is the amount.
15. 30 is the base. 5 is the amount. The unknown percent is the rate.
17. 5.5% is the rate. The tax, \$3.30, is the amount. The unknown selling price is the base.
19. The base is 9,000. The rate is 6%. The unknown number of additional students is the amount.

21. False 23. 210 25. 90 27. 1,000 29. 8% 31. 9%
33. 170% 35. 575 37. 500 39. 450 41. 880 43. 4,320
45. 175% 47. 400% 49. 500 51. 850 53. 25.5 55. 705
57. 157.5 59. 7.5% 61. $66\frac{2}{3}\%$ 63. 62.5% 65. 4,000
67. 450 69. 2,600 71. $R = 25\%$, $B =$ unknown, $A = 225$ mL
73. $R = 3.5\%$, $B = 938$ g, $A =$ unknown

Activity 17 :: A Matter of Interest

When you put your money into savings for investment purposes, you will often leave it for some time, allowing it to earn interest and grow. Typically, the interest your investment earns is computed periodically as a percent of your investment. The investment is referred to as the **principal,** and we use the following **interest** formula:

Interest = principal × rate × time

or $I = P \times R \times T$. If we use 1 year for time, the formula becomes $I = P \times R$. Note the following (for time = 1 year):

Interest = principal × rate

Suppose that your original investment is $1,000 and that your money earns interest at a rate of 4% (per year). Let us further suppose that the interest is computed at the end of each year and then added onto the principal. The principal then grows, and the amount of interest in the following year will be greater. To see how this works, complete the following table.

Year	Principal	Interest	Investment at End of Year
1	$1,000	$40	$1,040
2	1,040		
3			
4			
5			
6			
7			

After 7 years, how much has your investment grown?

For how many years must the money sit to earn total interest that is 50% of your original investment? (*Hint:* Continue the calculations in the table.)

6.4

Applications of Percent Problems

< 6.4 Objectives >

1 > Solve applications of percents

2 > Solve applications that involve percent increase and decrease

3 > Solve percent applications involving interest

The concept of percent is perhaps the most frequently encountered arithmetic idea considered in this text. In this section, we show some of the many applications of percent and the special terms that are used in these applications.

In Example 1, we solve a percent application in which the amount is the unknown quantity.

If the rate is *less than* 100%, then the amount will be *less than* the base.

20 is 40% of 50 and $20 < 50$

If the rate is *greater than* 100%, then the amount will be *greater than* the base.

75 is 150% of 50 and $75 > 50$

Example 1 Solving a Percent Application with an Unknown Amount

< Objective 1 >

A student needs to answer at least 70% of the questions correctly on a 50-question exam in order to pass. How many questions must the student get right?

In this case, the rate is 70%, so $r = 70$, and the base, or total, is 50 questions, so $B = 50$. The amount A is unknown.

We write the percent proportion and solve.

$$\frac{A}{50} = \frac{70}{100}$$

$$100A = 70 \cdot 50 \qquad \text{If } \frac{a}{b} = \frac{c}{d}, \text{ then } ad = bc.$$

$$100A = 3{,}500 \qquad \text{The coefficient of the variable is 100.}$$

$$\frac{100A}{100} = \frac{3{,}500}{100} \qquad \text{Divide both sides by the coefficient of the variable.}$$

$$A = 35 \qquad 3{,}500 \div 100 = 35$$

The student must answer at least 35 questions correctly in order to pass the exam.

Check Yourself 1

Generally, 72% of the students in a chemistry course pass the class. If there are 150 students in the class, how many are expected to pass?

Let us now look at an application involving an unknown rate.

If the amount is *less than* the base, then the rate will be *less than* 100%.

If the amount is *greater than* the base, then the rate will be *greater than* 100%.

Instructor's note: In this section, we use proportions to solve percent problems. After introducing students to algebra, we use an equations approach in Section 11.5.

Example 2 Solving a Percent Application with an Unknown Rate

Simon waits tables at La Catalana, an upscale restaurant. A family left a $45 tip on a $250 meal. What percent of the bill did the family leave as a tip?

We are asked to find the rate given a base $B = \$250$ and an amount $A = \$45$. To find the rate, we use the percent proportion.

$$\frac{45}{250} = \frac{r}{100}$$

$$250r = 4{,}500 \qquad 45 \cdot 100 = 4{,}500$$

$$\frac{250r}{250} = \frac{4{,}500}{250}$$

$$r = 18 \qquad 4{,}500 \div 250 = 18$$

NOTE

Remember to write your answer as a percent.

Therefore, the family left a tip that was 18% of the bill.

Check Yourself 2

Last year, Xian reported an income of $27,500 on her tax return. Of that, she paid $6,600 in taxes. What percent of her income did she pay in taxes?

We can now look at an application involving an unknown base.

Example 3 Solving a Percent Application with an Unknown Base

A computer ran 60% of a scan in 120 seconds (s). How long should it take to complete an entire scan?

In this case, the rate is 60% and the amount is 120 s. We employ the percent proportion again, and solve.

$$\frac{120}{B} = \frac{60}{100}$$

$$60B = 12{,}000$$

$$B = \frac{12{,}000}{60} \qquad \text{Divide by the coefficient of the variable, 60.}$$

$$B = 200$$

The entire scan should take 200 s.

Check Yourself 3

An indexing program takes 4 minutes to check 30% of the files on a laptop computer. How long should it take to index all the files (to the nearest second)?

Percents are used in too many ways for us to list. Notice the variety in the following examples, which illustrate some additional situations in which you will find percents.

Example 4 Solving a Percent Application: Commission

A salesman sells a used car for $9,500. His commission rate is 4%. What is his commission for the sale?

NOTE

A **commission** is the amount that a person is paid for a sale.

The base is the total of the sale, in this problem, \$9,500. The rate is 4%, and we want to find the commission. This is the amount. By the percent proportion

$$\frac{A}{9{,}500} = \frac{4}{100}$$

$$100A = 4 \cdot 9{,}500 = 38{,}000$$

$$A = \frac{38{,}000}{100}$$

$$A = 380$$

The salesman's commission is \$380.

Check Yourself 4

Jenny sells a \$36,000 building lot. If her real estate commission rate is 5%, what commission does she earn on the sale?

Example 5 Solving a Percent Application: Commission

A clerk sold \$3,500 in merchandise during 1 week. If he received a commission of \$140, what was the commission rate?

The base is \$3,500, and the amount is the commission of \$140. Using the percent proportion, we have

$$\frac{140}{3{,}500} = \frac{r}{100}$$

$$3{,}500r = 140 \cdot 100 = 14{,}000$$

$$r = \frac{14{,}000}{3{,}500}$$

$$r = 4$$

So $R = 4\%$. The commission rate is 4%.

Check Yourself 5

On a purchase of \$500 you pay a sales tax of \$21. What is the tax rate?

Example 6, involving a commission, shows how to find the total amount sold.

Example 6 Solving a Percent Application: Commission

A saleswoman has a commission rate of 3.5%. To earn \$280, how much must she sell?

The rate is 3.5%. The amount is the commission, \$280. We want to find the base. In this case, this is the amount that the saleswoman needs to sell.

By the percent proportion

$$\frac{280}{B} = \frac{3.5}{100} \quad \text{or} \quad 3.5B = 280 \cdot 100$$

$$B = \frac{28{,}000}{3.5}$$

$$B = 8{,}000$$

The saleswoman must sell \$8,000 to earn \$280 in commissions.

Check Yourself 6

Kerri earns a commission rate of 5.5%. If she wants to earn $825 in commissions, find the total sales that she must make.

Another common application of percents involves tax rates.

Example 7 Solving a Percent Application: Tax

A state taxes sales at 7%. If a 30-GB iPod is listed for $300, what is the total you will have to pay?

The tax you pay is the amount A (the part of the whole). Here the base B is the purchase price, $300. The rate R is 7%, so $r = 7$.

NOTE

In an application involving taxes, the tax paid is always the amount.

$$\frac{A}{300} = \frac{7}{100} \quad \text{or} \quad 100A = 300 \cdot 7$$

$$A = \frac{2,100}{100} = 21$$

The sales tax is $21. You will have to pay the sum: $300 + $21, or $321.

Check Yourself 7

Suppose that a state has a sales tax rate of $6\frac{1}{2}$%. If you buy a used car for $1,200, what is the total you will have to pay?

In applications that involve discounts or markups, the base B always represents the original price. This might be the price before the discount, or it might be the wholesale price prior to a markup. The amount A is usually the amount of the discount, or the amount of the markup.

Example 8 Solving a Percent Application: Discount

A kitchen store offers an All-Clad saucepan on sale for $92. The saucepan normally sells for $115. What is the discount rate?

We begin by identifying the base as the original price, $115, and the rate as the unknown. The amount A is the amount of the discount:

> CAUTION

The amount is not $92. The amount is the size of the discount.

$$A = \$115 - \$92 = \$23$$

Now we are ready to apply the percent proportion to solve this problem.

$$\frac{23}{115} = \frac{r}{100}$$

$115r = 2,300$ — $23 \cdot 100 = 2,300$

$r = \frac{2,300}{115}$ — Divide both sides by the coefficient of the variable, 115.

$r = 20$ — $2,300 \div 115 = 20$.

Therefore, the discount rate is 20%.

NOTE

The *markup* is the amount a store adds to the price of an item to cover expenses and profit. Retailers usually mark an item up by a percentage of its wholesale cost.

Check Yourself 8

An electronics store sells a certain Kicker amplifier for a car stereo system for $250. If the store pays $200 for the amplifier, what is the markup rate?

A common type of application involves *percent increase* or *percent decrease*. *Percent increase* and *percent decrease* always describe the change starting from the base.

Example 9 Solving a Percent Application: Percent Decrease

< Objective 2 >

NOTE

The base is the *original* population.

The population of a town decreased 15% in a 3-year period. If the original population was 12,000, what was the population at the end of the period?

Since the original population was 12,000, this is the base B. The rate of decrease R is 15%. The amount of the decrease A is unknown.

$$\frac{A}{12{,}000} = \frac{15}{100} \quad \text{so} \quad 100A = 15 \cdot 12{,}000$$

$$A = \frac{180{,}000}{100}$$

$$A = 1{,}800$$

Since the amount of the decrease is 1,800, the population at the end of the period must be:

$$12{,}000 - 1{,}800 = 10{,}200$$

Original population (12,000); Decrease (1,800); New population (10,200)

Check Yourself 9

A school's enrollment increased by 8% from a given year to the next. If the enrollment was 550 students the first year, how many students were enrolled the second year?

Example 10 Solving a Percent Application: Percent Increase

Enrollment at a school increased from 800 to 888 students from a given year to the next. What was the rate of increase?

First we must subtract to find the amount of the increase.

Increase: $888 - 800 = 88$ students

NOTE

We use the *original* enrollment, 800, as our base. The size of the increase is the amount.

Now to find the rate, we have

$$\frac{88}{800} = \frac{r}{100} \quad \text{so} \quad 800r = 88 \cdot 100$$

$$r = \frac{8{,}800}{800}$$

$$r = 11$$

The enrollment increased at a rate of 11%.

Check Yourself 10

Car sales at a dealership increased from 350 units one year to 378 units the next. What was the rate of increase?

Example 11 Solving a Percent Application: Percent Increase

A company hired 18 new employees in 1 year. If this was a 15% increase, how many employees did the company have before the increase?

The rate is 15%. The amount is 18, the number of new employees. The base in this problem is the number of employees *before the increase.* So

NOTE

The size of the increase is the amount. The original number of employees is the base.

$$\frac{18}{B} = \frac{15}{100}$$

$$15B = 18 \cdot 100$$

$$B = \frac{1{,}800}{15}$$

$$B = 120$$

The company had 120 employees before the increase.

Check Yourself 11

A school had 54 fewer students in one term than in the previous term. If this was a 12% decrease over the previous term, how many students were there before the decrease?

NOTE

The money borrowed or invested is called the **principal.**

Another common application of percent is interest. When you take out a home loan, you pay interest; when you invest money in a savings account, you earn interest. Interest is a percent of the whole, and the percent is called the **interest rate.**

When we work with interest on a certain amount of money (the principal) for a specific time period, the interest is called **simple interest.**

In the applications here, we will confine our study to interest earned or owed after one year. We will again put the percent proportion to use. In this case, the *interest* plays the same role as the "amount," and the *principal* takes the part of the "base."

Example 12 Solving a Percent Application: Simple Interest

< Objective 3 >

Find the interest you must pay if you borrow \$2,000 for 1 year at an interest rate of $9\frac{1}{2}\%$.

The principal, \$2,000, is the base B. The interest rate R is 9.5%, so $r = 9.5$. We want the amount of interest A.

$$\frac{A}{2{,}000} = \frac{9.5}{100}$$

$$100 \cdot A = 2{,}000 \cdot 9.5$$

$$\frac{100 \cdot A}{100} = \frac{19{,}000}{100}$$

$$A = 190$$

The amount of interest is \$190.

Check Yourself 12

You invest \$5,000 for 1 year at an annual rate of $8\frac{1}{2}\%$. How much interest will you earn?

As with other percent problems, you can find the principal or the rate using the percent proportion.

Example 13 Solving a Percent Application: Simple Interest

Ms. Hobson agrees to pay 11% interest on a loan for her new car. She is charged \$2,200 interest on the loan for 1 year. How much did she borrow?

The rate is 11% and the interest (or amount) is \$2,200. We need to find the principal (or base), which is the size of the loan.

As before, we set up the percent proportion to solve it.

$$\frac{2,200}{B} = \frac{11}{100}$$

$$11B = 220,000 \qquad 2,200 \cdot 100 = 220,000$$

$$\frac{11B}{11} = \frac{220,000}{11} \qquad \text{The coefficient of the variable is 11.}$$

$$B = 20,000 \qquad 220,000 \div 11 = 20,000$$

Ms. Hobson borrowed \$20,000 to purchase her car.

Check Yourself 13

Sue pays \$210 in interest for a 1-year loan at 10.5% interest. What is the size of her loan?

The true power of interest to earn money over time comes from the idea of **compound interest.** This means that once you earn (or are charged) interest, you start earning (or paying) interest on the interest. This is what is meant by compounding.

Compound interest is an exceptionally powerful idea. For many people, their retirement plans are not based on the amount of money invested, but rather on the fact that their retirement account grows with time.

The earnings on someone's retirement investments *compound* over decades and grow into much more than the original investments. This is why financial advisors always suggest that you should start saving for retirement as early as possible. The more time an investment has to grow, the larger it gets.

We conclude this section by looking at an example involving the compounding of interest.

Example 14 Solving a Percent Application: Compound Interest

Suppose you invest \$1,000 at 5% (compounded annually) in a savings account for 2 years. How much will you have in the account at the end of the 2-year period?

After the first year, you earn 5% interest on your \$1,000 principal.

$$\frac{A}{1,000} = \frac{5}{100}$$

$$100A = 5,000$$

$$A = \frac{5,000}{100}$$

$$A = 50$$

So, you earn \$50 after 1 year. The compounding comes into play in the second year when your account begins with \$1,000 + \$50 = \$1,050 in it. This is your new principal.

$$\underset{\text{Start}}{\$1,000} \xrightarrow{\text{At 5\%}} \underset{\text{Year 1}}{\$1,050}$$

In the second year, you earn 5% interest on this new principal. This process is called *compound interest.*

$$\frac{A}{1{,}050} = \frac{5}{100}$$

$$100A = 5{,}250 \qquad 5 \cdot 1{,}050 = 5{,}250$$

$$A = \frac{5{,}250}{100}$$

$$A = 52.5 \qquad 5{,}250 \div 100 = 52.5$$

You earn \$52.50 in the second year of your investment, therefore, your account balance will be \$1,050 + \$52.50 = \$1,102.50.

$$\underset{\text{Start}}{\$1{,}000} \xrightarrow{\text{At } 5\%} \underset{\text{Year 1}}{\$1{,}050} \xrightarrow{\text{At } 5\%} \underset{\text{Year 2}}{\$1{,}102.50}$$

Check Yourself 14

If you invest \$6,000 at 4% (compounded annually) for 2 years, how much will you have after 2 years?

Check Yourself ANSWERS

1. 108 students **2.** 24% **3.** 800 s **4.** \$1,800 **5.** 4.2% **6.** \$15,000 **7.** \$1,278 **8.** 25% **9.** 594 students **10.** 8% **11.** 450 students **12.** \$425 **13.** \$2,000 **14.** \$6,489.60

Reading Your Text

The following fill-in-the-blank exercises are designed to ensure that you understand some of the key vocabulary used in this section.

SECTION 6.4

(a) If the rate is greater than 100%, then the amount will be ____________ than the base.

(b) In an application involving taxes, the tax paid is always the ____________.

(c) The ____________ is the amount a store adds to the price of an item to cover expenses and profit.

(d) In an interest application, the money borrowed or invested is called the ____________.

6.4 exercises

Basic Skills | Challenge Yourself | Calculator/Computer | Career Applications | Above and Beyond

Name ______________

Section ________ Date ________

Answers

1. ______________
2. ______________
3. ______________
4. ______________
5. ______________
6. ______________
7. ______________
8. ______________
9. ______________
10. ______________
11. ______________
12. ______________
13. ______________
14. ______________
15. ______________
16. ______________

< Objectives 1–3 >

Solve each application.

1. **Business and Finance** What interest will you pay on a \$3,400 loan for 1 year if the interest rate is 12%?

2. **Science and Medicine** A chemist has 300 milliliters (mL) of solution that is 18% acid. How many milliliters of acid are in the solution?

3. **Business and Finance** If a salesman is paid a \$140 commission on the sale of a \$2,800 sailboat, what is his commission rate?

4. **Business and Finance** Ms. Jordan has been given a loan of \$2,500 for 1 year. If the interest charged is \$275, what is the interest rate on the loan?

5. **Statistics** On a test, Alice had 80% of the problems right. If she had 20 problems correct, how many questions were on the test? > Videos

6. **Business and Finance** A state sales tax rate is 3.5%. If the tax on a purchase was \$7, what was the price of the purchase?

7. **Business and Finance** A state sales tax is levied at a rate of 6.4%. How much tax would one pay on a purchase of \$260?

8. **Business and Finance** Betty must make a $9\frac{1}{2}\%$ down payment on the purchase of a \$6,000 motorcycle. What is her down payment?

9. **Social Science** A study has shown that 102 of the 1,200 people in the workforce of a small town are unemployed. What is the town's unemployment rate? > Videos

10. **Social Science** A survey of 400 people found that 66 were left-handed. What percent of those surveyed were left-handed?

11. **Statistics** In a recent survey, 65% of those responding were in favor of a freeway improvement project. If 780 people were in favor of the project, how many people responded to the survey?

12. **Social Science** A college finds that 42% of the students taking a foreign language are enrolled in Spanish. If 1,512 students are taking Spanish, how many foreign language students are there?

13. **Business and Finance** An appliance dealer marks up refrigerators 22% (based on cost). If the wholesale cost of one model is \$1,200, what should its selling price be?

14. **Social Science** A school had 900 students at the start of a school year. If there is an enrollment increase of 7% by the beginning of the next year, what is the new enrollment?

15. **Business and Finance** The price of a new van has increased \$2,030, which amounts to a 14% increase. What was the price of the van before the increase?

16. **Business and Finance** A television set is marked down \$75, to be placed on sale. If this is a 12.5% decrease from the original price, what was the selling price before the sale?

17. **Business and Finance** Carlotta received a monthly raise of $162.50. If this represented a 6.5% increase, what was her monthly salary before the raise?

18. **Business and Finance** Mr. Hernandez buys stock for $15,000. At the end of 6 months, the stock's value has decreased 7.5%. What is the stock worth at the end of the period?

chapter 6 > Make the Connection

19. **Social Science** The population of a town increases 14% in 2 years. If the population was 6,000 originally, what is the population after the increase?

20. **Business and Finance** A store marks up merchandise 25% to allow for profit. If an item costs the store $11, what will its selling price be?

21. **Business and Finance** A virus scanning program is checking every file for viruses. It has completed checking 40% of the files in 300 seconds. How long should it take to check all the files?

22. **Social Science** In 1990, there were an estimated 145.0 million passenger cars registered in the United States. The total number of vehicles registered in the United States for 1990 was estimated at 194.5 million. What percent of the vehicles registered were passenger cars? Round to the nearest tenth percent.

23. **Social Science** Gasoline accounts for 85% of the motor fuel consumed in the United States every day. If 8,882 thousand barrels (bbl) of motor fuel is consumed each day, how much gasoline is consumed each day in the United States? Round to the nearest thousand barrels.

24. **Social Science** In 1999, transportation accounted for 67% of U.S. petroleum consumption. If 13.3 million bbl of petroleum were used each day for transportation in the United States, what was the approximate total daily petroleum consumption by all sources in the United States?

25. **Science and Medicine** Each year, 540 million metric tons (t) of carbon dioxide is added to the atmosphere by the United States. Burning gasoline and other transportation fuels is responsible for 35% of the carbon dioxide emissions in the United States. How much carbon dioxide is emitted each year by the burning of transportation fuels in the United States?

26. **Social Science** The progress of the local Lions club fund drive is shown here. What percent of the goal has been achieved so far?

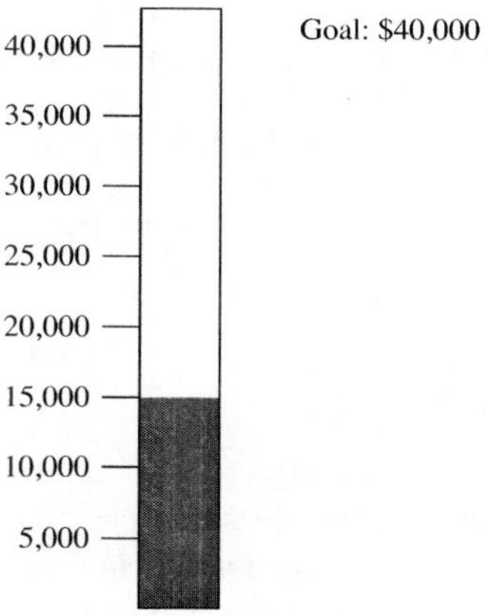

Answers

17. ______

18. ______

19. ______

20. ______

21. ______

22. ______

23. ______

24. ______

25. ______

26. ______

Basic Skills | **Challenge Yourself** | Calculator/Computer | Career Applications | Above and Beyond

Answers

27.

28.

29.

30.

31.

32.

33.

34.

35.

36.

37.

38.

The chart shows U.S. trade with Mexico from 1997 to 2002. Use this information for exercises 27 to 30.

U.S. Trade with Mexico, 1997–2002

	(millions of dollars) MEXICO		
Year	**Exports**	**Imports**	**Trade Balance[1]**
1997	71,389	85,938	−14,549
1998	78,773	94,629	−15,856
1999	86,909	109,721	−22,812
2000	111,349	135,926	−24,577
2001	101,297	131,338	−30,041
2002	97,470	134,616	−37,146

(1) Totals may not add due to rounding.
Source: U.S. Census Bureau.

27. What is the rate of increase (to the nearest whole percent) of exports from 1997 to 2002?

28. What is the rate of increase (to the nearest whole percent) of imports from 1997 to 2002?

29. By what percent did imports exceed exports in 1997?

30. By what percent did imports exceed exports in 2002?

In exercises 31 to 34, assume the interest is compounded annually (at the end of each year) and find the amount in an account with the given interest rate and principal.

31. \$4,000, 6%, 2 years

chapter 6 > Make the Connection

32. \$3,000, 7%, 2 years

33. \$4,000, 5%, 3 years

34. \$5,000, 6%, 3 years

Use the number line to complete exercises 35 to 38.

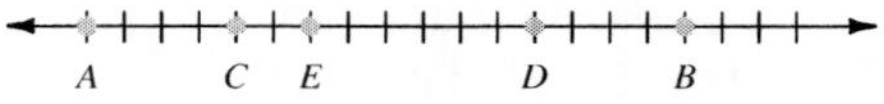

35. Length AC is what percent of length AB?

36. Length AD is what percent of AB?

37. Length AE is what percent of AB?

38. Length AE is what percent of AD?

Basic Skills | Challenge Yourself | **Calculator/Computer** | Career Applications | Above and Beyond

In many everyday applications of percent, the computations required can become quite messy. The calculator can be a great help. Whether we use the proportion approach or the equation approach in solving such an application, we typically set up the problem and isolate the desired variable before doing any calculations.

In some percent increase or percent decrease applications, we can set up the problem so it can be done in one step. (Previously, we did these as two-step problems.) For example, suppose that a store marks up an item 22.5%. If the original cost to the store was \$36.40, we want to know what the selling price will be. Since the selling price is the cost to the store plus the markup, the selling price will be 122.5% of the store's cost (100% + 22.5%). We can restate the problem as "What is 122.5% of \$36.40?" The base is \$36.40 and the rate is 122.5%, and we want the amount.

$$\frac{A}{36.40} = \frac{122.5}{100} \quad \text{so} \quad A = \frac{36.40 \times 122.5}{100}$$

We enter

36.40 [×] 122.5 [÷] 100 [=]

The selling price should be \$44.59.

Suppose now that a certain card collection *decreases* 8.2% in value from \$750. Note that 100% − 8.2% = 91.8%. To find the new value, we can restate the problem as: "What is 91.8% of \$750?" We set up the problem accordingly:

$$\frac{A}{750} = \frac{91.8}{100} \quad \text{so} \quad A = \frac{750 \times 91.8}{100}$$

Entering 750 [×] 91.8 [÷] 100 [=], we get \$688.50.

Use your calculator to solve each application.

39. **Social Science** The population of a town increases 4.2% in 1 year. If the original population was 19,500, what is the population after the increase?

40. **Business and Finance** A store marks up items 42.5% to allow for profit. If an item costs a store \$24.40, what will its selling price be?

41. **Business and Finance** A jacket that originally sold for \$98.50 is marked down by 12.5% for a sale. Find its sale price (to the nearest cent).

42. **Business and Finance** Jerry earned \$18,500 one year and then received a 10.5% raise. What is his new yearly salary?

43. **Business and Finance** Carolyn's salary is \$1,740 per month. If deductions average 24.6%, what is her take-home pay?

44. **Business and Finance** Yi Chen made a \$6,400 investment at the beginning of a year. By the end of the year, the value of the investment had decreased by 8.2%. What was its value at the end of the year?

chapter 6 > Make the Connection

Basic Skills | Challenge Yourself | Calculator/Computer | **Career Applications** | Above and Beyond

Solve each application.

45. **Allied Health** How much 25% alcohol solution can be prepared using 225 milliliters (mL) of ethyl alcohol?

46. **Information Technology** An Ethernet network transmits a maximum packet size of 1,500 bytes. 1.7% of each packet is "overhead." How much information (in bytes) in a maximum-size packet is overhead?

Answers

39. ______

40. ______

41. ______

42. ______

43. ______

44. ______

45. ______

46. ______

Answers

47. ______

48. ______

49. ______

50. ______

51. ______

52. ______

47. **Agricultural Technology** Milk that is labeled "3.5%" is made up of 3.5% butterfat. How many grams of butterfat are in 1 liter (938 g) of 3.5% milk?

48. **Environmental Technology** In some communities, "green" laws require that 40% of a lot remains green (covered in grass or other vegetation). How much green space is required in a 12,680-square-foot lot?

Basic Skills | Challenge Yourself | Calculator/Computer | Career Applications | **Above and Beyond**

49. **Business and Finance** The two ads pictured appeared last week and this week in the local paper. Is this week's ad accurate? Explain.

50. **Business and Finance** At True Grip hardware, you pay \$10 in tax for a barbecue grill, which is 6% of the purchase price. At Loose Fit hardware, you pay \$10 in tax for the same grill, but it is 8% of the purchase price. At which store do you get the better buy? Why?

51. It is customary when eating in a restaurant to leave a 15% tip.

(a) Outline a method to do a quick approximation for the amount of tip to leave.

(b) Use this method to figure a 15% tip on a bill of \$47.76.

52. The dean of enrollment management at a college states, "Last year was not a good year. Our enrollments were down 25%. But this year we increased our enrollment by 30% over last year. I think we have turned the corner." Evaluate the dean's analysis.

Answers

1. \$408 **3.** 5% **5.** 25 questions **7.** \$16.64 **9.** 8.5% **11.** 1,200 people **13.** \$1,464 **15.** \$14,500 **17.** \$2,500 **19.** 6,840 people **21.** 750 s **23.** 7,550 thousand bbl **25.** 189 million t **27.** 37% **29.** 20% **31.** \$4,494.40 **33.** \$4,630.50 **35.** 25% **37.** 37.5% **39.** 20,319 people **41.** \$86.19 **43.** \$1,311.96 **45.** 900 mL **47.** 32.83 g **49.** Above and Beyond **51.** Above and Beyond

Activity 18 ::
Population Changes Revisited

The following table gives the population for the United States and each of the six largest states from both the 1990 census and the 2000 census. Use this table to answer the questions that follow. Round all computations of percents to the nearest tenth of a percent.

	1990 Population	2000 Population
United States	248,709,873	281,421,906
California	29,760,021	33,871,648
Texas	16,986,510	20,851,820
New York	17,990,455	18,976,457
Florida	12,937,926	15,982,378
Illinois	11,430,602	12,419,293
Pennsylvania	11,881,643	12,281,054

1. Find the percent increase in the U.S. population from 1990 to 2000.
2. By examining the table (no actual calculations yet!), predict which state had the greatest percent increase.
3. Predict which state had the smallest percent increase.
4. Now find the percent increase in population during this period for each state.

   California: Texas:

   New York: Florida:

   Illinois: Pennsylvania:

5. Which state had the greatest percent increase during this period? Which had the smallest?
6. The population of the six largest states combined represented what percent of the U.S. population in 1990?
7. The population of the six largest states combined represented what percent of the U.S. population in 2000?
8. Determine the percent increase in population from 1990 to 2000 for the combined six largest states.

Definition/Procedure	Example	Reference
Writing Percents as Fractions and Decimals		Section 6.1
Percent Another way of naming parts of a whole. *Percent* means per hundred.	Fractions and decimals are other ways of naming parts of a whole. $21\% = 21\left(\frac{1}{100}\right) = \frac{21}{100} = 0.21$	p. 367
To write a percent as a fraction, replace the percent symbol with $\frac{1}{100}$ and then multiply and simplify.	$40\% = 40\left(\frac{1}{100}\right) = \frac{40}{100} = \frac{2}{5}$	p. 368
To write a percent as a decimal, remove the percent symbol and move the decimal point two places to the left.	$37\% = 0.37$	p. 369
Writing Decimals and Fractions as Percents		Section 6.2
To write a decimal as a percent, move the decimal point two places to the right and attach the percent symbol.	$0.581 = 58.1\%$	p. 377
There are two methods for writing a fraction as a percent. *Method 1 The Proportion Method* Use proportions to write an equivalent fraction with a denominator of 100. Then, write the fraction as a percent.	$\frac{3}{5} = \frac{x}{100} \Rightarrow 3 \cdot 100 = 5x$ $\frac{300}{5} = \frac{5x}{5} \Rightarrow 60 = x$ Therefore, $\frac{3}{5} = 60\%$.	p. 380
Method 2 The Decimal Method Write the decimal equivalent of the fraction, and then write that decimal as a percent.	$\frac{3}{5} = 0.6 = 60\%$	p. 379
The Three Types of Percent Problems		Section 6.3
Every percent problem has the following three parts: **1.** The *base, B.* This is the whole amount or starting amount in the problem. It is the standard used for comparison. **2.** The *amount, A.* This is the part of the whole being compared to the base. **3.** The *rate, R.* This is the ratio of the amount to the base. The rate is generally written as a percent.	45 is 30% of 150. ↑ A ↑ R ↑ B	p. 389

Definition/Procedure	Example	Reference
Percent problems are solved by identifying A, B, R, and r. The rate R is related to r as: $R = \frac{r}{100}$ The base B, the amount A, and r are related by the **percent proportion:** $\frac{A}{B} = \frac{r}{100}$	Suppose that $A = 45, B = 150, R = 30\%$ If the rate R is 30%, then $r = 30$. Then, the percent proportion is $\frac{45}{150} = \frac{30}{100}$	*p.* 392
Use the percent proportion to solve percent problems. **Step 1** Substitute the two known values into the proportion. **Step 2** Solve the proportion for the unknown value.	What is 24% of 300? $\frac{A}{300} = \frac{24}{100}$ $100A = 7{,}200$ $A = 72$ 72 is 24% of 300.	*p.* 392
Applications of Percent Problems		**Section 6.4**
Applications involving percentages are varied and include solving problems related to commissions, taxes, discounts, markups, and rates of increase or decrease.	An electronics store normally sells a DVD player for \$130. During a sale, they apply a 15% discount to the price. What is the sale price? $B = \$130$ and $R = 15\%$ (so $r = 15$): $\frac{A}{130} = \frac{15}{100}$ $100A = 15 \cdot 130 = 1{,}950$ $A = \frac{1{,}950}{100}$ $= 19.50$ The sale price is $\$130 - \$19.50 = \$110.50$	*p.* 400

summary exercises :: chapter 6

This summary exercise set is provided to give you practice with each of the objectives of this chapter. Each exercise is keyed to the appropriate chapter section. When you are finished, you can check your answers to the odd-numbered exercises against those presented in the back of the text. If you have difficulty with any of these questions, go back and reread the examples from that section. The answers to the even-numbered exercises appear in the *Instructor's Solutions Manual.* Your instructor will give you guidelines on how to best use these exercises in your instructional setting.

6.1

1. Use a percent to name the shaded portion of the diagram.

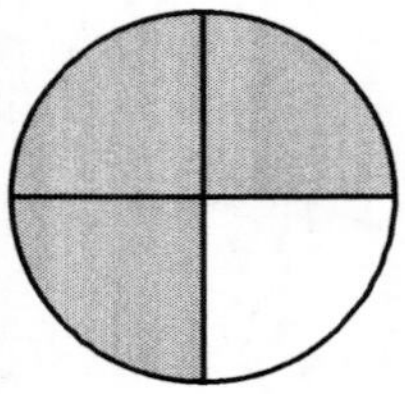

Write each percent as a common fraction or a mixed number.

2. 2%

3. 20%

4. 37.5%

5. 150%

6. $233\frac{1}{3}\%$

7. 300%

Write each percent as a decimal.

8. 75%

9. 4%

10. 6.25%

11. 13.5%

12. 0.6%

13. 225%

6.2 *Write as percents.*

14. 0.06

15. 0.375

16. 2.4

17. 7

18. 0.035

19. 0.005

20. $\frac{43}{100}$

21. $\frac{7}{10}$

22. $\frac{2}{5}$

23. $1\frac{1}{4}$

24. $2\frac{2}{3}$

25. $\frac{3}{11}$ (to nearest tenth of a percent)

6.3 *Find the unknown.*

26. 80 is 4% of what number?

27. 70 is what percent of 50?

28. 11% of 3,000 is what number?

29. 24 is what percent of 192?

30. Find the base if 12.5% of the base is 625.

31. 90 is 120% of what number?

32. What is 9.5% of 700?

33. Find 150% of 50.

34. Find the base if 130% of the base is 780.

35. 350 is what percent of 200?

36. 28.8 is what percent of 960?

6.4 *Solve each application.*

37. **Business and Finance** Joan works on a 4% commission basis. She sold $45,000 in merchandise during 1 month. What was the amount of her commission?

38. **Business and Finance** David buys a dishwasher that is marked down $77 from its original price of $350. What is the discount rate?

39. **Science and Medicine** A chemist prepares a 400-milliliter (mL) acid-water solution. If the solution contains 30 mL of acid, what percent of the solution is acid?

40. **Business and Finance** The price of a new compact car has increased $819 over that of the previous year. If this amounts to a 4.5% increase, what was the price of the car before the increase?

41. **Business and Finance** A store advertises, "Buy the red-tagged items at 25% off their listed price." If you buy a coat marked $136, what will you pay for the coat during the sale?

42. **Business and Finance** Tom has 6% of his salary deducted for a retirement plan. If that deduction is $168, what is his monthly salary?

43. **Social Science** A college finds that 35% of its science students take biology. If there are 252 biology students, how many science students are there altogether?

44. **Business and Finance** A company finds that its advertising costs increased from $72,000 to $76,680 in 1 year. What was the rate of increase?

45. **Business and Finance** A savings bank offers 5.25% interest on 1-year time deposits. If you place $3,000 in an account, how much will you have at the end of the year? chapter 6 > Make the Connection

46. **Business and Finance** Maria's company offers her a 4% pay raise. This will amount to a $126 per month increase in her salary. What is her monthly salary before and after the raise?

47. **Business and Finance** A virus scanning program is checking every file for viruses. It has completed 30% of the files in 150 seconds. How long should it take to check all the files?

self-test 6

The purpose of this self-test is to help you assess your progress so that you can find concepts that you need to review before the next exam. Allow yourself about an hour to take this test. At the end of that hour, check your answers against those given in the back of this text. If you miss any, go back to the appropriate section to reread the examples until you have mastered that particular concept.

Write as percents.

1. 0.03

2. 0.042

3. $\frac{2}{5}$

4. $\frac{5}{8}$

Solve the percent problems.

5. What is 4.5% of 250?

6. What percent of 300 is 60?

7. $33\frac{1}{3}$% of 1,500 is what number?

8. Find 125% of 600.

Solve each application.

9. Business and Finance A state taxes sales at 6.2%. What tax will you pay on a sweater that costs $80?

10. Statistics You receive a grade of 75% on a test of 80 questions. How many questions did you have correct?

11. Business and Finance A shirt that costs a store $54 is marked up 30% (based on cost). Find its selling price.

12. Business and Finance Mrs. Sanford pays $300 in interest on a $2,500 loan for 1 year. What is the interest rate for the loan?

13. Use a percent to name the shaded portion of the following diagram.

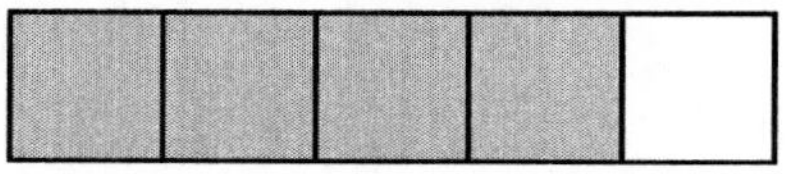

Write as decimals.

14. 42%

15. 6%

16. 160%

In exercises 17 to 19, identify the rate, base, and amount. Do not solve *at this point.*

17. 50 is 25% of 200.

18. What is 8% of 500?

19. Business and Finance A state sales tax rate is 6%. If the tax on a purchase is $30, what is the amount of the purchase?

Name ____________

Section ________ Date ________

Answers

1. ____________
2. ____________
3. ____________
4. ____________
5. ____________
6. ____________
7. ____________
8. ____________
9. ____________
10. ____________
11. ____________
12. ____________
13. ____________
14. ____________
15. ____________
16. ____________
17. ____________
18. ____________
19. ____________

Answers

20. ______

21. ______

22. ______

23. ______

24. ______

25. ______

26. ______

27. ______

28. ______

29. ______

30. ______

Solve the percent problems.

20. 875 is what percent of 500?

21. 96 is 12% of what number?

22. 8.5% of what number is 25.5?

23. 4.5 is what percent of 60?

Solve each application.

24. **Business and Finance** A car is marked down \$1,552 from its original selling price of \$19,400. What is the discount rate?

25. **Business and Finance** Sarah earns \$540 in commissions in one month. If her commission rate is 3%, what were her total sales?

26. **Social Science** A community college has 480 more students in fall 2008 than in fall 2007. If this is a 7.5% increase, what was the fall 2007 enrollment?

27. **Business and Finance** Shawn arranges financing for his new car. The interest rate for the financing plan is 12%, and he will pay \$2,220 interest for 1 year. How much money did he borrow to finance the car?

28. **Business and Finance** Jovita's monthly salary is \$2,200. If the deductions for taxes from her monthly paycheck are \$528, what percent of her salary goes for these deductions?

Write as fractions.

29. 7%

30. 72%

The following exercises are presented to help you review concepts from earlier chapters. This is meant as review material and not as a comprehensive exam. The answers are presented in the back of the text. Beside each answer is a section reference for the concept. If you have difficulty with any of these exercises, be certain to at least read through the summary related to that section.

Name ____________

Section ________ Date ________

Answers

1. ____________
2. ____________
3. ____________
4. ____________
5. ____________
6. ____________
7. ____________
8. ____________
9. ____________
10. ____________
11. ____________
12. ____________
13. ____________
14. ____________
15. ____________
16. ____________
17. ____________
18. ____________
19. ____________

1. What is the place value of 4 in the number 234,768?

Perform the indicated operations.

2. 56×203 **3.** $3{,}026 \div 34$

Evaluate each expression.

4. $8 - 5 + 2$ **5.** $15 - 3 \times 2$ **6.** $6 + 4 \times 3^2$

7. List the prime numbers between 50 and 70.

8. Write the prime factorization of 260.

9. Find the greatest common factor (GCF) of 84 and 140.

10. Find the least common multiple (LCM) of 18, 20, and 30.

Perform the indicated operations.

11. $3\frac{2}{5} \times 2\frac{1}{2}$ **12.** $5\frac{1}{3} \div 4$

13. $4\frac{3}{4} + 3\frac{5}{6}$ **14.** $7\frac{1}{6} - 2\frac{3}{8}$

15. A kitchen measures $5\frac{1}{2}$ yd by $3\frac{1}{4}$ yd. If vinyl flooring costs \$16 per yd^2, what will it cost to cover the floor?

16. If you drive 180 mi in $3\frac{1}{3}$ h, what is your average speed?

17. A bookshelf that is $54\frac{5}{8}$ in. long is cut from a board that is 8 ft long. If $\frac{1}{8}$ in. is wasted in the cut, what length board remains?

Find the indicated place values.

18. 8 in 4.2835 **19.** 4 in 6.09743

Answers

20. ______
21. ______
22. ______
23. ______
24. ______
25. ______
26. ______
27. ______
28. ______
29. ______
30. ______
31. ______
32. ______
33. ______
34. ______
35. ______
36. ______
37. ______
38. ______
39. ______
40. ______

Complete each statement with <, =, or >.

20. 6.28 ________ 6.3

21. 3.75 ________ 3.750

Write as a common fraction or a mixed number. Simplify.

22. 0.36

23. 5.125

Perform the indicated operations.

24. 2.8×4.03

25. $54.528 \div 3.2$

26. A television set has an advertised price of $599.95. You buy the set and agree to make payments of $29.50 per month for 2 years. How much extra are you paying on this installment plan?

27. Find the area of a rectangle with length 3.4 m and width 1.85 m.

28. Find the volume of a box with dimensions 5.1 ft × 3.6 ft × 2.4 ft.

Write each ratio in simplest form.

29. $8\frac{1}{2}$ to $12\frac{3}{4}$

30. 34 feet to 8 yards

Solve for the unknown.

31. $\frac{3}{7} = \frac{8}{x}$

32. $\frac{1.9}{y} = \frac{5.7}{1.2}$

33. On a map the scale is $\frac{1}{4}$ in. = 25 mi. How many miles apart are two towns that are $3\frac{1}{2}$ in. apart on the map?

34. Diane worked 23.5 hours on a part-time job and was paid $131.60. She is asked to work 25 hours the next week at the same pay rate. What salary will she receive?

35. Write 34% as a decimal and as a fraction.

36. Write $\frac{11}{20}$ as a decimal and as a percent.

37. Find 18% of 250.

38. 11% of what number is 55?

39. A company reduced the number of employees by 8% this year. 10 employees were laid off. How many were there last year?

40. The sales tax on an item priced at $72 is $6.12. What percent is the tax rate?

Answers to Prerequisite Tests, Reading Your Text, Summary Exercises, Self-Tests, and Cumulative Reviews

Reading Your Text

Section 1.1 **(a)** decimal; **(b)** digit; **(c)** comma; **(d)** million
Section 1.2 **(a)** natural; **(b)** addition; **(c)** order; **(d)** read
Section 1.3 **(a)** difference; **(b)** less; **(c)** read; **(d)** borrowing
Section 1.4 **(a)** rounding; **(b)** place value; **(c)** rounding; **(d)** less
Section 1.5 **(a)** reasonable; **(b)** product; **(c)** powers; **(d)** rectangle
Section 1.6 **(a)** quotient; **(b)** remainder; **(c)** zero; **(d)** subtraction
Section 1.7 **(a)** first; **(b)** exponent; **(c)** inside; **(d)** one

Summary Exercises for Chapter 1

1. Hundreds
3. Twenty-seven thousand, four hundred twenty-eight
5. 37,583 **7.** Commutative property of addition **9.** 1,416
11. 4,801 **13.** **(a)** 27; **(b)** 11; **(c)** 15 **15.** \$540
17. 18,800 **19.** 2,574 **21.** \$536 **23.** 7,000
25. 550,000 **27.** > **29.** 22 in.
31. Distributive property of multiplication over addition
33. 1,856 **35.** 154,602 **37.** 144 in.^3 **39.** 30,960
41. 0 **43.** 308 r 5 **45.** 497 r 1 **47.** 28 mi/gal
49. 21 **51.** 1,000 **53.** 4 **55.** 36 **57.** 33 **59.** 0

Self-Test for Chapter 1

1. 1,918 **2.** 13,103 **3.** 4,984 **4.** 55,414
5. Three hundred two thousand, five hundred twenty-five
6. 12 in. **7.** > **8.** < **9.** Hundred thousands
10. Distributive property of multiplication over addition
11. Associative property of addition
12. Associative property of multiplication
13. Commutative property of addition **14.** 76 r 7
15. 209 r 145 **16.** 2,430,000 **17.** 21,696 **18.** \$558,750
19. \$223 **20.** 12 in.^2 **21.** 280 ft^3 **22.** 55,978
23. 235 **24.** 40,555 **25.** 30,770 **26.** 12,220
27. 72 lb **28.** 39 **29.** 15 **30.** 7,700

Prerequisite Test for Chapter 2

1. No **2.** No **3.** Yes **4.** No **5.** Yes **6.** 1, 3, 9
7. 1, 2, 5, 10 **8.** 1, 17 **9.** 1, 2, 3, 4, 6, 8, 12, 16, 24, 48
10. 1, 2, 3, 4, 5, 6, 10, 12, 15, 20, 30, 60

Reading Your Text

Section 2.1 **(a)** One (1); **(b)** prime; **(c)** composite; **(d)** even
Section 2.2 **(a)** commutative; **(b)** prime; **(c)** common; **(d)** greatest
Section 2.3 **(a)** denominator; **(b)** proper; **(c)** mixed; **(d)** numerator
Section 2.4 **(a)** cross; **(b)** equivalent; **(c)** Fundamental; **(d)** common
Section 2.5 **(a)** simplest; **(b)** simplify; **(c)** reasonableness; **(d)** reasonable
Section 2.6 **(a)** reciprocal; **(b)** complex; **(c)** divisor; **(d)** units

Summary Exercises for Chapter 2

1. 1, 2, 4, 13, 26, 52 **3.** Prime: 2, 5, 7, 11, 17, 23, 43; composite: 14, 21, 27, 39 **5.** None **7.** $2 \times 2 \times 3 \times 5 \times 7$
9. $2 \times 3 \times 3 \times 5 \times 5 \times 5$ **11.** 1 **13.** 13 **15.** 11
17. Numerator: 17; denominator: 23
19. Fraction: $\frac{5}{6}$; numerator: 5; denominator: 6 **21.** $6\frac{5}{6}$
23. $7\frac{2}{3}$ **25.** $\frac{61}{8}$ **27.** $\frac{37}{7}$ **29.** No **31.** $\frac{2}{3}$ **33.** $\frac{7}{9}$
35. Yes **37.** $\frac{1}{9}$ **39.** $1\frac{1}{2}$ **41.** $9\frac{3}{5}$ **43.** 8 **45.** \$204
47. \$45 **49.** 408 mi **51.** $\frac{5}{8}$ **53.** $\frac{2}{3}$ **55.** $\frac{3}{16}$
57. $\frac{3}{7}$ **59.** $\frac{3}{4}$ ft **61.** 56 mi/h **63.** 48 lots

Self-Test for Chapter 2

1. 12 **2.** 8 **3.** $4\frac{1}{4}$ **4.** $\frac{7}{9}$ **5.** $\frac{3}{7}$ **6.** $\frac{8}{23}$ **7.** $\frac{10}{21}$
8. 4 **9.** $\frac{5}{8}$ **10.** $3\frac{3}{7}$ **11.** $\frac{4}{15}$ **12.** $2\frac{2}{3}$ **13.** $\frac{9}{16}$
14. $1\frac{1}{7}$ **15.** $9\frac{1}{5}$ **16.** $1\frac{3}{11}$
17. Prime: 5, 13, 17, 31; composite: 9, 22, 27, 45
18. $\frac{5}{6}$; numerator: 5; denominator: 6
19. $\frac{5}{8}$; numerator: 5; denominator: 8
20. $\frac{3}{5}$; numerator: 3; denominator: 5 **21.** \$1.32
22. 48 books **23.** $4\frac{1}{4}$ **24.** 15 **25.** $9\frac{1}{4}$ **26.** 3
27. $2 \times 2 \times 2 \times 3 \times 11$
28. Proper: $\frac{10}{11}, \frac{1}{8}$; improper: $\frac{9}{5}, \frac{7}{7}, \frac{8}{1}$; mixed: $2\frac{3}{5}$ **29.** 47 homes
30. 20 yd^2 **31.** 190 mi **32.** 2, 3 **33.** Yes **34.** Yes
35. No **36.** $\frac{37}{7}$ **37.** $\frac{35}{8}$ **38.** $\frac{74}{9}$

Cumulative Review Chapters 1–2

[1.1] **1.** Hundred thousands
2. Three hundred two thousand, five hundred twenty-five
3. 2,430,000 **[1.2]** **4.** Commutative property of addition
5. Additive identity **6.** Associative property of addition
7. 966 **8.** 23,351 **[1.4]** **9.** 5,900 **10.** 950,000
11. 7,700 **12.** > **13.** < **[1.3]** **14.** 3,861 **15.** 17,465
[1.2] **16.** 905 **17.** \$17,579
[1.5] **18.** Associative property of multiplication
19. Commutative property of multiplication
20. Distributive property **21.** 378,214 **22.** 686,000
23. \$1,008 **[1.6]** **24.** 67 r 43 **25.** 103 r 176
[1.7] **26.** 38 **27.** 56 **28.** 36 **29.** 8 **30.** \$58
[2.1] **31.** Prime: 5, 13, 17, 31; composite: 9, 22, 27, 45
32. 2 and 3 **[2.2]** **33.** $2 \times 2 \times 2 \times 3 \times 11$ **34.** 12 **35.** 8
[2.3] **36.** Proper: $\frac{7}{12}, \frac{3}{7}$; improper: $\frac{10}{8}, \frac{9}{9}, \frac{7}{1}$; mixed numbers: $3\frac{1}{5}, 2\frac{2}{3}$
[2.4] **37.** $2\frac{4}{5}$ **38.** 4 **39.** $\frac{13}{3}$ **40.** $\frac{63}{8}$ **41.** Yes
42. No **43.** $\frac{2}{3}$ **44.** $\frac{3}{8}$ **[2.5]** **45.** $\frac{8}{27}$ **46.** $\frac{4}{15}$
47. $5\frac{2}{5}$ **48.** $22\frac{2}{3}$ **49.** $\frac{3}{4}$ **[2.6]** **50.** $1\frac{1}{3}$ **51.** $4\frac{1}{2}$
52. $\frac{5}{6}$ **53.** $1\frac{1}{2}$ **54.** \$540 **55.** 88 sheets

Prerequisite Test for Chapter 3

1. $2 \times 2 \times 2 \times 3$ **2.** $2 \times 2 \times 3 \times 3$ **3.** $2 \times 3 \times 3 \times 5$
4. $\frac{14}{3}$ **5.** $\frac{32}{5}$ **6.** $\frac{91}{10}$ **7.** $7\frac{1}{4}$ **8.** 7 **9.** 1 **10.** 27

Reading Your Text

Section 3.1 **(a)** like; **(b)** numerators; **(c)** simplify; **(d)** difference
Section 3.2 **(a)** multiples; **(b)** smallest; **(c)** denominator; **(d)** greater
Section 3.3 **(a)** LCM; **(b)** unlike; **(c)** equivalent; **(d)** numerator
Section 3.4 **(a)** LCD; **(b)** regrouping; **(c)** like; **(d)** smaller
Section 3.5 **(a)** grouping; **(b)** exponents; **(c)** invert; **(d)** improper
Section 3.6 **(a)** dual; **(b)** estimation; **(c)** approximations; **(d)** estimation

Summary Exercises for Chapter 3

1. $\frac{2}{3}$ **3.** $1\frac{2}{13}$ **5.** $1\frac{1}{3}$ **7.** $1\frac{2}{9}$ **9.** 12 **11.** 72 **13.** 60
15. 72 **17.** $\frac{7}{12}, \frac{5}{8}$ **19.** > **21.** < **23.** $\frac{36}{120}, \frac{75}{120}, \frac{70}{120}$
25. 36 **27.** 200 **29.** 132 **31.** 24 **33.** $\frac{19}{24}$ **35.** $\frac{7}{12}$
37. $1\frac{17}{90}$ **39.** $\frac{7}{8}$ **41.** $1\frac{13}{72}$ **43.** $\frac{5}{9}$ **45.** $\frac{1}{2}$ **47.** $\frac{5}{24}$
49. $\frac{7}{18}$ **51.** $\frac{11}{24}$ **53.** $\frac{13}{42}$ **55.** $\frac{1}{3}$ **57.** $\frac{1}{4}$ **59.** $\frac{7}{60}$
61. $\frac{35}{72}$ **63.** $9\frac{37}{60}$ **65.** $4\frac{1}{3}$ **67.** $2\frac{19}{24}$ **69.** $\frac{5}{12}$ cup
71. $19\frac{9}{16}$ in. **73.** $53\frac{9}{16}$ in. **75.** $3\frac{7}{12}$ gal **77.** $1\frac{3}{4}$ yd
79. $\frac{37}{96}$ **81.** $\frac{1}{48}$ **83.** $1\frac{1}{2}$ **85.** $2,500 **87.** 24

Self-Test for Chapter 3

1. 60 **2.** 36 **3.** $10\frac{1}{4}$ **4.** $1\frac{11}{18}$ **5.** $\frac{9}{10}$ **6.** $\frac{25}{42}$
7. $\frac{23}{30}$ **8.** $9\frac{1}{7}$ **9.** $7\frac{11}{12}$ **10.** $\frac{2}{3}$ **11.** $13\frac{11}{20}$ **12.** $1\frac{11}{60}$
13. $\frac{1}{4}$ h **14.** $1\frac{5}{12}$ c **15.** 72 **16.** $\frac{1}{12}$ **17.** $\frac{299}{24}$ or $12\frac{11}{24}$
18. $\frac{4}{5}$ **19.** $1\frac{3}{4}$ **20.** $1\frac{8}{15}$ **21.** $\frac{1}{9}$ **22.** $\frac{19}{24}$ **23.** $3\frac{23}{24}$
24. $\frac{1}{3}$ **25.** $1\frac{23}{40}$ **26.** $7\frac{7}{10}$ **27.** $\frac{7}{12}$ **28.** $12\frac{3}{40}$
29. 39,000 c **30.** $5\frac{3}{4}$ h

Cumulative Review Chapters 1–3

[1.1–1.2] 1. 7,173 **2.** 1,918 **3.** 2,731 **4.** 13,103
[1.3] 5. 235 **6.** 12,220 **7.** 429 **8.** 3,239
[1.5] 9. 174 **10.** 1,911 **11.** 4,984 **12.** 55,414
[1.6] 13. 24 r191 **14.** 22 r21 **15.** 209 r145
[1.7] 16. 5 **17.** 7 **18.** 3 **19.** 16 **20.** 20 **21.** 3
[2.3] 22. Proper: $\frac{5}{7}, \frac{2}{5}$; improper: $\frac{15}{9}, \frac{8}{8}, \frac{11}{1}$; mixed numbers: $4\frac{5}{6}, 3\frac{5}{6}$
23. $1\frac{7}{9}$ **24.** $7\frac{1}{5}$ **25.** $\frac{23}{4}$ **26.** $\frac{55}{9}$ **[2.4] 27.** Yes
28. No **[2.5] 29.** $\frac{1}{9}$ **30.** $\frac{1}{6}$ **31.** $1\frac{1}{2}$ **32.** $2\frac{1}{8}$ **33.** $9\frac{3}{5}$
34. $11\frac{1}{3}$ **35.** 8 **[2.6] 36.** $\frac{2}{3}$ **37.** $\frac{5}{6}$ **38.** $\frac{3}{16}$
[3.1] 39. $\frac{4}{5}$ **40.** $\frac{61}{75}$ **41.** $1\frac{31}{40}$ **[3.3] 42.** $\frac{1}{2}$ **43.** $\frac{5}{36}$
44. $\frac{5}{9}$ **[3.4] 45.** $6\frac{2}{7}$ **46.** $8\frac{1}{24}$ **47.** $4\frac{5}{9}$ **48.** $4\frac{1}{24}$
49. $3\frac{5}{8}$ **50.** $3\frac{13}{24}$ **51.** $14\frac{19}{30}$ h **52.** $\frac{5}{8}$ in. **53.** $1\frac{11}{12}$ h

Prerequisite Test for Chapter 4

1. Three and seven tenths **2.** Six and twenty-nine hundredths
3. Seventeen and eighty-nine thousandths **4.** 257 **5.** 164
6. 6,390 **7.** 79 r2 **8.** 7 r 92 **9.** 136 ft^2 **10.** 225 $in.^2$

Reading Your Text

Section 4.1 **(a)** decimal; **(b)** places; **(c)** exact; **(d)** ten-thousandths
Section 4.2 **(a)** divide; **(b)** bar; **(c)** terminating; **(d)** places
Section 4.3 **(a)** decimal points; **(b)** value; **(c)** Perimeter; **(d)** following
Section 4.4 **(a)** add; **(b)** product; **(c)** zeros; **(d)** right
Section 4.5 **(a)** above; **(b)** past; **(c)** whole number; **(d)** left

Summary Exercises for Chapter 4

1. Hundredths **3.** 0.37 **5.** Seventy-one thousandths **7.** 4.5
9. > **11.** < **13.** 5.84 **15.** 4.876 **17.** $21\frac{857}{1,000}$
19. 0.429 **21.** 3.75 **23.** $\frac{21}{250}$ **25.** 3.47 **27.** 37.728
29. 23.32 **31.** 1.075 **33.** 28.02 cm **35.** 6.15 cm
37. $18.93 **39.** 0.000261 **41.** 0.0012275 **43.** 450
45. $287.50 **47.** $5,742 **49.** 4.65 **51.** 2.664 **53.** 1.273
55. 0.76 **57.** 0.0457 **59.** 39.3 mi/gal **61.** 29.8 mi/gal

Self-Test for Chapter 4

1. < **2.** > **3.** 0.4375 **4.** 0.429 **5.** $0.\overline{63}$
6. 0.004983 **7.** 0.00523 **8.** $\frac{9}{125}$ **9.** $4\frac{11}{25}$
10. Ten-thousandths **11.** Two and fifty-three hundredths
12. 0.598 **13.** 23.57 **14.** 36,000 **15.** 0.049
16. 12.017 **17.** 16.64 **18.** 10.54 **19.** 2.55
20. 1.4575 **21.** 2.35 **22.** 47.253 **23.** 17.437
24. 24.375 **25.** $543 **26.** 50.2 gal **27.** 32 lots
28. > **29.** 12.803 **30.** 7.525 $in.^2$ **31.** 735
32. 12,570 **33.** $573.40 **34.** $3.06 **35.** 3.888
36. 0.465 **37.** 0.02793 **38.** 2.385 **39.** $\frac{229}{500}$ **40.** 7.35
41. 0.051 **42.** 0.067

Cumulative Review Chapters 1–4

[1.1] 1. Two hundred eighty-six thousand, five hundred forty-three
2. Hundreds **[1.2] 3.** 34,594 **[1.3] 4.** 48,888
[1.5] 5. 5,063 **6.** 70,455 **[1.6] 7.** 17 **8.** 35 r11
[1.7] 9. 29 **[1.4] 10.** 4,000 **[1.8] 11.** *P*: 24 ft; *A*: 35 ft^2
[2.4] 12. $\frac{5}{17}$ **[2.5] 13.** $\frac{3}{4}$ **14.** $2\frac{6}{7}$ **[2.7] 15.** $\frac{9}{17}$
[3.1] 16. $\frac{5}{7}$ **[3.3] 17.** $\frac{7}{30}$ **[3.4] 18.** $3\frac{9}{10}$ **[4.3] 19.** 12.468
[4.5] 20. 3.9 **21.** 0.005238 **[4.4] 22.** 1.1385 **23.** 15,300
[4.2] 24. $\frac{43}{100}$ **25.** **(a)** 0.625; **(b)** 0.39 **[4.5] 26.** 0.429
[4.4] 27. 17.21 **[4.5] 28.** 39.829

Prerequisite Test for Chapter 5

1. $\frac{3}{4}$ **2.** $\frac{8}{15}$ **3.** $\frac{3}{4}$ **4.** $\frac{28}{5}$ **5.** $\frac{3}{4}$ **6.** 525 **7.** 35
8. 5.56 **9.** 7.22 **10.** No **11.** Yes

Reading Your Text

Section 5.1 **(a)** fraction; **(b)** like; **(c)** simplest; **(d)** mixed
Section 5.2 **(a)** like; **(b)** rate; **(c)** Mixed; **(d)** Unit
Section 5.3 **(a)** equal; **(b)** variable; **(c)** proportion; **(d)** rates
Section 5.4 **(a)** equation; **(b)** coefficient; **(c)** read; **(d)** proportional

Summary Exercises for Chapter 5

1. $\frac{4}{17}$ **3.** $\frac{5}{8}$ **5.** $\frac{4}{9}$ **7.** $\frac{7}{36}$ **9.** $100\frac{\text{mi}}{\text{h}}$ **11.** $50\frac{\text{cal}}{\text{oz}}$
13. $200\frac{\text{ft}}{\text{s}}$ **15.** $6\frac{1}{2}\frac{\text{hits}}{\text{game}}$ **17.** Marisa **19.** $\frac{9¢}{\text{oz}}$
21. $9.5\frac{\text{cents}}{\text{oz}}$ **23.** $14.95\frac{\text{dollars}}{\text{CD}}$ **25.** $\frac{4}{9} = \frac{20}{45}$
27. $\frac{110 \text{ mi}}{2 \text{ h}} = \frac{385 \text{ mi}}{7 \text{ h}}$ **29.** No **31.** Yes **33.** Yes **35.** Yes
37. $m = 2$ **39.** $t = 4$ **41.** $w = 180$ **43.** $x = 100$
45. $135 **47.** 15 in. **49.** 28 parts **51.** 140 g

Self-Test for Chapter 5

1. $4.8\frac{\text{mi}}{\text{gal}}$ **2.** $8.25\frac{\text{dollars}}{\text{h}}$ **3.** $x = 20$ **4.** $a = 18$
5. $\frac{\$2.56}{\text{gal}}$ **6.** $\frac{26}{33}; \frac{26}{7}$ **7.** $p = 3$ **8.** $m = 16$ **9.** $\frac{7}{19}$
10. $\frac{5}{3}$ **11.** $\frac{2}{3}$ **12.** $\frac{1}{12}$ **13.** $2.28 **14.** 576 miles
15. 600 mufflers **16.** 24 tsp **17.** Yes **18.** No
19. Yes **20.** No

Cumulative Review Chapters 1–5

[1.1] **1.** Forty-five thousand, seven hundred eighty-nine
2. Ten thousands [1.2] **3.** 26,304 [1.3] **4.** 47,806
[1.5] **5.** 4,408 [1.6] **6.** 78 r67 [1.3] **7.** $568
[1.7] **8.** 3 [1.8] **9.** P: 16 ft; A: 12 ft^2 **10.** $1,104
[2.2] **11.** $2 \times 2 \times 3 \times 7 \times 11$ **12.** 14 [2.4] **13.** $\frac{1}{4}$
[2.5] **14.** $1\frac{1}{5}$ **15.** 10 [2.7] **16.** $4\frac{1}{2}$ **17.** $1\frac{9}{13}$
[3.3] **18.** $\frac{25}{44}$ [3.4] **19.** $7\frac{7}{12}$ **20.** $4\frac{1}{2}$ [3.2] **21.** 180
[2.6] **22.** 176 mi [2.7] **23.** $48\frac{\text{mi}}{\text{h}}$ [4.2] **24.** 7.828
[4.5] **25.** 1.23 [4.3] **26.** 6.6015 [4.7] **27.** $\frac{9}{25}$
[4.6] **28.** 0.32 [4.2] **29.** 14.06 m [4.4] **30.** 50.24 cm^2
[5.1] **31.** $\frac{6}{13}$ **32.** $\frac{10}{3}$ **33.** $\frac{4}{5}$ [5.3] **34.** Yes **35.** No
[5.4] **36.** $x = 2$ **37.** $x = 15$ [5.2] **38.** $\frac{24.4¢}{\text{oz}}$
[5.4] **39.** 600 km **40.** 50

Prerequisite Test for Chapter 6

1. $\frac{11}{25}$ **2.** 0.3125 **3.** 41.6 **4.** 20 **5.** 120 **6.** 52.5
7. 48 **8.** $58\frac{1}{3}$ **9.** 70 **10.** 8,000

Reading Your Text

Section 6.1 **(a)** hundred; **(b)** fraction; **(c)** left; **(d)** greater
Section 6.2 **(a)** right; **(b)** decimal; **(c)** percent; **(d)** zeros
Section 6.3 **(a)** base; **(b)** rate; **(c)** rate; **(d)** amount
Section 6.4 **(a)** greater; **(b)** amount; **(c)** markup; **(d)** principal

Summary Exercises for Chapter 6

1. 75% **3.** $\frac{1}{5}$ **5.** $1\frac{1}{2}$ **7.** 3 **9.** 0.04 **11.** 0.135
13. 2.25 **15.** 37.5% **17.** 700% **19.** 0.5% **21.** 70%
23. 125% **25.** 27.3% **27.** 140% **29.** 12.5% **31.** 75
33. 75 **35.** 175% **37.** $1,800 **39.** 7.5% **41.** $102
43. 720 students **45.** $3,157.50 **47.** 500 s (8 min 20 s)

Self-Test for Chapter 6

1. 3% **2.** 4.2% **3.** 40% **4.** 62.5% **5.** 11.25 **6.** 20%
7. 500 **8.** 750 **9.** $4.96 **10.** 60 questions **11.** $70.20
12. 12% **13.** 80% **14.** 0.42 **15.** 0.06 **16.** 1.6
17. A: 50; R: 25%; B: 200 **18.** A: Unknown; R: 8%; B: 500
19. R: 6%; A: $30; B: amount of purchase **20.** 175% **21.** 800
22. 300 **23.** 7.5% **24.** 8% **25.** $18,000
26. 6,400 students **27.** $18,500 **28.** 24% **29.** $\frac{7}{100}$
30. $\frac{18}{25}$

Cumulative Review Chapters 1–6

[1.1] **1.** Thousands [1.5] **2.** 11,368 [1.6] **3.** 89
[1.7] **4.** 5 **5.** 9 **6.** 42 [2.1] **7.** 53, 59, 61, 67
[2.2] **8.** $2 \times 2 \times 5 \times 13$ **9.** 28 [3.2] **10.** 180
[2.5] **11.** $8\frac{1}{2}$ [2.7] **12.** $1\frac{1}{3}$ [3.4] **13.** $8\frac{7}{12}$ **14.** $4\frac{19}{24}$
[2.6] **15.** $286 [2.7] **16.** $54\frac{\text{mi}}{\text{h}}$ [3.4] **17.** $41\frac{1}{4}$ in.
[4.1] **18.** Hundredths **19.** Ten-thousandths **20.** <
21. = [4.7] **22.** $\frac{9}{25}$ **23.** $5\frac{1}{8}$ [4.3] **24.** 11.284
[4.5] **25.** 17.04 [4.3] **26.** $108.05 [4.4] **27.** 6.29 m^2
28. 44.064 ft^3 [5.1] **29.** $\frac{2}{3}$ **30.** $\frac{17}{12}$ [5.4] **31.** $x = 18\frac{2}{3}$
32. $y = 0.4$ **33.** 350 mi **34.** $140 [6.1] **35.** 0.34; $\frac{17}{50}$
[6.2] **36.** 0.55; 55% [6.4] **37.** 45 **38.** 500
39. 125 employees **40.** 8.5%

Prerequisite Test for Chapter 7

1. 428,400 **2.** 0.004284 **3.** $\frac{4}{3}$ **4.** $\frac{5}{12}$ **5.** $\frac{5}{2}$ **6.** $\frac{3}{5}$
7. $10.75/h **8.** $50\frac{\text{mi}}{\text{h}}$ **9.** $0.0514/fl oz **10.** $0.45/DVD-R
11. 54 in. **12.** 500 mm

Reading Your Text

Section 7.1 **(a)** metric; **(b)** volume; **(c)** one; **(d)** like
Section 7.2 **(a)** metric; **(b)** yard; **(c)** centi-; **(d)** Kilometers
Section 7.3 **(a)** gram; **(b)** milligram; **(c)** liter; **(d)** milliliter
Section 7.4 **(a)** substitution; **(b)** unit-ratio; **(c)** gravity; **(d)** Celsius

Summary Exercises for Chapter 7

1. 132 **3.** 24 **5.** 64 **7.** 4 **9.** 4 ft 11 in.
11. 9 lb 3 oz **13.** 5 ft 7 in. **15.** 4 h 15 min **17.** 33 h 35 min
19. **(a)** **21.** **(c)** **23.** mm **25.** cm **27.** 30
29. 8,000 **31.** 0.008 **33.** **(b)** **35.** **(b)** **37.** kg
39. 5,000 **41.** 5,000 **43.** **(c)** **45.** **(b)** **47.** L
49. mL or cm^3 **51.** 5,000 **53.** 9,000 **55.** 326.77
57. 6.75 **59.** 5.51 **61.** 62.6 **63.** 37 **65.** 15 **67.** 41

Self-Test for Chapter 7

1. 96 **2.** 48 **3.** 5,000 **4.** 3,000 **5.** 3 **6.** 101.6
7. 3.2 **8.** 55.1 **9.** 67.5 **10.** 30.5 **11.** 14.4

12. 75.2 **13.** 6 ft 9 in. **14.** 4 days 12 min **15.** 11 ft 5 in. **16.** 2 lb 9 oz **17.** 15 h 20 min **18.** 4 lb 6 oz **19.** (b) **20.** (b) **21.** (b) **22.** (b) **23.** $1,050 **24.** 8.6 lb **25.** $0.0013/mL

Cumulative Review Chapters 1–7

[1.5] 1. $896 **[1.6] 2.** $62 **[1.7] 3.** 16 **[2.2] 4.** $2 \times 2 \times 2 \times 3 \times 7$ **5.** 4 **[2.4] 6.** $\frac{3}{5}, \frac{5}{8}, \frac{2}{3}$ **[2.5] 7.** $\frac{3}{4}$ **[2.7] 8.** $\frac{5}{12}$ **[3.2] 9.** 60 **[3.3] 10.** $1\frac{1}{30}$ **[3.4] 11.** $3\frac{13}{24}$ **[4.2] 12.** $18.30 **[4.3] 13.** 27.84 cm^2 **[4.2] 14.** 21.5 cm **[4.6] 15.** 0.5625 **16.** 0.538 **[5.4] 17.** $x = 24$ **[5.5] 18.** 400 mi **19.** 450 mi **[6.2] 20.** 37.5% **[6.1] 21.** $\frac{1}{8}$ **[6.4] 22.** 3,526 **23.** 225% **24.** 150 **[6.5] 25.** $142,500 **[7.1] 26.** 120 **27.** 1 min 35 s **28.** 21 lb 11 oz **29.** 2 ft 9 in. **30.** 21 h 20 min **[7.2] 31.** 0.43 **[7.3] 32.** 62,000 **[7.2] 33.** 74 **[7.3] 34.** 14,000 **35.** 0.5 **[7.4] 36.** 13.3 **37.** 149.6 **38.** 29.4 **39.** 48.2

Prerequisite Test for Chapter 8

1. 25 **2.** 169 **3.** 78.5 **4.** 36 **5.** 17.4 **6.** $\frac{45}{2}$ **7.** 19.63 **8.** 7.0 in. **9.** 4.4 m **10.** 118 ft **11.** 144 mm^2 **12.** 173.25 $in.^2$

Reading Your Text

Section 8.1 **(a)** Earth; **(b)** perpendicular; **(c)** obtuse; **(d)** complementary
Section 8.2 **(a)** triangle; **(b)** regular; **(c)** sum; **(d)** nine
Section 8.3 **(a)** circumference; **(b)** radius; **(c)** composite; **(d)** area
Section 8.4 **(a)** equilateral; **(b)** isosceles; **(c)** similar; **(d)** corresponding
Section 8.5 **(a)** radical; **(b)** hypotenuse; **(c)** Pythagorean; **(d)** whole

Summary Exercises for Chapter 8

1. $\angle AOB$; acute; 70° **3.** $\angle AOC$; obtuse; 100° **5.** $\angle XYZ$; straight; 180° **7.** 135° **9.** 47° **11.** 73° **13.** 79° **15.** 67° **17.** $A = 750$ ft^2 **19.** $P = 60$ in.; $A = 216$ $in.^2$ **21.** $P = 93$ ft; $A = 457.5$ ft^2 **23.** 180 ft^2; 20 yd^2 **25.** $C = 37.7$ in.; $A = 113.0$ $in.^2$ **27.** $P = 56$ ft; $A = 128$ ft^2 **29.** 60°; equilateral **31.** 45°; isosceles **33.** 14.3 **35.** 32 m **37.** 28 **39.** 9.54 **41.** 15

Self-Test for Chapter 8

1. 60 mm **2.** 12 in. **3.** 256 yd **4.** 62 m **5.** 94.2 ft **6.** 91.7 ft **7.** 189 mm^2 **8.** 7 $in.^2$ **9.** 2,800 yd^2 **10.** 54 m^2 **11.** 706.5 ft^2 **12.** 332.8 ft^2 **13.** **(a)** Parallel; **(b)** neither; **(c)** perpendicular; **(d)** neither **14.** **(a)** Straight; **(b)** obtuse; **(c)** right **15.** 50° **16.** 135° **17.** 137° **18.** 66° **19.** Obtuse **20.** Right **21.** 67° **22.** 53.9° **23.** 21 **24.** 65 m **25.** 112 mm

Cumulative Review Chapters 1–8

[1.1] 1. Ten-thousands **[1.7] 2.** 64 **[2.1] 3.** $2 \cdot 3 \cdot 3 \cdot 5 \cdot 7$ **4.** 4 **5.** 120 **[2.5] 6.** $\frac{3}{4}$ **[2.6] 7.** $4\frac{1}{2}$ **8.** $578 **9.** $60\frac{\text{mi}}{\text{h}}$ **[3.3] 10.** $1\frac{13}{30}$ **[3.4] 11.** $3\frac{13}{24}$ **12.** $6\frac{7}{12}$ mi **[4.1] 13.** Hundredths **14.** Ten–thousandths **[4.4] 15.** $P = 24.2$ ft; $A = 35.04$ ft^2 **[4.2] 16.** $\frac{1}{8}$ **17.** 0.3125 **[5.2] 18.** $20,250/yr **[5.4] 19.** $w = 4$ **20.** 1,125 ft^2 **[6.1] 21.** 0.085 **22.** $\frac{3}{8}$ **[6.2] 23.** 67.5% **[6.4] 24.** 51.2 **25.** 1,500 **26.** 1,350 **[7.1–7.4] 27.** 5,280 **28.** 0.25 **29.** 5,800 **[8.1] 30.** 45° **31.** 49.6 ft **32.** 342 cm^2 **33.** 1,256 m^2 **34.** 60.63 ft^2 **[8.3] 35.** 73°; isosceles **[8.4] 36.** $x = 40$ **37.** 17 ft

Prerequisite Test for Chapter 9

1. $\frac{4}{5}$ **2.** $\frac{3}{4}$ **3.** 6 **4.** $\frac{17}{2}$ **5.** 27 **6.** 77 **7.** 90 **8.** 300 **9.** 62.5% **10.** $16.\overline{6}\%$ **11.** 0, 1, 2, 5, 7, 10, 11, 13 **12.** 7, 12, 21, 50, 55, 56, 81, 123 **13.** $1\frac{1}{8}$ in. **14.** 120°

Reading Your Text

Section 9.1 **(a)** mean; **(b)** median; **(c)** mode; **(d)** bimodal
Section 9.2 **(a)** rows; **(b)** cell; **(c)** pictograph; **(d)** legend
Section 9.3 **(a)** line; **(b)** future; **(c)** extrapolation; **(d)** predict
Section 9.4 **(a)** table; **(b)** approximation; **(c)** pie; **(d)** circle
Section 9.5 **(a)** quartiles; **(b)** three; **(c)** summary; **(d)** box-and-whisker

Summary Exercises for Chapter 9

1. 6 **3.** 120 **5.** 85 **7.** 19; 20 **9.** 29; 28 **11.** 92 **13.** 32,000 vehicles; 10,145,000 vehicles **15.** 60% **17.** 17.7% **19.** 60% **21.** 1 house = $100,000

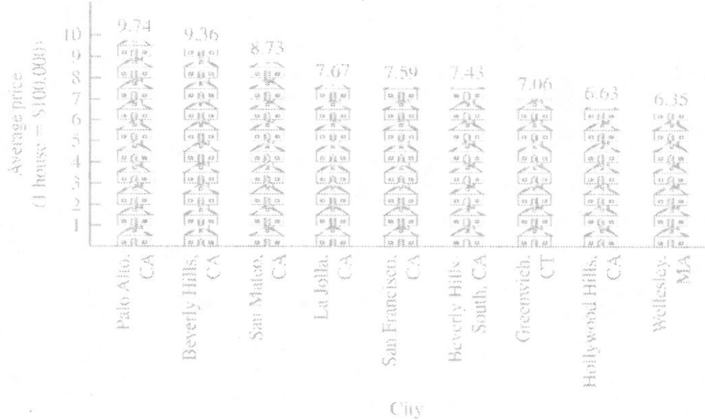

23. 5,000 students **25.** 250,000 computers **27.** About 400,000 computers **29.**

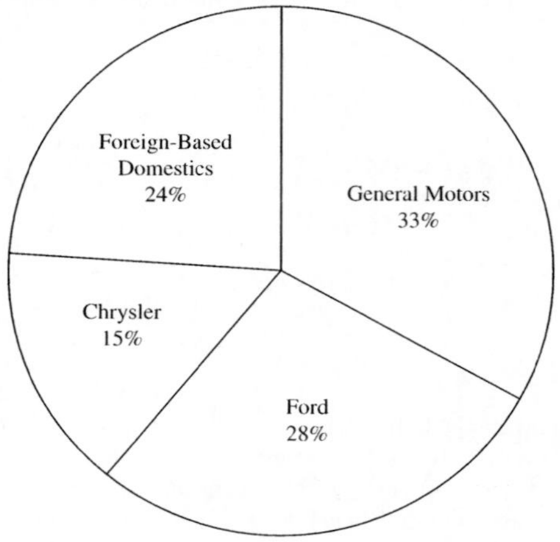

31. 47% **33.** 21, 24, 28, 30, 35

35. The data do not exhibit any striking features (the data set is mildly skewed right).

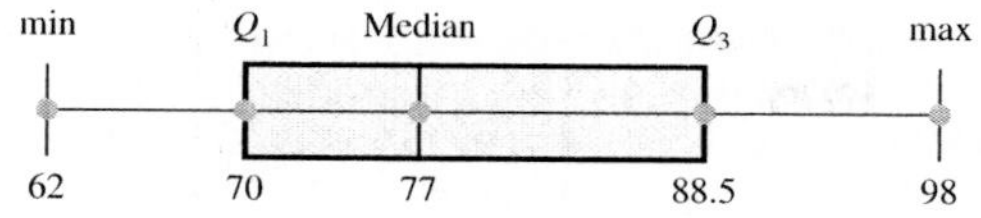

Self-Test for Chapter 9

1. 15 **2.** 8 **3.** 11 **4.** 6 **5.** 204 **6.** 93
7. Brown **8.** 31,162 **9.** 41,378 **10.** 324% **11.** 124%
12.

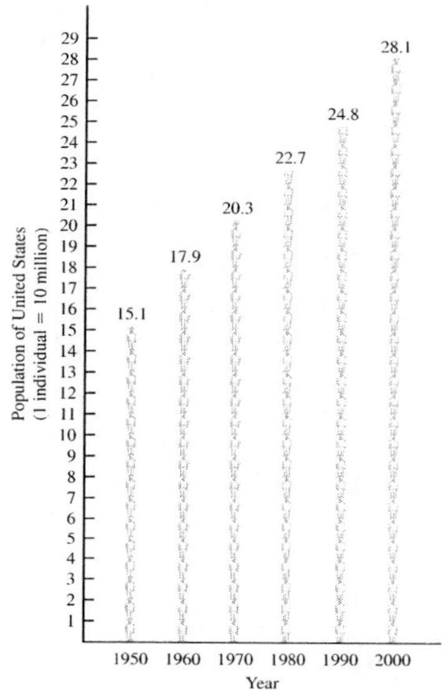

13. 16,000 people **14.** 30,000 people **15.** 10,000 people
16. 16,000 people **17.** 2000 to 2001 **18.** December
19. August and September
20. about 21 defects

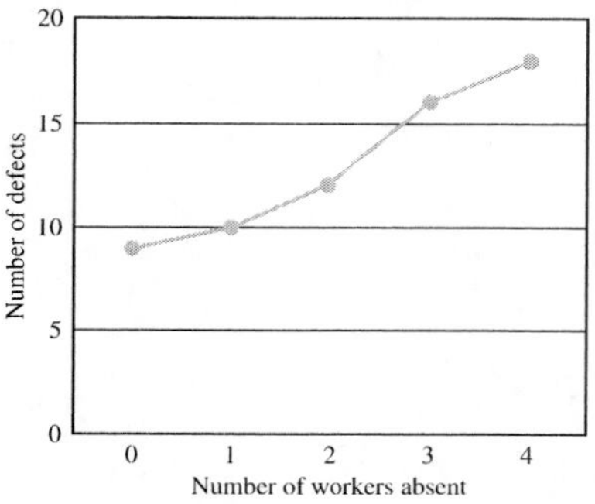

21.

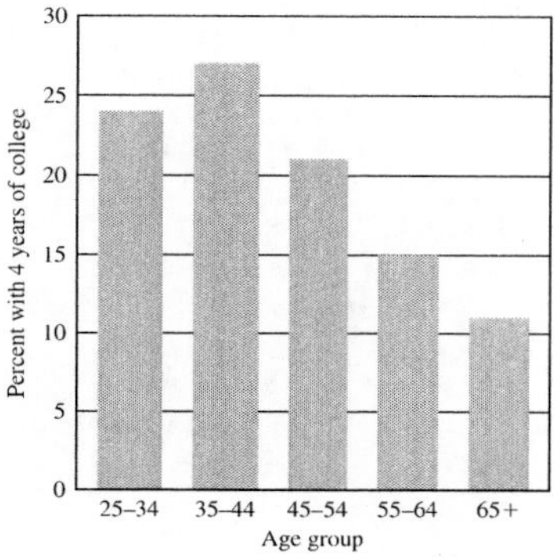

22.

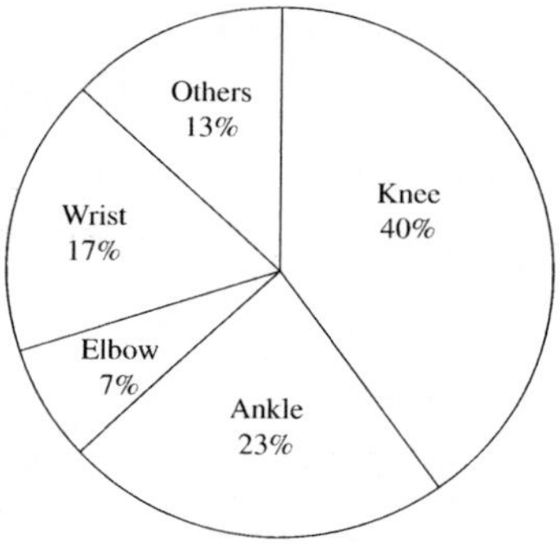

23. 45% **24.** 85%

25.

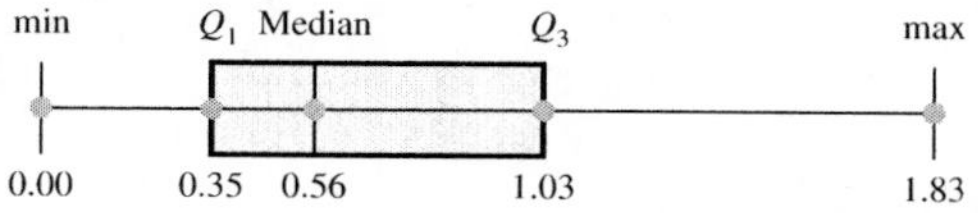

Cumulative Review Chapters 1–9

[1.1] 1. Thousands **[1.2] 2.** 32,278 **[1.3] 3.** 39,288
[1.5] 4. 26,230 **[1.6] 5.** 308 r 6 **[1.3] 6.** 48,588
[4.3] 7. 75.215 **[2.5] 8.** $\frac{2}{3}$ **[2.7] 9.** $\frac{6}{11}$ **[3.4] 10.** $7\frac{1}{12}$
[5.4] 11. $x = 14$ **12.** $x = 9$ **[6.1] 13.** 0.18; $\frac{9}{50}$
14. 0.425; 42.5% **[7.1] 15.** 11 lb 5 oz **16.** 1 min 35 s
[7.2] 17. 8,000 **[7.3] 18.** 3 **19.** 5 **20.** 250
[9.3] 21. 2002 and 2003
[9.4] 22.

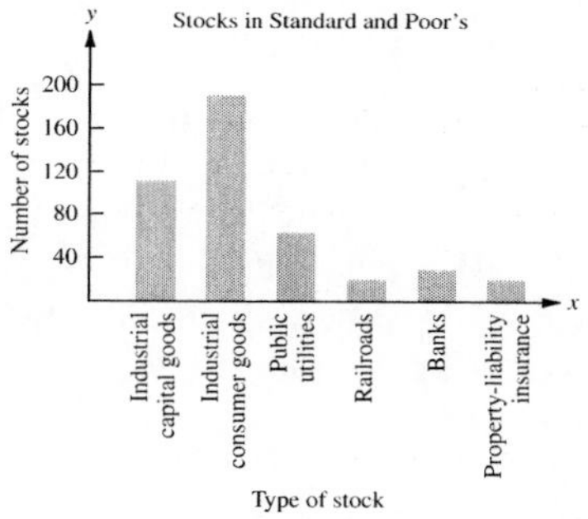

[9.1] 23. Mean: 9; median: 9; mode: 11 **[5.2] 24.** 70 gal
25. $88\ \frac{\text{ft}}{\text{s}}$ **26.** $19\ \frac{\text{pitches}}{\text{inning}}$ **[1.8] 27.** \$408 **28.** $48\ \frac{\text{mi}}{\text{h}}$
29. $28\frac{3}{5}$ cm **30.** $55\frac{1}{3}$ ft **[6.4] 31.** 133 **32.** 0.2%
33. 185 **[2.5] 34.** $4\frac{1}{3}$ **[6.5] 35.** 2,800 students

Prerequisite Test for Chapter 10

1. 21 **2.** 79 **3.** 368 **4.** $15\frac{1}{4}$ **5.** 187 **6.** 32
7. Commutative property of addition
8. Distributive property of multiplication over addition
9. Associative property of multiplication
10. Distributive property of multiplication over addition
11. 33.91 mm **12.** 91.56 mm^2

Reading Your Text

Section 10.1 **(a)** zero; **(b)** negative; **(c)** ascending; **(d)** absolute value
Section 10.2 **(a)** negative; **(b)** negative; **(c)** absolute; **(d)** zero
Section 10.3 **(a)** addition; **(b)** subtraction; **(c)** opposite; **(d)** positive

Section 10.4 **(a)** negative; **(b)** positive; **(c)** identity; **(d)** reciprocal
Section 10.5 **(a)** negative; **(b)** positive; **(c)** Division; **(d)** positive

Summary Exercises for Chapter 10

1.

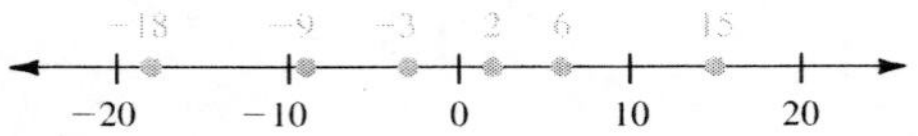

3. $-\frac{4}{5}, -\frac{2}{3}, -\frac{1}{2}, \frac{3}{5}, \frac{7}{10}, \frac{5}{6}$ **5.** Max: 8; min: −9 **7.** 9
9. −9 **11.** −4 **13.** −4 **15.** 6 **17.** −32 **19.** −1
21. −14 **23.** −17 **25.** −4 **27.** 2 **29.** 16
31. −4 **33.** −4 **35.** −2 **37.** −1 **39.** −70
41. 45 **43.** 0 **45.** $-\frac{3}{2}$ **47.** 80 **49.** 10 **51.** −2
53. −60 **55.** −9 **57.** 0 **59.** Undefined **61.** −1

Self-Test for Chapter 10

[10.1] 1.

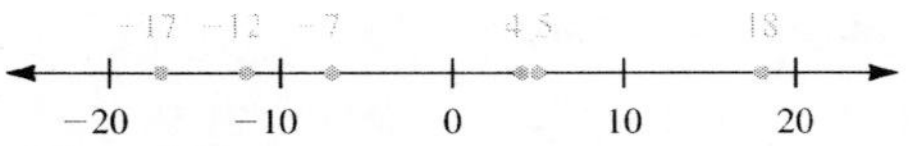

2. $-6, -3, -2, 0, \frac{1}{2}, \frac{3}{4}, 2, 4, 5$ **3.** Max: 6; min: −5 **4.** 7
5. 7 **6.** −13 **7.** −3 **8.** −6 **9.** −24 **10.** −40
11. 63 **12.** −25 **13.** 3 **14.** 11 **15.** 11 **16.** −21
17. 1 **18.** 9 **19.** 0 **20.** −27 **21.** −24 **22.** −5
23. Undefined **24.** −24 **25.** −10

Cumulative Review Chapters 1–10

[1.1] 1. Ten thousands **[1.2] 2.** 142,231 **[1.3] 3.** 29,573
[1.5] 4. 53,445 **[1.6] 5.** 402 r 28 **[4.2] 6.** 13.687
[4.3] 7. 1,837.353 **[2.5] 8.** $\frac{3}{7}$ **[2.7] 9.** 1
[3.4] 10. $8\frac{19}{54}$ **[5.4] 11.** $x = 4$ **[6.1] 12.** 0.58; $\frac{29}{50}$
[6.2] 13. 0.48; 48% **[7.1] 14.** 8 ft 10 in. **15.** 9 lb 4 oz
16. 12 ft 6 in. **17.** 2 lb 14 oz **18.** 10 h 30 min
19. 2 min 9 s **20.** 14 ft 8 in.
[5.2] 21. The three smaller bottles **[4.4] 22.** 49.02 cm^2
23. $72\frac{1}{4}$ $in.^2$ **24.** 25.7 ft **[6.4] 25.** 80 **[6.5] 26.** 7.5%
[7.3] 27. 0.017 **[7.2] 28.** 820 **[7.5] 29.** 160°
[9.2] 30. 5,000 students **[9.1] 31.** Mean: 17; median: 17; mode: 17 **[10.2] 32.** 4 **[10.3] 33.** 20 **34.** −32
35. −15 **36.** 31 **[10.4] 37.** 108 **[10.5] 38.** 4
39. 41 **40.** 72

Prerequisite Test for Chapter 11

1. 10 − 8 = 2 **2.** 3 + 5 × 6 = 33 **3.** $-\frac{1}{12}$ **4.** $\frac{8}{37}$
5. 1 **6.** 1 **7.** 1 **8.** 23 **9.** −64 **10.** 64
11. $14,117.65 **12.** $1.55

Reading Your Text

Section 11.1 **(a)** variables; **(b)** sum; **(c)** multiplication; **(d)** expression
Section 11.2 **(a)** evaluating; **(b)** variable; **(c)** operations; **(d)** positive
Section 11.3 **(a)** term; **(b)** number; **(c)** like; **(d)** distributive
Section 11.4 **(a)** equation; **(b)** true; **(c)** solution(s); **(d)** sentence
Section 11.5 **(a)** equivalent; **(b)** original; **(c)** dividing; **(d)** reciprocal
Section 11.6 **(a)** isolate; **(b)** addition; **(c)** original; **(d)** solved

Summary Exercises for Chapter 11

1. $y + 5$ **3.** $8a$ **5.** $5mn$ **7.** $17x + 3$ **9.** −7
11. 15 **13.** 19 **15.** 25 **17.** 1 **19.** −3
21. $4a^3, -3a^2$ **23.** $5m^2, -4m^2, m^2$ **25.** $12c$ **27.** $2a$
29. $3xy$ **31.** $19a + b$ **33.** $3x^3 + 9x^2$ **35.** $10a^3$
37. Yes **39.** Yes **41.** No **43.** $x = 2$ **45.** $x = -5$
47. $x = 5$ **49.** $x = 1$ **51.** $x = -7$ **53.** $x = 7$
55. $x = -4$ **57.** $x = 32$ **59.** $x = 27$ **61.** $x = 3$
63. $x = -2$ **65.** $x = \frac{7}{2}$ **67.** $x = 18$ **69.** $x = 6$
71. $x = \frac{2}{5}$ **73.** $x = 6$ **75.** $x = 6$ **77.** $x = 4$
79. $x = 5$ **81.** $x = \frac{1}{2}$

Self-Test for Chapter 11

1. $a - 5$ **2.** $6m$ **3.** $4(m + n)$ **4.** $4m + n$ **5.** No
6. Yes **7.** 11 **8.** 7 **9.** 3 **10.** 4 **11.** −12
12. 12 **13.** 7 **14.** 25 **15.** $-\frac{2}{3}$ **16.** −5 **17.** −4
18. 80 **19.** 144 **20.** 5 **21.** $15a$ **22.** $3x^2y$
23. $19x + 5y$ **24.** $4m^2 - 2m - 5$ **25.** 58 double lattes

Cumulative Review Chapters 1–11

[1.2] 1. Associative property of addition
[1.5] 2. Commutative property of multiplication
3. Distributive property **[1.4] 4.** 5,900 **5.** 950,000
[1.7] 6. 8 **[2.2] 7.** 2 × 2 × 2 × 3 × 11 **[3.2] 8.** 90
[2.3] 9. $3\frac{1}{7}$ **10.** $\frac{53}{8}$ **[2.5] 11.** $\frac{3}{4}$ **[2.6] 12.** $1\frac{1}{2}$
[3.4] 13. $8\frac{1}{24}$ **14.** $3\frac{5}{8}$ **15.** $\frac{5}{8}$ in. **[4.3] 16.** $3.06
[8.1] 17. 8.04 ft^2 **[4.5] 18.** 32 **[4.2] 19.** $0.\overline{72}$
[5.4] 20. $m = 112.5$ **[5.5] 21.** 12 in. **[6.2] 22.** 0.3%
23. 62.5% **24.** 350% **[6.4] 25.** 150 **26.** 600
27. $27,500 **[7.3] 28.** 0.3 **[9.3] 29.** 80
[10.2] 30. −8 **[10.1] 31.** 20 **32.** 12 **33.** 5
[10.2] 34. −18 **[10.3] 35.** −4 **[10.4] 36.** −90
37. −4 **[11.1] 38.** $3(x + y)$ **39.** $\frac{n-5}{3}$
[11.2] 40. −60 **41.** 27 **42.** 24 **43.** 3
[11.3] 44. $12a^2 + 3a$ **45.** $-2y$ **[11.4] 46.** 5
[11.5] 47. −24 **[11.6] 48.** $-\frac{2}{5}$ **49.** 5

index

 The Streeter/Hutchison Series in Mathematics Basic Mathematical Skills with Geometry